D1084306

Elementary Matrix Algebra

A series of advanced mathematics texts under the editorship of CARL B. ALLENDOERFER

Elementary Matrix
Algebra SECOND EDITION

FRANZ E. HOHN

Professor of Mathematics
University of Illinois

THE MACMILLAN COMPANY, NEW YORK

COLLIER-MACMILLAN LIMITED, LONDON

Fourth Printing, 1965

Preliminary editions copyright 1952 and 1957 by Franz E. Hohn

Library of Congress catalog card number : 64–16862

**THE MACMILLAN COMPANY, NEW YORK
COLLIER-MACMILLAN CANADA, LTD., TORONTO, ONTARIO**

Printed in the United States of America

DESIGN BY R. A. KASELER

PREFACE TO THE FIRST EDITION

This text has been developed over a period of years for a course in Linear Transformations and Matrices given at the University of Illinois. The students have been juniors, seniors, and graduates whose interests have included such diverse subjects as aeronautical engineering, agricultural economics, chemistry, econometrics, education, electrical engineering, high speed computation, mechanical engineering, metallurgy, physics, psychology, sociology, statistics, and pure mathematics.

The book makes no pretense of being in any sense "complete." On the other hand, to meet as well as possible the needs of so varied a group, I have searched the literature of the various applications to find what aspects of matrix algebra and determinant theory are most commonly used. The book presents this most essential material as simply as possible and in a logical order with the objective of preparing the reader to study intelligently the applications of matrices in his special field. The topics are separated so far as possible into distinct, self-contained chapters in order to make the book more useful as a reference volume. With the same purpose in view, the principal results are listed as numbered theorems, identified as to chapter and section, and printed in italics. Formulas are similarly numbered, but the numbers are always enclosed in parentheses so as to distinguish formulas from theorems. Again for reference purposes, I have added appendices on the Σ and Π notations and on the algebra of complex numbers, for many readers will no doubt be in need of review of these matters.

The exercises often present formal aspects of certain applications, but no knowledge of the latter is necessary for working any problem. To keep down the size of the volume, detailed treatment of applications was omitted. The exercises range from purely formal computation and extremely simple proofs to a few fairly difficult problems designed to challenge the reader. I hope that every reader will find it possible to work most of the simpler exercises and at least to study the rest, for many useful results are contained in them, and, also, there is no way to learn the techniques of computation and of proof except through practice. The exercises marked with an asterisk (*) are of particular importance for immediate or later use and should not be overlooked.

In order to make the learning and the teaching of matrix algebra as easy as possible, I have tried always to proceed by means of ample explanations from the familiar and the concrete to the abstract. Abstract algebraic concepts themselves are not the prime concern of the volume. However, I have not hesitated to make an important mathematical point where the need and the motivation for it are clear, for it has been my purpose that in addition to learning useful methods of manipulating matrices, the reader should progress significantly in mathematical maturity as a result of careful study of this book. In fact, since the definitions of fields, groups, and vector spaces as well as of other abstract concepts appear and are used here, I believe that a course of this kind is not only far more practical but is also better preparation for later work in abstract algebra than is the traditional course in the theory of equations. I also believe that some appreciation of these abstract ideas will help the student of applications to read and work in his own field with greater insight and understanding.

The chief claim to originality here is in the attempt to reduce this material to the junior-senior level. Although a few proofs and many exercises are believed to be new, my debt to the standard authors—M. Bôcher, L. E. Dickson, W. L. Ferrar, C. C. McDuffee, F. J. Murnaghan, G. Birkhoff and S. MacLane, O. Schreier and E. Sperner, among others—is a very great one, and I acknowledge it with respect and gratitude.

I am particularly indebted to Professor A. B. Coble for permission to adapt to my needs his unpublished notes on determinants. The credit is his for all merit in the organization of Chapter Two. I am also indebted to Professor William G. Madow who helped to encourage and guide my efforts in their early stages. The value of the critical assistance of Professors Paul Bateman, Albert Wilansky, and Wilson Zaring cannot be overemphasized. Without their severe but kindly criticisms, this book would have been much less acceptable. However, I alone am responsible for any errors of fact or judgment which still persist. For additional critical aid, and for many of the problems, I owe thanks to a host of students and colleagues who have had contact with this effort. Finally, I owe thanks to Mrs. Betty Kaplan and to Mrs. Rachel Dyal for their faithful and competent typing of the manuscript, to Wilson Zaring and Russell Welker for assistance with reading proof, and to the staff of The Macmillan Company for their patient and helpful efforts during the production of this book.

FRANZ E. HOHN

Urbana, Illinois

PREFACE TO THE SECOND EDITION

This second edition of *Elementary Matrix Algebra* retains the point of view and the scope of the first edition. Some of the topics have been reordered to make the exposition simpler. For example, the partitioning of matrices is now treated in Chapter One so that it can be used to greater advantage. The theorem on the determinant of the product of two matrices is proved without use of the Laplace expansion in Chapter Two. Thus the material on the Laplace expansion may be omitted entirely if that is desired since it is not essential to later developments. Similar changes occur in following chapters. A number of topics which are useful in applications (projections, for example) have been introduced in various places. This has been done in such a way that these topics need not be made part of the classroom work. An exceptionally detailed index, referencing also symbols and those exercises which contain important contributions to the theory, has been provided. Finally, a number of errors have been corrected and a great many new exercises have been included. It is hoped that the net effect of all these changes is to make the book easier to read and more useful as a text and as a reference. Exactly the same type of course can be taught from it as before.

The author wishes to thank his colleagues, Professors Richard L. Bishop and Hiram Paley, for their careful reading of the revised manuscript and of the proof, respectively. Many corrections and improvements are the direct result of their efforts. Professor Gene Golub provided a number of interesting and important exercises. Thanks are also due the many users of the first edition who have sent the author helpful suggestions, exercises, corrections, and letters of encouragement. Finally, the author is most grateful to the staff of The Macmillan Company and to the printers for their exceptionally cordial and able assistance.

FRANZ E. HOHN

Philo, Illinois

CONTENTS

Nine. Bilinear, Quadratic, and Hermitian Forms

Appendix I.   The Notations Σ and Π

Elementary Matrix Algebra

CHAPTER ONE

Introduction to Matrix Algebra

THE BASIC OPERATIONS

1.1 Matrices

There are many situations in both pure and applied mathematics in which we have to deal with rectangular arrays of numbers or functions. An array of this kind may be represented by the symbol

$$(1.1.1) \qquad A = \begin{bmatrix} a_{11} & a_{12} & \cdots & a_{1n} \\ a_{21} & a_{22} & \cdots & a_{2n} \\ \vdots & & & \\ a_{m1} & a_{m2} & \cdots & a_{mn} \end{bmatrix}.$$

The numbers or functions a_{ij} of this array are called its **elements** and in this book are assumed to have real or complex values. Such an array, subject to rules of operation to be defined below, is called a **matrix**. We shall denote matrices with pairs of square brackets, but pairs of double bars, $\| \ \|$, and pairs of parentheses, $(\ )$, are also used for this purpose. The subscripts i and j of the element a_{ij} of a matrix identify respectively the **row** and the **column** thereof in which a_{ij} is located. When there is no need to distinguish between rows and columns, we call them simply **lines** of the matrix.

A matrix A with m rows and n columns is called a **matrix of order** (m, n) or **an $m \times n$ ("m by n") matrix**. When $m = n$ so that the matrix is square, it is called a **matrix of order n**. When A is of order n, the elements $a_{11}, a_{22}, \ldots,$ a_{nn} are said to constitute the **main diagonal** of A and the elements $a_{n1},$ $a_{n-1,2}, \ldots, a_{1n}$ constitute its **secondary diagonal**.

It is often convenient to abbreviate the symbol (1.1.1) to the form

$[a_{ij}]_{(m,n)}$, which means "the matrix of order (m, n) whose elements are the a_{ij}'s." When the order of the matrix need not be specified or is clear from the context, this is abbreviated further to the form $[a_{ij}]$. Another convenient procedure which we shall follow is to denote matrices by capital letters such as A, B, X, Y, etc., whenever it is not necessary to indicate explicitly the elements or the orders of the matrices in question.

A simple illustration of the matrix concept is the following: The coefficients of x and y in the system of linear equations

(1.1.2)
$$2x + 6y - 1 = 0,$$
$$4x - y + 3 = 0,$$

provide the matrix of order 2:

$$\begin{bmatrix} 2 & 6 \\ 4 & -1 \end{bmatrix},$$

which is called the **coefficient matrix** of the system. The 2×3 matrix

$$\begin{bmatrix} 2 & 6 & -1 \\ 4 & -1 & 3 \end{bmatrix}$$

containing the coefficients of x and y and the constant terms as well is called the **augmented matrix** of the system. The coefficient and augmented matrices of systems of equations are useful in investigating their solutions, as we shall see later.

1.2 Equality of Matrices

Two matrices $[a_{ij}]_{(m,n)}$ and $[b_{ij}]_{(m,n)}$ are defined to be **equal** if and only if $a_{ij} = b_{ij}$ for each pair of subscripts i and j. In words, *two matrices are equal if and only if they have the same order and have equal corresponding elements throughout.*

From this definition and from the properties of equality in ordinary algebra, there follow four properties of the equality of matrices:

(a) If A and B are any two matrices, either $A = B$ or $A \neq B$ (the **determinative** property).
(b) If A is any matrix, $A = A$ (the **reflexive** property).
(c) If $A = B$, then $B = A$ (the **symmetric** property).
(d) If $A = B$ and $B = C$, then $A = C$ (the **transitive** property).

Many mathematical relationships other than equality of matrices possess these same four properties. (The similarity of triangles is a simple example. Can you think of others?) Any relation between pairs of mathematical objects which possesses these properties is called an **equivalence relation**. Several types of equivalence relations will be defined and used in this book.

Because equality means that matrices are in fact identical, *a matrix may be substituted for any equal matrix in the following operations.*

1.3 Addition of Matrices

If $A = [a_{ij}]_{(m,n)}$, and $B = [b_{ij}]_{(m,n)}$, we define the **sum** $A + B$ to be the matrix $[(a_{ij} + b_{ij})]_{(m,n)}$. That is, the sum of two matrices of the same order is found by adding the corresponding elements thereof. For example,

$$\begin{bmatrix} 1 - t & 2 \\ 3 & 1 + t \end{bmatrix} + \begin{bmatrix} 1 + t & -2 \\ -3 & 1 - t \end{bmatrix} = \begin{bmatrix} 2 & 0 \\ 0 & 2 \end{bmatrix}.$$

Two matrices of the same order are said to be **conformable for addition**.

Since the sum of any two $m \times n$ matrices is again an $m \times n$ matrix, we say that the set of all $m \times n$ matrices is **closed with respect to addition**.

1.4 Commutative and Associative Laws of Addition

Throughout this book, the real and the complex numbers and functions thereof will be called **scalars** to distinguish them from the arrays which are called matrices. In scalar algebra, the fact that $a + b = b + a$ for any two scalars a and b is known as the **commutative law of addition**. The fact that $a + (b + c) = (a + b) + c$ for any three scalars a, b, and c is known as the **associative law of addition**. It is not hard to see that these laws extend to matrix addition also.

Let A, B, C be arbitrary matrices of the same order. Then, using the definition of the sum of two matrices and the commutative law of addition of scalars, we have in the abbreviated notation

$$A + B = [a_{ij} + b_{ij}] = [b_{ij} + a_{ij}] = B + A.$$

Similarly, applying the associative law for the addition of scalars, we have

$$A + (B + C) = [a_{ij} + (b_{ij} + c_{ij})] = [(a_{ij} + b_{ij}) + c_{ij}] = (A + B) + C.$$

We have thus proved

Theorem 1.4.1: *The addition of matrices is both commutative and associative, that is, if A, B, and C are conformable for addition,*

(1.4.1) $$A + B = B + A,$$

(1.4.2) $$A + (B + C) = (A + B) + C.$$

The reader who finds the above notation a little too condensed should write out the details in full for matrices of order, say, $(2, 3)$.

These two laws, applied repeatedly if necessary, enable us to arrange the terms of a sum in any order we wish, and to group them in any fashion we wish. In particular, they justify the absence of parentheses in an expression like $A + B + C$, which (for given A, B, C of the same order) has a uniquely defined meaning.

Another important property of matrix addition is given in

Theorem 1.4.2: $A + C = B + C$ *if and only if* $A = B$.

The fact that $A + C = B + C$ implies $A = B$ is called **the cancellation law for addition**.

Indeed, $A + C = B + C$ if and only if $a_{ij} + c_{ij} = b_{ij} + c_{ij}$ in every case. But $a_{ij} + c_{ij} = b_{ij} + c_{ij}$ if and only if $a_{ij} = b_{ij}$, by the cancellation law of addition in the complex domain. This implies $A + C = B + C$ if and only if $A = B$.

1.5 Subtraction of Matrices

A matrix all of whose elements are zero is called a **zero matrix** and is denoted by 0, or by 0_n, or by $0_{m \times n}$ when the order needs emphasis. The basic property of the matrix $0_{m \times n}$ is that, for all $m \times n$ matrices A,

$$(1.5.1) \qquad\qquad A + 0 = A,$$

that is, the zero matrix is an **identity element for addition**.

The **negative** of an $m \times n$ matrix $A = [a_{ij}]$ is defined to be $-A = [-a_{ij}]$. That is, the negative of A is formed by changing the sign of every element of A. The reason for this definition is, of course, to guarantee that

$$(1.5.2) \qquad\qquad A + (-A) = 0.$$

Thus $-A$ is the **inverse of A with respect to addition**.

Instead of $A + (-A) = 0$, we agree to write $A - A = 0$. In general, we define

$$(1.5.3) \qquad\qquad A - B = A + (-B).$$

This implies that the difference $A - B$ may be found by subtracting corresponding elements.

For example,

$$\begin{bmatrix} 2 & 1 & -3 \\ -4 & 0 & 1 \end{bmatrix} - \begin{bmatrix} 1 & -1 & 2 \\ 0 & 1 & 0 \end{bmatrix} = \begin{bmatrix} 1 & 2 & -5 \\ -4 & -1 & 1 \end{bmatrix}.$$

An important consequence of the preceding definitions is that, if X, A, and B are all of the same order, then a solution of the equation

$$(1.5.4) \qquad\qquad X + A = B$$

is

$$X = B - A.$$

In fact, replacement of X by $B - A$ in $X + A$ yields

$$(B - A) + A = (B + (-A)) + A$$
$$= B + ((-A) + A)$$
$$= B + 0$$
$$= B,$$

which shows that $B - A$ is indeed a solution of (1.5.4). [Note that (1.5.2), (1.4.2), (1.4.1), and (1.5.1) were all employed in the proof.] Moreover it is the *only* solution, for, if Y is any solution, then

$$Y + A = B,$$

so that, by substitution,

$$(Y + A) + (-A) = B + (-A),$$
$$Y + (A + (-A)) = B - A,$$
$$Y + 0 = B - A,$$

and finally

$$Y = B - A.$$

(Each use of a basic law should be identified here by the reader.) In summary, $B - A$ is the *unique* solution of the equation $X + A = B$.

In particular, this proves that the equations

$$X + A = A$$

and

$$X + A = 0$$

have respectively the unique solutions 0 and $-A$; that is, for a given order (m, n), *the additive identity element is unique*, and *each matrix A has a unique inverse with respect to addition*, namely, the matrix $-A$ defined above.

In summary, with respect to addition, the set of all $m \times n$ matrices has the same properties as the set of complex numbers. This is because matrix addition is effected by mn independent scalar additions—one in each of the mn positions.

1.6 Scalar Multiples of Matrices

If $A = [a_{ij}]$ and if α is a scalar, we define $\alpha A = A\alpha = [\alpha a_{ij}]$. In words, to multiply a matrix A by a scalar α, multiply every element of A by α. This definition is, of course, suggested by the fact that, if we add n A's, we obtain a matrix whose elements are those of A each multiplied by n. For example,

$$\begin{bmatrix} a & b \\ c & d \end{bmatrix} + \begin{bmatrix} a & b \\ c & d \end{bmatrix} = \begin{bmatrix} 2a & 2b \\ 2c & 2d \end{bmatrix} = 2\begin{bmatrix} a & b \\ c & d \end{bmatrix}.$$

The operation of multiplying a matrix by a scalar has these basic properties:

$$1 \cdot A = A,$$
$$(\alpha + \beta)A = \alpha A + \beta A,$$
$$\alpha(A + B) = \alpha A + \alpha B,$$
$$\alpha(\beta A) = (\alpha\beta)A.$$

All four are readily proved by appealing to the definition. In the case of the second, we have $(\alpha + \beta)A = [(\alpha + \beta)a_{ij}] = [\alpha a_{ij} + \beta a_{ij}] = [\alpha a_{ij}] + [\beta a_{ij}] = \alpha A + \beta A$. We leave it as an exercise to the reader to prove the other laws in a similar fashion.

1.7 The Multiplication of Matrices

Frequently in the mathematical treatment of a problem, the work can be simplified by the introduction of new variables. Translations of axes, effected by equations of the form

$$x = x' + h,$$
$$y = y' + k,$$

and rotations of axes, effected by

$$x = x' \cos\theta - y' \sin\theta,$$
$$y = x' \sin\theta + y' \cos\theta,$$

are the most familiar examples. A rotation of axes is a special case of a change of variables of the type

(1.7.1)
$$x = a_{11}x' + a_{12}y',$$
$$y = a_{21}x' + a_{22}y',$$

in which the a's are constants. Substitutions of this latter kind are called **linear homogeneous transformations** of the variables and are of great usefulness. The properties of these transformations suggest the law that should be adopted for the multiplication of matrices, which we now proceed to illustrate.

Let us consider, for example, the effect on the system of linear functions

(1.7.2)
$$2x + 3y,$$
$$3x - 4y,$$
$$-5x + 6y,$$

resulting from an application of the linear transformation (1.7.1). Substitution from (1.7.1) into (1.7.2) yields the new system of linear functions

$$(2a_{11} + 3a_{21})x' + (2a_{12} + 3a_{22})y',$$

(1.7.3)
$$(3a_{11} - 4a_{21})x' + (3a_{12} - 4a_{22})y',$$

$$(-5a_{11} + 6a_{21})x' + (-5a_{12} + 6a_{22})y'.$$

From the three systems of linear expressions, (1.7.1), (1.7.2), and (1.7.3), we obtain three coefficient matrices. Since the third matrix is in a sense the "product" of the first two, we shall relate them by the following *matrix equation*:

$$\begin{bmatrix} 2 & 3 \\ 3 & -4 \\ -5 & 6 \end{bmatrix} \cdot \begin{bmatrix} a_{11} & a_{12} \\ a_{21} & a_{22} \end{bmatrix} = \begin{bmatrix} (2a_{11} + 3a_{21}) & (2a_{12} + 3a_{22}) \\ (3a_{11} - 4a_{21}) & (3a_{12} - 4a_{22}) \\ (-5a_{11} + 6a_{21}) & (-5a_{12} + 6a_{22}) \end{bmatrix}.$$

The question now is, "What rule for 'multiplying' matrices does this equation imply?" The element $(2a_{11} + 3a_{21})$ in the *first row and first column* of the matrix on the right may be obtained by multiplying the elements of the *first row* of the extreme left matrix respectively by the corresponding elements of the *first column* of the second matrix on the left and then adding the results: (first × first) + (second × second). If we multiply the elements of the *second row* of the extreme left matrix respectively by the corresponding elements of the *first column* of the second matrix and add, we obtain the entry $(3a_{11} - 4a_{21})$ in the *second row and first column* on the right. A similar procedure is followed for every other entry on the right. (The reader should check them all.)

This example suggests the following general definition. Let A be an $m \times p$ matrix and let B be a $p \times n$ matrix. The **product** AB is then defined to be the $m \times n$ matrix whose element in the ith row and jth column is found by multiplying corresponding elements of the ith row of A and of the jth column of B, and then adding the results. Symbolically, we may write,

$$\begin{bmatrix} a_{11} & a_{12} & \cdots & a_{1p} \\ a_{21} & a_{22} & \cdots & a_{2p} \\ \vdots & & & \\ a_{m1} & a_{m2} & \cdots & a_{mp} \end{bmatrix} \cdot \begin{bmatrix} b_{11} & b_{12} & \cdots & b_{1n} \\ b_{21} & b_{22} & \cdots & b_{2n} \\ \vdots & & & \\ b_{p1} & b_{p2} & \cdots & b_{pn} \end{bmatrix} = \begin{bmatrix} c_{11} & c_{12} & \cdots & c_{1n} \\ c_{21} & c_{22} & \cdots & c_{2n} \\ \vdots & & & \\ c_{m1} & c_{m2} & \cdots & c_{mn} \end{bmatrix},$$

where

$$c_{ij} = a_{i1}b_{1j} + a_{i2}b_{2j} + \cdots + a_{ip}b_{pj} = \sum_{k=1}^{p} a_{ik}b_{kj}.$$

(The arrows have been used for emphasis and are not customarily part of the notation.)

Two things should be noted particularly. First, the product AB has the same number of rows as the matrix A and the same number of columns as the matrix B. Second, the number of columns in A and the number of rows in B must be the same since otherwise there will not always be corresponding elements to multiply together. When the number of columns of a matrix A is the same as the number of rows of a matrix B, **A is said to be conformable to B for multiplication.**

These matters are illustrated further in the examples which follow:

(a)
$$\begin{bmatrix} 1 & -1 & 2 \\ 3 & 0 & 1 \end{bmatrix}_{(2,3)} \begin{bmatrix} 1 & 2 & 0 \\ 0 & -1 & 1 \\ 1 & 2 & -1 \end{bmatrix}_{(3,3)}$$

$$= \begin{bmatrix} (1\cdot1+(-1)\cdot0+2\cdot1) & (1\cdot2+(-1)(-1)+2\cdot2) & (1\cdot0+(-1)\cdot1+2\cdot(-1)) \\ (3\cdot1+0\cdot0+1\cdot1) & (3\cdot2+0\cdot(-1)+1\cdot2) & (3\cdot0+0\cdot1+1\cdot(-1)) \end{bmatrix}$$

$$= \begin{bmatrix} 3 & 7 & -3 \\ 4 & 8 & -1 \end{bmatrix}_{(2,3)}$$

(b) $[x_1, x_2]_{(1,2)} \cdot \begin{bmatrix} 1 & 2 & 4 \\ -1 & 3 & -2 \end{bmatrix}_{(2,3)}$

$$= [(x_1 - x_2), \quad (2x_1 + 3x_2), \quad (4x_1 - 2x_2)]_{(1,3)}.$$

(c) $[x_1, x_2, x_3]_{(1,3)} \cdot \begin{bmatrix} y_1 \\ y_2 \\ y_3 \end{bmatrix}_{(3,1)} = [(x_1y_1 + x_2y_2 + x_3y_3)]_{(1,1)}.$

1.8 The Properties of Matrix Multiplication

In the product AB we say that B is **premultiplied** by A and that A is **postmultiplied** by B. This terminology is essential since ordinarily $AB \neq BA$. In fact, if A has order (m, p) and B has order (p, n) with $m \neq n$, the product AB is defined but the product BA is not. Thus the fact that A is conformable to B for multiplication *does not imply* that B is conformable to A for multiplication. Even if $m = n$, we need not have $AB = BA$. That is, *matrix* *multiplication is not in general commutative.* We give some numerical examples in which the reader should verify every detail:

(a)
$$\begin{bmatrix} 0 & 1 & 2 & 3 \\ 3 & 2 & 1 & 0 \end{bmatrix} \cdot \begin{bmatrix} 0 & 3 \\ 1 & 2 \\ 2 & 1 \\ 3 & 0 \end{bmatrix} = \begin{bmatrix} 14 & 4 \\ 4 & 14 \end{bmatrix},$$

but

$$\begin{bmatrix} 0 & 3 \\ 1 & 2 \\ 2 & 1 \\ 3 & 0 \end{bmatrix} \cdot \begin{bmatrix} 0 & 1 & 2 & 3 \\ 3 & 2 & 1 & 0 \end{bmatrix} = \begin{bmatrix} 9 & 6 & 3 & 0 \\ 6 & 5 & 4 & 3 \\ 3 & 4 & 5 & 6 \\ 0 & 3 & 6 & 9 \end{bmatrix}.$$

(b)
$$\begin{bmatrix} 2 & -1 \\ -1 & 2 \end{bmatrix} \cdot \begin{bmatrix} 1 & 4 \\ -1 & 1 \end{bmatrix} = \begin{bmatrix} 3 & 7 \\ -3 & -2 \end{bmatrix},$$

but

$$\begin{bmatrix} 1 & 4 \\ -1 & 1 \end{bmatrix} \cdot \begin{bmatrix} 2 & -1 \\ -1 & 2 \end{bmatrix} = \begin{bmatrix} -2 & 7 \\ -3 & 3 \end{bmatrix}.$$

This last example shows that multiplication is not commutative even in the case of square matrices.

The fact that "multiplication is not, in general, commutative" does not mean that we *never* have $AB = BA$. There are, in fact, important special cases when this equality holds. Examples will appear later in this chapter.

The familiar rule of scalar algebra that if a product is zero, then one of the factors must be zero, also fails to hold for matrix multiplication. An example is the product

$$\begin{bmatrix} 1 & 2 & 0 \\ 1 & 1 & 0 \\ -1 & 4 & 0 \end{bmatrix} \cdot \begin{bmatrix} 0 & 0 & 0 \\ 0 & 0 & 0 \\ 1 & 4 & 9 \end{bmatrix} = \begin{bmatrix} 0 & 0 & 0 \\ 0 & 0 & 0 \\ 0 & 0 & 0 \end{bmatrix}.$$

Here neither factor is a zero matrix, although the product is.

When a product $AB = 0$ but neither A nor B is 0, then the factors A and B are called **divisors of zero**. Thus, in the algebra of matrices, there exist divisors of zero whereas in the algebra of complex numbers there do not.

We make a final assault on the laws of scalar algebra by means of the following example. Let

$$A = \begin{bmatrix} 1 & 2 & 0 \\ 1 & 1 & 0 \\ -1 & 4 & 0 \end{bmatrix}, \qquad B = \begin{bmatrix} 1 & 2 & 3 \\ 1 & 1 & -1 \\ 2 & 2 & 2 \end{bmatrix}, \qquad C = \begin{bmatrix} 1 & 2 & 3 \\ 1 & 1 & -1 \\ 1 & 1 & 1 \end{bmatrix}.$$

Then

$$AB = \begin{bmatrix} 3 & 4 & 1 \\ 2 & 3 & 2 \\ 3 & 2 & -7 \end{bmatrix} = AC.$$

Thus we can have $AB = AC$ without having $B = C$. In other words, we cannot ordinarily cancel A from $AB = AC$ even if $A \neq 0$. However, there is an important special case when the cancellation is possible, as we shall see later.

In summary, then, three fundamental properties of multiplication in scalar algebra do not carry over to matrix algebra:

(a) *The commutative law $AB = BA$ does not hold true generally.*

(b) *From $AB = 0$, we cannot conclude that at least one of A and B must be zero; that is, there exist divisors of zero.*

(c) *From $AB = AC$ or $BA = CA$ we cannot in general conclude that $B = C$, even if $A \neq 0$; that is, the cancellation law does not hold in general in multiplication.*

These rather staggering losses might make one wonder whether matrix multiplication is not a nearly useless operation. This is, of course, not the case, for, as we shall prove, the most vital properties—the associative and the distributive laws—still remain. However, it should be clear at this point why we have been, and must continue to be, so careful to prove the validity of the matrix operations which we employ.

Theorem 1.8.1:   *The multiplication of matrices is associative.*

Let

$$A = [a_{ij}]_{(m,n)}, \qquad B = [b_{jk}]_{(n,p)}, \qquad C = [c_{kr}]_{(p,q)}.$$

Then the theorem says that

$$(AB)C = A(BC).$$

Applying the definition of multiplication, we see first that

$$AB = \left[\sum_{j=1}^{n} a_{ij}b_{jk} \right]_{(m,p)}$$

Here i ranges from 1 to m and denotes the row of the element in parentheses, whereas k ranges from 1 to p and denotes its column.

We apply the definition now to AB and C. The new summation will be on the column subscript k of AB, which is the row subscript of C, so that

$$(AB)C = \left[\sum_{k=1}^{p} \left(\sum_{j=1}^{n} a_{ij}b_{jk} \right) c_{kr} \right]_{(m,q)}.$$

Multiplying the factor c_{kr} into each sum in parentheses, we obtain

$$(AB)C = \left[\sum_{k=1}^{p} \left(\sum_{j=1}^{n} a_{ij}b_{jk}c_{kr} \right) \right]_{(m,q)},$$

in which the row subscript i ranges from 1 to m while the column subscript r ranges from 1 to q.

In the same way we find

$$A(BC) = \left[\sum_{j=1}^{n} \left(\sum_{k=1}^{p} a_{ij}b_{jk}c_{kr} \right) \right]_{(m,q)}.$$

Since the order of summation is arbitrary in a finite sum, we have

$$\sum_{k=1}^{n} \left(\sum_{j=1}^{n} a_{ij}b_{jk}c_{kr} \right) = \sum_{j=1}^{n} \left(\sum_{k=1}^{p} a_{ij}b_{jk}c_{kr} \right)$$

for each pair of values of i and r, so that $(AB)C = A(BC)$.

If the uses made of the $\sum$ sign in this proof are unfamiliar to the reader, he may refer to an explanation of these matters in Appendix I. It would also help to write out the proof in full for 2×2 matrices.

Theorem 1.8.2: *Matrix multiplication is distributive with respect to addition.*

To make this explicit, let

$$A = [a_{ik}]_{(m,n)}, \qquad B = [b_{kj}]_{(n,p)}, \qquad C = [c_{kj}]_{(n,p)}.$$

Here A is conformable to B and also to C for multiplication, and B is conformable to C for addition. Then the theorem says that

$$A(B + C) = AB + AC.$$

Indeed

$$A(B + C) = [a_{ik}]_{(m,n)}[(b_{kj} + c_{kj})]_{(n,p)}$$

$$= \left[\sum_{k=1}^{n} a_{ik}(b_{kj} + c_{kj}) \right]_{(m,p)}$$

$$= \left[\sum_{k=1}^{n} a_{ik}b_{kj} + \sum_{k=1}^{n} a_{ik}c_{kj} \right]_{(m,p)}$$

$$= \left[\sum_{k=1}^{n} a_{ik}b_{kj} \right]_{(m,p)} + \left[\sum_{k=1}^{n} a_{ik}c_{kj} \right]_{(m,p)}$$

$$= AB + AC.$$

The theorem also says that, assuming conformability,

$$(D + E)F = DF + EF.$$

This second distributive law is distinct from the first, since matrix multiplication is not in general commutative. It is proved in the same manner as the first, however, and details are left to the reader.

The proofs of the last two theorems involve a detailed examination of the elements of the matrices involved. They are thus essentially scalar in nature. As the theory develops, we shall increasingly employ proofs involving only manipulations with matrices. Such proofs are typically more compact than are scalar-type proofs of the same results and, hence, are to be preferred. The reader's progress in learning *matrix* algebra will be accelerated if in the exercises he avoids the use of the scalar-type proof whenever this is possible. For example, to prove that, for conformable matrices,

$$(A + B)(C + D) = AC + BC + AD + BD,$$

we do not again resort to a scalar type of proof. We simply note that, by the first distributive law above, $(A + B)(C + D) = (A + B)C + (A + B)D$, so that, by the second distributive law,

$$(A + B)(C + D) = AC + BC + AD + BD.$$

1.9 Exercises

Throughout this book, exercises marked with an asterisk (*) develop an important part of the theory and should not be overlooked.

In many problems, conditions of conformability for addition or multiplication must be satisfied for the problem to have meaning. These conditions are usually rather obvious, so that we shall frequently omit statement of them. The reader is then expected to make the necessary assumptions in working the exercises.

In these exercises, the words "prove" and "show" are to be taken as synonymous.

1. Prove that $(A + B) - C = A + (B - C)$ and name each property used in the proof. Why is $(A - B) + C \neq A - (B + C)$ in general?

2. Perform the matrix multiplications:

(a) $\begin{bmatrix} 1 & -1 & 1 \\ 2 & 0 & 1 \\ 3 & -1 & 2 \end{bmatrix} \cdot \begin{bmatrix} 1 & 2 \\ -1 & 1 \\ 1 & 3 \end{bmatrix}$,

(b) $[1 \quad 2 \quad 3 \quad 4] \cdot \begin{bmatrix} 1 \\ 2 \\ 3 \\ 4 \end{bmatrix}$,

(c) $\begin{bmatrix} 1 & 0 & 0 \\ 0 & 1 & 0 \\ 0 & 0 & 1 \end{bmatrix} \cdot \begin{bmatrix} a_1 & a_2 & a_3 \\ b_1 & b_2 & b_3 \\ c_1 & c_2 & c_3 \end{bmatrix}$,

(d) $\begin{bmatrix} \alpha_1 & 0 & 0 \\ 0 & \alpha_2 & 0 \\ 0 & 0 & \alpha_3 \end{bmatrix} \cdot \begin{bmatrix} a_1 & a_2 \\ b_1 & b_2 \\ c_1 & c_2 \end{bmatrix}$,

(e) $\begin{bmatrix} a_1 & a_2 \\ b_1 & b_2 \\ c_1 & c_2 \end{bmatrix} \cdot \begin{bmatrix} \alpha_1 & 0 \\ 0 & \alpha_2 \end{bmatrix},$

(f) $\begin{bmatrix} 1 \\ 2 \\ 3 \\ 4 \end{bmatrix} \cdot [1 \quad 2 \quad 3 \quad 4],$

(g) $[2 \quad 1 \quad -1] \begin{bmatrix} 4 & -1 & 2 \\ -1 & 0 & 1 \\ 2 & 1 & 0 \end{bmatrix} \cdot \begin{bmatrix} 2 \\ 1 \\ -1 \end{bmatrix},$

(h) $\begin{bmatrix} 1 & 0 \\ i & 1 \end{bmatrix} \cdot \begin{bmatrix} 1 & i \\ -i & 0 \end{bmatrix} \cdot \begin{bmatrix} 1 & -i \\ 0 & 1 \end{bmatrix},$

where $i^2 = -1$.

3. (a) Using

$$A = \begin{bmatrix} 1 & -1 & 1 \\ 2 & 0 & 1 \end{bmatrix}, \quad B = \begin{bmatrix} 1 & -1 & 0 \\ 0 & 1 & -1 \\ 1 & 1 & 1 \end{bmatrix}, \quad C = \begin{bmatrix} 1 & 0 \\ 0 & 1 \\ 1 & 1 \end{bmatrix},$$

test the rule $(AB)C = A(BC)$.

(b) Under what conditions is a matrix product $ABCD$ defined? According to the associative law, what are the various ways of computing it?

4. Prove in detail the second distributive law

$$(D + E)F = DF + EF.$$

5. Given that A is a square matrix, define $A^{p+1} = A^p \cdot A$ for $p \geqslant 1$. By induction on q, prove that, for each positive integer p,

$$A^p A^q = A^{p+q} \quad \text{and} \quad (A^p)^q = A^{pq}$$

for all positive integers q. (Note that neither the definition nor the proof is of the scalar type.)

6. If $A = \begin{bmatrix} 0 & i \\ i & 0 \end{bmatrix}$, compute A^2, A^3, A^4. (Here $i^2 = -1$.) Give a general rule for A^n. (You may treat the cases n even and n odd separately.)

***7.** Show that, if $\alpha A = 0$ where α is a scalar, then either $\alpha = 0$ or $A = 0$. Show also that, if $\alpha A = \alpha B$ and $\alpha \neq 0$, then $A = B$, and that, if $A = B$, then $\alpha A = \alpha B$ for all scalars α.

***8.** Prove:

(a) $\alpha A \cdot \beta B = \alpha \beta \cdot AB$ (α, β scalars).

(b) $(-1) \cdot A = -A$.

(c) $(-A) \cdot (-B) = AB$.

(d) $A(\alpha B) = (\alpha A)B = \alpha(AB)$.

9. (a) Explain why in matrix algebra

$$(A + B)^2 \neq A^2 + 2AB + B^2,$$

and

$$(A + B)(A - B) \neq A^2 - B^2,$$

except in special cases. Under what circumstances would equality hold?

(b) Expand $(A + B)^3$.

10. Let $AB = C$ where A and B are of order n. If, in the ith row of A, $a_{ik} = 1$, where i and k are fixed, but all other elements of the ith row are zero, what can be said about the ith row of C? What is the analogous fact for columns?

11. Let A, B be of order n and let

$$C_1 = \alpha_1 A + \beta_1 B,$$
$$C_2 = \alpha_2 A + \beta_2 B,$$

where α_1, α_2, β_1, β_2 are scalars such that $\alpha_1 \beta_2 \neq \alpha_2 \beta_1$. Show that $C_1 C_2 = C_2 C_1$ if and only if $AB = BA$.

12. Let

$$A = \begin{bmatrix} 3 & 4 & 2 \\ -2 & -1 & -1 \\ -1 & -3 & -1 \end{bmatrix}, \qquad B = \begin{bmatrix} -1 & -1 & -1 \\ 2 & 2 & 2 \\ 1 & 1 & 1 \end{bmatrix}.$$

Compare the products AB and BA.

13. For what values of x will

$$\begin{bmatrix} x & 4 & 1 \end{bmatrix} \cdot \begin{bmatrix} 2 & 1 & 0 \\ 1 & 0 & 2 \\ 0 & 2 & 4 \end{bmatrix} \cdot \begin{bmatrix} x \\ 4 \\ 1 \end{bmatrix} = 0?$$

*14. A square matrix of the form

$$D_n = \begin{bmatrix} d_{11} & 0 & \cdots & 0 \\ 0 & d_{22} & \cdots & 0 \\ \vdots & & & \\ 0 & 0 & \cdots & d_{nn} \end{bmatrix},$$

that is, one in which $d_{ij} = 0$ if $i \neq j$, is called a **diagonal matrix** of order n. (Note that this does *not* say $d_{ii} \neq 0$.) Let A be any matrix of order (p, q) and evaluate the products $D_p A$ and $A D_q$. Describe the results in words. What happens in the special cases $d_{11} = d_{22} = \cdots = \alpha$ and $d_{11} = d_{22} = \cdots = 1$?

*15. (a) Show that any two diagonal matrices of the same order commute.

(b) Give a formula for D^p where D is diagonal and p is a positive integer.

(c) Show that if D is diagonal with *non-negative* elements, then $A D^p = D^p A$ if and only if $AD = DA$.

16. Prove by induction that if B, C are of order n and if $A = B + C, C^2 = 0$, and $BC = CB$, then for every positive integer k, $A^{k+1} = B^k(B + (k + 1)C)$.

17. If $AB = BA$, the matrices A and B are said to be **commutative** or to **commute**. Show that for all values of a, b, c, d, the matrices

$$A = \begin{bmatrix} a & b \\ -b & a \end{bmatrix} \quad \text{and} \quad B = \begin{bmatrix} c & d \\ -d & c \end{bmatrix}$$

commute.

18. What must be true about a, b, c, d if the matrices

$$\begin{bmatrix} a & b \\ c & d \end{bmatrix} \quad \text{and} \quad \begin{bmatrix} 1 & 1 \\ -1 & 1 \end{bmatrix}$$

are to commute?

19. If $AB = -BA$, the matrices A and B are said to be **anticommutative** or to **anticommute**. Show that each of the matrices

$$\sigma_x = \begin{bmatrix} 0 & 1 \\ 1 & 0 \end{bmatrix}, \quad \sigma_y = \begin{bmatrix} 0 & -i \\ i & 0 \end{bmatrix}, \quad \sigma_z = \begin{bmatrix} 1 & 0 \\ 0 & -1 \end{bmatrix}, \quad (i^2 = -1),$$

anticommutes with the others. These are the **Pauli spin matrices** which are used in the study of electron spin in quantum mechanics.

20. The matrix $AB - BA$ (A and B of order n) is called the **commutator** of A and B. Using Exercise 19, show that the commutators of σ_x and σ_y, σ_y and σ_z, and σ_z and σ_x are respectively $2i\sigma_z$, $2i\sigma_x$, and $2i\sigma_y$.

*21. Show by induction that, if A is square and $AB = \lambda B$, where λ is a scalar, then $A^p B = \lambda^p B$ for every positive integer p.

22. If

$$A_i = \begin{bmatrix} \cos \theta_i & -\sin \theta_i \\ \sin \theta_i & \cos \theta_i \end{bmatrix}, \quad i = 1, 2,$$

show that A_1 and A_2 commute. What is the connection with transformations used in plane analytic geometry?

23. The sum of the main diagonal elements a_{ii}, $i = 1, 2, \ldots, n$, of a square matrix A is called the **trace** of A:

$$\operatorname{tr} A = a_{11} + a_{22} + \cdots + a_{nn}.$$

(a) If A and B are of order n, show that

$$\operatorname{tr} (A + B) = \operatorname{tr} A + \operatorname{tr} B.$$

(b) If C is of order (m, n) and G is of order (n, m), show that

$$\operatorname{tr} CG = \operatorname{tr} GC.$$

24. Prove that, if A has identical rows and AB is defined, AB has identical rows also.

25. A matrix A such that $A^p = 0$ for some positive integer p is called **nilpotent**. Show that every 2×2 nilpotent matrix A such that $A^2 = 0$ may be written in the form

$$\begin{bmatrix} \lambda\mu & \mu^2 \\ -\lambda^2 & -\lambda\mu \end{bmatrix},$$

where λ and μ are scalars, and that every such matrix is nilpotent. If A is real, must λ and μ also be real?

26. Given that $\alpha A = \beta A$ and $A \neq 0$, prove that $\alpha = \beta$ (α and β scalars).

27. Given that A, B, C all have order n, use Exercise 23(b) to show that

$$\operatorname{tr} ABC = \operatorname{tr} BCA = \operatorname{tr} CAB = \operatorname{tr} ACB = \operatorname{tr} BAC = \operatorname{tr} CBA.$$

What is the generalization of this observation?

28. A matrix A such that $A^2 = A$ is called **idempotent**. Determine all diagonal matrices of order n which are idempotent. How many are there?

29. Prove that conformability for addition is an equivalence relation for matrices whereas conformability for multiplication is not. What properties cannot, in consequence, hold for matrix multiplication?

30. Given that

$$
\begin{bmatrix} 1 & 0 & 0 \\ 0 & 2 & 0 \\ 0 & 0 & -3 \end{bmatrix} \cdot A \cdot \begin{bmatrix} 1 & 0 & 0 \\ 0 & 0 & 1 \\ 0 & 1 & 0 \end{bmatrix} = \begin{bmatrix} 1 & 2 & 3 \\ 4 & 5 & 4 \\ 3 & 2 & 1 \end{bmatrix},
$$

find the matrix A.

*31. Given that $AB = BA$, show that, for all positive integers r and s, $A^r B^s = B^s A^r$.

1.10 Linear Equations in Matrix Notation

In a great variety of applications of mathematics, there appear systems of linear equations of the general form

$$
\begin{aligned}
a_{11}x_1 + a_{12}x_2 + \cdots + a_{1n}x_n &= b_1 \\
a_{21}x_1 + a_{22}x_2 + \cdots + a_{2n}x_n &= b_2 \\
&\vdots \\
a_{m1}x_1 + a_{m2}x_2 + \cdots + a_{mn}x_n &= b_m,
\end{aligned}
$$

(1.10.1)

where the number m of equations is not necessarily equal to the number n of unknowns. In view of the definition of matrix multiplication, such a system of equations may be written as the single matrix equation

(1.10.2)
$$
\begin{bmatrix} a_{11} & a_{12} & \cdots & a_{1n} \\ a_{21} & a_{22} & \cdots & a_{2n} \\ \vdots & & & \\ a_{m1} & a_{m2} & \cdots & a_{mn} \end{bmatrix} \cdot \begin{bmatrix} x_1 \\ x_2 \\ \vdots \\ x_n \end{bmatrix} = \begin{bmatrix} b_1 \\ b_2 \\ \vdots \\ b_m \end{bmatrix}.
$$

In fact, if we compute the matrix product on the left, this equation becomes

(1.10.3)
$$
\begin{bmatrix}
(a_{11}x_1 + a_{12}x_2 + \cdots + a_{1n}x_n) \\
(a_{21}x_1 + a_{22}x_2 + \cdots + a_{2n}x_n) \\
\vdots \\
(a_{m1}x_1 + a_{m2}x_2 + \cdots + a_{mn}x_n)
\end{bmatrix}
=
\begin{bmatrix}
b_1 \\
b_2 \\
\vdots \\
b_m
\end{bmatrix}.
$$

Since these two matrices are equal if and only if all their corresponding elements are equal, this single equation is equivalent to the system of (1.10.1). If we now put

$$
A =
\begin{bmatrix}
a_{11} & a_{12} & \cdots & a_{1n} \\
a_{21} & a_{22} & \cdots & a_{2n} \\
\vdots & & & \\
a_{m1} & a_{m2} & \cdots & a_{mn}
\end{bmatrix},
\qquad
X =
\begin{bmatrix}
x_1 \\
x_2 \\
\vdots \\
x_n
\end{bmatrix},
\qquad
B =
\begin{bmatrix}
b_1 \\
b_2 \\
\vdots \\
b_m
\end{bmatrix},
$$

the bulky equation (1.10.2) may be written in the highly compact form

(1.10.4) $AX = B.$

When a system of equations is written in the form (1.10.2) or (1.10.4), in which one matrix equation replaces the entire system of scalar equations, it is said to be represented in the **matrix notation**.

Single column matrices, such as X and B in the above discussion, are called **vectors**. The relation between this concept of a vector and the usual one will be developed later. For the present, *a vector is simply a column matrix*. The elements of such a matrix are commonly called its **components**. The vector X above is called an **n-vector** since it has n components. By the same token, B is an m-vector. Frequently, to save space, an n-vector is written in the form $\{a_1, a_2, \ldots, a_n\}$, the curly braces being used to identify it as a column matrix. In some books **row matrices**, i.e., matrices consisting of a single row, are also called vectors.

By using this new terminology, we see that, whenever we know a set of values of $x_1, x_2, \ldots, x_n$ which simultaneously satisfy the scalar equations (1.10.1), we also know the components of a vector which satisfies the matrix equation (1.10.4), and conversely. Such a vector is called a **solution** of (1.10.4). The problems of solving the system of scalar equations (1.10.1) and of solving the matrix equation (1.10.4) are thus seen to be equivalent. In Chapter Five, we shall treat the solution of such equations in detail.

1.11 The Transpose of a Matrix

The matrix A^T of order (n, m) obtained by interchanging rows and columns in a matrix A of order (m, n) is called the **transpose** of A. For example, the transpose of

$$\begin{bmatrix} 2 & 0 & -1 \\ 1 & 1 & 4 \end{bmatrix} \quad \text{is} \quad \begin{bmatrix} 2 & 1 \\ 0 & 1 \\ -1 & 4 \end{bmatrix}.$$

Theorem 1.11.1:   *If A^T and B^T are the transposes of A and B, and if α is a scalar, then:*

(a) $(A^\mathsf{T})^\mathsf{T} = A$.
(b) $(A + B)^\mathsf{T} = A^\mathsf{T} + B^\mathsf{T}$.
(c) $(\alpha A)^\mathsf{T} = \alpha A^\mathsf{T}$.
(d) $(AB)^\mathsf{T} = B^\mathsf{T} A^\mathsf{T}$.

The first three of these rules are easy to think through. Detailed proofs are left to the reader. Only (d) will be proved here. Let $A = [a_{ik}]_{(m,n)}$, $B = [b_{kj}]_{(n,p)}$. Then $AB = [c_{ij}]_{(m,p)}$, where $c_{ij} = \sum_{k=1}^{n} a_{ik}b_{kj}$. Here i, ranging from 1 to m, identifies the row, and j, ranging from 1 to p, identifies the column of the element c_{ij}.

Now B^T is of order (p, n) and A^T is of order (n, m), so that B^T is conformable to A^T for multiplication. To compute the element γ_{ji} in the jth row and the ith column of $B^\mathsf{T} A^\mathsf{T}$, we must multiply the jth row of B^T into the ith column of A^T. Observing that the second subscript of an element in B or A identifies the row and the first subscript identifies the column in which it appears in B^T or A^T, we see that

$$B^\mathsf{T} A^\mathsf{T} = [\gamma_{ji}]_{(p,m)} = \left[\sum_{k=1}^{n} b_{kj} a_{ik} \right]_{(p,m)} = \left[\sum_{k=1}^{n} a_{ik} b_{kj} \right]_{(p,m)}.$$

Here j ranges from 1 to p and identifies the row of γ_{ji}, whereas i ranges from 1 to m and identifies the column. Thus $\gamma_{ji} = c_{ij}$ but with the meanings of i and j for rows and columns just opposite in the two cases, so that $B^\mathsf{T} A^\mathsf{T} = (AB)^\mathsf{T}$. The reader would do well to construct a numerical example.

The preceding proof illustrates the fact that the expression for the typical element of a matrix may at times assume a complicated form, but that an essential aspect of the expression is a *pair of subscripts* which may be used to identify the row and the column of the element. Such subscripts are called **free subscripts**. Thus, in the above expression,

$$c_{ij} = \sum_{k=1}^{n} a_{ik}b_{kj},$$

the free subscripts are i and j. Moreover, i is used to designate the row and j the column of the element. The index k is an **index of summation**. It has nothing to do with the row–column position of the element c_{ij}. On the other hand, in the expression

$$\gamma_{ji} = \sum_{k=1}^{n} b_{kj} a_{ik}$$

used in the foregoing, the free subscripts j and i designate respectively the row and the column of the element γ_{ji}. This illustrates the fact that, whereas the index i is frequently used as a row index and j as a column index, this is not necessary nor is it always convenient. Any convenient index symbol may be used for either purpose. Indeed, in the sum represented by c_{ij} in the foregoing, the index k is used both ways—as a column index in a_{ik} and as a row index in b_{kj}. It is this freedom to use indices in both ways that enabled us to prove the foregoing theorem in a simple fashion.

As another example illustrating these matters, let

$$a_{ij} = \sum_{k=1}^{n} r_{ik} s_{jk},$$

where i denotes the row and j the column of the element a_{ij}. If i ranges from 1 to m and j from 1 to p, then we can interpret r_{ik} as the entry in the ith row and kth column of a matrix $R_{m \times n}$. In s_{jk}, k must play the role of a *row* index if we want to represent the matrix $A = [a_{ij}]_{m \times p}$ as a product. Assuming that normally the first subscript is the row subscript, it follows that the element s_{jk} is the element in the jth column and kth row of a matrix $(S_{p \times n})^{\mathsf{T}}$. That is

$$A = RS^{\mathsf{T}}.$$

Consider finally the sum

$$c_{ij} = \sum_{k_2=1}^{n} \sum_{k_1=1}^{n} a_{ik_1} a_{k_1 k_2} a_{k_2 j}, \qquad i,j = 1, 2, \ldots, n,$$

which we can write

$$c_{ij} = \sum_{k_2=1}^{n} \left(\sum_{k_1=1}^{n} a_{ik_1} a_{k_1 k_2} \right) a_{k_2 j}.$$

The sum in parentheses is the element in row i and column k_2 of A^2. Hence the second sum represents the element in row i and column j of $A^2 \cdot A$. That is, we have

$$[c_{ij}]_{n \times n} = A^3.$$

1.12 Symmetric, Skew-Symmetric, and Hermitian Matrices

A **symmetric matrix** is a square matrix A such that $A = A^{\mathsf{T}}$. A **skew-symmetric matrix** is a square matrix A such that $A = -A^{\mathsf{T}}$. These definitions may also be stated in terms of the individual elements: A is symmetric if and only if $a_{ij} = a_{ji}$ for all pairs of subscripts; it is skew-symmetric if and only if $a_{ij} = -a_{ji}$ for all pairs of subscripts. The reader should demonstrate the equivalence of the alternative definitions in each case.

The following are examples of symmetric and skew-symmetric matrices respectively:

$$
(a) \quad \begin{bmatrix} 0 & 1 & 2 \\ 1 & 2 & 3 \\ 2 & 3 & 4 \end{bmatrix}; \quad (b) \quad \begin{bmatrix} 0 & 1 & 2 \\ -1 & 0 & 3 \\ -2 & -3 & 0 \end{bmatrix}.
$$

Example (b) illustrates the fact that the main diagonal elements of a skew-symmetric matrix must all be zero. Why is this true?

A matrix is called a **real matrix** if and only if all its elements are real. In the applications, real symmetric matrices occur most frequently. However, matrices of complex elements are also of importance. When the elements of such a matrix A are replaced by their complex conjugates, the resulting matrix is called the **conjugate** of A and is denoted by $\bar{A}$. Evidently a matrix A is real if and only if $A = \bar{A}$. Transposing $\bar{A}$, we obtain the **transposed conjugate** or **tranjugate** $(\bar{A})^\mathsf{T}$ of A. This will be denoted by the symbol $A*$. ($A*$ is sometimes called the *adjoint* of A, but not in this book.) For example, if

$$
A = \begin{bmatrix} 1 - i & 2 \\ i & 1 + i \end{bmatrix},
$$

then

$$
\bar{A} = \begin{bmatrix} 1 + i & 2 \\ -i & 1 - i \end{bmatrix},
$$

and

$$
A* = \begin{bmatrix} 1 + i & -i \\ 2 & 1 - i \end{bmatrix}.
$$

When $A = A*$, that is, when $a_{ij} = \bar{a}_{ji}$ for all pairs of subscripts, A is called a **Hermitian matrix** (after the French mathematician, Charles Hermite, 1822–1901). When matrices of complex elements appear in the applications, for example, in the theory of atomic physics, they are often Hermitian. The matrices

$$
\begin{bmatrix} 0 & i \\ -i & 0 \end{bmatrix} \quad \text{and} \quad \begin{bmatrix} 4 & 1 - i \\ 1 + i & 2 \end{bmatrix}
$$

are simple examples of Hermitian matrices, as is readily verified. Why must the diagonal elements of a Hermitian matrix all be real numbers?

If the elements of A are real, $A^\mathsf{T} = A^*$, so that the property of being real and symmetric is a special case of the property of being Hermitian. The following pages will contain a great many results about Hermitian matrices. The reader interested only in the real case may interpret the word "Hermitian" as "symmetric," and all will be well.

1.13 Scalar Matrices

A square matrix of the form

$$\begin{bmatrix} \alpha & 0 & 0 & \cdots & 0 \\ 0 & \alpha & 0 & \cdots & 0 \\ \vdots & & & & \\ 0 & 0 & 0 & \cdots & \alpha \end{bmatrix}_n$$

in which each element of the main diagonal equals the scalar α and all other elements are zero, is called a **scalar matrix** of order n. In matrix multiplication, a scalar matrix behaves like a scalar, as the following equations show:

$$\begin{bmatrix} \alpha & 0 & \cdots & 0 \\ 0 & \alpha & \cdots & 0 \\ \vdots & & & \\ 0 & 0 & \cdots & \alpha \end{bmatrix}_m \cdot \begin{bmatrix} a_{11} & a_{12} & \cdots & a_{1n} \\ a_{21} & a_{22} & \cdots & a_{2n} \\ \vdots & & & \\ a_{m1} & a_{m2} & \cdots & a_{mn} \end{bmatrix}$$

$$= \begin{bmatrix} a_{11} & a_{12} & \cdots & a_{1n} \\ a_{21} & a_{22} & \cdots & a_{2n} \\ \vdots & & & \\ a_{m1} & a_{m2} & \cdots & a_{mn} \end{bmatrix} \cdot \begin{bmatrix} \alpha & 0 & \cdots & 0 \\ 0 & \alpha & \cdots & 0 \\ \vdots & & & \\ 0 & 0 & \cdots & \alpha \end{bmatrix}_n = \alpha \begin{bmatrix} a_{11} & a_{12} & \cdots & a_{1n} \\ a_{21} & a_{22} & \cdots & a_{2n} \\ \vdots & & & \\ a_{m1} & a_{m2} & \cdots & a_{mn} \end{bmatrix}.$$

The scalar matrices are even more fundamentally like scalars, however, for if α and β are any two scalars, and if

(1.13.1)
$$\alpha + \beta = \gamma,$$
$$\alpha\beta = \delta,$$

then

$$
\begin{bmatrix}
\alpha & 0 & \cdots & 0 \\
0 & \alpha & \cdots & 0 \\
\vdots & & & \\
0 & 0 & \cdots & \alpha
\end{bmatrix}_n
+
\begin{bmatrix}
\beta & 0 & \cdots & 0 \\
0 & \beta & \cdots & 0 \\
\vdots & & & \\
0 & 0 & \cdots & \beta
\end{bmatrix}_n
=
\begin{bmatrix}
\gamma & 0 & \cdots & 0 \\
0 & \gamma & \cdots & 0 \\
\vdots & & & \\
0 & 0 & \cdots & \gamma
\end{bmatrix}_n ,
$$

(1.13.2)

$$
\begin{bmatrix}
\alpha & 0 & \cdots & 0 \\
0 & \alpha & \cdots & 0 \\
\vdots & & & \\
0 & 0 & \cdots & \alpha
\end{bmatrix}_n
\cdot
\begin{bmatrix}
\beta & 0 & \cdots & 0 \\
0 & \beta & \cdots & 0 \\
\vdots & & & \\
0 & 0 & \cdots & \beta
\end{bmatrix}_n
=
\begin{bmatrix}
\delta & 0 & \cdots & 0 \\
0 & \delta & \cdots & 0 \\
\vdots & & & \\
0 & 0 & \cdots & \delta
\end{bmatrix}_n .
$$

These equations show that corresponding to the arithmetic of the real numbers, for example, there is a strictly analogous arithmetic of scalar matrices of a fixed order n in which the scalar matrix with main diagonal elements α corresponds to the real number α. In the same way, corresponding to the arithmetic of complex numbers, there is an analogous arithmetic of scalar matrices the main diagonal elements of which are complex numbers. Many other examples of such a correspondence between a set of scalars and a corresponding set of scalar matrices could be constructed.

There are three essential points to be noted in this situation. First, we deal with a collection $\mathscr{S}$ of scalars such that, if α and β belong to $\mathscr{S}$, and if $\alpha + \beta = \gamma$, $\alpha\beta = \delta$, then γ and δ also belong to $\mathscr{S}$. (In the two examples cited in the foregoing, the sum and the product of two real numbers are again real numbers, and the sum and the product of two complex numbers are again complex numbers.) Secondly, we deal with a collection $\mathscr{M}$ of scalar matrices of a fixed order n such that to each scalar α in $\mathscr{S}$ there corresponds the unique scalar matrix of $\mathscr{M}$ the main diagonal elements of which are all equal to α. Conversely, to each scalar matrix in $\mathscr{M}$ with diagonal elements α there corresponds the unique scalar α of $\mathscr{S}$. That is, the scalars in $\mathscr{S}$ are in *one-to-one correspondence* with the scalar matrices in $\mathscr{M}$. The third point to be noted is that, if α and β are in the set $\mathscr{S}$ of scalars, and if (1.13.1) hold, then so do (1.13.2). That is, to the sum and the product of two scalars in $\mathscr{S}$ there correspond respectively the sum and the product of the corresponding scalar matrices of $\mathscr{M}$. This collection of ideas we identify by saying that the set $\mathscr{S}$ of scalars and the set $\mathscr{M}$ of corresponding matrices are **isomorphic**, or that there is an **isomorphism** between $\mathscr{S}$ and $\mathscr{M}$. [Isomorphic means *of the same* (iso-) *form* (morphos).]

The notion of isomorphism developed here is a particular application of a general concept of isomorphism which is one of the powerful tools of modern abstract algebra. (See Appendix III.)

1.14 The Identity Matrix

The scalar matrix of order n corresponding to the scalar 1 will be denoted by the symbol I_n, or simply by I if the order need not be emphasized:

$$I_n = \begin{bmatrix} 1 & 0 & 0 & \cdots & 0 \\ 0 & 1 & 0 & \cdots & 0 \\ \vdots & & & & \\ 0 & 0 & 0 & \cdots & 1 \end{bmatrix}_n.$$

It is called the **identity matrix** or the **unit matrix** of order n because it plays in matrix algebra the role corresponding to that played by the integer 1 in scalar algebra, as the isomorphism just explained would lead us to expect. However, the role extends beyond the domain of scalar matrices, for if A is any $m \times n$ matrix, we have

$$I_m A = A I_n = A,$$

as is readily verified.

From the isomorphism explained in the foregoing, it is clear that, since 1 is the only scalar satisfying the equations $xa = ax = a$ for every scalar a, I_n is likewise the only scalar matrix of order n satisfying the matrix equations $XA = AX = A$ for every scalar matrix A of order n. It therefore follows that I_n is the only matrix of order n satisfying the equations $XA = AX = A$ for every matrix A, scalar or not, of order n. This latter conclusion may also be proved directly. In fact, let B be any matrix of order n such that $AB = BA = A$ for *every* matrix A of order n. Letting $A = I_n$ in particular, we have $I_n B = B I_n = I_n$ or $B = I_n$; that is, the identity matrix is uniquely defined by the property that it behaves like the scalar 1 in matrix multiplication.

In conclusion, we note that every scalar matrix is related to the identity matrix as follows:

$$\begin{bmatrix} \alpha & 0 & \cdots & 0 \\ 0 & \alpha & \cdots & 0 \\ \vdots & & & \\ 0 & 0 & \cdots & \alpha \end{bmatrix}_n = \alpha I_n.$$

This is a convenient way of reducing bulky notation.

1.15 The Inverse of a Matrix

For any scalar $\alpha \neq 0$, there exists another scalar α^{-1}, the reciprocal or inverse of α, such that

$$\alpha\alpha^{-1} = \alpha^{-1}\alpha = 1.$$

The analogous equation for scalar matrices, indicated by the isomorphism just pointed out, is

$$(\alpha^{-1}I_n)(\alpha I_n) = (\alpha I_n)(\alpha^{-1}I_n) = I_n.$$

Hence we say that the matrix $\alpha^{-1}I_n$ is the *inverse* of the matrix αI_n, and we write

$$\alpha^{-1}I_n = (\alpha I_n)^{-1}, \qquad (\alpha \neq 0).$$

For example,

$$2 \cdot \tfrac{1}{2} = \tfrac{1}{2} \cdot 2 = 1,$$

and

$$\begin{bmatrix} 2 & 0 \\ 0 & 2 \end{bmatrix} \cdot \begin{bmatrix} \tfrac{1}{2} & 0 \\ 0 & \tfrac{1}{2} \end{bmatrix} = \begin{bmatrix} \tfrac{1}{2} & 0 \\ 0 & \tfrac{1}{2} \end{bmatrix} \cdot \begin{bmatrix} 2 & 0 \\ 0 & 2 \end{bmatrix} = \begin{bmatrix} 1 & 0 \\ 0 & 1 \end{bmatrix}.$$

From the isomorphism between scalars and scalar matrices, it follows that a nonzero scalar matrix has only one inverse which is a scalar matrix.

These observations lead us at once to a more general problem of which the foregoing is just a special case. This problem is to determine, when a matrix A of order n is given, any and all matrices B of the same order as A which have the property $AB = BA = I_n$. If such a matrix B exists, we call it an **inverse** of A.

Suppose now that we have both $AB = BA = I$ and $AC = CA = I$. Then, premultiplying both sides of $AC = I$ by B, we find $B(AC) = BI = B$. Similarly, from $BA = I$, we obtain $(BA)C = IC = C$. But $B(AC) = (BA)C$ by the associative law. Hence $B = C$. Thus we have

Theorem 1.15.1:   *A square matrix A has at most one inverse, that is, the inverse is unique if it exists.*

In view of this result, it is proper to refer to *the* inverse of a matrix A and to denote it by the convenient symbol A^{-1}, when the inverse exists.

In some cases, the inverse is readily found by inspection. For instance, we have, in the case of a diagonal matrix D,

$$D = \begin{bmatrix} d_1 & 0 & \cdots & 0 \\ 0 & d_2 & \cdots & 0 \\ \vdots & & & \\ 0 & 0 & \cdots & d_n \end{bmatrix} \quad \text{and} \quad D^{-1} = \begin{bmatrix} d_1^{-1} & 0 & \cdots & 0 \\ 0 & d_2^{-1} & \cdots & 0 \\ \vdots & & & \\ 0 & 0 & \cdots & d_n^{-1} \end{bmatrix},$$

provided that all the d_j are different from zero, for it is easily verified that, in this case, $DD^{-1} = D^{-1}D = I_n$.

That an inverse does not always exist is shown by the following example. The product

$$\begin{bmatrix} a & b \\ c & d \end{bmatrix} \cdot \begin{bmatrix} 0 & 1 \\ 0 & 0 \end{bmatrix} = \begin{bmatrix} 0 & a \\ 0 & c \end{bmatrix}$$

shows that there is no way to choose a, b, c, and d so as to make the right member equal to I_2. Hence the matrix $\begin{bmatrix} 0 & 1 \\ 0 & 0 \end{bmatrix}$ has no inverse.

That a nonsquare matrix does not have an inverse in the aforementioned sense follows from the fact that the products AB and BA cannot be equal in this case, whereas $AB = BA$ is required by the definition. Separate "left" and "right" inverses can be defined, however (see Exercise 8, Section 5.21).

Ordinarily, one cannot determine simply by casual inspection whether or not a given square matrix has an inverse. The answer to this question and a formula for the inverse are readily obtained from determinant theory, which we shall develop in the next chapter. Before turning to that matter, we shall examine two other applications of the concept of isomorphism.

1.16 The Product of a Row Matrix into a Column Matrix

The product of a row matrix into a column matrix is a matrix of order 1:

$$[x_1, x_2, \ldots, x_n]_{(1,n)} \cdot \{y_1, y_2, \ldots, y_n\}_{(n,1)}$$

$$= [(x_1y_1 + x_2y_2 + \cdots + x_ny_n)]_{(1,1)}.$$

Let the elements of the row matrix and the column matrix, and hence the element of their product, belong to a set of scalars $\mathscr{S}$ such as was described in Section 1.13. Now the set of all 1×1 matrices whose elements belong to $\mathscr{S}$ is isomorphic to $\mathscr{S}$. In fact, if α and β are any two scalars of $\mathscr{S}$, we have, for the corresponding 1×1 matrices, $[\alpha] + [\beta] = [\alpha + \beta]$ and $[\alpha][\beta] = [\alpha\beta]$, so that the matrices behave exactly like scalars with respect to addition and multiplication. Furthermore, the 1×1 matrices have no important properties not possessed by scalars. Hence *we redefine the product of a row matrix into a column matrix to be the scalar corresponding to the 1×1 product matrix, thus*:

$$[x_1, x_2, \ldots, x_n] \cdot \{y_1, y_2, \ldots, y_n\} = (x_1y_1 + x_2y_2 + \cdots + x_ny_n).$$

This kind of product arises most commonly in the form $X^\mathsf{T}Y$, where X and Y are both column matrices, that is, vectors. It is called the **scalar product** of the two vectors. Whereas one may treat every 1×1 matrix product as a scalar, one can replace a scalar by a product of matrices only if the rule of conformability is satisfied.

There is another, closely related, function of two vectors X and Y. Reflecting the fact that X and Y may have complex elements, the **inner product** of X and Y, *in that order*, is defined to be X^*Y. The inner product is commonly denoted by the symbol $\langle X,\ Y \rangle$ so that

$$\langle X,\ Y \rangle = X^*Y = [\bar{x}_1, \bar{x}_2, \ldots, \bar{x}_n] \cdot \{y_1, y_2, \ldots, y_n\}$$

$$= \bar{x}_1 y_1 + \bar{x}_2 y_2 + \cdots + \bar{x}_n y_n.$$

In the particular case when X and Y are restricted to the real domain, this reduces to

$$\langle X,\ Y \rangle = X^\mathsf{T} Y = x_1 y_1 + x_2 y_2 + \cdots + x_n y_n,$$

that is, in the real case, the inner product and the scalar product are the same.

1.17 Polynomial Functions of Matrices

Consider a polynomial

$$f(x) = a_p x^p + a_{p-1} x^{p-1} + \cdots + a_1 x + a_0$$

of degree p in an indeterminate x, with either real or complex coefficients. With any such polynomial, we can associate a **polynomial function** of an $n \times n$ matrix A:

$$f(A) = a_p A^p + a_{p-1} A^{p-1} + \cdots + a_1 A + a_0 I_n$$

simply by replacing the constant term a_0 by the scalar matrix $a_0 I_n$ and by replacing x by A throughout. For example, if

$$f(x) = x^2 - 3x - 2,$$

then, for any matrix A of order n,

$$f(A) = A^2 - 3A - 2I_n.$$

Now suppose $f(x)$ and $g(x)$ have only real coefficients. Then if

$$f(x) + g(x) = h(x) \qquad \text{and} \qquad f(x) \cdot g(x) = q(x),$$

$h(x)$ and $q(x)$ are again polynomials with real coefficients. Moreover, since scalars commute with matrices, since the distributive and associative laws hold, and since the exponent laws hold for positive integral powers of A, we may conclude also that

$$f(A) + g(A) = h(A) \qquad \text{and} \qquad f(A) \cdot g(A) = q(A).$$

Hence the set of all real polynomials in an indeterminate x is isomorphic to the set of all real polynomials in an indeterminate matrix A of order n. A similar statement holds true for polynomials with complex coefficients.

This isomorphism implies that the matrix polynomial $f(A)$ is factorable in the same manner as the scalar polynomial $f(x)$. For example, if

$$f(x) = x^3 - 3x^2 + 2x = x(x - 1)(x - 2),$$

then

$$f(A) = A^3 - 3A^2 + 2A = A(A - I_n)(A - 2I_n).$$

Now suppose that the solutions of

$$f(x) = a_p x^p + a_{p-1} x^{p-1} + \cdots + a_1 x + a_0 = 0$$

are $\alpha_1, \alpha_2, \ldots, \alpha_p$ so that

$$f(x) \equiv a_p(x - \alpha_1)(x - \alpha_2) \cdots (x - \alpha_p).$$

Hence, by the isomorphism just explained,

(1.17.1) $$f(A) \equiv a_p(A - \alpha_1 I)(A - \alpha_2 I) \cdots (A - \alpha_p I),$$

so that the matrix equation $f(A) = 0$ has for solutions the *scalar* matrices $\alpha_1 I, \ldots, \alpha_p I$. Moreover, it has no other *scalar* matrices as solutions. However, since the product of matrices (1.17.1) may be zero even though no factor is zero, the equation $f(A) = 0$ may also have nonscalar matrices as solutions. For example, the equation

$$A^2 + I_2 = 0$$

has for solutions the scalar matrices

$$\begin{bmatrix} i & 0 \\ 0 & i \end{bmatrix}, \quad \begin{bmatrix} -i & 0 \\ 0 & -i \end{bmatrix},$$

corresponding to the solutions i and $-i$ of the equation $x^2 + 1 = 0$. It also has (among others) the nonscalar solution

$$\begin{bmatrix} 1 & 2 \\ -1 & -1 \end{bmatrix},$$

as the reader should verify.

The fact that in scalar algebra a polynomial equation of degree p in a single unknown x has exactly p solutions therefore does not hold true in matrix algebra, where the number of solutions is always at least p. The notion of isomorphism has thus led us to discover another important difference between matrix algebra and scalar algebra.

1.18 Exercises

1. (a) Verify that $B^\mathsf{T}A^\mathsf{T} = (AB)^\mathsf{T}$ when

$$A = \begin{bmatrix} 1 & -1 & 2 \\ 2 & 1 & 0 \end{bmatrix}, \qquad B = \begin{bmatrix} 1 & 2 \\ 2 & 0 \\ -1 & 1 \end{bmatrix}.$$

(b) Prove that $(A^\mathsf{T}B^\mathsf{T})^\mathsf{T} = BA$.

2. (a) Illustrate the definition of the equality of two matrices by writing the system of equations $x_j = a_j$, $j = 1, 2, \ldots, 12$, as a single matrix equation. Can you do this in more than one way?

(b) Interpret the matrix equation

$$\begin{bmatrix} 1 & -4 \\ 3 & 2 \end{bmatrix} \cdot \begin{bmatrix} 5 \\ -2 \end{bmatrix} = \begin{bmatrix} 13 \\ 11 \end{bmatrix}$$

as a fact about a system of linear equations in two unknowns.

(c) What is the geometrical significance of the matrix equation

$$\begin{bmatrix} x \\ y \end{bmatrix} = \begin{bmatrix} x_1 \\ y_1 \end{bmatrix} + t \begin{bmatrix} x_2 - x_1 \\ y_2 - y_1 \end{bmatrix}?$$

What is the corresponding equation in three dimensions?

*3. Generalize statements (b) and (d) of Theorem 1.11.1 and prove the generalized forms by induction.

*4. Show that ordinarily $AA^\mathsf{T} \neq A^\mathsf{T}A$, but that AA^T and $A^\mathsf{T}A$ are both symmetric. Also show that if A has real elements, the principal diagonal elements of AA^T and $A^\mathsf{T}A$ are non-negative.

5. What may be said about the main diagonal elements of AA^T when A is a real skew-symmetric matrix? What about those of A^2?

6. Show that if A is symmetric or skew-symmetric, $AA^\mathsf{T} = A^\mathsf{T}A$ and A^2 is symmetric.

7. Show that every square matrix A can be represented uniquely in the form

$$A = A^{(S)} + A^{(SS)}$$

where $A^{(S)}$ is symmetric and $A^{(SS)}$ is skew-symmetric. (Hint: If $A = A^{(S)} + A^{(SS)}$, then $A^\mathsf{T} = A^{(S)} - A^{(SS)}$, etc.)

8. Show by means of an example that even though A and B are both symmetric and are of the same order, AB need not necessarily be symmetric.

*9. Prove that if A and B of order n are both symmetric or both skew-symmetric *and commute*, then AB is symmetric.

10. Find by inspection inverses for the following matrices:

(a) $\begin{bmatrix} 1 & 1 & 0 \\ 0 & 1 & 1 \\ 0 & 0 & 1 \end{bmatrix}$, (b) $D = \begin{bmatrix} 0 & 0 & \cdots & 0 & d_n \\ 0 & 0 & \cdots & d_{n-1} & 0 \\ \vdots & & & & \\ 0 & d_2 & \cdots & 0 & 0 \\ d_1 & 0 & \cdots & 0 & 0 \end{bmatrix}$

(The elements $d_1, d_2, \ldots, d_n$ are assumed to be different from zero.)

(c) $\begin{bmatrix} 1 & 0 & 0 & 0 \\ 0 & 1 & 0 & 1 \\ 0 & 0 & 1 & 0 \\ 0 & 0 & 0 & 1 \end{bmatrix}$,   (d) $\begin{bmatrix} 0 & 0 & 1 & 0 \\ 0 & 1 & 0 & 0 \\ 1 & 0 & 0 & 0 \\ 0 & 0 & 0 & 1 \end{bmatrix}$,   (e) $\begin{bmatrix} 1 & 0 & 0 & 0 \\ 0 & 1 & 0 & 0 \\ 0 & 0 & 1 & 0 \\ a & b & c & 1 \end{bmatrix}$.

11. Evaluate the product

$$\begin{bmatrix} a_{11} & a_{12} \\ a_{21} & a_{22} \end{bmatrix} \cdot \begin{bmatrix} a_{22} & -a_{12} \\ -a_{21} & a_{11} \end{bmatrix},$$

and thereby determine an inverse for the first factor of the product. Under what conditions is there no inverse?

12. Find all scalar matrices which satisfy the matrix equations:

(a) $A^2 - 5A + 7I_2 = 0$.

(b) $2A^3 + 3A^2 - 4A - 6I_2 = 0$.

(c) $A^3 - I_n = 0$.

(d) $A^3 - A = 0$.

13. (a) Determine all diagonal matrices of order n which satisfy a polynomial matrix equation $f(A) = 0$ of degree p.

(b) Determine all solutions of the form $\begin{bmatrix} 0 & a \\ b & 0 \end{bmatrix}$ of the equation $A^3 + A = 0$.

14. Show that the nonscalar matrix

$$A = \begin{bmatrix} 3 & 1 \\ -1 & 2 \end{bmatrix}$$

is a solution of the equation $A^2 - 5A + 7I_2 = 0$.

15. Find all second-order matrices which satisfy the equation $A^2 - 2\alpha A + \beta I_2 = 0$. Specialize to the case $\alpha = 0$, $\beta = -1$, and interpret the results.

16. Prove that if $B = P^{-1}AP$, then $B^k = P^{-1}A^kP$. Hence show that, if

$$f(A) = a_p A^p + a_{p-1} A^{p-1} + \cdots + a_1 A + a_0 I = 0,$$

and if $B = P^{-1}AP$, then also $f(B) = 0$.

17. Show that, if α and β are real numbers, then the set of all matrices

$$\begin{bmatrix} \alpha & -\beta \\ \beta & \alpha \end{bmatrix}$$

is isomorphic to the set of all complex numbers $\alpha + i\beta$. Hence show that every such matrix has an inverse except when $\alpha = \beta = 0$. What is this inverse? Review also Exercise 17 in Section 1.9 in this connection.

18. (a) Use the isomorphism established in Exercise 17 to find two additional matrix roots of the equation given in Exercise 14.

(b) Find all square roots of the form

$$\begin{bmatrix} 0 & a \\ b & 0 \end{bmatrix} \quad (a,\, b \text{ real})$$

of the matrix

$$\begin{bmatrix} -\lambda^2 & 0 \\ 0 & -\lambda^2 \end{bmatrix},$$

where λ is real. The latter matrix corresponds to a negative number, but you will be finding square roots all elements of which are real. Use the isomorphism concept to explain the two simplest cases.

19. Show that

$$\sigma_x{}^2 = \sigma_y{}^2 = \sigma_z{}^2 = I_2{}^2 = I_2,$$

where σ_x, σ_y, σ_z are the Pauli spin matrices defined in Section 1.9, Exercise 19. What rule about roots in scalar algebra fails to carry over into matrix algebra?

*20. Show that, if α is a scalar, $(\alpha A)^* = \bar{\alpha} A^*$. Show also that $A = \bar{\bar{A}}$, $(\bar{A})^{\mathsf{T}} = \overline{(A^{\mathsf{T}})}$, $(A^*)^* = A$, $(A + B)^* = A^* + B^*$, $\overline{AB} = \bar{A}\bar{B}$, and $(AB)^* = B^*A^*$.

*21. Show that, for every matrix A, A^*A, and AA^* are Hermitian matrices. What may be said about the diagonal entries of A^*A and AA^*? Show also that, if H is Hermitian, so is B^*HB for every conformable matrix B.

22. Show that, if A and B are of order n, then A and B commute if and only if $A - \lambda I_n$ and $B - \lambda I_n$ commute for every scalar λ.

23. Show that any two polynomial functions of a square matrix A commute.

24. Show that arbitrary polynomials $f(A)$ and $g(B)$ in fixed matrices A and B of order n commute if and only if A and B commute. (It suffices to show that $A^rB^s = B^sA^r$ for all positive integers r and s if and only if $AB = BA$.)

25. Show that, if A and B are both $m \times n$ matrices, then $A = B$ if and only if $AX = BX$ for all n-vectors X.

Show similarly that $AX = 0$ for all n vectors X if and only if $A = 0$.

26. Show that a matrix A of order n is scalar if and only if it commutes with every matrix B of order n.

27. If A is square and if $A = -A^*$, that is, if $a_{ij} = -\bar{a}_{ji}$ for all i and j, A is called **skew-Hermitian**. Show that every square matrix A can be written in the form $A = A^{(H)} + A^{(SH)}$ where $A^{(H)}$ is Hermitian and $A^{(SH)}$ is skew-Hermitian. Show also that the diagonal elements of a skew-Hermitian matrix are pure imaginaries.

28. Show that every Hermitian matrix H may be written in the form $A + iB$, where A is real and symmetric, B is real and skew-symmetric, and $i^2 = -1$. Then show that H^*H is real if and only if $AB = -BA$, that is, if and only if A and B anticommute.

29. Give an example to illustrate that $\langle X, Y \rangle$ and $\langle Y, X \rangle$ are not always equal in the complex case.

30. Given that $A = [a_{ij}]_{n \times n}$ and $B = [b_{ij}]_{n \times n}$, represent each of the following as a matrix product:

$$\left[\sum_{k=1}^{n} a_{ik}b_{jk}\right], \qquad \left[\sum_{k=1}^{n} a_{ki}b_{jk}\right],$$

$$\left[\sum_{k=1}^{n} b_{ik}a_{kj}\right], \qquad \left[\sum_{k=1}^{n} b_{kj}a_{ik}\right].$$

Assume in each case that i designates the row and j the column of the element in the product.

*31. Denoting by E_j an n-vector with 1 in the jth row, all other components being 0, interpret each of the products

$$E_j{}^\mathsf{T}A, \qquad AE_j, \qquad E_i{}^\mathsf{T}AE_j, \qquad E_j{}^\mathsf{T}E_k, \qquad E_jE_k{}^\mathsf{T},$$

where A is an arbitrary matrix of order n. The vectors E_j are called the **elementary n-vectors**.

32. Let $W_n = \sum_{j=1}^{n} E_j$. Then how are AW_n and $W_n{}^\mathsf{T}A$ related to A? Evaluate $W_n{}^\mathsf{T}X$, where X is an arbitrary n-vector.

33. Suppose that $AB = C$, and let X denote a matrix with a single column whose elements are the sums of the elements in the corresponding rows of B. Similarly, let Y denote a column matrix whose elements are the row sums of C. Then show that $AX = Y$. (This fact may be used to check matrix multiplication and is useful in machine computation.) *Hint:* Use Exercise 32.

34. Evaluate each of the following products, then express the results in words. The E's are the n-vectors defined in Exercise 31.

$$(E_{i_1} + E_{i_2} + \cdots + E_{i_k})^\mathsf{T}A_{n \times m}, \qquad B_{p \times n}(E_{j_1} + E_{j_2} + \cdots + E_{j_r}),$$

$$(E_{i_1} + E_{i_2} + \cdots + E_{i_k})^\mathsf{T}C(E_{j_1} + E_{j_2} + \cdots + E_{j_r}).$$

35. Given that $X = \{x_1, x_2, \ldots, x_n\}$, show that

$$X^\mathsf{T}E_j = x_j,$$

and hence that

$$X = \sum_{j=1}^{n} (X^\mathsf{T}E_j)E_j.$$

Why can one not write $(X^\mathsf{T}E_j)E_j = X^\mathsf{T}(E_jE_j)$?

36. Denoting by E_{ij} an $n \times n$ matrix with a 1 in the ith row and jth column and 0's elsewhere, evaluate the products

$$E_{ij}E_{jk}, \qquad E_{ij}E_{km}, \qquad AE_{ij}, \qquad E_{ij}A, \qquad E_{ij}AE_{jk}, \qquad E_{ij}AE_{km}.$$

Show that

$$E_{ij} = E_iE_j{}^\mathsf{T}, \qquad E_{jj}{}^2 = E_{jj},$$

and

$$(E_{ij}E_{jk})^\mathsf{T} = E_{ki} = E_{kj}E_{ji}.$$

37. Show that, for arbitrary $n \times n$ matrices A and B,

$$A = \sum_{i,j=1}^{n} a_{ij}E_{ij}, \qquad B = \sum_{j,k=1}^{n} b_{jk}E_{jk},$$

and, hence, with the aid of the preceding exercise, that $(AB)^{\mathsf{T}} = B^{\mathsf{T}}A^{\mathsf{T}}$.

38. A matrix A such that $A^2 = I$ is called **involutory**. Show that A is involutory if and only if

$$(A - I)(A + I) = 0.$$

Does it follow that $A = I$ or $-I$? Why? Defend your answer with an example.

39. Determine all involutory matrices of the form

$$\begin{bmatrix} 1 & 2a & b & c \\ 0 & -1 & d & e \\ 0 & 0 & 1 & 2f \\ 0 & 0 & 0 & -1 \end{bmatrix}.$$

40. Express as matrix products if i denotes the row and j the column of the entry; $i = 1, 2, \ldots, m; j = 1, 2, \ldots, n$:

(a)
$$\left[\sum_{r=1}^{q} \left(\sum_{k=1}^{p} a_{ik}b_{kr} \right) c_{rj} \right].$$

(b)
$$\left[\sum_{r=1}^{q} c_{jr} \left(\sum_{k=1}^{p} a_{ki}b_{kr} \right) \right].$$

41. Given that

$$S_n = \begin{bmatrix} 0 & 1 & 0 & \cdots & 0 & 0 \\ 0 & 0 & 1 & \cdots & 0 & 0 \\ & \vdots & & & & \\ 0 & 0 & 0 & \cdots & 0 & 1 \\ 0 & 0 & 0 & \cdots & 0 & 0 \end{bmatrix}_n,$$

give a rule for evaluating S_nA, where A is any $n \times n$ matrix. Use this result to develop a rule for evaluating S_n^p, where p is any positive integer.

42. Given that $A = [a_{ij}]_{m \times n}$, evaluate S_mA, AS_n, $S_m^{\mathsf{T}}A$, AS_n^{T}, $S_m^{\mathsf{T}}AS_n$, $S_mAS_n^{\mathsf{T}}$, $S_m^pAS_n^q$.

43. Given that $f(x) = a_0 + a_1x + a_2x^2 + \cdots + a_rx^r + \cdots$, show that

$$f(S_n) = \begin{bmatrix} a_0 & a_1 & a_2 & \cdots & a_{n-2} & a_{n-1} \\ 0 & a_0 & a_1 & \cdots & a_{n-3} & a_{n-2} \\ 0 & 0 & a_0 & \cdots & a_{n-4} & a_{n-3} \\ & \vdots & & & & \\ 0 & 0 & 0 & \cdots & a_0 & a_1 \\ 0 & 0 & 0 & \cdots & 0 & a_0 \end{bmatrix},$$

where S_n is as defined in Exercise 41.

44. A square matrix A such that $a_{ij} = 0$ whenever $i \geqslant j$ is called an **upper matrix**. For example,

$$\begin{bmatrix} 0 & -1 & 3 \\ 0 & 0 & 2 \\ 0 & 0 & 0 \end{bmatrix}$$

is an upper matrix. Prove that every upper matrix U is nilpotent.

45. A square matrix B such that B^{T} is upper is called a **lower matrix**. Prove that every lower matrix is nilpotent.

46. Show that the sum and the product of any two $n \times n$ upper matrices whose elements are complex numbers or functions thereof are again upper matrices, that is, that the set of all such matrices is closed under the operations of addition and multiplication.

47. Let U denote an upper matrix of order n. Prove that $(I_n + U)^p = I_n$ if and only if $U = 0$. (*Hint:* Expand the left member, then consider successively the **superdiagonals**, that is, the diagonals above the main diagonal, of U.)

48. Prove that, if U is nilpotent and if $U^n = 0$ but $U^{n-1} \neq 0$, then $I + U$ has an inverse, namely,

$$(I + U)^{-1} = I - U + U^2 - U^3 + \cdots + (-1)^{n-1}U^{n-1}.$$

49. Prove that, if U is nilpotent and the polynomial $f(x)$ has no constant term, then $f(U)$ is nilpotent.

50. Prove that, if U is nilpotent and $(I + U)^p = I$, then

$$U(I + f(U)) = 0,$$

where $f(U)$ is a polynomial with constant term zero.

51. Use Exercises 48, 49, 50 to show that, if U is nilpotent and $(I + U)^p = I$, then $U = 0$.

52. Given that $t_k = \operatorname{tr} A^k$, where A is of order n, prove that, for every positive integer k,

$$\left[\frac{\partial t_k}{\partial a_{ij}}\right]^{\mathsf{T}} = kA^{k-1}.$$

THE PARTITIONING OF MATRICES

1.19 Partitioned Matrices

At many points in the following chapters we shall find it desirable to subdivide or partition matrices into rectangular blocks of elements. We shall now investigate the consequences of treating these blocks as matrices, that is, of treating the original matrix as a matrix whose elements are matrices. The blocks are called **submatrices** of the original matrix.

Before proceeding formally, we give a few illustrations. If there were any advantage to it, we could write, for example,

$$\begin{bmatrix} 1 & 0 \\ -1 & -3 \\ 2 & 1 \end{bmatrix},$$

as $[A_1, A_2]$, where

$$A_1 = \begin{bmatrix} 1 \\ -1 \\ 2 \end{bmatrix} \quad \text{and} \quad A_2 = \begin{bmatrix} 0 \\ -3 \\ 1 \end{bmatrix},$$

or as

$$\begin{bmatrix} B_1 \\ B_2 \\ B_3 \end{bmatrix}$$

where

$$B_1 = [1, \quad 0], \quad B_2 = [-1, \quad -3], \quad B_3 = [2, \quad 1],$$

or as

$$\begin{bmatrix} C_1 \\ C_2 \end{bmatrix}$$

where

$$C_1 = \begin{bmatrix} 1 & 0 \\ -1 & -3 \end{bmatrix} \quad \text{and} \quad C_2 = [2, \quad 1].$$

The manner in which a matrix is to be partitioned is often indicated by dashed lines, and the resulting parts of the given matrix are then treated as submatrices thereof. Thus

$$\begin{bmatrix} 1 & 2 & -1 \\ 3 & 0 & 2 \\ 1 & 1 & 1 \end{bmatrix} = \left[\begin{array}{cc:c} 1 & 2 & -1 \\ 3 & 0 & 2 \\ \hdashline 1 & 1 & 1 \end{array}\right] = \begin{bmatrix} A & B \\ C & D \end{bmatrix},$$

where A, B, C, and D denote the submatrices.

As in the preceding example, we shall say that two matrices, partitioned or not, are **equal** if and only if their nonpartitioned forms are equal.

Of course, if we wish to treat these blocks of elements as matrices, we must do so subject to all the laws of computation with matrices. For example, if we wish to write the equation

$$\begin{bmatrix} A_1 & B_1 \\ C_1 & D_1 \end{bmatrix} + \begin{bmatrix} A_2 & B_2 \\ C_2 & D_2 \end{bmatrix} = \begin{bmatrix} (A_1 + A_2) & (B_1 + B_2) \\ (C_1 + C_2) & (D_1 + D_2) \end{bmatrix},$$

we must first make sure that A_1 and A_2 have the same order, and similarly for B_1 and B_2, C_1 and C_2, D_1 and D_2.

In general, let A and B be matrices of the same order. We shall then say that A and B are **identically partitioned** if the resulting matrices *of matrices* contain the same number of rows and the same number of columns and if, in addition, corresponding blocks have the same order. Thus the matrices

$$\begin{bmatrix} 1 & -2 & 3 \\ 4 & -1 & 6 \\ \hline 1 & 1 & 1 \end{bmatrix} \quad \text{and} \quad \begin{bmatrix} a & b & c \\ d & e & f \\ \hline g & h & k \end{bmatrix}$$

are identically partitioned. It is then a simple matter to see that identically partitioned matrices are equal if and only if corresponding submatrices are equal throughout and that they may be added by adding corresponding submatrices throughout.

To show how partitioning into submatrices is used in the multiplication of matrices, we consider first several examples.

(1) Let

$$A = \begin{bmatrix} 1 & 0 & 2 \\ 0 & 1 & -2 \end{bmatrix} \quad \text{and} \quad B = \begin{bmatrix} 1 & 0 \\ 0 & 1 \\ \hline 3 & -1 \end{bmatrix}.$$

Then we observe that if we treat the submatrices as if they were elements, we have

$$\begin{bmatrix} \begin{bmatrix} 1 & 0 \\ 0 & 1 \end{bmatrix} & \begin{bmatrix} 2 \\ -2 \end{bmatrix} \end{bmatrix} \cdot \begin{bmatrix} \begin{bmatrix} 1 & 0 \\ 0 & 1 \end{bmatrix} \\ [3 \ -1] \end{bmatrix} = \begin{bmatrix} \begin{bmatrix} 1 & 0 \\ 0 & 1 \end{bmatrix} \cdot \begin{bmatrix} 1 & 0 \\ 0 & 1 \end{bmatrix} + \begin{bmatrix} 2 \\ -2 \end{bmatrix} \cdot [3 \ -1] \end{bmatrix}$$

$$= \begin{bmatrix} \begin{bmatrix} 1 & 0 \\ 0 & 1 \end{bmatrix} + \begin{bmatrix} 6 & -2 \\ -6 & 2 \end{bmatrix} \end{bmatrix} = \begin{bmatrix} 7 & -2 \\ -6 & 3 \end{bmatrix}$$

$$= AB.$$

(2) Let

$$A = \begin{bmatrix} 2 & 1 & 0 & 0 \\ 1 & -1 & 0 & 0 \\ 0 & 0 & 0 & 1 \\ 0 & 0 & 2 & 0 \end{bmatrix} \quad \text{and} \quad B = \begin{bmatrix} 0 & 0 & 1 & 0 \\ 0 & 0 & 0 & 1 \\ 0 & 2 & 0 & 0 \\ -2 & 0 & 0 & 0 \end{bmatrix}.$$

Then, again treating the submatrices as though they were elements, we note that because of the zero matrices appearing we have as the product

$$\begin{bmatrix} \begin{bmatrix} 0 & 0 \\ 0 & 0 \end{bmatrix} & \begin{bmatrix} 2 & 1 \\ 1 & -1 \end{bmatrix} \cdot \begin{bmatrix} 1 & 0 \\ 0 & 1 \end{bmatrix} \\ \begin{bmatrix} 0 & 1 \\ 2 & 0 \end{bmatrix} \cdot \begin{bmatrix} 0 & 2 \\ -2 & 0 \end{bmatrix} & \begin{bmatrix} 0 & 0 \\ 0 & 0 \end{bmatrix} \end{bmatrix} = \begin{bmatrix} 0 & 0 & 2 & 1 \\ 0 & 0 & 1 & -1 \\ -2 & 0 & 0 & 0 \\ 0 & 4 & 0 & 0 \end{bmatrix} = AB.$$

Note that when the multiplication is complete, the internal brackets may be dropped.

(3) Let

$$A = \begin{bmatrix} a_{11} & a_{12} & a_{13} \\ a_{21} & a_{22} & a_{23} \\ a_{31} & a_{32} & a_{33} \end{bmatrix} \quad \text{and} \quad B = \begin{bmatrix} b_{11} & b_{12} \\ b_{21} & b_{22} \\ b_{31} & b_{32} \end{bmatrix}.$$

Let us partition A and B, designating the submatrices with double subscripts.

$$A = \begin{bmatrix} a_{11} & a_{12} & a_{13} \\ a_{21} & a_{22} & a_{23} \\ a_{31} & a_{32} & a_{33} \end{bmatrix} = \begin{bmatrix} A_{11} & A_{12} \\ A_{21} & A_{22} \end{bmatrix}, \quad B = \begin{bmatrix} b_{11} & b_{12} \\ b_{21} & b_{22} \\ b_{31} & b_{32} \end{bmatrix} = \begin{bmatrix} B_{11} \\ B_{21} \end{bmatrix}.$$

Then

$$\begin{bmatrix} A_{11} & A_{12} \\ A_{21} & A_{22} \end{bmatrix} \cdot \begin{bmatrix} B_{11} \\ B_{21} \end{bmatrix}$$

$$= \begin{bmatrix} (A_{11}B_{11} + A_{12}B_{21}) \\ (A_{21}B_{11} + A_{22}B_{21}) \end{bmatrix}$$

$$= \begin{bmatrix} \begin{bmatrix} (a_{11}b_{11} + a_{12}b_{21}) & (a_{11}b_{12} + a_{12}b_{22}) \\ (a_{21}b_{11} + a_{22}b_{21}) & (a_{21}b_{12} + a_{22}b_{22}) \end{bmatrix} + \begin{bmatrix} a_{13}b_{31} & a_{13}b_{32} \\ a_{23}b_{31} & a_{23}b_{32} \end{bmatrix} \\ [(a_{31}b_{11} + a_{32}b_{21}) \quad (a_{31}b_{12} + a_{32}b_{22})] + [a_{33}b_{31} \quad a_{33}b_{32}] \end{bmatrix}$$

$$= \begin{bmatrix} \begin{bmatrix} a_{11}b_{11} + a_{12}b_{21} + a_{13}b_{31} & a_{11}b_{12} + a_{12}b_{22} + a_{13}b_{32} \\ a_{21}b_{11} + a_{22}b_{21} + a_{23}b_{31} & a_{21}b_{12} + a_{22}b_{22} + a_{23}b_{32} \end{bmatrix} \\ \begin{bmatrix} a_{31}b_{11} + a_{32}b_{21} + a_{33}b_{31} & a_{31}b_{12} + a_{32}b_{22} + a_{33}b_{32} \end{bmatrix} \end{bmatrix}$$

$= AB$ after the internal brackets are dropped.

In each of the above examples, we partitioned the matrices A and B and multiplied them, treating the submatrices as elements. When the multiplication was complete, we dropped the internal brackets, thus in effect undoing the partitioning. The result was in each case the product AB.

The results stated in the last paragraph hold true in general, provided that the partitioning is so carried out that the matrices to be multiplied are all conformable. Let A be of order (m, n) and let B be of order (n, p) so that A is conformable to B for multiplication. Let A_{ij} and B_{ij} be used to denote submatrices. Then we write

$$\overbrace{\phantom{n_1 \text{ cols.}}}^{n_1 \text{ cols.}} \overbrace{\phantom{n_2 \text{ cols.}}}^{n_2 \text{ cols.}} \cdots \overbrace{\phantom{n_\nu\text{-cols.}}}^{n_\nu\text{-cols.}}$$

$$A = \begin{bmatrix} a_{11} & a_{12} & \cdots & a_{1n} \\ a_{21} & a_{22} & \cdots & a_{2n} \\ \vdots & & & \\ a_{m1} & a_{m2} & \cdots & a_{mn} \end{bmatrix} = \left[\begin{array}{c|c|c|c} A_{11} & A_{12} & \cdots & A_{1\nu} \\ \hline A_{21} & A_{22} & \cdots & A_{2\nu} \\ \hline \vdots & & & \\ \hline A_{\mu 1} & A_{\mu 2} & \cdots & A_{\mu\nu} \end{array} \right] \begin{array}{l} \}m_1 \text{ rows} \\ \}m_2 \text{ rows} \\ \vdots \\ \}m_\mu \text{ rows} \end{array} \quad,$$

where $n_1 + n_2 + \cdots + n_\nu = n$, and $m_1 + m_2 + \cdots + m_\mu = m$.

The matrix B is then partitioned thus:

$$\overbrace{\phantom{p_1 \text{ cols.}}}^{p_1 \text{ cols.}} \overbrace{\phantom{p_2 \text{ cols.}}}^{p_2 \text{ cols.}} \cdots \overbrace{\phantom{p_\rho \text{ cols.}}}^{p_\rho \text{ cols.}}$$

$$B = \begin{bmatrix} b_{11} & b_{12} & \cdots & b_{1p} \\ b_{21} & b_{22} & \cdots & b_{2p} \\ \vdots & & & \\ b_{n1} & b_{n2} & \cdots & b_{np} \end{bmatrix} = \begin{array}{l} n_1 \text{ rows } \{ \\ n_2 \text{ rows } \{ \\ \vdots \\ n_\nu \text{ rows } \{ \end{array} \left[\begin{array}{c|c|c|c} B_{11} & B_{12} & \cdots & B_{1\rho} \\ \hline B_{21} & B_{22} & \cdots & B_{2\rho} \\ \hline \vdots & & & \\ \hline B_{\nu 1} & B_{\nu 2} & \cdots & B_{\nu\rho} \end{array} \right] \quad,$$

where $p_1 + p_2 + \cdots + p_\rho = p$.

As indicated, the column partitioning of A must be similar to the row partitioning of B so that the matrices A_{ij} will be conformable to the matrices B_{jk} for $j = 1, 2, \ldots, \nu$. However, the row partitioning of A and the column partitioning of B are quite arbitrary, being governed only by considerations of convenience.

We could now show that

$$AB = [C_{ik}]_{(\mu, \rho)},$$

where

$$C_{ik} = \sum_{j=1}^{\nu} A_{ij}B_{jk},$$

that is, we could show that, if we multiply the partitioned A and B according to the rule outlined above, the end result would be precisely AB. The proof will be left to the reader to think through. Example 3 gives the key: Show that $[C_{ik}]_{(\mu, \rho)}$ gives each element of AB, in its proper place, by building it up as a sum of groups of products.

1.20 Exercises

1. Compute the product using the indicated partitioning

$$
\begin{bmatrix}
1 & 2 & 0 & 0 & 0 \\
-2 & 1 & 0 & 0 & 0 \\
\hline
0 & 0 & 1 & 0 & 0 \\
0 & 0 & 0 & 1 & 0 \\
0 & 0 & 0 & 0 & 1
\end{bmatrix}
\cdot
\begin{bmatrix}
0 & 0 & 0 & 2 & 1 \\
0 & 0 & 0 & 1 & -2 \\
0 & 0 & 1 & 0 & 0 \\
0 & 1 & 0 & 0 & 0 \\
1 & 0 & 0 & 0 & 0
\end{bmatrix}.
$$

2. Compute A^2, using the indicated partitioning, where

$$
A =
\begin{bmatrix}
1 & 0 & 0 & 0 & 0 & 1 \\
0 & 1 & 0 & 0 & 0 & 1 \\
0 & 0 & 1 & 0 & 0 & 1 \\
\hline
0 & 0 & 0 & 1 & 0 & 0 \\
0 & 0 & 0 & 0 & 1 & 0 \\
\hline
1 & 1 & 1 & 0 & 0 & 1
\end{bmatrix}.
$$

3. In the preceding exercise, we have a symmetric matrix, symmetrically partitioned, which is probably the most important case to arise in practice. Write out a generalized scheme for the symmetric partitioning of two symmetric matrices A and B of order n and write a formula for the product AB. Show that, before the internal brackets are removed, the product AB is partitioned in the same way as were A and B.

*4. Let A be of order (m, n) and let B be of order (n, p). Then we can partition A into rows and B into columns, thus:

$$
A =
\begin{bmatrix}
A^{(1)} \\
A^{(2)} \\
\vdots \\
A^{(m)}
\end{bmatrix},
\qquad
B = [B_1, B_2, \ldots, B_p],
$$

or we can partition A into columns and B into rows:

$$
A = [A_1, A_2, \ldots, A_n],
\qquad
B =
\begin{bmatrix}
B^{(1)} \\
B^{(2)} \\
\vdots \\
B^{(n)}
\end{bmatrix}.
$$

Form the product of the partitioned matrices in each case and observe how these products are related to the product AB.

5. Let A_1 and B_1 be square and of the same order. Let the same be true for A_2 and $B_2, \ldots, A_n$ and B_n. Furthermore, let

$$
A = \begin{bmatrix} A_1 & 0 & \cdots & 0 \\ 0 & A_2 & \cdots & 0 \\ \vdots & & & \\ 0 & 0 & \cdots & A_n \end{bmatrix}, \qquad
B = \begin{bmatrix} B_1 & 0 & \cdots & 0 \\ 0 & B_2 & \cdots & 0 \\ \vdots & & & \\ 0 & 0 & \cdots & B_n \end{bmatrix}.
$$

Determine the sum and the product of A and B. The matrices A and B here are called **decomposable matrices** or **quasi-diagonal matrices**. This problem then shows that the sum and the product of two decomposable matrices of the same kind are decomposable matrices of the same kind. If we abbreviate $A = D[A_1, A_2, \ldots, A_n]$, what can be said about $f(A)$ where $f(A)$ is any polynomial function of A?

6. If X_1 is a k_1-vector and X_2 is a k_2-vector, indicate what orders the A_{ij} must have for the product

$$
[X_1{}^\mathsf{T}, X_2{}^\mathsf{T}] \cdot \begin{bmatrix} A_{11} & A_{12} \\ A_{21} & A_{22} \end{bmatrix} \cdot \begin{bmatrix} X_1 \\ X_2 \end{bmatrix}
$$

to have meaning, and compute the product.

7. Show that, if $A = [A_{ij}]$, where the A_{ij} are *submatrices*, then $[A_{ij}]^\mathsf{T} = [A_{ji}{}^\mathsf{T}]$.

8. Given that $A_1, A_2, \ldots, A_k$ are all n-rowed matrices of complex numbers, simplify the expression

$$
[A_1{}^*, A_2{}^*, \ldots, A_k{}^*]^*.
$$

9. Notice that

$$
\begin{bmatrix} 0 & 1 \\ 0 & 0 \end{bmatrix} \cdot \begin{bmatrix} 0 & 0 \\ 1 & 0 \end{bmatrix} = \begin{bmatrix} 1 & 0 \\ 0 & 0 \end{bmatrix},
$$

$$
\begin{bmatrix} 0 & 1 & 0 \\ 0 & 0 & 1 \\ 0 & 0 & 0 \end{bmatrix} \cdot \begin{bmatrix} 0 & 0 & 0 \\ 1 & 0 & 0 \\ 0 & 1 & 0 \end{bmatrix} = \begin{bmatrix} 1 & 0 & 0 \\ 0 & 1 & 0 \\ 0 & 0 & 0 \end{bmatrix},
$$

$$
\begin{bmatrix} 0 & 0 & 1 \\ 0 & 0 & 0 \\ 0 & 0 & 0 \end{bmatrix} \cdot \begin{bmatrix} 0 & 0 & 0 \\ 0 & 0 & 0 \\ 1 & 0 & 0 \end{bmatrix} = \begin{bmatrix} 1 & 0 & 0 \\ 0 & 0 & 0 \\ 0 & 0 & 0 \end{bmatrix}.
$$

Generalize these to matrices of arbitrary orders and use the E_j's to prove the result.

*10. Given that $A_{m \times n} = [A_1, A_2, \ldots, A_n]$ and $B = [b_{ij}]_{n \times p}$, expand the product

$$[A_1, A_2, \ldots, A_n] \cdot \begin{bmatrix} b_{11} & b_{12} & \cdots & b_{1p} \\ b_{21} & b_{22} & \cdots & b_{2p} \\ \vdots & & & \\ b_{n1} & b_{n2} & \cdots & b_{np} \end{bmatrix}$$

as it stands and show that it is, in fact, AB.

11. Given that $AB = C$, that is, that

$$A[B_1, B_2, \ldots, B_p] = [C_1, C_2, \ldots, C_p],$$

where B and C are partitioned into columns, prove that

$$A \sum_{j=1}^{p} B_j = \sum_{j=1}^{p} C_j.$$

Compare with Exercise 33, Section 1.18.

12. Consider the matrix

$$S_n = \begin{bmatrix} 0 & 1 & 0 & \cdots & 0 \\ 0 & 0 & 1 & \cdots & 0 \\ \vdots & & & & \\ 0 & 0 & 0 & \cdots & 1 \\ 0 & 0 & 0 & \cdots & 0 \end{bmatrix}_n .$$

Give a rule for evaluating $S_n{}^p$, where p is a positive integer. (*Hint:* Write

$$S_n{}^2 = \begin{bmatrix} E_2{}^\mathsf{T} \\ E_3{}^\mathsf{T} \\ \vdots \\ E_n{}^\mathsf{T} \\ 0 \end{bmatrix} \cdot [0, E_1, E_2, \ldots, E_{n-1}],$$

and use Exercise 31, Section 1.18.)

*13. Let D denote a quasi-diagonal matrix of order n, and let A denote any matrix of order n which is partitioned similarly to D. What is the nature of the products DA and AD?

14. Use second-order solutions of $A^2 - 5A + 7I_2 = 0$ to build up quasi-diagonal fourth-order solutions of the equation $A^2 - 5A + 7I_4 = 0$.

*15. If $A = [A_1, A_2, \ldots, A_m]$, where the A_j are n-vectors, find representations of A^T, A^*, and the ij-entry of AA^T in terms of the A_j.

16. Show that the algebra of complex matrices of the form $A + iB$, where A and B are real matrices of order n, is isomorphic to the algebra of those real matrices of order $2n$ which have the form

$$\begin{bmatrix} A & -B \\ B & A \end{bmatrix}.$$

(See Exercise 17, Section 1.18.)

Show that under this isomorphism "tranjugate" corresponds to transpose and, consequently, "Hermitian" corresponds to "symmetric," and "skew-Hermitian" corresponds to "skew-symmetric."

Show that multiplication by the complex scalar $a + ib$ corresponds to multiplication by the matrix of order $2n$,

$$\begin{bmatrix} aI & -bI \\ bI & aI \end{bmatrix},$$

and that these matrices commute with all of those of the form

$$\begin{bmatrix} A & -B \\ B & A \end{bmatrix}.$$

Finally, show that the matrices of this latter form are exactly those which commute with

$$\begin{bmatrix} 0 & -I \\ I & 0 \end{bmatrix}.$$

(Note that this isomorphism can be used to derive theorems about Hermitian matrices from theorems about symmetric matrices.)

CHAPTER TWO

Determinants

As has been pointed out in Chapter One, a certain amount of determinant theory is useful in the study of matrix algebra. Moreover, determinants have numerous applications in other branches of mathematics as well as in applied fields. For these reasons, we give in this chapter a systematic treatment of the most important results of determinant theory, starting with the theory of permutations and inversions. Some of the applications are indicated in the exercises, but knowledge of the area of application is never necessary to solve any problem. The reader already familiar with determinants may skim this chapter and concentrate on the applications made to matrix theory.

PERMUTATIONS AND INVERSIONS

2.1 Permutations

The n integers $1, 2, \ldots, n$, listed in the order used in counting, are said to be in the **natural order**. In general, whenever the members of a collection of distinct positive integers are listed in increasing order, they are said to be in the natural order. Thus the sets of integers 1, 2, 3, 4, 5 and 2, 4, 7, 9 are both in the natural order. When no confusion is introduced thereby, it is customary to write such sets of integers without commas: 12345 and 2479, for example. The integers are still read as though the commas were present. When integers greater than 9 are present, commas are essential to make the meaning clear.

The six sets of integers

$$123 \qquad 213 \qquad 312$$
$$132 \qquad 231 \qquad 321$$

are called *permutations* of the integers 123. The twenty-four sets of integers,

1234	2134	3124	4123
1243	2143	3142	4132
1324	2314	3214	4213
1342	2341	3241	4231
1423	2413	3412	4312
1432	2431	3421	4321

are permutations of the integers 1234. More generally, if each of $j_1, j_2, \ldots, j_n$ denotes one of the integers from 1 to n (always inclusive here) and if each of the integers from 1 to n appears once and only once among the j's, then we call the set of integers $j_1 j_2 \cdots j_n$ a **permutation** of the integers from 1 to n. In the permutation 2314 we have, for example, $j_1 = 2, j_2 = 3, j_3 = 1, j_4 = 4$. The permutations of 123 and 1234 listed above suggest the following result:

Theorem 2.1.1:   *There are $n!$ permutations of the integers from 1 to n.*

The first integer of a permutation may be selected in n ways, and for each choice of the first, the second may be selected in any one of the $n - 1$ remaining ways, so that the first two may be selected in $n(n - 1)$ ways. For each choice of the first two integers of the permutation, the third may then be selected in $n - 2$ ways, making $[n(n - 1)](n - 2)$ choices for the first three. Proceeding thus until all the integers of the permutation have been chosen, we find there are altogether

$$n(n - 1)(n - 2) \cdots 3 \cdot 2 \cdot 1 = n!$$

distinct permutations possible.

2.2 Inversions

In a permutation of the integers from 1 to n, an integer may precede another smaller integer. When this occurs, we say that the permutation contains an **inversion**. The **total number of inversions** in a permutation is, by definition, found by counting the number of smaller integers following each integer of the permutation. Thus 614325 has eight inversions since 6 is followed by 1, 4, 3, 2, and 5; 4 is followed by 3 and 2; 3 is followed by 2. A permutation is defined to be **even** or **odd** according as the total number of inversions in it is even or odd. The natural order $123 \cdots n$ is an even permutation since the number of inversions in it is the even number zero. The permutation 4312 is an odd permutation since it has five inversions. When two permutations are both even or both odd, they are said to have the **same parity**. When one is even and the other is odd, they are said to have **opposite parity**.

The interchange of two adjacent integers of a permutation will be called an **adjacent transposition**. The interchange of any two integers of a permutation, whether adjacent or not, is called a **transposition**.

Theorem 2.2.1: *An adjacent transposition changes a given permutation into one of opposite parity.*

This theorem may be illustrated by considering some of the twenty-four permutations of 1234 listed above. For example, 1234 is even, 1243 is odd, and 2143 is even again.

We prove the theorem by noting that the two integers to be interchanged are necessarily unequal and that, after the interchange, these two integers will still follow or precede all *other* integers in the permutation, just as before. Thus the total number of inversions is either increased or decreased by exactly one, and the theorem is proved.

Theorem 2.2.2: *If a permutation has a total of k inversions, then it can be reduced to the natural order by exactly k adjacent transpositions.*

Thus, for example, 51243 has five inversions. It may be reduced to the natural order by interchanging the integer 5 successively with the integers 1, 2, 4, and 3, and then interchanging the integers 4 and 3. This example suggests a general method for proving the theorem: In the permutation, let n be followed by i_n smaller integers, $n - 1$ by i_{n-1} smaller integers, etc. Then the total number of inversions is $\sum\limits_{r=2}^{n} i_r = k$. As a first step toward restoring the natural order, it takes i_n adjacent transpositions to put n in the natural position. *Thereafter* it takes i_{n-1} adjacent transpositions to put $n - 1$ in the natural position, etc. The complete task of restoring the natural order can therefore be accomplished by $\sum\limits_{r=2}^{n} i_r = k$ adjacent transpositions.

One can, of course, restore the natural order by numbers of adjacent transpositions other than k. The theorem only says that it *can* be done with exactly k of them.

Theorem 2.2.3: *An even (odd) permutation may be reduced to the natural order only by an even (odd) number of adjacent transpositions.*

If it were possible to reduce a permutation to the natural order both by an even number and by an odd number of adjacent transpositions, then it would be possible to obtain the given permutation in two ways from the (even) natural order by reversing each of these two sequences of transpositions. Hence, by Theorem 2.2.1, the permutation would be both even and odd, which is impossible.

From Theorems 2.2.2 and 2.2.3 we conclude next:

Theorem 2.2.4: *A permutation is even (odd) if and only if an even (odd) number of adjacent transpositions is required to reduce it to the natural order.*

We have finally the very important result:

Theorem 2.2.5: *If any two integers of a given permutation are inter-changed, a permutation of opposite parity results.*

In the permutation

$$j_1 j_2 \cdots j_{k-1} \uparrow \overline{j_k j_{k+1} \cdots j_{p-1}} \downarrow j_p j_{p+1} \cdots j_n,$$

with 2 above and 1 below,

let us interchange j_k and j_p by making two sequences of adjacent trans-positions, the first of which puts j_p between j_{k-1} and j_k by means of $(p-1) - (k-1)$ successive adjacent transpositions. The second then puts j_k between j_{p-1} and j_{p+1} by means of $(p-1) - k$ more adjacent trans-positions. The exchange thus requires altogether $2p - 2k - 1$ adjacent transpositions. Since this is necessarily an odd number, the desired result follows from Theorem 2.2.1.

2.3 The Epsilon Symbols

For each permutation $j_1 j_2 \cdots j_n$ of the integers from 1 to n, we define an **epsilon symbol** as follows:

$$\epsilon_{j_1 j_2 \cdots j_n} = \begin{cases} 1 & \text{if } j_1 j_2 \cdots j_n \text{ is an even permutation,} \\ -1 & \text{if } j_1 j_2 \cdots j_n \text{ is an odd permutation.} \end{cases}$$

The reader should note that if k is the number of inversions in $j_1 j_2 \cdots j_n$, then

$$\epsilon_{j_1 j_2 \cdots j_n} = (-1)^k.$$

We shall make extensive use of this symbol later in the chapter.

2.4 Exercises

1. Prove that if a permutation with a total of k inversions is restored to normal order by adjacent transpositions, then at least k such transpositions are required, so that, by Theorem 2.2.2, k is the *minimum* number of adjacent transpositions that will accomplish the result.

*2. Prove that for $n \geqslant 2$, there are equal numbers of even and odd permuta-tions of the integers from 1 to n.

3. Prove that a permutation $j_1 j_2 \cdots j_n$ is even or odd depending upon whether the following product is positive or negative:

$$\prod_{n \geqslant k > p \geqslant 1} (j_k - j_p) = (j_n - j_{n-1})(j_n - j_{n-2}) \cdots (j_n - j_2)(j_n - j_1)$$
$$(j_{n-1} - j_{n-2}) \cdots (j_{n-1} - j_2)(j_{n-1} - j_1)$$
$$\vdots$$
$$(j_3 - j_2)(j_3 - j_1)$$
$$(j_2 - j_1).$$

4. Prove that the number of inversions in a permutation may also be found by counting the number of larger integers preceding each integer of the permutation.

5. Evaluate the $n!$ epsilon symbols for $n = 2, 3, 4$.

6. Prove that at most $n(n-1)/2$ adjacent transpositions are required to restore a given permutation of $1, 2, \ldots, n$ to the natural order.

7. Prove that

$$\epsilon_{k_1 k_2 \cdots k_n} \cdot \epsilon_{j_{k_1} j_{k_2} \cdots j_{k_n}} = \epsilon_{j_1 j_2 \cdots j_n}.$$

8. Prove Theorem 2.2.5 by a method which involves counting inversions.

THE SIMPLEST PROPERTIES OF DETERMINANTS

2.5 The Determinant of a Square Matrix

Square matrices appear in a wide variety of problems, sometimes independently and sometimes as submatrices of other matrices. A **submatrix** of a given matrix is the array remaining when certain rows and columns of the given matrix are deleted. For example, the coefficient matrix (see p. 136),

$$\begin{bmatrix} a_{11} & a_{12} \\ a_{21} & a_{22} \end{bmatrix}$$

of the system of equations

(2.5.1)
$$a_{11}x_1 + a_{12}x_2 = b_1,$$
$$a_{21}x_1 + a_{22}x_2 = b_2,$$

may be considered independently or may be regarded as a square submatrix obtained by deleting the last column from the augmented matrix

$$\begin{bmatrix} a_{11} & a_{12} & -b_1 \\ a_{21} & a_{22} & -b_2 \end{bmatrix}$$

of the system.

The conclusion that square matrices are of particular importance in matrix algebra is suggested by the developments at the end of Chapter One. This importance rests largely on the fact, to be proved in Chapter Five, that only a square matrix can have an inverse. For example, the reader who has solved Exercise 11 in Section 1.18 will have found that the matrix

$$A = \begin{bmatrix} a_{11} & a_{12} \\ a_{21} & a_{22} \end{bmatrix}$$

has an inverse if and only if the scalar $\Delta = a_{11}a_{22} - a_{12}a_{21}$ is different from zero. The inverse is readily seen to be

$$A^{-1} = \begin{bmatrix} \dfrac{a_{22}}{\Delta} & \dfrac{-a_{12}}{\Delta} \\[2ex] \dfrac{-a_{21}}{\Delta} & \dfrac{a_{11}}{\Delta} \end{bmatrix}, \quad (\Delta \neq 0),$$

because $AA^{-1} = A^{-1}A = I$.

If we now write the system (2.5.1) in matrix form in the manner of Chapter One,

$$AX = B,$$

and, assuming $\Delta \neq 0$, premultiply on both sides by A^{-1}, we find $(A^{-1}A)X = A^{-1}B$ or

$$X = A^{-1}B,$$

from which it is easy to compute by matrix multiplication the familiar solution

$$x_1 = \frac{b_1 a_{22} - b_2 a_{12}}{\Delta},$$

(2.5.2) $(\Delta \neq 0)$

$$x_2 = \frac{b_2 a_{11} - b_1 a_{21}}{\Delta}.$$

This example illustrates the use of the inverse of a matrix in the process of solving a system of linear equations.

It is natural to wish to extend this procedure to more extensive systems of equations. In order ultimately to do this, we begin by associating with each square matrix $A = [a_{ij}]_n$, $n \geqslant 1$, a uniquely defined scalar which we call **the determinant of A** and denote by the symbol "det A." In particular, when A is the second-order matrix used in the foregoing, det A is precisely the scalar Δ. (It will appear later that, as in the case of matrices of order 2, A has an inverse if and only if det A is different from zero.) To define the scalar, det A, we first select n elements a_{ij} from A in such a way that each row and each column of A is represented exactly once among the subscripts of these n elements. Then we form the product of the selected elements, keeping the row subscripts in the natural order:

$$a_{1j_1} a_{2j_2} \cdots a_{nj_n}.$$

In this product, $j_1 j_2 \cdots j_n$ will be a permutation of the integers from 1 to n since we have selected one element from each column. Next we multiply this product by $\epsilon_{j_1 j_2 \ldots j_n}$ to get the term

$$\epsilon_{j_1 j_2 \ldots j_n} a_{1j_1} a_{2j_2} \cdots a_{nj_n}.$$

This amounts to multiplying the product by $+1$ if $j_1 j_2 \cdots j_n$ is an even permutation and by -1 if it is an odd permutation. Proceeding thus, we form one such term for each possible permutation $j_1 j_2 \cdots j_n$ of $1, 2, \ldots, n$ and then add the results to obtain det A:

(2.5.3) $$\det A = \sum_{(j)} \epsilon_{j_1 j_2 \cdots j_n} a_{1 j_1} a_{2 j_2} \cdots a_{n j_n}.$$

The symbol (j) denotes that the summation is to be extended only over the $n!$ permutations $j_1 j_2 \cdots j_n$ of $1, 2, \ldots, n$.

The determinant of a 1×1 matrix $[a]$ is defined to be a.

For $n = 2$ and $n = 3$, we have by (2.5.3):

(2.5.4a) $\det \begin{bmatrix} a_{11} & a_{12} \\ a_{21} & a_{22} \end{bmatrix} = \epsilon_{12} a_{11} a_{22} + \epsilon_{21} a_{12} a_{21} = a_{11} a_{22} - a_{12} a_{21}.$

(2.5.4b) $\det \begin{bmatrix} a_{11} & a_{12} & a_{13} \\ a_{21} & a_{22} & a_{23} \\ a_{31} & a_{32} & a_{33} \end{bmatrix} = \begin{array}{l} \epsilon_{123} a_{11} a_{22} a_{33} + \epsilon_{231} a_{12} a_{23} a_{31} \\ + \epsilon_{312} a_{13} a_{21} a_{32} + \epsilon_{132} a_{11} a_{23} a_{32} \\ + \epsilon_{213} a_{12} a_{21} a_{33} + \epsilon_{321} a_{13} a_{22} a_{31} \end{array}$

$$= a_{11} a_{22} a_{33} + a_{12} a_{23} a_{31} + a_{13} a_{21} a_{32} - a_{11} a_{23} a_{32} - a_{12} a_{21} a_{33} - a_{13} a_{22} a_{31}.$$

A numerical example is given by

$$\det \begin{bmatrix} 1 & -1 \\ 3 & -2 \end{bmatrix} = +(1)(-2) - (-1)(3) = -2 + 3 = 1.$$

Note that the signs introduced by the epsilons act independently of the signs the elements may possess. Again, if $i^2 = -1$,

$$\det \begin{bmatrix} 0 & i & -i \\ i & 0 & i \\ -i & i & 0 \end{bmatrix} = \begin{array}{l} 0 \cdot 0 \cdot 0 + i \cdot i \cdot (-i) + (-i) \cdot i \cdot i - 0 \cdot i \cdot i \\ - i \cdot i \cdot 0 - (-i) \cdot 0 \cdot (-i) = -2i^3 = 2i. \end{array}$$

The reader should write out det $[a_{ij}]_4$ in a form similar to (2.5.4) just to get the feel of the definition. In practice, however, we rarely if ever find it necessary to apply the definition in this way. We use instead various results, derived from the definition, which often make the evaluation of a determinant a far simpler task than the definition itself would suggest.

As one example of how the determinant of a matrix may be used, we note that by (2.5.2) and (2.5.4a), the solution of the system of equations (2.5.1) may be written in determinant form thus:

(2.5.5) $$x_1 = \frac{\det \begin{bmatrix} b_1 & a_{12} \\ b_2 & a_{22} \end{bmatrix}}{\Delta}, \qquad x_2 = \frac{\det \begin{bmatrix} a_{11} & b_1 \\ a_{21} & b_2 \end{bmatrix}}{\Delta}$$

where

$$\Delta = \det \begin{bmatrix} a_{11} & a_{12} \\ a_{21} & a_{22} \end{bmatrix},$$

provided $\Delta \neq 0$.

Applied to the system

$$tx - 3y = 1,$$
$$3x + ty = 4,$$

these formulas give the solution

$$\Delta = \det \begin{bmatrix} t & -3 \\ 3 & t \end{bmatrix} = t^2 + 9,$$

$$x = \frac{\det \begin{bmatrix} 1 & -3 \\ 4 & t \end{bmatrix}}{\Delta} = \frac{t + 12}{t^2 + 9}, \qquad y = \frac{\det \begin{bmatrix} t & 1 \\ 3 & 4 \end{bmatrix}}{\Delta} = \frac{4t - 3}{t^2 + 9},$$

provided $t^2 + 9 \neq 0$, that is, provided $t \neq \pm 3i$.

The extension of this process to systems of n equations in n unknowns, and other applications of determinants, will be developed in later sections.

The reader already familiar with determinants may well wonder why we have written, for example,

$$\det \begin{bmatrix} a_{11} & a_{12} \\ a_{21} & a_{22} \end{bmatrix},$$

instead of the more familiar symbol,

$$\begin{vmatrix} a_{11} & a_{12} \\ a_{21} & a_{22} \end{vmatrix}.$$

Our purpose has been, of course, to emphasize the fact that *the square array of scalars is the matrix, whereas the determinant is just one scalar, associated with the matrix according to a definite rule.* In what follows, we shall also make use of the usual vertical bars to denote the determinant of a square array contained between them, but the *array* and the *determinant of the array* should be carefully distinguished.

To emphasize this point, it is well to review the concept of *function.* The most familiar type of function may be regarded as a rule that determines a unique number corresponding to each given number of some fixed set. For example, the squaring function assigns the unique number x^2 to each number x, the sine function assigns a unique number $\sin x$ to each number x, etc. In each of these examples, the set from which x is chosen may be any subset of the set of complex numbers. The number $f(x)$ associated by the function f with the number x is called the *value of the function f at x.*

It is important to distinguish between the function as a rule for computation, and the function value. For example, if the function is "square the given number," then x^2 denotes the *value* of the function at x, not the function itself. In this case the function could conveniently be represented by the symbol $(\ )^2$. Similarly, the function represented by $\sqrt{1 - (\ )^2}$ associates a real number $\sqrt{1 - x^2}$ with each real number x such that $-1 \leqslant x \leqslant 1$.

The function concept is not limited to sets of numbers, however. Let $\mathfrak{A}$ and $\mathfrak{B}$ denote arbitrary sets of objects. Then any rule which assigns to each member of $\mathfrak{A}$ a unique member of $\mathfrak{B}$ is called a function from $\mathfrak{A}$ to $\mathfrak{B}$.

We have already dealt with functions in this larger sense, for a polynomial function associates a matrix $a_0 A^p + a_1 A^{p-1} + \cdots + a_p I_n$ with each given $n \times n$ matrix A. In this case the sets $\mathfrak{A}$ and $\mathfrak{B}$ are the same set of matrices.

The determinant of a matrix provides another illustration of the function concept. Let $\mathfrak{A}$ be the set of *square* matrices whose elements belong to the set $\mathfrak{B}$ of complex numbers, for example. Then the determinant function associates with each matrix A of $\mathfrak{A}$ a unique complex number b of $\mathfrak{B}$: $b = \det A$.

These two examples illustrate the fact that some functions of matrices have *matrices* as function values whereas others have *scalars* as function values. In particular, the determinant of a matrix is a scalar. Another important scalar function of a square matrix is the *trace* (defined in Chapter One).

2.6 Three Basic Properties of Determinants

The fact that each of the row subscripts $1, 2, \ldots, n$ and each of the column subscripts $1, 2, \ldots, n$ appears once and only once in each term of

$$(2.6.1) \qquad \det A = \sum_{(j)} \epsilon_{j_1 j_2 \cdots j_n} a_{1 j_1} a_{2 j_2} \cdots a_{n j_n}$$

is equivalent to the following:

Property 1:   Exactly one element from each row and one element from each column appears in each term of the expansion of $\det A$.

Since the elements of any one row or column appear only to the *first* degree, $\det A$ is *linear* in these elements. Since all the terms of $\det A$ are of the *same* degree in the elements of any one row or column, we say $\det A$ is *homogeneous* in these elements. Property 1 may therefore be stated thus: $\det A$ is a linear, homogeneous function of the elements of any given row (and of any given column) of A. The examples of the previous section illustrate these remarks.

The particular arrangement (2.6.1) of the terms of $\det A$ is called the **row expansion** of $\det A$ since the row subscripts are kept in the natural order in the formation of each term of the sum.

Property 2:   *Another formula for* det A *is*

$$\det A = \sum_{(i)} \epsilon_{i_1 i_2 \cdots i_n} a_{i_1 1} a_{i_2 2} \cdots a_{i_n n},$$

the summation being extended over all $n!$ *permutations*

$$i_1 i_2 \cdots i_n \quad of \quad 1, 2, \ldots, n.$$

This arrangement of the terms of det A is called the **column expansion** of det A, so that Property 2 states that *the row and column expansions of* det A *are algebraically identical expressions.*

To prove Property 2, we observe first that every product $a_{1j_1} a_{2j_2} \cdots a_{nj_n}$ of the row expansion appears also in the column expansion, for if the factors of any product are rearranged so that the column subscripts are in the natural order, the row subscripts will thereby be arranged in a corresponding permutation $i_1 i_2 \cdots i_n$ of $1, 2, \ldots, n$. Thus, for example, $a_{12} a_{23} a_{31} = a_{31} a_{12} a_{23}$ when $n = 3$. Similarly, each product of the column expansion appears also in the row expansion. It therefore remains only to show that the *signs* of a given product will be the same in both expressions. To do this, let us transpose factors of $a_{1j_1} a_{2j_2} \cdots a_{nj_n}$ in such a way as to reduce the column subscripts *to* the natural order. We will then simultaneously be using the *same transpositions* to obtain the corresponding permutation $i_1 i_2 \cdots i_n$ of the row subscripts *from* the natural order. Thus the permutations $i_1 i_2 \cdots i_n$ and $j_1 j_2 \cdots j_n$ are either both even or both odd so that the signs attached to the product in question will be the same.

Property 3:   *If any two parallel lines of A are interchanged, the determinant of the resulting matrix is* $-\det A$.

In the case of the interchange of the kth and pth rows ($k < p$), the result follows thus:

$$\det A = \sum_{(j)} \epsilon_{j_1 \cdots j_k \cdots j_p \cdots j_n} a_{1j_1} \cdots a_{kj_k} \cdots a_{pj_p} \cdots a_{nj_n}.$$

In each term of this sum we can interchange the scalar factors a_{kj_k} and a_{pj_p} since multiplication is commutative for scalars:

$$\det A = \sum_{(j)} \epsilon_{j_1 \cdots j_k \cdots j_p \cdots j_n} a_{1j_1} \cdots a_{pj_p} \cdots a_{kj_k} \cdots a_{nj_n}.$$

The products of a_{ij}'s in this sum are those that come from a matrix the same as A, except with rows k and p interchanged. However, the column subscripts j_k and j_p do not appear in the corresponding order on the ϵ symbols. Exchanging these, we have, by Theorem 2.2.5:

$$\det A = \sum_{(j)} (-\epsilon_{j_1 \cdots j_p \cdots j_k \cdots j_n}) a_{1j_1} \cdots a_{pj_p} \cdots a_{kj_k} \cdots a_{nj_n}$$

$$= -\left(\sum_{(j)} \epsilon_{j_1 \cdots j_p \cdots j_k \cdots j_n} a_{1j_1} \cdots a_{pj_p} \cdots a_{kj_k} \cdots a_{nj_n} \right),$$

and the expression in the parentheses is the determinant of a matrix the same as A except that it has rows k and p interchanged. The procedure is similar for two columns.

2.7 Further Properties of Determinants

From the three basic properties of the last section we can derive many useful results. We begin with

Theorem 2.7.1:   *For every square matrix A, $\det A = \det A^{\mathsf{T}}$.*

In words, this says that when the rows and columns of a matrix are interchanged, the determinant remains the same. For example, as is readily verified,

$$\det \begin{bmatrix} 3 & 2 & a \\ -2 & a & 3 \\ -a & -3 & 0 \end{bmatrix} = \det \begin{bmatrix} 3 & -2 & -a \\ 2 & a & -3 \\ a & 3 & 0 \end{bmatrix} = a^3 + 27.$$

The proof of the theorem consists in observing that the row expansion of $\det A$ and the column expansion of $\det A^{\mathsf{T}}$ are identical.

The importance of this theorem is that it shows that *in every theorem about determinants, we may interchange the roles of rows and columns throughout, and another true theorem will result.*

In an expansion of $\det A$ we may collect all terms containing the *fixed element a_{ij}* as a factor and write their sum in the factored form $a_{ij}A_{ij}$. Here A_{ij} denotes the factor remaining when the element a_{ij} is factored out. We call A_{ij} the **cofactor** of a_{ij} in $\det A$. For example, from (2.5.4) we have

$$\det \begin{bmatrix} a_{11} & a_{12} & a_{13} \\ a_{21} & a_{22} & a_{23} \\ a_{31} & a_{32} & a_{33} \end{bmatrix} = \left\{ \begin{aligned} & a_{11}(a_{22}a_{33} - a_{23}a_{32}) \\ + & a_{12}(a_{23}a_{31} - a_{21}a_{33}) \\ + & a_{13}(a_{21}a_{32} - a_{22}a_{31}) \end{aligned} \right\} = \left\{ \begin{aligned} & a_{13}(a_{21}a_{32} - a_{22}a_{31}) \\ + & a_{23}(a_{12}a_{31} - a_{11}a_{32}) \\ + & a_{33}(a_{11}a_{22} - a_{12}a_{21}) \end{aligned} \right\},$$

so that

$$A_{11} = a_{22}a_{33} - a_{23}a_{32}, \quad A_{12} = a_{23}a_{31} - a_{21}a_{33}, \quad A_{13} = a_{21}a_{32} - a_{22}a_{31},$$

$$A_{23} = a_{12}a_{31} - a_{11}a_{32}, \quad A_{33} = a_{11}a_{22} - a_{12}a_{21}.$$

The other four cofactors may be found similarly by the reader.

From Property 1 it follows that A_{ij} contains no elements from either the ith row or the jth column of A.

As the preceding example illustrates, if we repeat the process described in the last paragraph for each element of a fixed line of A, we obtain one of the following expansions of $\det A$:

(2.7.1) $\det A = a_{i1}A_{i1} + a_{i2}A_{i2} + \cdots + a_{in}A_{in}$

(2.7.2) $\det A = a_{1j}A_{1j} + a_{2j}A_{2j} + \cdots + a_{nj}A_{nj}$ $i, j = 1, 2, \ldots, n.$

In fact, by Property 1, every term of det A includes one and only one of $a_{i1}, a_{i2}, \ldots, a_{in}$, and hence appears once and only once in the right member of (2.7.1) and, likewise, every term of det A includes one and only one of $a_{1j}, a_{2j}, \ldots, a_{nj}$, and hence appears once and only once in the right member of (2.7.2). Thus these equations are fully justified.

The expression (2.7.1) is called **the expansion of det A in terms of the elements of the *i*th row** and (2.7.2) is called **the expansion of det A in terms of the elements of the *j*th column.**

A little later, we shall give explicitly the formula for A_{ij} but first we shall use (2.7.1) and (2.7.2) to derive some properties of det A depending only on the behavior of the elements of some line of A. These formulas are particularly useful for this purpose.

Theorem 2.7.2: *If all the elements of any line of A are zero, or if all the cofactors in* det A *of the elements of any line of A are zero, then* det $A = 0$.

This result is immediate from (2.7.1) and (2.7.2), as is also the next:

Theorem 2.7.3: *The expressions*

$$c_1 A_{i1} + c_2 A_{i2} + \cdots + c_n A_{in},$$

and

$$c_1 A_{1j} + c_2 A_{2j} + \cdots + c_n A_{nj},$$

are determinants of matrices the same as A except that the elements of the ith row and of the jth column respectively have been replaced by the elements $c_1, c_2, \ldots, c_n$.

Indeed, if we regard $a_{i1}, a_{i2}, \ldots, a_{in}$ as variables and assign them the values $c_1, c_2, \ldots, c_n$, we obtain the first of these expansions from the right member of (2.7.1). The second expression is obtained in the same way from the right member of (2.7.2).

An example is the following:

$$c_1 A_{11} + c_2 A_{12} + c_3 A_{13} = \det \begin{bmatrix} c_1 & c_2 & c_3 \\ a_{21} & a_{22} & a_{23} \\ a_{31} & a_{32} & a_{33} \end{bmatrix}.$$

Theorem 2.7.4: *If A has two identical parallel lines, then* det $A = 0$.

Prove this, using Property 3 above.

Theorem 2.7.5: *The sum of the products of the elements of one line of A by the cofactors in* det A *of the corresponding elements of a different parallel line of A is always zero:*

$$a_{i1} A_{k1} + a_{i2} A_{k2} + \cdots + a_{in} A_{kn} = 0, \qquad i \neq k,$$

$$a_{1j} A_{1k} + a_{2j} A_{2k} + \cdots + a_{nj} A_{nk} = 0, \qquad j \neq k.$$

Prove this by using first Theorem 2.7.3 and then Theorem 2.7.4.

We now define the symbol known as the **Kronecker delta**:

$$(2.7.3) \qquad \delta_{ik} = \begin{cases} 1, & \text{if } i = k \\ 0, & \text{if } i \neq k. \end{cases}$$

By using this symbol, we may combine the results of (2.7.1), (2.7.2), and Theorem 2.7.5 thus:

$$a_{i1}A_{k1} + a_{i2}A_{k2} + \cdots + a_{in}A_{kn} = \delta_{ik} \det A,$$

$$a_{1j}A_{1k} + a_{2j}A_{2k} + \cdots + a_{nj}A_{nk} = \delta_{jk} \det A,$$

or, using the $\sum$ notation,

$$(2.7.4) \qquad \sum_{j=1}^{n} a_{ij}A_{kj} = \delta_{ik} \det A, \qquad \sum_{i=1}^{n} a_{ij}A_{ik} = \delta_{jk} \det A.$$

The example

$$\begin{vmatrix} a_{11} & a_{12} \\ ka_{21} & ka_{22} \end{vmatrix} = a_{11} \cdot ka_{22} - a_{12} \cdot ka_{21} = k(a_{11}a_{22} - a_{12}a_{21}) = k \begin{vmatrix} a_{11} & a_{12} \\ a_{21} & a_{22} \end{vmatrix}$$

serves to illustrate

Theorem 2.7.6: *Let B be a square matrix the same as A except that all the elements of some line of B are k times the corresponding elements of the corresponding line of A. Then* $\det B = k \det A$.

This result follows at once from (2.7.1) and (2.7.2). In fact, if B is the same as A except that $b_{i1} = ka_{i1}$, $b_{i2} = ka_{i2}, \ldots, b_{in} = ka_{in}$, then, by (2.7.1),

$$\det B = (ka_{i1})A_{i1} + (ka_{i2})A_{i2} + \cdots + (ka_{in})A_{in}$$

$$= k(a_{i1}A_{i1} + a_{i2}A_{i2} + \cdots + a_{in}A_{in}) = k \det A.$$

Similarly for columns. The following examples illustrate how this theorem is used for the removal of, or the introduction of, factors:

(a) $$\begin{vmatrix} a + b & a + b \\ a - b & 0 \end{vmatrix} = (a + b) \begin{vmatrix} 1 & 1 \\ a - b & 0 \end{vmatrix} = (a + b)(a - b) \begin{vmatrix} 1 & 1 \\ 1 & 0 \end{vmatrix}.$$

(b) $$\begin{vmatrix} \frac{1}{2} & -1 & 2 \\ \frac{1}{3} & -1 & 3 \\ 0 & 1 & 1 \end{vmatrix} = \frac{1}{6} \begin{vmatrix} 1 & -2 & 4 \\ 1 & -3 & 9 \\ 0 & 1 & 1 \end{vmatrix} \quad \text{or} \quad \frac{1}{6} \begin{vmatrix} 3 & -1 & 2 \\ 2 & -1 & 3 \\ 0 & 1 & 1 \end{vmatrix}.$$

In the first example, $(a + b)$ was factored from the first row and $(a - b)$ was factored from the second. In the second example the first row was multiplied by 2 and the second row by 3. These changes were paid for by writing the 1/6 in front as a coefficient. In the second part of the example, the first column was multiplied by 6 and this was paid for with the coefficient 1/6.

Since the statement of the next theorem is a little complicated, we introduce some examples first to show that the idea involved is really very simple. Direct expansion of the determinants involved shows that

$$\begin{vmatrix} a_1 + b_1 & c_1 & d_1 \\ a_2 + b_2 & c_2 & d_2 \\ a_3 + b_3 & c_3 & d_3 \end{vmatrix} = \begin{vmatrix} a_1 & c_1 & d_1 \\ a_2 & c_2 & d_2 \\ a_3 & c_3 & d_3 \end{vmatrix} + \begin{vmatrix} b_1 & c_1 & d_1 \\ b_2 & c_2 & d_2 \\ b_3 & c_3 & d_3 \end{vmatrix}.$$

The reader should supply full details. Here the first column on the left is a column of binomials. The first columns on the right consist respectively of the first and second terms of these binomials, the other columns remaining the same throughout. Similarly, we have

$$\begin{vmatrix} a_1 + b_1 + c_1 & a_2 + b_2 + c_2 \\ d_1 & d_2 \end{vmatrix} = \begin{vmatrix} a_1 & a_2 \\ d_1 & d_2 \end{vmatrix} + \begin{vmatrix} b_1 & b_2 \\ d_1 & d_2 \end{vmatrix} + \begin{vmatrix} c_1 & c_2 \\ d_1 & d_2 \end{vmatrix},$$

where the trinomial elements of the first row on the left are broken up to give the three first rows on the right, the second row remaining the same throughout.

Theorem 2.7.7:   *If each element of the kth column of a matrix A is expressed as the sum of p terms, then* det A *may be expressed as the sum of the determinants of p matrices, the elements of whose kth columns are respectively the first, second, . . ., pth terms of the corresponding elements of the kth column of A. All other columns are the same throughout. A corresponding result holds for rows.*

Suppose in fact that the elements of the kth column of A are given by

$$a_{ik} = b_i^{(1)} + b_i^{(2)} + \cdots + b_i^{(p)} = \sum_{j=1}^{p} b_i^{(j)}, i = 1, 2, \ldots, n.$$

Then, expanding det A in terms of the elements of the kth column, we have from (2.7.2),

$$\det A = \sum_{i=1}^{n} a_{ik} A_{ik} = \sum_{i=1}^{n} \left(\sum_{j=1}^{p} b_i^{(j)} \right) A_{ik}.$$

Reversing the order of summation, we obtain

$$\det A = \sum_{j=1}^{p} \left(\sum_{i=1}^{n} b_i^{(j)} A_{ik} \right).$$

Now, by Theorem 2.7.3, $\sum_{i=1}^{n} b_i^{(j)} A_{ik}$ is the column expansion of the determinant of a matrix the same as A except that the kth column has been replaced by $\{b_1^{(j)}, b_2^{(j)}, \ldots, b_n^{(j)}\}$, so that the theorem is proved for columns.

By Theorem 2.7.1, a separate proof for rows is unnecessary, of course, but it would provide a good exercise for the reader to carry out the additional manipulations with the $\sum$ sign.

If the use of the $\sum$ signs in this proof bothers you, some of the mystery may be dispelled by a study of Appendix I.

Theorem 2.7.8: *If in A we add any multiple of one line to a different, parallel line, the determinant of the new matrix equals* det *A*.

For example,

(a)
$$\begin{vmatrix} x & y & 1 \\ 2 & 4 & 1 \\ 1 & 2 & 1 \end{vmatrix} = \begin{vmatrix} x & y & 1 \\ 0 & 0 & -1 \\ 1 & 2 & 1 \end{vmatrix}.$$

Here -2 times the third row was added to the second row. This, of course, involves no change in the third row. Whenever this theorem is applied, it should be recalled that *the line used as a* tool *to effect changes in a parallel line is itself* unaltered *in the process.*

(b)
$$\begin{vmatrix} 4 & -1 \\ 8 & -2 \end{vmatrix} = \begin{vmatrix} 4 & 0 \\ 8 & 0 \end{vmatrix}.$$

Here $1/4$ times the first column was added to the second column.

(c)
$$\begin{vmatrix} 2 & -3 \\ 1 & 4 \end{vmatrix} = \begin{vmatrix} (2 - 3x) & -3 \\ (1 + 4x) & 4 \end{vmatrix}.$$

Here x times the last column was added to the first column. Expand these last two determinants and verify that the equality holds regardless of the value of x.

The theorem follows from successive use of Theorems 2.7.7, 2.7.6, and 2.7.4. The details are left to the reader as an exercise.

The reader would do well at this point to recall Properties 1, 2, and 3 and reconsider the dependence of the results of Section 2.7 on them. It simplifies the learning of mathematics to organize the details of a topic about a few basic ideas instead of attempting to memorize a large body of inadequately organized information. In fact, if one learns the principles well, much of the related information will take care of itself without any memorization at all.

2.8 The Cofactor of an Element

An explicit formula for the cofactor of an element was not necessary in the proofs of the theorems of the last section, but it is necessary in various other connections. We therefore prove:

Theorem 2.8.1: *The cofactor A_{ij} of a_{ij} in* det *A is $(-1)^{i+j}$ times the determinant of the submatrix of order $n - 1$ obtained by deleting the ith row and the jth column from A.*

The second example in Section 2.7 illustrates this fact for the case $n = 3$.

Consider first A_{nn}, the cofactor of a_{nn} in det A. It is the sum of all terms of the form

$$\epsilon_{j_1 j_2 \cdots j_{n-1} n} a_{1 j_1} a_{2 j_2} \cdots a_{n-1 j_{n-1}},$$

where $j_1 j_2 \cdots j_{n-1}$ is a permutation of $1, 2, \ldots, n-1$ only. (The reader should compute A_{33} and A_{44} in the cases when $n = 3$ and $n = 4$.) Since the n in the permutation $j_1 j_2 \cdots j_{n-1} n$ is in the natural position, we see that

$$\epsilon_{j_1 j_2 \cdots j_{n-1} n} = \epsilon_{j_1 j_2 \cdots j_{n-1}},$$

the latter ϵ being one of the next lower order. Thus we have

$$A_{nn} = \sum \epsilon_{j_1 j_2 \cdots j_{n-1}} a_{1 j_1} a_{2 j_2} \cdots a_{n-1 j_{n-1}},$$

the summation being extended over the $(n-1)!$ permutations $j_1 j_2 \cdots j_{n-1}$ of $1, 2, \ldots, n-1$. This is therefore an expansion of

$$\begin{vmatrix} a_{11} & a_{12} & \cdots & a_{1,n-1} \\ \vdots & & & \\ a_{n-1,1} & a_{n-1,2} & \cdots & a_{n-1,n-1} \end{vmatrix}.$$

Since $(-1)^{i+j} = (-1)^{2n} = 1$ here, the theorem follows for A_{nn}.

To prove the result for any other A_{ij}, we reduce the problem to the preceding case. We first rewrite the matrix A thus:

$$A = \begin{bmatrix} B & C & E \\ F & a_{ij} & G \\ H & J & K \end{bmatrix},$$

where the capital letters are simply abbreviations for the appropriate blocks of terms. Then we move a_{ij} by successive interchanges of adjacent parallel lines to the lower right corner, noticing that E, G, K each have $n - j$ columns and H, J, K each have $n - i$ rows:

$$\det A = \begin{vmatrix} B & C & E \\ F & a_{ij} & G \\ H & J & K \end{vmatrix} = (-1)^{n-j} \begin{vmatrix} B & E & C \\ F & G & a_{ij} \\ H & K & J \end{vmatrix}$$

$$= (-1)^{n-j}(-1)^{n-i} \begin{vmatrix} B & E & C \\ H & K & J \\ F & G & a_{ij} \end{vmatrix}.$$

In the last determinant, $\begin{vmatrix} B & \vdots & E \\ \cdots & \vdots & \cdots \\ H & \vdots & K \end{vmatrix}$ is the cofactor of a_{ij} by the special case, so that the cofactor of a_{ij} in det A must be $(-1)^{2n-i-j} = (-1)^{i+j}$ times this in view of the above identities. But $\begin{bmatrix} B & \vdots & E \\ \cdots & \vdots & \cdots \\ H & \vdots & K \end{bmatrix}$ may be obtained from A in precisely the manner stated in the theorem, which is therefore now completely proved.

To illustrate, in

$$\begin{vmatrix} x & 0 & 0 & y \\ 2 & 0 & 0 & 0 \\ 3 & 3 & 0 & 0 \\ 4 & 4 & 4 & 0 \end{vmatrix},$$

the cofactor of the element y is

$$(-1)^{1+4} \begin{vmatrix} 2 & 0 & 0 \\ 3 & 3 & 0 \\ 4 & 4 & 4 \end{vmatrix} = -24.$$

Hence, applying (2.7.2) to the elements of the last column, we see that, because of the three zeros, the indicated determinant is simply $-24y$.

2.9 The Computation of Determinants

In the computation of the determinant of a matrix A with simple elements we can frequently use Theorem 2.7.8—repeatedly if necessary and as appropriately as possible—to reduce to zero all but one of the elements of some line of the matrix. Then, if in the altered matrix a'_{kp} denotes the nonzero element in a line of otherwise zero elements, and if A'_{kp} denotes the cofactor of a'_{kp} in the determinant of this matrix, we have from (2.7.1) or (2.7.2) that det $A = a'_{kp} A'_{kp}$. By Theorem 2.8.1, we see that the problem has thus been reduced to computing in a similar way the determinant of a matrix of order $n-1$. This procedure may be continued until the computation of the remaining determinant becomes sufficiently simple to be performed directly. The example of the last section illustrates these remarks, as does also the following example. Let the determinant to be computed be

$$d = \begin{vmatrix} 1 & 2 & 1 & -4 \\ -1 & 2 & -1 & 3 \\ 0 & 4 & 4 & -1 \\ 1 & 1 & 0 & -1 \end{vmatrix}.$$

When the second row is added to each of the first and fourth rows, we obtain

$$d = \begin{vmatrix} 0 & 4 & 0 & -1 \\ -1 & 2 & -1 & 3 \\ 0 & 4 & 4 & -1 \\ 0 & 3 & -1 & 2 \end{vmatrix}.$$

Expansion in terms of elements of the first column as in (2.7.2) then gives

$$d = (-1) \cdot (-1)^{2+1} \cdot \begin{vmatrix} 4 & 0 & -1 \\ 4 & 4 & -1 \\ 3 & -1 & 2 \end{vmatrix} = \begin{vmatrix} 4 & 0 & -1 \\ 4 & 4 & -1 \\ 3 & -1 & 2 \end{vmatrix}.$$

Here we add four times the last column to the first and obtain

$$d = \begin{vmatrix} 0 & 0 & -1 \\ 0 & 4 & -1 \\ 11 & -1 & 2 \end{vmatrix} = 11 \cdot (-1)^{3+1} \cdot \begin{vmatrix} 0 & -1 \\ 4 & -1 \end{vmatrix} = 44.$$

Note that other similar steps could have been employed to effect a quick determination of d. *We emphasize that in operations such as these, the tool line is not altered. Only the line (parallel to the tool line) which we wish to change in some way is altered.*

In the following example, we apply (2.7.2) repeatedly to compute the determinant of a frequently useful type of matrix:

$$\begin{vmatrix} a_{11} & a_{12} & a_{13} & \cdots & a_{1n} \\ 0 & a_{22} & a_{23} & \cdots & a_{2n} \\ 0 & 0 & a_{33} & \cdots & a_{3n} \\ \vdots & & & & \\ 0 & 0 & 0 & \cdots & a_{nn} \end{vmatrix} = a_{11} \begin{vmatrix} a_{22} & a_{23} & \cdots & a_{2n} \\ 0 & a_{33} & \cdots & a_{3n} \\ \vdots & & & \\ 0 & 0 & \cdots & a_{nn} \end{vmatrix}$$

$$= a_{11}a_{22} \begin{vmatrix} a_{33} & \cdots & a_{3n} \\ \vdots & & \\ 0 & \cdots & a_{nn} \end{vmatrix}$$

$$= \cdots = a_{11}a_{22}\cdots a_{nn}.$$

A matrix like this with $a_{ij} = 0$ when $i > j$ is called an **upper triangular matrix**. We shall make use of the results of this example in the next section.

As another example, we point out that the equation of the straight line through two distinct points (x_1, y_1) and (x_2, y_2) can be written in the form

$$\begin{vmatrix} x & y & 1 \\ x_1 & y_1 & 1 \\ x_2 & y_2 & 1 \end{vmatrix} = 0,$$

for the expansion is linear in x and y by Property 1, and the determinant vanishes if either x_1 and y_1 or x_2 and y_2 are substituted for x and y, by Theorem 2.7.4. If we now subtract the second row from each of the first and third rows, we have

$$\begin{vmatrix} (x - x_1) & (y - y_1) & 0 \\ x_1 & y_1 & 1 \\ (x_2 - x_1) & (y_2 - y_1) & 0 \end{vmatrix} = 0,$$

from which

$$(x_2 - x_1)(y - y_1) = (y_2 - y_1)(x - x_1),$$

which is the familiar two-point form of the equation of a straight line.

Occasionally we are able to reduce all the elements of some line to zero, in which case the determinant is, of course, zero. Not infrequently, it is quicker to reduce all but a few of the elements of some line to zero, rather than all but one. Then after applying (2.7.1) or (2.7.2) to this line, we will have several determinants of order $n - 1$ to compute.

At times, Theorem 2.7.6 is useful in computing a determinant by the foregoing procedure. For example, let

$$h = \begin{vmatrix} 1 & 1 + i & 1 - i \\ 1 - i & 1 & i \\ 1 + i & -i & 1 \end{vmatrix}.$$

If we multiply the second row by $1 + i$ and the third by $1 - i$, we have, since $(1 + i)(1 - i) = 2$,

$$h = \tfrac{1}{2} \begin{vmatrix} 1 & 1 + i & 1 - i \\ 2 & 1 + i & -1 + i \\ 2 & -1 - i & 1 - i \end{vmatrix}.$$

Now subtracting twice the first row from the second and the third, we find

$$h = \tfrac{1}{2} \begin{vmatrix} 1 & 1+i & 1-i \\ 0 & -1-i & -3+3i \\ 0 & -3-3i & -1+i \end{vmatrix} = \tfrac{1}{2} \begin{vmatrix} -1-i & -3+3i \\ -3-3i & -1+i \end{vmatrix} = -8.$$

As a final example, by applying Theorems 2.7.6, 2.7.8, and 2.7.4, we have

$$\begin{vmatrix} 18 & 11 & 13 \\ 27 & 23 & 26 \\ 45 & 87 & 92 \end{vmatrix} = 9 \begin{vmatrix} 2 & 11 & 13 \\ 3 & 23 & 26 \\ 5 & 87 & 92 \end{vmatrix} = 9 \begin{vmatrix} 2 & 11 & 2 \\ 3 & 23 & 3 \\ 5 & 87 & 5 \end{vmatrix} = 0.$$

Often, as here, Theorem 2.7.8 can be used to diminish the absolute values of some of the elements of a matrix of integers, thereby simplifying considerably the computation of the determinant.

2.10 The "Sweep-Out" Process for Computing Determinants

When we find it necessary to compute the determinant of a matrix like

$$A = \begin{bmatrix} 0.87632 & 0.31141 & 0.11232 \\ 0.31141 & 0.24418 & 0.10214 \\ 0.11232 & 0.10214 & 0.014971 \end{bmatrix},$$

it pays to apply the procedures of the last section in a systematic form. If an automatic desk calculator is available, the following process is convenient. In the case of this example, $a_{11} \neq 0$, so that we may divide the elements of the first row by a_{11}, thus obtaining

$$\det A = 0.87632 \begin{vmatrix} 1 & 0.35536 & 0.12817 \\ 0.31141 & 0.24418 & 0.10214 \\ 0.11232 & 0.10214 & 0.014971 \end{vmatrix}.$$

Now subtracting 0.31141 times the first row from the second and 0.11232 times the first row from the third, we have

$$\det A = 0.87632 \begin{vmatrix} 1 & 0.35536 & 0.12817 \\ 0 & 0.13352 & 0.06223 \\ 0 & 0.06223 & 0.00058 \end{vmatrix}.$$

Next, by dividing the second row of this last determinant by the element in the 22-position, we obtain

$$\det A = 0.87632 \times 0.13352 \begin{vmatrix} 1 & 0.35536 & 0.12817 \\ 0 & 1 & 0.4661 \\ 0 & 0.06223 & 0.00058 \end{vmatrix}.$$

By subtracting 0.06223 times the second row from the third, we have next

$$\det A = 0.87632 \times 0.13352 \begin{vmatrix} 1 & 0.35536 & 0.12817 \\ 0 & 1 & 0.4661 \\ 0 & 0 & -0.02843 \end{vmatrix},$$

so that, finally,

$$\det A = 0.87632 \times 0.13352 \times (-0.02843) = -0.003326.$$

The principle of the method is, of course, to reduce the given matrix to triangular form, which is why it is called the "sweep-out" process, and the method may be extended at once to matrices of any order. If operations are counted, it will appear that, in the third-order case, one might almost as well have applied the definition of a determinant directly, especially if the available machine is equipped with automatic multiplication. However, when $n = 4$, the number of operations involved in this method is only about half the number of operations involved in applying the definition of a determinant directly. The advantage increases rapidly with n, as a little study will disclose.

For performing computations of this kind, a good computational form is essential. One possible form for our method, which avoids unnecessary rewriting of information, is given in Table 2.10.1.

Table 2.10.1

Key to Operations

0.87632	0.31141	0.11232	Row (1)
0.31141	0.24418	0.10214	Row (2)
0.11232	0.10214	0.014971	Row (3)
1	0.35536	0.12817	$(1)' \equiv (1) \div 0.87632$
0.31141	0.11066	0.03991	$(1)'' \equiv (1)' \times 0.31141$
0.11232	0.03991	0.014396	$(1)''' \equiv (1)' \times 0.11232$
0	*0.13352*	0.06223	$(2)' \equiv (2) - (1)''$
0	0.06223	0.00058	$(3)' \equiv (3) - (1)'''$
0	1	0.4661	$(2)'' \equiv (2)' \div 0.13352$
0	0.06223	0.02901	$(2)''' \equiv (2)'' \times 0.06223$
0	0	*-0.02843*	$(3)'' \equiv (3)' - (2)'''$

After the dividing, multiplying, and subtracting have been completed, the determinant is evaluated by multiplying together all numbers used as divisors and the final entry in the array. These numbers are italicized in the table.

In the event that accidental zeros appear, it may be necessary to alter the process slightly by interchanging some rows, but the number of operations required will in this event be reduced. At times, as this example suggests, the subtractions to be performed result in the loss of significant figures. This may become a serious problem. (For various computational procedures in evaluating determinants and for an excellent discussion of computation with approximate numbers, see P. S. Dwyer, *Linear Computations*, New York, John Wiley, 1951.)

2.11 The Determinant of the Product of Two Matrices

If matrices A and B have orders (m, n) and (n, m) respectively, AB is a square matrix of order m. The nature of det AB will now be investigated since we will have frequent occasion to use the results.

To facilitate the discussion, we make the following definitions: A **major determinant** of a matrix of order (p, q) is any determinant of maximum order of the matrix. For example,

$$\det \begin{bmatrix} a_{11} & a_{13} \\ a_{21} & a_{23} \end{bmatrix}$$

is a major determinant of

$$\begin{bmatrix} a_{11} & a_{12} & a_{13} \\ a_{21} & a_{22} & a_{23} \end{bmatrix},$$

but not of the matrix

$$\begin{bmatrix} a_{11} & a_{12} & a_{13} \\ a_{21} & a_{22} & a_{23} \\ a_{31} & a_{32} & a_{33} \end{bmatrix}.$$

In fact, *the* determinant of a square matrix is its *only* major determinant.

Suppose now that A is of order (m, n) and that B is of order (n, m), where $m \leqslant n$. Then a major determinant of the matrix A and a major determinant of the matrix B are said to be **corresponding majors** of A and B if and only if the columns of A used to form the major of A have the same indices as do the rows of B used to form the major of B. For example, in

$$
\begin{bmatrix} \alpha_1 & \alpha_2 & \alpha_3 \\ \beta_1 & \beta_2 & \beta_3 \end{bmatrix}
\quad \text{and} \quad
\begin{bmatrix} a_1 & b_1 \\ a_2 & b_2 \\ a_3 & b_3 \end{bmatrix}
$$

$$
\det \begin{bmatrix} \alpha_1 & \alpha_3 \\ \beta_1 & \beta_3 \end{bmatrix} \text{ (\textit{columns} 1 and 3)}
\quad \text{and} \quad
\det \begin{bmatrix} a_1 & b_1 \\ a_3 & b_3 \end{bmatrix} \text{ (\textit{rows} 1 and 3)}
$$

are corresponding majors. What are the other two pairs of corresponding majors?

We shall now establish

Theorem 2.11.1: *If A is a matrix of order (m, n) and B is a matrix of order (n, m), and if $m \leqslant n$, then $\det AB$ is equal to the sum of the products of the corresponding majors of A and B.*

For example,

$$
\det \left(\begin{bmatrix} x_1 & x_2 & x_3 \\ y_1 & y_2 & y_3 \end{bmatrix} \cdot \begin{bmatrix} x_1 & y_1 \\ x_2 & y_2 \\ x_3 & y_3 \end{bmatrix} \right) = \begin{vmatrix} x_1 & x_2 \\ y_1 & y_2 \end{vmatrix} \cdot \begin{vmatrix} x_1 & y_1 \\ x_2 & y_2 \end{vmatrix} + \begin{vmatrix} x_1 & x_3 \\ y_1 & y_3 \end{vmatrix} \cdot \begin{vmatrix} x_1 & y_1 \\ x_3 & y_3 \end{vmatrix}
$$

$$
+ \begin{vmatrix} x_2 & x_3 \\ y_2 & y_3 \end{vmatrix} \cdot \begin{vmatrix} x_2 & y_2 \\ x_3 & y_3 \end{vmatrix}
$$

$$
= \begin{vmatrix} x_1 & x_2 \\ y_1 & y_2 \end{vmatrix}^2 + \begin{vmatrix} x_1 & x_3 \\ y_1 & y_3 \end{vmatrix}^2 + \begin{vmatrix} x_2 & x_3 \\ y_2 & y_3 \end{vmatrix}^2.
$$

To prove the theorem, we first write A as a matrix of n m-vectors, and then form the product AB:

$$
AB = [A_1, A_2, \ldots, A_n] \cdot \begin{bmatrix} b_{11} & b_{12} & \cdots & b_{1m} \\ b_{21} & b_{22} & \cdots & b_{2m} \\ \vdots & & & \\ b_{n1} & b_{n2} & \cdots & b_{nm} \end{bmatrix}
$$

$$
= [(b_{11}A_1 + b_{21}A_2 + \cdots + b_{n1}A_n),
$$

$$
(b_{12}A_1 + b_{22}A_2 + \cdots + b_{n2}A_n), \ldots, (b_{1m}A_1 + b_{2m}A_2 + \cdots + b_{nm}A_n)].
$$

If we now proceed to expand $\det AB$ by repeated application of Theorem 2.7.7, we note that, by decomposing the first column, we obtain n determinants. From *each* of these, by decomposing the second column, we obtain

n more determinants, etc. When the process is complete, we will have obtained n^m determinants in which all possible combinations, including repetitions, of the columns $A_1, A_2, \ldots, A_n$ appear:

$$\det AB = \sum_{j_1, j_2, \ldots, j_m = 1}^{n} \det [(b_{j_1 1} A_{j_1}), (b_{j_2 2} A_{j_2}), \ldots, (b_{j_m m} A_{j_m})].$$

Evidently, every term in the above sum in which $j_1, j_2, \ldots, j_m$ are not all distinct will vanish because of proportional columns. Thus the summation needs to be extended only over the $P_m^n = n!/(n-m)!$ permutations of the integers $1, 2, \ldots, n$ taken m at a time. Designating such a sum by $\sum\limits_{(j)}'$ and factoring out the b's, we have

$$\det AB = \sum_{(j)}' (b_{j_1 1} b_{j_2 2} \cdots b_{j_m m}) \det [A_{j_1}, A_{j_2}, \ldots, A_{j_m}].$$

The terms of this sum may be grouped into sets of $m!$ terms, each set involving only permutations $j_1 j_2 \cdots j_m$ *of the same* m *digits.* Let $k_1 k_2 \cdots k_m$ denote such a set of m digits arranged in the natural order, and let

$$\epsilon_{j_1 j_2 \cdots j_m}^{k_1 k_2 \cdots k_m} = \pm 1,$$

depending on whether $j_1 j_2 \cdots j_m$ is an even or odd permutation of $k_1 k_2 \cdots k_m$. Then

$$\det [A_{j_1}, A_{j_2}, \ldots, A_{j_m}] = \epsilon_{j_1 j_2 \cdots j_m}^{k_1 k_2 \cdots k_m} \det [A_{k_1}, A_{k_2}, \ldots, A_{k_m}],$$

so that we can write

$$\det AB = \sum_{(k)} \left(\sum_{(j)} \epsilon_{j_1 j_2 \cdots j_m}^{k_1 k_2 \cdots k_m} b_{j_1 1} b_{j_2 2} \cdots b_{j_m m} \right) \det [A_{k_1}, A_{k_2}, \ldots, A_{k_m}].$$

Here the inner sum is now extended over all permutations $j_1 \cdots j_m$ of $k_1 \cdots k_m$, and the outer sum is extended over all C_m^n natural-order combinations of m of the digits $1, 2, \ldots, n$. Examination of the sum in parentheses reveals that it is the major determinant of B formed from the rows with indices $k_1, k_2, \ldots, k_m$. This is precisely the corresponding major of the major, $\det [A_{k_1}, A_{k_2}, \ldots, A_{k_m}]$, of A. Since the summation $\sum\limits_{(k)}$ includes all possible pairs of such majors, the theorem has been proved.

In the case $m = n$, each matrix has just one major, so we have proved

Corollary 2.11.2: *For two matrices A and B of order n,*

(2.11.1) $\det AB = \det A \det B.$

For example, we have

$$\begin{bmatrix} 7 & 2 \\ 3 & -4 \end{bmatrix} \cdot \begin{bmatrix} a & b \\ c & d \end{bmatrix} = \begin{bmatrix} 7a + 2c & 7b + 2d \\ 3a - 4c & 3b - 4d \end{bmatrix},$$

and, taking determinants of these matrices,

$$-34(ad - bc) = -34ad + 34bc.$$

There remains the case $m > n$. It is easy to verify that we may write

$$AB = \begin{bmatrix} a_{11} & \cdots & a_{1n} \\ a_{21} & \cdots & a_{2n} \\ \vdots & & \\ a_{m1} & \cdots & a_{mn} \end{bmatrix} \cdot \begin{bmatrix} b_{11} & b_{12} & \cdots & b_{1m} \\ \vdots & & & \\ b_{n1} & b_{n2} & \cdots & b_{nm} \end{bmatrix}$$

$$= \begin{bmatrix} a_{11} & \cdots & a_{1n} & 0 & \cdots & 0 \\ a_{21} & \cdots & a_{2n} & 0 & \cdots & 0 \\ \vdots & & & & & \\ a_{m1} & \cdots & a_{mn} & 0 & \cdots & 0 \end{bmatrix} \cdot \begin{bmatrix} b_{11} & b_{12} & \cdots & b_{1m} \\ \vdots & & & \\ b_{n1} & b_{n2} & \cdots & b_{nm} \\ 0 & 0 & \cdots & 0 \\ \vdots & & & \\ 0 & 0 & \cdots & 0 \end{bmatrix} \left.\rule{0pt}{40pt}\right\} m - n \text{ rows}$$

$$\underbrace{\phantom{a_{m1} \cdots a_{mn} 0 \cdots 0}}_{m - n \text{ cols.}}$$

Here the matrices of the last product are square and of order m. Since each of the latter matrices has determinant 0, we conclude that $\det AB = 0$ also; that is, we have

   Theorem 2.11.3:   *If A is a matrix of order (m, n) and B is a matrix of order (n, m), and if $m > n$, then $\det AB = 0$.*

2.12 Exercises

   1. Compute by first reducing to triangular form by the "sweep-out" process developed in Section 2.10:

(a) $\begin{vmatrix} 1 & 2 & 3 & 4 \\ -1 & 1 & 2 & 3 \\ 1 & -1 & 1 & 2 \\ -1 & 1 & -1 & 1 \end{vmatrix}$,

(b) $\begin{vmatrix} 1 & -2 & 0 & 3 & 6 \\ 2 & -4 & 1 & 5 & 11 \\ -1 & 2 & 3 & -2 & -5 \\ 3 & -6 & 4 & 1 & 10 \\ -3 & 7 & 2 & -7 & -16 \end{vmatrix}$.

   2. Use the methods of Section 2.9 to compute the determinants

(a) $\begin{vmatrix} 1 & 3 & 4 & -1 \\ 2 & 2 & 0 & 0 \\ 0 & -1 & 1 & 4 \\ -2 & 0 & -1 & 2 \end{vmatrix}$,

(b) $\begin{vmatrix} x & y & z & 1 \\ 1 & 1 & 1 & 1 \\ 0 & 1 & 1 & 1 \\ 1 & 0 & 1 & 1 \end{vmatrix}$.

(c) $\begin{vmatrix} 0 & i & -i & 1+i \\ i & 0 & i & -1 \\ -i & i & 0 & i \\ 1+i & -1 & i & 0 \end{vmatrix}$,

(d) $\begin{vmatrix} a_1 & a_2 & 0 & 0 \\ 0 & a_1 & a_2 & 0 \\ 0 & 0 & a_1 & a_2 \\ a_2 & 0 & 0 & a_1 \end{vmatrix}$.

3. Compute the determinant of the lower triangular matrix:

$$\begin{bmatrix} a_{11} & 0 & 0 & \cdots & 0 \\ a_{21} & a_{22} & 0 & \cdots & 0 \\ a_{31} & a_{32} & a_{33} & \cdots & 0 \\ \vdots & & & & \\ a_{n1} & a_{n2} & a_{n3} & \cdots & a_{nn} \end{bmatrix} .$$

4. Suppose that a square matrix A of order $m + n$ can be written in the form

$$A = \begin{bmatrix} a_{11} & 0 & 0 & \cdots & 0 & \\ a_{21} & a_{22} & 0 & \cdots & 0 & \\ \vdots & & & & & \mathbf{0} \\ a_{n1} & a_{n2} & a_{n3} & \cdots & a_{nn} & \\ \hline & & B & & & C \end{bmatrix} ,$$

where B is an $m \times n$ block of terms, C is an $m \times m$ block of terms, and $\bigcirc$ is an $n \times m$ block of zeros. Show that $\det A = a_{11}a_{22} \cdots a_{nn} \det C$.

5. Evaluate the determinant of the matrix

$$\begin{bmatrix} 0 & 0 & \cdots & 0 & a_{1n} \\ 0 & 0 & \cdots & a_{2,n-1} & a_{2n} \\ \vdots & & & & \\ 0 & a_{n-1,2} & \cdots & a_{n-1,n-1} & a_{n-1,n} \\ a_{n1} & a_{n2} & \cdots & a_{n,n-1} & a_{nn} \end{bmatrix} ,$$

with only zeros above the secondary diagonal. (Here it is easy to jump at the wrong conclusion.)

6. Show that no matter what may be the values of the x's and the y's,

$$\begin{vmatrix} a_{11} & a_{12} \\ a_{21} & a_{22} \end{vmatrix} = \begin{vmatrix} a_{11} & a_{12} & 0 \\ a_{21} & a_{22} & 0 \\ x_1 & x_2 & 1 \end{vmatrix} = \begin{vmatrix} a_{11} & a_{12} & x_1 & y_1 \\ a_{21} & a_{22} & x_2 & y_2 \\ 0 & 0 & 1 & y_3 \\ 0 & 0 & 0 & 1 \end{vmatrix} .$$

*7. Prove that, if the corresponding elements of two parallel lines of a square matrix A are proportional, its determinant is zero. Is the converse true?

*8. Prove that det $(\alpha A) = \alpha^n \det A$, where α is a scalar and A is of order n.

*9. Prove that, if A is skew-symmetric and of odd order, det $A = 0$.

10. Show that, if in a square matrix A all the elements for which the sum of the subscripts is odd are multiplied by -1, the determinant of the new matrix equals det A.

*11. Prove that det $\bar{A} = \overline{\det A}$.

12. Use Property 1 to prove that the expansion

$$\det A = \sum \epsilon_{j_1 j_2 \ldots j_n} a_{1 j_1} a_{2 j_2} \cdots a_{n j_n},$$

where the a_{ij}'s are indeterminates, is not a factorable polynomial. (*Hint*: If det $A = fg$, and if f contains an element from row (column) j, then, by Property 1, g cannot contain any element from row (column) j, etc.)

13. Write complete proofs for Theorems 2.7.4, 2.7.5, and 2.7.8.

14. By using the properties developed in Section 2.7, show without expanding that

$$\begin{vmatrix} a-b & 1 & a \\ b-c & 1 & b \\ c-a & 1 & c \end{vmatrix} \equiv \begin{vmatrix} a & 1 & b \\ b & 1 & c \\ c & 1 & a \end{vmatrix}.$$

15. Show without expanding that

$$\begin{vmatrix} 1 & \alpha & \beta\gamma \\ 1 & \beta & \gamma\alpha \\ 1 & \gamma & \alpha\beta \end{vmatrix} \equiv \begin{vmatrix} 1 & \alpha & \alpha^2 \\ 1 & \beta & \beta^2 \\ 1 & \gamma & \gamma^2 \end{vmatrix}.$$

16. With the aid of the properties developed in Section 2.7, express as a product of four linear factors:

$$\begin{vmatrix} a^3 & b^3 & c^3 \\ a & b & c \\ 1 & 1 & 1 \end{vmatrix}.$$

(There are a great many problems like 14, 15, 16 scattered throughout the literature.)

17. Prove that, if

$$A_j = \begin{bmatrix} a_j & d & g \\ b_j & e & h \\ c_j & f & k \end{bmatrix}, \quad j = 1, 2, \ldots, p,$$

then

$$\det \left(\sum_{j=1}^{p} A_j \right) = p^2 \sum_{j=1}^{p} (\det A_j).$$

18. Let A be an $n \times n$-partitioned matrix:

$$A = [A_1, A_2, A_3],$$

where A_1 and A_2 each have r columns. Let B be an arbitrary $r \times r$ matrix. Prove that

$$\det [A_1 + A_2 B, A_2, A_3] = \det A.$$

State a similar result for rows.

19. (a) Show by an example that $\det (A + B) \neq \det A + \det B$.

(b) Given that

$$A = \begin{vmatrix} a_{11} & a_{12} \\ a_{21} & a_{22} \end{vmatrix}, \qquad B = \begin{vmatrix} b_{11} & b_{12} \\ b_{21} & b_{22} \end{vmatrix},$$

show that $\det (A + B) = \det A + \det B$ if and only if

$$\det \begin{vmatrix} a_{11} & b_{12} \\ a_{21} & b_{22} \end{vmatrix} + \det \begin{vmatrix} b_{11} & a_{12} \\ b_{21} & a_{22} \end{vmatrix} = 0.$$

20. Prove that two matrices

$$\begin{vmatrix} a & b \\ 0 & c \end{vmatrix} \quad \text{and} \quad \begin{vmatrix} \alpha & \beta \\ 0 & \gamma \end{vmatrix}$$

commute if and only if

$$\det \begin{vmatrix} b & a - c \\ \beta & \alpha - \gamma \end{vmatrix} = 0.$$

21. Prove that

$$\begin{vmatrix} (a_{12} + a_{13}) & (a_{13} + a_{11}) & (a_{11} + a_{12}) \\ (a_{22} + a_{23}) & (a_{23} + a_{21}) & (a_{21} + a_{22}) \\ (a_{32} + a_{33}) & (a_{33} + a_{31}) & (a_{31} + a_{32}) \end{vmatrix} = 2 \begin{vmatrix} a_{11} & a_{12} & a_{13} \\ a_{21} & a_{22} & a_{23} \\ a_{31} & a_{32} & a_{33} \end{vmatrix}.$$

*22. Show that, if $i_1, i_2, \ldots, i_n$ and $j_1, j_2, \ldots, j_n$ are any permutations of $1, 2, \ldots, n$, and if $A = [a_{ij}]_n$, then

$$\det \begin{bmatrix} a_{i_1 j_1} & a_{i_1 j_2} & \cdots & a_{i_1 j_n} \\ a_{i_2 j_1} & a_{i_2 j_2} & \cdots & a_{i_2 j_n} \\ \vdots & & & \\ a_{i_n j_1} & a_{i_n j_2} & \cdots & a_{i_n j_n} \end{bmatrix} = \epsilon_{i_1 i_2 \cdots i_n} \epsilon_{j_1 j_2 \cdots j_n} \det A.$$

*23. Prove that, if the E_{j_i}'s are a permutation of the elementary n-vectors (see Exercise 31, Section 1.18), then

$$\det [E_{j_1}, E_{j_2}, \ldots, E_{j_n}] = \epsilon_{j_1 j_2 \cdots j_n}.$$

24. Show that $\det [\delta_{ij} a_{ij}] = \prod_{j=1}^{n} a_{jj}$, where δ_{ij} is the Kronecker delta.

25. Let

$$d_n = \det \begin{bmatrix} 0 & k & k & \cdots & k & k \\ k & 0 & k & \cdots & k & k \\ k & k & 0 & \cdots & k & k \\ \vdots & & & & & \\ k & k & k & \cdots & 0 & k \\ k & k & k & \cdots & k & r \end{bmatrix}_n .$$

Take $d_1 = r$, and prove by mathematical induction that $d_n = (-k)^{n-1}[(n-1)k - (n-2)r]$. (The result may also be established by the methods of Section 2.9.)

*26. Prove by induction that

$$\begin{vmatrix} x_1^{n-1} & x_1^{n-2} & \cdots & x_1 & 1 \\ x_2^{n-1} & x_2^{n-2} & \cdots & x_2 & 1 \\ \vdots & & & & \\ x_n^{n-1} & x_n^{n-2} & \cdots & x_n & 1 \end{vmatrix} = \prod_{1 \leqslant i < j \leqslant n} (x_i - x_j).$$

(See Appendix I for an explanation of the $\prod$ notation.) This determinant has a number of important applications which rest on the fact that it vanishes if and only if $x_i = x_j$ for at least one pair of integers i and j such that $1 \leqslant i < j \leqslant n$. It is known as the **Vandermonde determinant** and the corresponding matrix is called a **Vandermonde matrix**.

27. Prove that, if

$$d_n = \det \begin{vmatrix} 2\cos\theta & 1 & 0 & 0 & \cdots & 0 & 0 & 0 \\ 1 & 2\cos\theta & 1 & 0 & \cdots & 0 & 0 & 0 \\ 0 & 1 & 2\cos\theta & 1 & \cdots & 0 & 0 & 0 \\ \vdots & & & & & & & \\ 0 & 0 & 0 & 0 & \cdots & 1 & 2\cos\theta & 1 \\ 0 & 0 & 0 & 0 & \cdots & 0 & 1 & 2\cos\theta \end{vmatrix},$$

then

$$d_n = 2d_{n-1}\cos\theta - d_{n-2}, \qquad (n \geqslant 3),$$

and hence, by induction, that, if $\theta \neq k\pi$, then

$$d_n = \csc\theta \sin(n+1)\theta.$$

Finally show that, if $\theta = k\pi$, then

$$d_n = (-1)^{k(n+1)}(n+1).$$

(The matrix here is an example of a **triple-diagonal matrix**, that is, one in which nonzero entries appear only on the main diagonal and the two adjacent diagonals.)

28. The determinant

$$
\begin{vmatrix}
1 - n & 1 & 1 & \cdots & 1 \\
1 & 1 - n & 1 & \cdots & 1 \\
1 & 1 & 1 - n & \cdots & 1 \\
\vdots & & & & \\
1 & 1 & 1 & \cdots & 1 - n
\end{vmatrix}_n
$$

arises in a statistical connection. Show that it is zero.

29. Prove that

$$
\det \begin{bmatrix}
x + \lambda & x & x & \cdots & x \\
x & x + \lambda & x & \cdots & x \\
\vdots & & & & \\
x & x & x & \cdots & x + \lambda
\end{bmatrix}_n = \lambda^{n-1}(nx + \lambda).
$$

Exercise 28 is a special case of this frequently useful result.

30. Show by inspection that the equation

$$
\begin{vmatrix}
0 & \alpha - x & \beta - x \\
-\alpha - x & 0 & \gamma - x \\
-\beta - x & -\gamma - x & 0
\end{vmatrix} = 0
$$

has at least one real root. (See Exercise 9.) When will it have a multiple root? (This and other interesting problems concerning determinants and matrices may be found in the problem sections of the *American Mathematical Monthly*.)

31. Express the product

$$
\begin{vmatrix}
a_{11} & a_{12} & 0 & 0 \\
a_{21} & a_{22} & 0 & 0 \\
0 & 0 & a_{33} & a_{34} \\
0 & 0 & a_{43} & a_{44}
\end{vmatrix} \cdot \begin{vmatrix}
\alpha_1 & \alpha_2 \\
\beta_1 & \beta_2
\end{vmatrix}
$$

as the determinant of a single fourth-order matrix.

32. Two quadratic equations

$$
a_0 x^2 + a_1 x + a_2 = 0, \qquad a_0 \neq 0,
$$
$$
b_0 x^2 + b_1 x + b_2 = 0, \qquad b_0 \neq 0,
$$

have a common root if and only if the determinant

$$
\begin{vmatrix}
a_0 & a_1 & a_2 & 0 \\
0 & a_0 & a_1 & a_2 \\
b_0 & b_1 & b_2 & 0 \\
0 & b_0 & b_1 & b_2
\end{vmatrix}
$$

vanishes. Use this fact to show that, for any values of α and β, the equations

$$\alpha x^2 + x + (1 - \alpha) = 0,$$

$$(1 - \beta)x^2 + x + \beta = 0,$$

will have a common root. (The determinant above is a special case of the resultant of two polynomials, the vanishing of which is a necessary and sufficient condition that the polynomials have at least one root in common, provided we assume the polynomials have nonvanishing, leading coefficients. See M. Bôcher, *Introduction to Higher Algebra*, Macmillan, New York, 1907, p. 195, where resultants are discussed in detail.)

33. In the study of the stability of oscillating electrical or vibrating dynamical systems, the following definition is important. An algebraic equation with real coefficients is said to be a **stable equation** if and only if all its roots have negative real parts. The following tests are due to Hermite.

The equations ($a_0 > 0$ in each case)

(α) $\qquad\qquad\qquad a_0 + a_1 x + a_2 x^2 = 0,$

(β) $\qquad\qquad\qquad a_0 + a_1 x + a_2 x^2 + a_3 x^3 = 0,$

(γ) $\qquad\qquad\qquad a_0 + a_1 x + a_2 x^2 + a_3 x^3 + a_4 x^4 = 0,$

are respectively stable if and only if

(α') $\qquad a_1 > 0, \qquad a_2 > 0,$

(β') $\qquad a_1 > 0, \qquad \begin{vmatrix} a_1 & a_3 \\ a_0 & a_2 \end{vmatrix} > 0, \qquad a_3 > 0.$

(γ') $\qquad a_1 > 0, \qquad \begin{vmatrix} a_1 & a_3 \\ a_0 & a_2 \end{vmatrix} > 0, \qquad \begin{vmatrix} a_1 & a_3 & 0 \\ a_0 & a_2 & a_4 \\ 0 & a_1 & a_3 \end{vmatrix} > 0, \qquad a_4 > 0,$

with similar tests for higher order equations. Using these tests, investigate the stability of the equations:

(a) $\qquad\qquad\qquad 1 + 2x + 3x^2 = 0,$

(b) $\qquad\qquad\qquad 1 + 2x + 3x^2 + x^3 = 0,$

(c) $\qquad\qquad\qquad 1 + 2x + 3x^2 + x^3 + 2x^4 = 0.$

Also show that, if (γ) is stable, (β) is stable, and if (β) is stable, (α) is stable, but not conversely.

34. In problems in vibrations, it becomes necessary to solve equations similar to the following for λ:

$$\begin{vmatrix} 4 - \lambda & -1 & 0 \\ -1 & 4 - \lambda & -1 \\ 0 & -1 & 4 - \lambda \end{vmatrix} = 0.$$

Expand the determinant and solve the resulting equation. The values of λ found in this way are used to obtain the "normal modes of vibration."

*35. Prove the following theorem. If the elements a_{ij} of a matrix A of order n are differentiable functions of a parameter t, then $d(\det A)/(dt)$ is the sum of the determinants of n matrices, each the same as A except that, in the first, the elements of the first row have been replaced by their derivatives with respect to t, in the second the elements of the second row have been replaced by their derivatives with respect to t, etc. (A similar result holds for columns by Theorem 2.7.1.) Then show that

$$\frac{d}{dt} (\det A) = \sum_{i,j=1}^{n} A_{ij} \frac{da_{ij}}{dt}.$$

36. Compute the derivative of the determinant

$$\begin{vmatrix} 1+t & 1-t & 1 \\ 1-t & 1+t & 0 \\ 1 & 0 & t \end{vmatrix}$$

according to the rule given in Exercise 35.

37. Let $A = [a_{ij} + \delta_{ij}x]$, where the a_{ij} are constant and δ_{ij} is the Kronecker delta. Compute $d(\det A)/dx$.

38. Treating the elements of $A = [a_{ij}]_n$ as n^2 independent variables, evaluate

$$\frac{\partial}{\partial a_{ij}} (\det A).$$

39. The volume V of a tetrahedron whose six sides are known is found from the formula

$$288 \, V^2 = \begin{vmatrix} 0 & c^2 & b^2 & \alpha^2 & 1 \\ c^2 & 0 & a^2 & \beta^2 & 1 \\ b^2 & a^2 & 0 & \gamma^2 & 1 \\ \alpha^2 & \beta^2 & \gamma^2 & 0 & 1 \\ 1 & 1 & 1 & 1 & 0 \end{vmatrix},$$

where the sides a, b, c emanate from one vertex and α, β, γ are the opposite sides respectively. Find by means of this formula the volume of a regular tetrahedron with sides all equal to s.

40. Show that

$$\begin{vmatrix} y & 1 & x & x^2 \\ y_0 & 1 & x_0 & x_0^2 \\ y_0' & 0 & 1 & 2x_0 \\ y_0'' & 0 & 0 & 2 \end{vmatrix} = 0,$$

is the equation of a parabola which passes through the point (x_0, y_0) with slope y_0' and with second derivative y_0'' at that point.

41. Show that in the rectangular coordinates (x, y, z) of three-dimensional analytic geometry,

$$\begin{vmatrix} x & y & z & 1 \\ 1 & 2 & -1 & 1 \\ 0 & 1 & 0 & 1 \\ 1 & 1 & 1 & 1 \end{vmatrix} = 0,$$

is the equation of a plane through the points $(1, 2, -1)$, $(0, 1, 0)$, and $(1, 1, 1)$ and write the equation in expanded form.

42. The line $ax + by + c = 0$ is tangent to a nondegenerate conic

$$Ax^2 + Bxy + Cy^2 + Dx + Ey + F = 0$$

if and only if

$$\begin{vmatrix} 2A & B & D & a \\ B & 2C & E & b \\ D & E & 2F & c \\ a & b & c & 0 \end{vmatrix} = 0.$$

Prove that, for fixed p and all values of m, the line $y = mx + (p/m)$ is tangent to the parabola $y^2 = 4px$.

43. Define

$$\Delta = \left\{ \begin{vmatrix} y_1 & z_1 & 1 \\ y_2 & z_2 & 1 \\ y_3 & z_3 & 1 \end{vmatrix}^2 + \begin{vmatrix} z_1 & x_1 & 1 \\ z_2 & x_2 & 1 \\ z_3 & x_3 & 1 \end{vmatrix}^2 + \begin{vmatrix} x_1 & y_1 & 1 \\ x_2 & y_2 & 1 \\ x_3 & y_3 & 1 \end{vmatrix}^2 \right\}^{1/2}.$$

Then the distance between the plane on the three points, $P_1: (x_1, y_1, z_1)$, $P_2: (x_2, y_2, z_2)$, $P_3: (x_3, y_3, z_3)$, and the point $P_0: (x_0, y_0, z_0)$ is the absolute value of

$$\frac{1}{\Delta} \cdot \begin{vmatrix} x_0 & y_0 & z_0 & 1 \\ x_1 & y_1 & z_1 & 1 \\ x_2 & y_2 & z_2 & 1 \\ x_3 & y_3 & z_3 & 1 \end{vmatrix}.$$

Find the distance between the point $P_0: (1, 1, 1)$ and the plane $x + y + z = 4$ by means of this formula.

44. Define

$$k = \left\{ \begin{vmatrix} b_1 & c_1 \\ b_2 & c_2 \end{vmatrix}^2 + \begin{vmatrix} c_1 & a_1 \\ c_2 & a_2 \end{vmatrix}^2 + \begin{vmatrix} a_1 & b_1 \\ a_2 & b_2 \end{vmatrix}^2 \right\}^{1/2}.$$

Then the distance between the two skew lines

$$\frac{x - x_1}{a_1} = \frac{y - y_1}{b_1} = \frac{z - z_1}{c_1} \quad \text{and} \quad \frac{x - x_2}{a_2} = \frac{y - y_2}{b_2} = \frac{z - z_2}{c_2},$$

that is, the length of their common perpendicular, is given by the absolute value of

$$\frac{1}{k} \cdot \begin{vmatrix} x_2 - x_1 & y_2 - y_1 & z_2 - z_1 \\ a_1 & b_1 & c_1 \\ a_2 & b_2 & c_2 \end{vmatrix}.$$

Determine by means of this formula the value of λ for which the lines defined by

$$(x_1, y_1, z_1) = (\lambda, 2, -5), \qquad a_1, b_1, c_1 = 1, 2, -5,$$

and

$$(x_2, y_2, z_2) = (-1, 4, 3), \qquad a_2, b_2, c_2 = 2, -1, 1$$

will intersect.

45. Prove that, if one chooses a_1, a_2, a_3 so that the point (a_1, a_2, a_3) lies in the plane $y_1 + y_2 = y_3$ in 3-space, then the three points

$$(0, a_1), \qquad \left(\frac{1}{2}, \frac{a_3}{2}\right), \qquad \text{and} \qquad (1, a_2),$$

if plotted in the $x_1 x_2$-plane, are collinear.

46. On what surface will the point (a_1, a_2, a_3) lie if the points

$$(0, a_1), \qquad (1, a_2), \qquad \text{and} \qquad \left(\frac{a_3}{a_3 + 1}, \frac{a_3^2}{a_3 + 1}\right)$$

plotted in the $x_1 x_2$-plane are collinear? (This problem and the preceding one are adapted from Levens: *Nomography*, New York, Wiley, 1959, in which determinants are used extensively to construct nomograms.)

47. Use the sweep-out process to evaluate

(a) $\begin{vmatrix} 1 & 2 & 3 \\ 2 & 2 & 2 \\ 3 & 2 & 3 \end{vmatrix}$,   (b) $\begin{vmatrix} 0.6151 & 0.2234 & 0.1476 \\ 0.2234 & 0.5945 & 0.1162 \\ 0.1476 & 0.1162 & 0.7129 \end{vmatrix}$.

48. Show that the number of multiplications and divisions required in computing a determinant by sweep-out is

$$\frac{n - 1}{3} (n^2 + n + 3).$$

49. Show that $\det [a + (i - 1)n + j]_n = 0$ if $n > 2$ and i and j are row and column indices respectively.

50. Given $A_{n \times p}, B_{n \times q}, C_{n \times r}$, where $p + q + r = 2n$, prove that

$$\det \begin{bmatrix} A & B & 0 \\ A & 0 & C \end{bmatrix} = \pm \det \begin{bmatrix} B & A & 0 \\ B & 0 & C \end{bmatrix}.$$

When should the negative sign be used? Generalize this result.

51. From the example following the statement of Theorem 2.11.1, show that

$$(x_1{}^2 + x_2{}^2 + x_3{}^2)(y_1{}^2 + y_2{}^2 + y_3{}^2) - (x_1 y_1 + x_2 y_2 + x_3 y_3)^2$$

$$= \begin{vmatrix} x_1 & x_2 \\ y_1 & y_2 \end{vmatrix}^2 + \begin{vmatrix} x_1 & x_3 \\ y_1 & y_3 \end{vmatrix}^2 + \begin{vmatrix} x_2 & x_3 \\ y_2 & y_3 \end{vmatrix}^2 .$$

This identity is useful in analytical geometry.

*52. If $X = \{x_1, x_2, \ldots, x_n\}$ and $Y = \{y_1, y_2, \ldots, y_n\}$, show by means of Theorem 2.11.1 that

$$(X^{\mathsf{T}}X)(Y^{\mathsf{T}}Y) - (X^{\mathsf{T}}Y)^2 = \sum_{1 \leqslant i < j \leqslant n} \begin{vmatrix} x_i & x_j \\ y_i & y_j \end{vmatrix}^2 ,$$

from which

$$(X^{\mathsf{T}}X)(Y^{\mathsf{T}}Y) \geqslant (X^{\mathsf{T}}Y)^2,$$

in case the components of X and Y are real. This last is one form of the famous Cauchy-Schwarz inequality. Prove that equality holds if and only if there exist scalars α and β such that $\alpha X = \beta Y$.

*53. Prove that, if A and B are both of order n,

(a) $\det A^{\mathsf{T}}B = \det AB^{\mathsf{T}} = \det A^{\mathsf{T}}B^{\mathsf{T}} = \det AB,$

(b) $\det A^*B^* = \overline{\det AB}.$

54. Compute the product matrix and verify that (2.11.1) holds in this example:

$$\begin{bmatrix} 1 & 0 & 0 \\ 1 & 2 & 0 \\ 1 & 2 & 3 \end{bmatrix} \begin{bmatrix} 0 & 0 & x \\ 0 & y & 1 \\ z & 1 & 1 \end{bmatrix} .$$

*55. Prove that, if A and B are of order n and if $AB = I_n$, then neither $\det A$ nor $\det B$ can be zero.

*56. Show that, if A is a square matrix, $\det A^*A$ is a non-negative real number and that, if A is Hermitian, $\det A$ is real.

57. What can one conclude about $\det A$ if $A^k = A$ for some positive integer k?

*58. Prove by induction that the determinant of the product of k $n \times n$ matrices is the product of their determinants.

*59. Given that A and C are square, prove that

$$\det \begin{bmatrix} A & 0 \\ \hline B & C \end{bmatrix} = \det A \cdot \det C$$

by using the definition of a determinant and noting which terms are necessarily zero.

*60. Generalize Exercise 59 and prove the result by induction.

LAPLACE'S EXPANSION AND RELATED RESULTS

2.13 Definitions

The expansions (2.7.1) and (2.7.2) of det A in terms of the elements of some row or of some column of A are special cases of an expansion in terms of the elements of a number of rows or of a number of columns of A. This more general result, known as **Laplace's expansion**, is what we shall now establish. We begin with some definitions.

If we strike out $n - r$ rows and $n - r$ columns from a square matrix A of order n, the remaining elements form a **square submatrix** of A. The determinant of such a square submatrix is called a **minor determinant** of order r of A or an $(n - r)$th minor determinant of A. The word "determinant" is commonly omitted here. For example,

$$\begin{vmatrix} a_{11} & a_{13} \\ a_{21} & a_{23} \end{vmatrix},$$

is a minor of order 2, or a first minor of the matrix

$$\begin{bmatrix} a_{11} & a_{12} & a_{13} \\ a_{21} & a_{22} & a_{23} \\ a_{31} & a_{32} & a_{33} \end{bmatrix},$$

since it is the determinant of the submatrix obtained when the third row and the second column of the given matrix are deleted. It is useful to define the **minor of order zero** of an arbitrary square matrix A to be 1.

The $n - r$ rows one deletes in order to obtain a minor of order r may be chosen in $C_{n-r}^{n} = n!/((n - r)!r!)$ ways. The same is true for the $n - r$ columns to be deleted so that there are $(C_{n-r}^{n})^2$ such minors. (The symbol C_{n-r}^{n} denotes "the number of combinations of n things $n - r$ at a time." For an explanation with examples, see P. R. Rider, *College Algebra*, New York, Macmillan, 1955, Chapter XVI.) For example, a third-order matrix has $(C_{3-2}^{3})^2 = 9$ minors of order 2; a matrix of order 4 has $(C_{4-2}^{4})^2 = 36$ minors of order 2. Since $C_{n-r}^{n} = C_{n-r}^{n}$, it follows that there are equally many minors of orders r and $n - r$.

When the rows and columns struck out of a square matrix A have the same indices, the remaining submatrix is located symmetrically with respect to the main diagonal of A, and we call the corresponding minor a **principal minor** of A. The minor

$$\begin{vmatrix} a_{11} & \cdots & a_{1r} \\ \vdots & & \\ a_{r1} & \cdots & a_{rr} \end{vmatrix}$$

is called the **leading principal minor of order r**.

The **zero*th* minor** of A is just det A. A **first minor** M_{ij} of A is the determinant of the submatrix of order $n - 1$ of A obtained by striking out the ith row and the jth column of A. From Theorem 2.8.1 we see then that the cofactor of a_{ij} in det A is given by

$$A_{ij} = (-1)^{i+j} M_{ij}.$$

An $(n - 1)$th minor of A is just an element a_{ij} of A.

If the integers $i_1 i_2 \cdots i_r$ identify the rows and $j_1 j_2 \cdots j_r$ the columns struck out of A in constructing the minor, then we shall denote the minor by the symbol

$$M_{i_1 i_2 \cdots i_r, j_1 j_2 \cdots j_r}$$

or, more briefly, by $M_{(i)(j)}$.

A slight deviation from this notation is used for a first minor, which is commonly denoted by the symbol M_{ij}, as pointed out above. Here the comma has been omitted from between the two subscripts. Note that the initial set of subscripts identifies the rows and the second set the columns *not represented* in the minor.

If $i_1 i_2 \cdots i_r$, $n > r \geqslant 1$, is any set of r numbers chosen from $1, 2, \ldots, n$ and arranged in natural order, and if $k_1 k_2 \cdots k_{n-r}$ is the set of $n - r$ remaining integers, also arranged in natural order, then $i_1 i_2 \cdots i_r$ and $k_1 k_2 \cdots k_{n-r}$ are called **complementary sets of indices**. For example, if $n = 8$, then 147 and 23568 are such complementary sets of indices.

If $i_1 i_2 \cdots i_r$ and $k_1 k_2 \cdots k_{n-r}$ are complementary sets of row indices, and if $j_1 j_2 \cdots j_r$ and $p_1 p_2 \cdots p_{n-r}$ are complementary sets of column indices, then the two minor determinants $M_{i_1 i_2 \cdots i_r, j_1 j_2 \cdots j_r}$ and $M_{k_1 k_2 \cdots k_{n-r}, p_1 p_2 \cdots p_{n-r}}$, or, as we shall write them, $M_{(i)(j)}$ and $M_{(k)(p)}$, are called **complementary minors** of A. For example, if $n = 5$, we have as complementary minors of A,

$$M_{145,135} = \begin{vmatrix} a_{22} & a_{24} \\ a_{32} & a_{34} \end{vmatrix} \quad \text{and} \quad M_{23,24} = \begin{vmatrix} a_{11} & a_{13} & a_{15} \\ a_{41} & a_{43} & a_{45} \\ a_{51} & a_{53} & a_{55} \end{vmatrix}.$$

Notice that, if we strike out of A the complete rows and columns of A represented in one minor, there remain just the elements of the complementary minor.

We make a final definition. If $M_{(i)(j)}$ and $M_{(k)(p)}$ are complementary minors, then the quantity $A_{(k)(p)}$ defined by

$$A_{(k)(p)} = (-1)^{\Sigma k + \Sigma p} M_{(k)(p)}$$

is called the **algebraic complement** or **cofactor** of $M_{(i)(j)}$. Evidently the cofactor of $M_{(k)(p)}$ is

$$A_{(i)(j)} = (-1)^{\Sigma i + \Sigma j} M_{(i)(j)}.$$

If in particular we let $M_{(k)(p)}$ be the element a_{ij}, then we see that the cofactor of a_{ij} is

$$A_{ij} = (-1)^{i+j} M_{ij},$$

which agrees with the result of Section 2.8.

The reader may show that $(-1)^{\Sigma i + \Sigma j} = (-1)^{\Sigma p + \Sigma p}$, where complementary sets of subscripts are involved as above, so that the cofactors of $M_{(i)(j)}$ and $M_{(k)(p)}$ are respectively $M_{(k)(p)}$ and $M_{(i)(j)}$ or $-M_{(k)(p)}$ and $-M_{(i)(j)}$ depending upon whether $\Sigma i + \Sigma j$ is even or odd.

Examination of the definition of $A_{(k)(p)}$ shows that the exponent on (-1) is simply the sum of the indices of the rows and columns *present* in $M_{(i)(j)}$. This observation makes writing down the cofactor of $M_{(i)(j)}$ a simple matter. For example, consider the matrix

$$\begin{bmatrix} 1 & 0 & 2 & 0 \\ 2 & 0 & 1 & 0 \\ 0 & 4 & 0 & 3 \\ 0 & 3 & 0 & 4 \end{bmatrix}.$$

The cofactor of $\begin{vmatrix} 1 & 0 \\ 2 & 0 \end{vmatrix}$, the upper-left principal minor of order 2, is

$$(-1)^{(1+2)+(1+2)} \begin{vmatrix} 0 & 3 \\ 0 & 4 \end{vmatrix}$$

since $\begin{vmatrix} 0 & 3 \\ 0 & 4 \end{vmatrix}$ is the complementary minor of $\begin{vmatrix} 1 & 0 \\ 2 & 0 \end{vmatrix}$ in this case.

2.14 The Laplace Expansion

The sequence of theorems to follow will provide a derivation of the Laplace expansion of a determinant. To motivate these theorems and also to provide further illustrations of the foregoing definitions, we shall give an example of how Laplace's expansion operates before launching into the proof.

Laplace's theorem says that, if we select any r rows of A, form all possible r-rowed minors from these r rows, multiply each of these minors by its cofactor, and then add the results, we obtain det A.

In the matrix given in Section 2.13, let the first two rows be the r rows from which to form minors. We denote this fact by a dashed line:

$$\begin{bmatrix} 1 & 0 & 2 & 0 \\ 2 & 0 & 1 & 0 \\ \hdashline 0 & 4 & 0 & 3 \\ 0 & 3 & 0 & 4 \end{bmatrix}.$$

Since the formation of a minor from the first two rows requires the selection of two columns from the four, we will have $C_2^4 = 6$ minors possible. We shall select the columns systematically thus: 1 and 2, 1 and 3, 1 and 4, 2 and 3, 2 and 4,

3 and 4. Then applying Laplace's theorem as stated above, and the verbal rule for finding the sign of the cofactor given in Section 2.13, we have

$$
\begin{vmatrix} 1 & 0 & 2 & 0 \\ 2 & 0 & 1 & 0 \\ \hline 0 & 4 & 0 & 3 \\ 0 & 3 & 0 & 4 \end{vmatrix} = \begin{vmatrix} 1 & 0 \\ 2 & 0 \end{vmatrix} \cdot (-1)^{1+2+1+2} \begin{vmatrix} 0 & 3 \\ 0 & 4 \end{vmatrix}
$$

$$
+ \begin{vmatrix} 1 & 2 \\ 2 & 1 \end{vmatrix} \cdot (-1)^{1+2+1+3} \begin{vmatrix} 4 & 3 \\ 3 & 4 \end{vmatrix} + \begin{vmatrix} 1 & 0 \\ 2 & 0 \end{vmatrix} \cdot (-1)^{1+2+1+4} \begin{vmatrix} 4 & 0 \\ 3 & 0 \end{vmatrix}
$$

$$
+ \begin{vmatrix} 0 & 2 \\ 0 & 1 \end{vmatrix} \cdot (-1)^{1+2+2+3} \begin{vmatrix} 0 & 3 \\ 0 & 4 \end{vmatrix} + \begin{vmatrix} 0 & 0 \\ 0 & 0 \end{vmatrix} \cdot (-1)^{1+2+2+4} \begin{vmatrix} 0 & 0 \\ 0 & 0 \end{vmatrix}
$$

$$
+ \begin{vmatrix} 2 & 0 \\ 1 & 0 \end{vmatrix} \cdot (-1)^{1+2+3+4} \begin{vmatrix} 0 & 4 \\ 0 & 3 \end{vmatrix} = 21.
$$

The full expansion was written here for illustrative purposes but, clearly, to obtain the end result, we would only have needed to write the single nonzero term of the sum. Someone with only a little experience in these matters would have noticed this at once and would have been able to write the result, "21," by inspection. The example shows that the Laplace expansion is useful for evaluating certain special numerical determinants, but it is even more useful in deriving other theorems.

We shall now establish several preliminary theorems by way of preparing for the main result.

Theorem 2.14.1: *If* $i_1 i_2 \cdots i_r$ *and* $k_1 k_2 \cdots k_{n-r}$ *are complementary sets of indices, then the permutation* $i_1 i_2 \cdots i_r k_1 k_2 \cdots k_{n-r}$ *may be obtained from the natural order* 1, 2, ..., n *by* $(\sum i) - r(r+1)/2$ *adjacent transpositions.*

(The given permutation may therefore be reduced to the natural order by the same number of adjacent transpositions.)

For if we start with the natural order 1, 2, ..., n, it takes $i_1 - 1$ adjacent transpositions to put i_1 into the first position and then, because $i_2 > i_1$ it takes $i_2 - 2$ more to put i_2 in the second position, etc. Finally, it takes $i_r - r$ adjacent transpositions to put i_r in the rth position. The natural order of the remaining integers has not been disturbed, so that no further transpositions are needed to construct the desired permutation. Thus we use altogether $(i_1 - 1) + (i_2 - 2) + \cdots + (i_r - r) = (\sum i) - r(r+1)/2$ adjacent transpositions since $1 + 2 + \cdots + r = r(r+1)/2$.

Theorem 2.14.2: *If* $i_1 i_2 \cdots i_r$ *and* $k_1 k_2 \cdots k_{n-r}$ *are complementary sets of row indices, and if* $j_1 j_2 \cdots j_r$ *and* $p_1 p_2 \cdots p_{n-r}$ *are complementary sets of column indices, then*

$$
(-1)^{\Sigma i + \Sigma j} a_{i_1 j_1} \cdots a_{i_r j_r} a_{k_1 p_1} \cdots a_{k_{n-r} p_{n-r}}
$$

is a term in the expansion of det A.

Because (i), (k) and (j), (p) here are complementary sets of row and column subscripts, every row and every column of A is represented once and only once in the above product. Hence we need only show that the sign is correct. To decide what sign would be attached to the product

$$a_{i_1 j_1} \cdots a_{i_r j_r} a_{k_1 p_1} \cdots a_{k_{n-r} p_{n-r}}$$

in the expansion of det A, we note that by the preceding theorem, it will take $(\sum i) - r(r+1)/2$ adjacent transpositions of these factors to restore their row subscripts to the natural order $1, 2, \ldots, n$. Then we can determine the sign to be attached to this product by investigating the permutation represented by the column subscripts. There are $(\sum j) - r(r+1)/2$ transpositions needed to obtain the *initially given* set of column subscripts from the natural order. Since the unscrambling of the row subscripts then imposes $(\sum i) - r(r+1)/2$ *additional* transpositions on the column subscripts, the sign of the term should be determined by

$$(-1)^{\Sigma i - r(r+1)/2 + \Sigma j - r(r+1)/2} = (-1)^{\Sigma i + \Sigma j},$$

which is just what was used above, so that the theorem is proved.

Theorem 2.14.3: *With complementary sets of row and column indices as in Theorem 2.14.2, every term in the product*

$$M_{(k)(p)} A_{(i)(j)} \equiv M_{(k)(p)} (-1)^{\Sigma i + \Sigma j} M_{(i)(j)}$$

of a minor of A and its cofactor is a term in the expansion of det A.

Since every row and column subscript will appear once and only once in each such term, it is again only the sign of such a term that needs to be investigated. A general term of this product may be written thus:

$$(-1)^{\Sigma i + \Sigma j} [(-1)^{\mu_j'} a_{i_1 j_1'} a_{i_2 j_2'} \cdots a_{i_r j_r'}] \cdot [(-1)^{\mu_p'} a_{k_1 p_1'} a_{k_2 p_2'} \cdots a_{k_{n-r} p_{n-r}'}],$$

where the bracketed expressions are terms from the row expansions of the two minors and where μ_j' is the number of adjacent transpositions required to produce the permutation $j_1' j_2' \cdots j_r'$ from $j_1 j_2 \cdots j_r$, with a similar definition for μ_p'.

Now to determine the sign that the product

$$a_{i_1 j_1'} a_{i_2 j_2'} \cdots a_{i_r j_r'} a_{k_1 p_1'} a_{k_2 p_2'} \cdots a_{k_{n-r} p_{n-r}'}$$

would have in the expansion of det A, we put the i's and the k's back into the natural order $1, 2, \ldots, n$ by transposing factors. This may be accomplished by $(\sum i) - r(r+1)/2$ adjacent transpositions, and it induces further scrambling of the column scripts. Checking through the matter chronologically, we see that the final arrangement of the column scripts may be obtained by a total of

$$\left(\left(\sum j \right) - \frac{r(r+1)}{2} \right) + \mu_j' + \mu_p' + \left(\left(\sum i \right) - \frac{r(r+1)}{2} \right)$$

transpositions from the natural order, and hence the sign attached to the product in question should be determined by

$$(-1)^{\Sigma i + \Sigma j + \mu_j' + \mu_p'},$$

as is indeed the case in the signed product above. Therefore each term in this product is actually a term from det A.

Theorem 2.14.4: *If $i_1 i_2 \cdots i_r$ is any fixed set of r row indices in the natural order, and if $j_1 j_2 \cdots j_r$ runs over every set of r column indices, each set also in the natural order, then we have*

$$\det A = \sum_{(j)} M_{(k)(p)} A_{(i)(j)},$$

where the i's and k's and the j's and p's are complementary sets of row and column indices respectively, and where the summation extends over all the sets of r column indices described above.

This is called the **Laplace expansion** of det A in terms of minors of order r formed from the given r rows. A similar result holds, of course, for columns.

To prove the result, we note first that the expansion of every term in this summation will contain only terms of det A by the preceding theorem. Since no two sets of subscripts $j_1 j_2 \cdots j_r$ are the same, it follows next that these terms of det A are all different. Finally, the two minors appearing in each summand have respectively $r!$ and $(n - r)!$ terms, and there are $C_r^n = n!/(r!(n - r)!)$ ways to select $j_1 j_2 \cdots j_r$ from $1, 2, \ldots, n$. Hence there are altogether

$$r!(n - r)! \frac{n!}{r!(n - r)!} = n!$$

terms of det A in the complete expansion of the above sum, just as there are $n!$ terms in det A. These three facts taken together prove the theorem.

As a second illustration of Laplace's expansion we give the following example involving literal elements rather than integers. The student should check the signs of the various terms.

We make the definition

$$p_{ij} = \begin{vmatrix} x_i & x_j \\ y_i & y_j \end{vmatrix}, \qquad i, j = 1, 2, 3, 4.$$

Then we have $p_{ii} \equiv 0$ and $p_{ij} \equiv -p_{ji}$ in any case. Among the nonidentically vanishing p_{ij}'s, there exists a simple identity. It is found by applying Laplace's expansion to the following vanishing determinant:

$$0 = \begin{vmatrix} x_1 & x_2 & x_3 & x_4 \\ y_1 & y_2 & y_3 & y_4 \\ \hline x_1 & x_2 & x_3 & x_4 \\ y_1 & y_2 & y_3 & y_4 \end{vmatrix} = \begin{vmatrix} x_1 & x_2 \\ y_1 & y_2 \end{vmatrix} \cdot \begin{vmatrix} x_3 & x_4 \\ y_3 & y_4 \end{vmatrix} - \begin{vmatrix} x_1 & x_3 \\ y_1 & y_3 \end{vmatrix} \cdot \begin{vmatrix} x_2 & x_4 \\ y_2 & y_4 \end{vmatrix}$$

$$+ \begin{vmatrix} x_1 & x_4 \\ y_1 & y_4 \end{vmatrix} \cdot \begin{vmatrix} x_2 & x_3 \\ y_2 & y_3 \end{vmatrix} + \begin{vmatrix} x_2 & x_3 \\ y_2 & y_3 \end{vmatrix} \cdot \begin{vmatrix} x_1 & x_4 \\ y_1 & y_4 \end{vmatrix}$$

$$- \begin{vmatrix} x_2 & x_4 \\ y_2 & y_4 \end{vmatrix} \cdot \begin{vmatrix} x_1 & x_3 \\ y_1 & y_3 \end{vmatrix} + \begin{vmatrix} x_3 & x_4 \\ y_3 & y_4 \end{vmatrix} \cdot \begin{vmatrix} x_1 & x_2 \\ y_1 & y_2 \end{vmatrix},$$

or

$$p_{12}p_{34} - p_{13}p_{24} + p_{14}p_{23} + p_{23}p_{14} - p_{24}p_{13} + p_{34}p_{12} \equiv 0,$$

which reduces without difficulty to

$$(2.14.1) \qquad p_{12}p_{34} + p_{13}p_{42} + p_{14}p_{23} \equiv 0,$$

when we use the fact that $p_{ij} \equiv -p_{ji}$. This identity is important in the study of line geometry, where these p's are used as coordinates (the Plücker coordinates of a line).

2.15 The Determinant of a Product of Two Square Matrices

As an application of the Laplace expansion, we prove this basic result, which was proved in another way in Section 2.11.

Theorem 2.15.1:   *The determinant of the product of two square matrices of order n is equal to the product of their determinants.*

In symbols, if A and B are matrices of order n with elements a_{ij} and b_{ij} respectively, and if C is the matrix of order n such that $AB = C$, that is, if C has elements c_{ij} defined by

$$c_{ij} = a_{i1}b_{1j} + a_{i2}b_{2j} + \cdots + a_{in}b_{nj},$$

then

$$\det A \det B = \det C.$$

To prove the theorem, we note first that by the Laplace expansion

$$\det A \det B = \begin{vmatrix} a_{11} & a_{12} & \cdots & a_{1n} & 0 & 0 & \cdots & 0 \\ a_{21} & a_{22} & \cdots & a_{2n} & 0 & 0 & \cdots & 0 \\ \vdots & & & \vdots & & & & \\ a_{n1} & a_{n2} & \cdots & a_{nn} & 0 & 0 & \cdots & 0 \\ -1 & 0 & \cdots & 0 & b_{11} & b_{12} & \cdots & b_{1n} \\ 0 & -1 & \cdots & 0 & b_{21} & b_{22} & \cdots & b_{2n} \\ \vdots & & & & \vdots & & & \\ 0 & 0 & \cdots & -1 & b_{n1} & b_{n2} & \cdots & b_{nn} \end{vmatrix},$$

since the upper left-hand submatrix of order n is the only one formed from the first n rows whose determinant is not identically zero. The lower left-hand block is, of course, arbitrary here, but the choice shown makes possible a neat proof.

We now eliminate the first row of b's in the lower right-hand block of the array on the right by adding b_{11} times the first column, b_{12} times the first column, ..., b_{1n} times the first column respectively to the columns with indices $n + 1$, $n + 2, \ldots, 2n$. This yields the result

$$\det A \det B = \begin{vmatrix} a_{11} & a_{12} & \cdots & a_{1n} & a_{11}b_{11} & a_{11}b_{12} & \cdots & a_{11}b_{1n} \\ a_{21} & a_{22} & \cdots & a_{2n} & a_{21}b_{11} & a_{21}b_{12} & \cdots & a_{21}b_{1n} \\ \vdots & & & & \vdots & & & \\ a_{n1} & a_{n2} & \cdots & a_{nn} & a_{n1}b_{11} & a_{n1}b_{12} & \cdots & a_{n1}b_{1n} \\ -1 & 0 & \cdots & 0 & 0 & 0 & \cdots & 0 \\ 0 & -1 & \cdots & 0 & b_{21} & b_{22} & \cdots & b_{2n} \\ \vdots & & & & \vdots & & & \\ 0 & 0 & \cdots & -1 & b_{n1} & b_{n2} & \cdots & b_{nn} \end{vmatrix}.$$

We next add b_{21} times, b_{22} times, ..., b_{2n} times the second column to the columns with indices $n + 1, n + 2, \ldots, 2n$ respectively. This eliminates the second row of b's from the lower right-hand block:

$$\det A \det B = \begin{vmatrix} a_{11} & a_{12} & \cdots & a_{1n} & (a_{11}b_{11} + a_{12}b_{21}) & \cdots & (a_{11}b_{1n} + a_{12}b_{2n}) \\ a_{21} & a_{22} & \cdots & a_{2n} & (a_{21}b_{11} + a_{22}b_{21}) & \cdots & (a_{21}b_{1n} + a_{22}b_{2n}) \\ \vdots & & & & \vdots & & \\ a_{n1} & a_{n2} & \cdots & a_{nn} & (a_{n1}b_{11} + a_{n2}b_{21}) & \cdots & (a_{n1}b_{1n} + a_{n2}b_{2n}) \\ -1 & 0 & \cdots & 0 & 0 & \cdots & 0 \\ 0 & -1 & \cdots & 0 & 0 & \cdots & 0 \\ & & & & b_{31} & \cdots & b_{3n} \\ \vdots & & & & \vdots & & \\ 0 & 0 & \cdots & -1 & b_{n1} & \cdots & b_{nn} \end{vmatrix}.$$

Continuing thus until all the rows of the lower right-hand block are eliminated we obtain the result

$$\begin{vmatrix} a_{11} & a_{12} & \cdots & a_{1n} & c_{11} & c_{12} & \cdots & c_{1n} \\ a_{21} & a_{22} & \cdots & a_{2n} & c_{21} & c_{22} & \cdots & c_{2n} \\ \vdots & & & & \vdots & & & \\ a_{n1} & a_{n2} & \cdots & a_{nn} & c_{n1} & c_{n2} & \cdots & c_{nn} \\ -1 & 0 & \cdots & 0 & 0 & 0 & \cdots & 0 \\ 0 & -1 & \cdots & 0 & 0 & 0 & \cdots & 0 \\ \vdots & & & & \vdots & & & \\ 0 & 0 & \cdots & -1 & 0 & 0 & \cdots & 0 \end{vmatrix},$$

where the c_{ij}'s are just as described in the statement of the theorem.

Now we apply the Laplace expansion in terms of minors of the first n rows once more and obtain

$$\det A \, \det B = (-1)^{[1+2+\cdots+n]+[(n+1)+(n+2)+\cdots+2n]}(-1)^n \det C$$

$$= \det C.$$

2.16 The Adjoint Matrix

If A is a matrix of order n and A_{ij} is the cofactor of a_{ij} in $\det A$, then the matrix

(2.16.1)
$$\mathscr{A} = [A_{ij}]^{\mathsf{T}} = \begin{bmatrix} A_{11} & A_{21} & \cdots & A_{n1} \\ A_{12} & A_{22} & \cdots & A_{n2} \\ \vdots & & & \\ A_{1n} & A_{2n} & \cdots & A_{nn} \end{bmatrix}$$

is called the **adjoint matrix of A** and $\det \mathscr{A}$ is called the **adjoint determinant of A**. In the next chapter we shall use the adjoint matrix in discussing the inverse of a matrix, but here we wish to give several results that are useful in a number of applications.

Theorem 2.16.1: $\det \mathscr{A} = (\det A)^{n-1}$.

We have by (2.7.4)

(2.16.2)
$$A \cdot \mathscr{A} = \begin{bmatrix} a_{11} & a_{12} & \cdots & a_{1n} \\ a_{21} & a_{22} & \cdots & a_{2n} \\ \vdots & & & \\ a_{n1} & a_{n2} & \cdots & a_{nn} \end{bmatrix} \cdot \begin{bmatrix} A_{11} & A_{21} & \cdots & A_{n1} \\ A_{12} & A_{22} & \cdots & A_{n2} \\ \vdots & & & \\ A_{1n} & A_{2n} & \cdots & A_{nn} \end{bmatrix} = (\det A)I_n,$$

so that, by Theorem 2.15.1 and Exercise 8, Section 2.12

$$\det A \cdot \det \mathscr{A} = (\det A)^n.$$

Since this is *a polynomial identity in the* a_{ij}'s and $\det A \not\equiv 0$ in these variables we have, by cancelling $\det A$ from both members, the desired result. (See M. Bôcher, *Introduction to Higher Algebra*, New York, Macmillan, 1907, p. 7, last sentence. See also Exercise 8, Section 5.8, this book.)

This theorem is generalized in the next:

Theorem 2.16.2: *If* $\mathscr{M}_{(p)(k)}$ *is a minor of order* r *of* $\mathscr{A}$ *and if* $M_{(i)(j)}$ *is a minor of order* $n-r$ *of* A *such that the* i's *and* k's *as well as the* j's *and* p's *are complementary sets of subscripts, then*

$$\mathscr{M}_{(p)(k)} = (-1)^{\Sigma i + \Sigma j}(\det A)^{r-1}M_{(i)(j)} = (\det A)^{r-1}A_{(i)(j)}.$$

(Note that in $\mathscr{A}$, and hence in $\mathscr{M}$ also, the p's identify rows and the k's identify columns.)

The theorem is proved by considering the following product:

$$
\begin{bmatrix}
a_{i_1 j_1} & \cdots & a_{i_1 j_r} & a_{i_1 p_1} & \cdots & a_{i_1 p_{n-r}} \\
\vdots & & & \vdots & & \\
a_{i_r j_1} & \cdots & a_{i_r j_r} & a_{i_r p_1} & \cdots & a_{i_r p_{n-r}} \\
a_{k_1 j_1} & \cdots & a_{k_1 j_r} & a_{k_1 p_1} & \cdots & a_{k_1 p_{n-r}} \\
\vdots & & & \vdots & & \\
a_{k_{n-r} j_1} & \cdots & a_{k_{n-r} j_r} & a_{k_{n-r} p_1} & \cdots & a_{k_{n-r} p_{n-r}}
\end{bmatrix}
$$

$$
\cdot
\begin{bmatrix}
A_{i_1 j_1} & \cdots & A_{i_r j_1} & 0 & 0 & \cdots & 0 \\
\vdots & & & & \vdots & & \\
A_{i_1 j_r} & \cdots & A_{i_r j_r} & 0 & 0 & \cdots & 0 \\
A_{i_1 p_1} & \cdots & A_{i_r p_1} & 1 & 0 & \cdots & 0 \\
\vdots & & & & \vdots & & \\
A_{i_1 p_{n-r}} & \cdots & A_{i_r p_{n-r}} & 0 & 0 & \cdots & 1
\end{bmatrix}
$$

$$
=
\begin{bmatrix}
\det A & 0 & \cdots & 0 & a_{i_1 p_1} & \cdots & a_{i_1 p_{n-r}} \\
0 & \det A & \cdots & 0 & \vdots & & \\
0 & 0 & \cdots & \det A & a_{i_r p_1} & \cdots & a_{i_r p_{n-r}} \\
0 & 0 & \cdots & 0 & a_{k_1 p_1} & \cdots & a_{k_1 p_{n-r}} \\
\vdots & & & & \vdots & & \\
0 & 0 & \cdots & 0 & a_{k_{n-r} p_1} & \cdots & a_{k_{n-r} p_{n-r}}
\end{bmatrix}.
$$

Now, taking determinants of both sides and employing Exercise 22 of Section 2.12, Theorem 2.14.1, and Theorems 2.15.1 and 2.14.4, we obtain the identity

$$(-1)^{\Sigma i + \Sigma j} \det A \cdot \mathscr{M}_{(p)(k)} = (\det A)^r \cdot M_{(i)(j)}.$$

Canceling $\det A$ from both sides and multiplying both sides by $(-1)^{\Sigma i + \Sigma j}$, we have, finally,

$$\mathscr{M}_{(p)(k)} = (-1)^{\Sigma i + \Sigma j}(\det A)^{r-1} M_{(i)(j)} = (\det A)^{r-1} A_{(i)(j)}$$

as stated.

Certain special cases are frequently useful. If we put $r = n - 1$ and let $\mathscr{A}_{pk}$ denote the *cofactor* of the element in the pth row and kth column of $\mathscr{A}$, then

$$\mathscr{A}_{pk} = (\det A)^{n-2} a_{kp}.$$

Putting $r = 2$, we find

$$
\begin{vmatrix}
A_{i_1 j_1} & A_{i_2 j_1} \\
A_{i_1 j_2} & A_{i_2 j_2}
\end{vmatrix}
= \mathscr{M}_{p_1 \cdots p_{n-2}, k_1 \cdots k_{n-2}} = A_{i_1 i_2, j_1 j_2} \det A.
$$

The reader should think through the special cases $r = n$ and $r = 1$ with some care.

2.17 The Row-and-Column Expansion

The theorem of this section has, among others, applications to statistics and to the study of quadric surfaces.

In the statement of the theorem, $A_{1i,1j}$ represents the cofactor of the second-order minor

$$\begin{vmatrix} a_{11} & a_{1j} \\ a_{i1} & a_{ij} \end{vmatrix}$$

of the matrix $A = [a_{ij}]_n$, the notation being that explained in Section 2.13.

Theorem 2.17.1: $\det A = a_{11}A_{11} - \sum\limits_{i,j=2}^{n} a_{i1}a_{1j}A_{1i,1j}.$

This is called the *expansion of* $\det A$ *in terms of the elements of the first row and the elements of the first column.*

By (2.7.1), the expansion in terms of the elements of the first row is

(2.17.1) $$\det A = a_{11}A_{11} + \sum_{j=2}^{n} a_{1j}A_{1j}.$$

Now

$$A_{1j} = (-1)^{1+j}M_{1j},$$

and expanding M_{1j} in terms of elements of its first column, we see that

$$M_{1j} = \sum_{i=2}^{n} a_{i1}(-1)^{(i-1)+1}M_{1i,1j},$$

so that

$$A_{1j} = \sum_{i=2}^{n} a_{i1}(-1)^{i+j+1}M_{1i,1j}$$

$$= -\sum_{i=2}^{n} a_{i1}((-1)^{1+i+1+j}M_{1i,1j}),$$

or

$$A_{1j} = -\sum_{i=2}^{n} a_{i1}A_{1i,1j}.$$

Substitution for A_{1j} in (2.17.1) now gives the desired result.

2.18 The Diagonal Expansion of the Determinant of a Matrix

It is easy to verify by direct computation that

$$\begin{vmatrix} d_1 & b_{12} \\ b_{21} & d_2 \end{vmatrix} = \begin{vmatrix} 0 & b_{12} \\ b_{21} & 0 \end{vmatrix} + d_1 d_2,$$

and that

$$\begin{vmatrix} d_1 & b_{12} & b_{13} \\ b_{21} & d_2 & b_{23} \\ b_{31} & b_{32} & d_3 \end{vmatrix} = \begin{vmatrix} 0 & b_{12} & b_{13} \\ b_{21} & 0 & b_{23} \\ b_{31} & b_{32} & 0 \end{vmatrix} + d_1 \begin{vmatrix} 0 & b_{23} \\ b_{32} & 0 \end{vmatrix}$$

$$+ d_2 \begin{vmatrix} 0 & b_{13} \\ b_{31} & 0 \end{vmatrix} + d_3 \begin{vmatrix} 0 & b_{12} \\ b_{21} & 0 \end{vmatrix} + d_1 d_2 d_3.$$

These two examples suggest

Theorem 2.18.1: *Let*

$$A = B + D$$

denote an arbitrary $n \times n$ matrix, where

$$B = \begin{bmatrix} 0 & b_{12} & b_{13} & \cdots & b_{1,n-1} & b_{1n} \\ b_{21} & 0 & b_{23} & \cdots & b_{2,n-1} & b_{2n} \\ \vdots & & & & & \\ b_{n1} & b_{n2} & b_{n3} & \cdots & b_{n,n-1} & 0 \end{bmatrix},$$

and

$$D = \begin{bmatrix} d_1 & 0 & \cdots & 0 \\ 0 & d_2 & \cdots & 0 \\ \vdots & & & \\ 0 & 0 & \cdots & d_n \end{bmatrix}.$$

Then,

$$\det A = \det B + \sum_{i=1}^{n} d_i B_{ii} + \sum_{1 \leqslant i < j \leqslant n} d_i d_j B_{ij,ij}$$

$$+ \sum_{1 \leqslant i < j < k \leqslant n} d_i d_j d_k B_{ijk,ijk} + \cdots + d_1 d_2 \cdots d_n.$$

This is called the **diagonal expansion** *of* $\det A$.

To prove this, let us first write

$$A = [B_1 + D_1, B_2 + D_2, \ldots, B_n + D_n],$$

where B_j denotes the jth column of B and D_j denotes the jth column of D. By applying Theorem 2.7.7 to the first column of A, we obtain

$$\det A = \det [B_1, B_2 + D_2, \ldots, B_n + D_n]$$
$$+ \det [D_1, B_2 + D_2, \ldots, B_n + D_n].$$

Then applying Theorem 2.7.7 to the second columns of these matrices, and to the third columns of the resulting matrices, etc., we obtain finally,

$$\det A = \sum \det [C_1, C_2, \ldots, C_n],$$

where each C_j is either B_j or D_j, so that there are altogether 2^n determinants in the sum.

Now by putting each $C_j = B_j$, we obtain $\det B$ as one term of the sum. By putting $C_k = D_k$, $C_j = B_j$ for $j \neq k$, we obtain all terms of the form $d_k B_{kk}$, etc. Finally, by putting each $C_j = D_j$, we obtain the term $d_1 d_2 \cdots d_n$. Note that no product of $n - 1$ d_j's will appear because every principal minor of order 1 of B is 0.

2.19 Exercises

1. Expand in minors of the first two rows

$$
\begin{vmatrix}
2 & 0 & 1 & 0 & 1 \\
1 & 0 & 1 & 0 & 2 \\
\hline
1 & 2 & 0 & 1 & 1 \\
1 & 1 & 0 & 2 & 1 \\
1 & 1 & 0 & 1 & 1
\end{vmatrix}.
$$

2. Expand in minors of the last two columns

$$
\begin{vmatrix}
0 & -2 & 4 & 1 & 1 \\
1 & 2 & 1 & 1 & 2 \\
1 & 2 & 1 & 2 & 2 \\
0 & 1 & -2 & 3 & 3 \\
1 & 0 & 1 & 4 & 4
\end{vmatrix}.
$$

3. Show that if $A_1, A_2, \ldots, A_n$ are square matrices which are used to build up a square matrix A,

$$
A = \begin{bmatrix}
A_1 & 0 & \cdots & 0 \\
0 & A_2 & \cdots & 0 \\
\vdots & & & \\
0 & 0 & \cdots & A_n
\end{bmatrix},
$$

where the 0's stand for blocks of elements all of which are zero, then

$$
\det A = \det A_1 \det A_2 \cdots \det A_n.
$$

Matrices of this type are useful in theoretical physics, numerical analysis, and in other applications.

4. Show that if A_{ij} is the cofactor of a_{ij} in $\det A$, and if $n > 1$, then

$$
\begin{vmatrix}
0 & u_1 & u_2 & \cdots & u_n \\
u_1 & a_{11} & a_{12} & \cdots & a_{1n} \\
u_2 & a_{21} & a_{22} & \cdots & a_{2n} \\
\vdots & & & & \\
u_n & a_{n1} & a_{n2} & \cdots & a_{nn}
\end{vmatrix} = -\sum_{i,j=1}^{n} A_{ij} u_i u_j.
$$

This application of Theorem 2.17.1 is used in the study of quadric surfaces and hypersurfaces.

5. Show that

$$
\begin{vmatrix}
a_1 & b_1 & c_1 & d_1 & 0 & 0 \\
a_2 & b_2 & c_2 & d_2 & 0 & 0 \\
a_3 & b_3 & c_3 & d_3 & 0 & 0 \\
0 & 0 & 0 & d_1 & e_1 & f_1 \\
0 & 0 & 0 & d_2 & e_2 & f_2 \\
0 & 0 & 0 & d_3 & e_3 & f_3
\end{vmatrix}
=
\begin{vmatrix}
a_1 & b_1 & c_1 & d_1 & 0 & 0 \\
a_2 & b_2 & c_2 & d_2 & 0 & 0 \\
a_3 & b_3 & c_3 & d_3 & 0 & 0 \\
-a_1 & -b_1 & -c_1 & 0 & e_1 & f_1 \\
-a_2 & -b_2 & -c_2 & 0 & e_2 & f_2 \\
-a_3 & -b_3 & -c_3 & 0 & e_3 & f_3
\end{vmatrix}.
$$

Now define

$$
(abc) = \det \begin{bmatrix}
a_1 & b_1 & c_1 \\
a_2 & b_2 & c_2 \\
a_3 & b_3 & c_3
\end{bmatrix}
$$

and similarly in other cases. Then show that

$$
(abc)(def) = (dbc)(aef) + (adc)(bef) + (abd)(cef).
$$

To what does this identity reduce if (def) is an identity matrix? If all corresponding entries d_i and f_i are identical? [Compare (2.14.1) with this last case.]

6. Prove Theorem 2.11.1 by applying the Laplace expansion to

$$
\begin{vmatrix}
A_{(m,n)} & 0_{(m,m)} \\
-I_n & B_{(n,m)}
\end{vmatrix}.
$$

7. Restate Theorem 2.17.1 in such a way that it will apply to any row and column with the same index.

8. Put

$$
q_{ij} = \begin{vmatrix} u_i & v_i \\ u_j & v_j \end{vmatrix} = \begin{vmatrix} u_i & u_j \\ v_i & v_j \end{vmatrix}
$$

and show that, if $A = [a_{ij}]_n$, then

$$
\begin{vmatrix}
a_{11} & a_{12} & \cdots & a_{1n} & u_1 & v_1 \\
a_{21} & a_{22} & \cdots & a_{2n} & u_2 & v_2 \\
\vdots & & & & & \\
a_{n1} & a_{n2} & \cdots & a_{nn} & u_n & v_n \\
u_1 & u_2 & \cdots & u_n & 0 & 0 \\
v_1 & v_2 & \cdots & v_n & 0 & 0
\end{vmatrix}
= \sum_{\substack{1 \leqslant i < j \leqslant n \\ 1 \leqslant k < m \leqslant n}} q_{ij} q_{km} A_{ij,km}.
$$

The matrices whose determinants are found in Exercises 4 and 8 are called **bordered matrices**.

9. Show that, if $A = [a_{ij}]_n$ and if A_{ij} is the cofactor of a_{ij} in det A, then

$$\det [a_{ij} + x]_n = \det A + x \sum_{i,j=1}^{n} A_{ij}.$$

10. How many identities of the form given in Theorem 2.16.2 are there when $n = 2$? $n = 3$? $n = 4$?

11. Evaluate

$$\det \begin{bmatrix} \lambda & -1 & 2 \\ 1 & \lambda & 4 \\ -2 & -4 & \lambda \end{bmatrix}$$

by the method of Theorem 2.18.1.

CHAPTER THREE

The Inverse of a Matrix

DEFINITION AND PROPERTIES OF THE INVERSE

3.1 The Inverse of a Matrix

We are now ready to treat in detail the problem of finding the inverse of a given square matrix A, when such an inverse exists. We begin with the following definition:

If A is a matrix of order n and A_{ij} is the cofactor of a_{ij} in det A, then the matrix

$$\mathscr{A} = [A_{ij}]^{\mathsf{T}} = \begin{bmatrix} A_{11} & A_{21} & \cdots & A_{n1} \\ A_{12} & A_{22} & \cdots & A_{n2} \\ \vdots & & & \\ A_{1n} & A_{2n} & \cdots & A_{nn} \end{bmatrix}$$

is called the **adjoint matrix of A** and det $\mathscr{A}$ is called the **adjoint determinant** of A. (In some books $\mathscr{A}$ is called the **adjugate** of A.)

We have by (2.7.4),

$$A \cdot \mathscr{A} = \begin{bmatrix} a_{11} & a_{12} & \cdots & a_{1n} \\ a_{21} & a_{22} & \cdots & a_{2n} \\ \vdots & & & \\ a_{n1} & a_{n2} & \cdots & a_{nn} \end{bmatrix} \cdot \begin{bmatrix} A_{11} & A_{21} & \cdots & A_{n1} \\ A_{12} & A_{22} & \cdots & A_{n2} \\ \vdots & & & \\ A_{1n} & A_{2n} & \cdots & A_{nn} \end{bmatrix}$$

$$= \begin{bmatrix} \det A & 0 & \cdots & 0 \\ 0 & \det A & \cdots & 0 \\ \vdots & & & \\ 0 & 0 & \cdots & \det A \end{bmatrix} = \mathscr{A} \cdot A.$$

That is, we have

(3.1.1) $A \cdot \mathscr{A} = \mathscr{A} \cdot A = (\det A)I_n.$

Let us now assume that $\det A \neq 0$ and define a matrix B as follows:

(3.1.2) $B = \dfrac{\mathscr{A}}{\det A} = \left[\dfrac{A_{ij}}{\det A}\right]^{\mathsf{T}} = \begin{bmatrix} \dfrac{A_{11}}{\det A} & \cdots & \dfrac{A_{n1}}{\det A} \\ \vdots & & \\ \dfrac{A_{1n}}{\det A} & \cdots & \dfrac{A_{nn}}{\det A} \end{bmatrix}.$

Then, dividing both members of (3.1.1) by the nonzero scalar $\det A$, we obtain the result

(3.1.3) $AB = BA = I_n.$

Hence B is an inverse of A according to the definition given in Section 1.15. Moreover, if B is any matrix satisfying (3.1.3),

$$\det A \det B = \det I_n = 1,$$

so that $\det A \neq 0$. Hence we have

Theorem 3.1.1: *A square matrix A has an inverse if and only if* $\det A \neq 0.$

It is customary to call a square matrix A such that $\det A \neq 0$ a **non-singular matrix**, whereas if $\det A = 0$, A is called **singular**. The above theorem then says that *A has an inverse if and only if A is nonsingular*. In some books, every nonsquare matrix is also called singular. We now conclude from Theorem 1.15.1,

Theorem 3.1.2: *If A is nonsingular, B as defined above is the only inverse of A.*

Henceforth we shall denote the matrix $\dfrac{\mathscr{A}}{\det A}$ by the customary symbol A^{-1}.

The procedure given above for forming the inverse may be stated in words as follows:

(a) Replace each element a_{ij} of A by its cofactor A_{ij}.
(b) Divide each element of this matrix of cofactors by $\det A$.
(c) Transpose the result.

For example, if

$$A = \begin{bmatrix} 8 & 4 & 2 \\ 2 & 8 & 4 \\ 1 & 2 & 8 \end{bmatrix},$$

the matrix of cofactors is

$$\begin{bmatrix} 56 & -12 & -4 \\ -28 & 62 & -12 \\ 0 & -28 & 56 \end{bmatrix}.$$

Since det $A = 392$, we have then

$$A^{-1} = \begin{bmatrix} \dfrac{56}{392} & \dfrac{-12}{392} & \dfrac{-4}{392} \\[2mm] \dfrac{-28}{392} & \dfrac{62}{392} & \dfrac{-12}{392} \\[2mm] \dfrac{0}{392} & \dfrac{-28}{392} & \dfrac{56}{392} \end{bmatrix}^{\mathsf{T}} = \begin{bmatrix} \dfrac{1}{7} & \dfrac{-1}{14} & 0 \\[2mm] \dfrac{-3}{98} & \dfrac{31}{196} & \dfrac{-1}{14} \\[2mm] \dfrac{-1}{98} & \dfrac{-3}{98} & \dfrac{1}{7} \end{bmatrix}.$$

3.2 Exercises

1. Determine *by inspection* (see Section 1.15) inverses for the following matrices.

(a) $\begin{bmatrix} 1 & 0 & k \\ 0 & 1 & 0 \\ 0 & 0 & 1 \end{bmatrix},$ (b) $\begin{bmatrix} 2 & 0 & 0 & 0 \\ 0 & 2 & 0 & 0 \\ 0 & 0 & 0 & 1 \\ 0 & 0 & 1 & 0 \end{bmatrix},$ (c) $\begin{bmatrix} 0 & -1 & 0 \\ 0 & 0 & -1 \\ 1 & 0 & 0 \end{bmatrix},$

(d) $\begin{bmatrix} 0 & 0 & 1 & 0 \\ 0 & 1 & 0 & 0 \\ 1 & 0 & 0 & 0 \\ 0 & 0 & 0 & 1 \end{bmatrix},$ (e) $\left[\begin{array}{ccc:cc} 1 & 1 & 1 & 0 & 0 \\ 0 & 1 & 0 & 0 & 0 \\ 0 & 0 & 1 & 0 & 0 \\ \hdashline 0 & 0 & 0 & 1 & 2 \\ 0 & 0 & 0 & 3 & 7 \end{array}\right].$

Use (3.1.2) to write formulas for inverses for the following matrices and state when the inverses exist.

(f) $\begin{bmatrix} a & b & 0 \\ 0 & a & b \\ b & 0 & a \end{bmatrix},$ (g) $\begin{bmatrix} a & 0 & b & 0 \\ 0 & a & 0 & b \\ b & 0 & a & 0 \\ 0 & b & 0 & a \end{bmatrix}.$

*2. Prove that, if A is nonsingular, then from $AB = AC$ we can conclude $B = C$. (B and C need not be square, of course.)

3. Prove that, if $\det A \neq 0$, $\det (A^{-1}) = (\det A)^{-1}$. Note the two meanings of the exponent -1 here.

4. Show that the inverse of the skew-symmetric matrix of order $2n$

$$\begin{bmatrix} 0 & 1 & 1 & 1 & \cdots & 1 \\ -1 & 0 & 1 & 1 & \cdots & 1 \\ -1 & -1 & 0 & 1 & \cdots & 1 \\ \vdots & & & & & \\ -1 & -1 & -1 & -1 & \cdots & 0 \end{bmatrix} \quad \text{is} \quad \begin{bmatrix} 0 & -1 & 1 & -1 & \cdots & -1 \\ 1 & 0 & -1 & 1 & \cdots & 1 \\ -1 & 1 & 0 & -1 & \cdots & -1 \\ \vdots & & & & & \\ 1 & -1 & 1 & -1 & \cdots & 0 \end{bmatrix}.$$

(*American Mathematical Monthly*, Vol. 58, 1951, p. 494.)

*5. Show that, if A^{-1} exists, then $(A^{\mathsf{T}})^{-1} = (A^{-1})^{\mathsf{T}}$, $(\bar{A})^{-1} = \overline{(A^{-1})}$, and $(A^*)^{-1} = (A^{-1})^*$.

*6. Show that, if $A, B, \ldots, M$, are all nonsingular and of order n, then the inverse of their product is the product of their inverses in the reverse order; then use this fact to find the inverse of the product

$$\begin{bmatrix} 1 & 0 & k \\ 0 & 1 & h \\ 0 & 0 & 1 \end{bmatrix} \cdot \begin{bmatrix} \alpha & 0 & 0 \\ 0 & \beta & 0 \\ 0 & 0 & \gamma \end{bmatrix} \cdot \begin{bmatrix} 1 & 0 & 0 \\ 0 & 0 & 1 \\ 0 & 1 & 0 \end{bmatrix}, \qquad \alpha\beta\gamma \neq 0,$$

without first evaluating the product.

7. Prove that, if $RAC = I$, where all four matrices have order n, then A^{-1} exists and $A^{-1} = CR$.

*8. We define $A^{-n} = (A^{-1})^n$ when A is nonsingular and n is a positive integer. We define $A^0 = I$ for an arbitrary square matrix A, singular or not. Show that the laws of exponents $A^m A^n = A^{m+n}$ and $(A^m)^n = A^{mn}$ now apply for *all* integral values of m and n when A is nonsingular.

9. If

$$A = \begin{bmatrix} \cosh x & \sinh x \\ \sinh x & \cosh x \end{bmatrix},$$

show that, for all integral values of n,

$$A^n = \begin{bmatrix} \cosh nx & \sinh nx \\ \sinh nx & \cosh nx \end{bmatrix}.$$

*10. Show that the inverse of a nonsingular symmetric matrix is also symmetric.

11. Prove that a matrix A of order n is nonsingular if and only if there exists a matrix B such that $B(AX) = X$ for all n-vectors X.

12. If $AWB = C$, where A and B are square, under what conditions can one certainly solve for the matrix W?

13. Prove that, if $AB = BA$ and $S^2 = B$, then also

$$(A^{-1}SA)^2 = B.$$

14. For some purposes it is desirable to employ systems of equations of the form

$$YA = R,$$

where Y and R denote rows. Given that A is nonsingular, prove that there exists a unique solution for such a system.

15. Given that D is diagonal and nonsingular and that

$$D = (I + A)^{-1} \cdot A,$$

prove that A is diagonal also.

16. Prove that, if $S_m = I + A + A^2 + \cdots + A^m$, and if $I - A$ is non-singular, then $S_m = (I - A^{m+1})(I - A)^{-1}$. See if you can define $\lim_{m \to \infty} A^{m+1}$ and then show that, when this limit is the zero matrix, $\lim_{m \to \infty} S_m = (I - A)^{-1}$.

17. For an arbitrary $m \times n$ matrix A, any $n \times m$ matrix B such that $AB = I_m$ is called a **right inverse** of A, and any $n \times m$ matrix C such that $CA = I_n$ is called a **left inverse** of A. Show that, if a square matrix A has a left (or a right) inverse B, then A^{-1} exists and is equal to B.

18. If $AB = 0$, where A and B are of order n but neither is the zero matrix, A and B are called **divisors of zero**. If $A^p = 0$ for some positive integer p, then A is called **nilpotent**. Show that all divisors of zero and all nilpotent matrices are singular.

19. Find A^{-1} if a, b, c, d are real numbers such that

$$a^2 + b^2 + c^2 + d^2 = 1,$$

and

$$A = \begin{bmatrix} a + ib & c + id \\ -c + id & a - ib \end{bmatrix}.$$

20. Given that A^{-1} exists, determine X so that

$$\begin{bmatrix} A^{-1} & 0 \\ \hline X & A^{-1} \end{bmatrix}$$

is the inverse of

$$\begin{bmatrix} A & O \\ \hline B & A \end{bmatrix}.$$

21. Find by Exercise 20 the inverses of the matrices

$$\text{(a)} \quad \begin{bmatrix} 1 & 0 & 0 & 0 \\ 1 & 1 & 0 & 0 \\ \hline 0 & 0 & 1 & 0 \\ 0 & 0 & 1 & 1 \end{bmatrix}, \qquad \text{(b)} \quad \begin{bmatrix} 1 & 0 & 0 & 0 \\ 1 & 1 & 0 & 0 \\ \hline 1 & 1 & 1 & 0 \\ 1 & 1 & 1 & 1 \end{bmatrix}.$$

22. Find by inspection the inverse of

$$\begin{bmatrix} 1 & 0 & 0 & 0 & \cdots & 0 & 0 \\ -1 & 1 & 0 & 0 & \cdots & 0 & 0 \\ 0 & -1 & 1 & 0 & \cdots & 0 & 0 \\ \vdots & & & & & & \\ 0 & 0 & 0 & 0 & \cdots & -1 & 1 \end{bmatrix}_n.$$

23. Prove that, if A and B are symmetric and commute, then $A^{-1}B$, AB^{-1}, and $A^{-1}B^{-1}$ are symmetric.

24. Explain why the notation A/B is ambiguous when A and B are matrices, even if $\det B \neq 0$.

25. Given that $f(A)$ and $g(A)$ are polynomial functions of A and that $[g(A)]^{-1}$ exists, prove that

$$f(A) \cdot [g(A)]^{-1} = [g(A)]^{-1} \cdot f(A).$$

Is the notation $f(A)/g(A)$ ambiguous? Why?

*26. Given that $AB = BA$ and that B^{-1} exists, prove that $AB^r = B^rA$ for all integer values of r. If A^{-1} also exists, prove that $A^rB^s = B^sA^r$ for all integers r and s. (See Exercise 31, Section 1.9.)

27. Show that, if $\det A = 1$, then A is the adjoint matrix of $\mathscr{A}$.

28. Show that, if A, B, D are of order n and if $AB = D$, then $\mathscr{D} = \mathscr{B}\mathscr{A}$; that is, the adjoint of the product of two matrices is the product of their adjoints in reverse order.

29. Prove that, if $\mathscr{A}_{ji}$ denotes a cofactor of the adjoint matrix $\mathscr{A}$ of A, then

$$\mathscr{A}_{ji} = a_{ij} \cdot (\det A)^{n-2}.$$

30. Given that A_{11}^{-1} and a_{nn}^{-1} exist, determine A^{-1}, where

$$A = \begin{bmatrix} A_{11} & 0 \\ \hline A_{21} & a_{nn} \end{bmatrix}.$$

(Note that this is a special case of Exercise 20.)

31. Determine when a matrix of the form

$$\begin{bmatrix} y & x & x & \cdots & x & x \\ x & y & x & \cdots & x & x \\ \vdots & & & & & \\ x & x & x & \cdots & y & x \\ x & x & x & \cdots & x & y \end{bmatrix}$$

is nonsingular, and show that the inverse, when it exists, is of the same form. (See Exercise 29, Section 2.12.)

32. Show that the square matrix

$$
k \left\{
\begin{array}{c}
\begin{bmatrix}
1 & 0 & \cdots & 0 & 1 & 1 & \cdots & 1 \\
0 & 1 & \cdots & 0 & 1 & 1 & \cdots & 1 \\
\vdots & & & & \vdots & & & \\
0 & 0 & \cdots & 1 & 1 & 1 & \cdots & 1 \\
\end{array}
\right.
$$

$$
n-k \left\{
\begin{array}{c}
1 & 1 & \cdots & 1 & \\
1 & 1 & \cdots & 1 & & & B & \\
\vdots & & & & \\
1 & 1 & \cdots & 1 & \\
\end{bmatrix}
\end{array}
\right.
$$

is nonsingular if and only if det B is *unequal* to k times the sum of its cofactors.

*33. Prove that the inverse of a nonsingular, upper-triangular matrix T is also upper triangular, and that the diagonal entries of the inverse are the reciprocals of the corresponding entries of T.

34. A **triple-diagonal matrix** is one whose elements are zero except possibly for those on the main diagonal, the diagonal immediately above the main diagonal, and the diagonal immediately below the main diagonal. Triple-diagonal matrices are important in certain applications and in linear computations. Obtain inverses for the triple-diagonal matrices

$$
\begin{bmatrix} 1 & -1 \\ -1 & 2 \end{bmatrix},
\quad
\begin{bmatrix} 1 & -1 & 0 \\ -1 & 2 & -1 \\ 0 & -1 & 2 \end{bmatrix},
\quad
\begin{bmatrix} 1 & -1 & 0 & 0 \\ -1 & 2 & -1 & 0 \\ 0 & -1 & 2 & -1 \\ 0 & 0 & -1 & 2 \end{bmatrix}.
$$

Then guess at the form of the inverse of an $n \times n$ matrix of the same structure and prove that your formula is correct.

35. Given that $A^* = A^{-1}$ and that

$$
A = \begin{bmatrix} 0 & 0 & \alpha & i\alpha \\ 0 & 0 & i\alpha & \alpha \\ \alpha & i\alpha & 0 & 0 \\ i\alpha & \alpha & 0 & 0 \end{bmatrix},
\qquad i^2 = -1,
$$

what are the possible values for α?

*36. Given that

$$
P = [E_{j_1}, E_{j_2}, \ldots, E_{j_n}],
$$

where the E_j's are a permutation of the n elementary n-vectors (see Exercise **31**, Section **1.18**), prove that

$$
P^{\mathsf{T}} = P^{-1}.
$$

37. Compute the inverse of

$$\alpha \begin{bmatrix} 1 & 0 \\ 0 & 1 \end{bmatrix} + \beta \begin{bmatrix} 0 & -1 \\ 1 & 0 \end{bmatrix},$$

where α and β are real numbers and write the inverse in this same form. Interpret by using the concept of isomorphism. (See Exercise 17, Section 1.18.)

LINEAR COMPUTATIONS

3.3 Cramer's Rule

With the concept of the inverse of a matrix to help us, we now consider the problem of solving simultaneously n linear equations in n unknowns. Let the system in question be

$$
\begin{aligned}
a_{11}x_1 + a_{12}x_2 + \cdots + a_{1n}x_n &= b_1, \\
a_{21}x_1 + a_{22}x_2 + \cdots + a_{2n}x_n &= b_2, \\
&\vdots \\
a_{n1}x_1 + a_{n2}x_2 + \cdots + a_{nn}x_n &= b_n.
\end{aligned}
$$

(3.3.1)

Here the coefficients a_{ij} and the right members b_i are assumed to be independent of $x_1, x_2, \ldots, x_n$, but are otherwise arbitrary. The problem is to find all sets of values of $x_1, x_2, \ldots, x_n$ which will simultaneously satisfy all n of these equations. Such a set of values is called a **simultaneous solution** or, more simply, a **solution** of the system.

The coefficients of this system define the **coefficient matrix** $A = [a_{ij}]$ thereof. We shall denote by A_j the matrix obtained from A by replacing the jth column of A by the column of b's. Then the following theorem gives what is commonly known as **Cramer's rule**:

Theorem 3.3.1:   *If* $\det A \neq 0$, *the system* (3.3.1) *has exactly one solution, namely, that given by*

$$x_j = \frac{\det A_j}{\det A}, \qquad j = 1, 2, \ldots, n.$$

We have already illustrated this theorem for systems of two equations in two unknowns in Section 2.5. As a further example, we note that the coefficient matrix of the system

$$
\begin{aligned}
y + az &= 1, \\
ax + z &= 2, \qquad a^3 + 1 \neq 0, \\
x + ay &= 3,
\end{aligned}
$$

has the determinant

$$
\begin{vmatrix} 0 & 1 & a \\ a & 0 & 1 \\ 1 & a & 0 \end{vmatrix} = a^3 + 1.
$$

Hence, according to the theorem, the solution of the given system is

$$x = \frac{\begin{vmatrix} 1 & 1 & a \\ 2 & 0 & 1 \\ 3 & a & 0 \end{vmatrix}}{(a^3 + 1)}, \qquad y = \frac{\begin{vmatrix} 0 & 1 & a \\ a & 2 & 1 \\ 1 & 3 & 0 \end{vmatrix}}{(a^3 + 1)}, \qquad z = \frac{\begin{vmatrix} 0 & 1 & 1 \\ a & 0 & 2 \\ 1 & a & 3 \end{vmatrix}}{(a^3 + 1)},$$

or

$$x = \frac{2a^2 - a + 3}{a^3 + 1}, \qquad y = \frac{3a^2 - 2a + 1}{a^3 + 1}, \qquad z = \frac{a^2 - 3a + 2}{a^3 + 1}.$$

The example illustrates the **basic pattern of the general solution**: *Each denominator contains the determinant of the coefficient matrix. To obtain the numerator of the solution for any given variable, we delete the column of coefficients of that variable from the coefficient matrix, substitute the column of constant terms in its place, and then find the determinant of the resulting matrix.*

To prove the theorem, we note that, as in Section 1.10, the system (3.3.1) can be written in matrix notation in the form

(3.3.2) $AX = B,$

where

$$A = \begin{bmatrix} a_{11} & \cdots & a_{1n} \\ \vdots & & \\ a_{n1} & \cdots & a_{nn} \end{bmatrix}, \qquad X = \begin{bmatrix} x_1 \\ \vdots \\ x_n \end{bmatrix}, \qquad B = \begin{bmatrix} b_1 \\ \vdots \\ b_n \end{bmatrix}.$$

Furthermore, as we have pointed out earlier, solving (3.3.2) is equivalent to solving (3.3.1).

First of all, since $\det A \neq 0$, A^{-1} exists. Hence, multiplying (3.3.2) on the left by A^{-1}, we have

(3.3.3) $X = A^{-1}B.$

That is, if the matrix equation (3.3.2) has a solution, it must be given by (3.3.3). However, by direct substitution, we see at once that (3.3.3) is indeed a solution of (3.3.2) and, hence, is the *one and only solution thereof.*

To express the solution in scalar form, we note from the formula for A^{-1} that

$$X = \frac{1}{\det A} \begin{bmatrix} A_{11} & A_{21} & \cdots & A_{n1} \\ A_{12} & A_{22} & \cdots & A_{n2} \\ \vdots & & & \\ A_{1n} & A_{2n} & \cdots & A_{nn} \end{bmatrix} \cdot \begin{bmatrix} b_1 \\ b_2 \\ \vdots \\ b_n \end{bmatrix},$$

or

$$\begin{bmatrix} x_1 \\ x_2 \\ \vdots \\ x_n \end{bmatrix} = \frac{1}{\det A} \begin{bmatrix} (b_1 A_{11} + b_2 A_{21} + \cdots + b_n A_{n1}) \\ (b_1 A_{12} + b_2 A_{22} + \cdots + b_n A_{n2}) \\ \vdots \\ (b_1 A_{1n} + b_2 A_{2n} + \cdots + b_n A_{nn}) \end{bmatrix}.$$

Equating corresponding elements and applying Theorem 2.7.3, we obtain the solution in the form stated in the theorem:

$$x_1 = \frac{1}{\det A}(b_1 A_{11} + b_2 A_{21} + \cdots + b_n A_{n1}) = \frac{\det A_1}{\det A},$$

$$x_2 = \frac{1}{\det A}(b_1 A_{12} + b_2 A_{22} + \cdots + b_n A_{n2}) = \frac{\det A_2}{\det A},$$

$$\vdots$$

$$x_n = \frac{1}{\det A}(b_1 A_{1n} + b_2 A_{2n} + \cdots + b_n A_{nn}) = \frac{\det A_n}{\det A}.$$

When $\det A = 0$, the system (3.3.1) may have infinitely many solutions or none at all. These possibilities will be discussed fully in Chapter Five. Equation (3.3.3) shows that, once we find A^{-1}, we can compute the solution of (3.3.1) by a simple matrix multiplication. This is one of the reasons that an important task of the modern electronic computer is to compute inverses of given matrices. Many different techniques are available for the detailed computation.

3.4 Solution of Equations by Synthetic Elimination

When the coefficients in a system of linear equations of type (3.3.1) are not simply whole numbers, solving the system by Cramer's rule becomes a very tedious process. We therefore indicate a more efficient method of computing the solution in this case. The method may be called **synthetic elimination** (in analogy to "synthetic division" in the theory of equations), because it provides in effect for a systematic elimination of the variables while involving only their coefficients. The method also has the advantages of being simple to use and easy to remember.

We introduce the method by means of a specific example. The study of a certain electric circuit (see M. B. Reed, *Alternating Current Circuit Theory*, New York, Harper, 1948, pp. 322–323) requires the solution of the following system of equations:

$$-1.700\ V_1 + 0.250\ V_2 + 0.500\ V_3 = -25.000,$$

$$0.250\ V_1 - 0.850\ V_2 + 0.100\ V_3 = -10.000,$$

$$0.500\ V_1 + 0.100\ V_2 - 1.700\ V_3 = 30.000.$$

The solution may be obtained by a method related to that used to evaluate a determinant in Section 2.10. In Table 3.4.1, we carry five decimal places throughout, and then round off the final answers to three significant figures

Table 3.4.1

Key to Operations					S
(1)	− 1.70000	0.25000	0.50000	− 25.00000	− 25.95000
(2)	0.25000	− 0.85000	0.10000	− 10.00000	− 10.50000
(3)	0.50000	0.10000	− 1.70000	30.00000	28.90000
(1′)	1	− 0.14706	− 0.29412	14.70588	15.26470
(2′)	1	− 3.40000	0.40000	− 40.00000	− 42.00000
(3′)	1	0.20000	− 3.40000	60.00000	57.80000
(2′) − (1′)		− 3.25294	0.69412	− 54.70588	− 57.26470
(3′) − (1′)		0.34706	− 3.10588	45.29412	42.53530
(2″)		1	− 0.21338	16.81736	17.60398
(3″)		1	− 8.94912	130.50804	122.55892
(3″) − (2″)			− 8.73574	113.69068	104.95494
(3‴)			1	− 13.01443	− 12.01443

$$V_3 \qquad\qquad\qquad\qquad\qquad\quad = -13.01443 \quad \text{from (3‴)}$$
$$V_2 = \qquad\qquad 130.50804 - 116.46770 = \quad 14.04034 \quad \text{from (3″)}$$
$$V_1 = 60.00000 - 2.80807 - \quad 44.24906 = \quad 12.94287 \quad \text{from (3′)}$$

To 3 significant figures: $V_1 = 12.9$, $V_2 = 14.0$, $V_3 = -13.0$

in accordance with the accuracy of the given coefficients. The purpose of carrying the extra decimal places is, of course, to avoid the possibility of losing all significant figures in some subtraction, and to avoid the possibility that the cumulative effect of rounding-off errors will be enough to introduce errors in the significant figures to be retained in the solution. When a computing machine is being used, carrying the extra decimal places involves but little extra work.

The arrangement of the tabular form is almost self-explanatory. Lines (1), (2), (3) contain, in effect, the augmented matrix of the given system of equations, together with a column S of row sums which are used for checking purposes. Lines (1′), (2′), (3′) contain the augmented matrix of the system of equations obtained from the given system by dividing each equation by its leading coefficient. The row sums here will equal the quotients of the previous row sums by the corresponding leading coefficients, provided that the computation has been correctly performed. (There may be slight discrepancies resulting from the cumulative effect of rounding-off errors.) In lines (2′) − (1′) and (3′) − (1′) we have in effect eliminated V_1 by subtraction, as the empty part of the first column indicates. Then we again divide by the leading coefficients to obtain (2″) and (3″), after which we eliminate V_2 in (3″) − (2″). The final division by the leading coefficient −8.73574 yields (3‴), which is equivalent to the equation $V_3 = -13.014$. At each step, we use the S column for checking purposes.

Once we have V_3, we substitute into (3″) [or into (2″)] to obtain V_2. Finally, we substitute both of these values into (3′) [or into (2′) or (1′)] to obtain V_1.

In this process, the vanishing of the leading coefficient of an equation is no cause for embarrassment when it occurs. This simply means that one elimination is unnecessary so that we need only recopy that equation unchanged into the next set of lines of the table. Other lines than (1′), (2″), ... may be used to effect the elimination of the 1's if that appears necessary or desirable.

In the case of two or three equations in as many unknowns, this method has little advantage over Cramer's rule. However, in the case of four or more equations, the amount of work which this method requires is far less than that required by the determinantal solution. In this connection, it is instructive to count the number of multiplications and divisions, and additions and subtractions, required in each of the two methods, when the number of unknowns is four.

This method of solution may be altered to follow closely the sweep-out process used in Section 2.10 to evaluate a determinant. The sweep-out process may also be replaced by a method patterned on the foregoing procedure.

3.5 Inversion of a Matrix by Synthetic Elimination

When the inverse of a matrix is desired, and the evaluation thereof by the formula $A^{-1} = [A_{ij}/\det A]^{\mathsf{T}}$ would be tedious, the following procedure is preferable since it is well adapted to computation with a desk calculator. Let

$$X = \{x_1, x_2, \ldots, x_n\}, \qquad Y = \{y_1, y_2, \ldots, y_n\},$$

and let $A = [a_{ij}]_n$ be the nonsingular matrix to be inverted. If the system of equations $AX = Y$ is solved for the x's in terms of the y's, the result is $X = A^{-1}Y$, so that the coefficient matrix of the y's is the required inverse. The work may be systematized as shown in the following example.

Let the matrix to be inverted be

$$\begin{bmatrix} 4 & -1 & 2 \\ 3 & 4 & 1 \\ -2 & -2 & 4 \end{bmatrix}.$$

The corresponding system of equations, to be solved for x_1, x_2, x_3, is

$$4x_1 - x_2 + 2x_3 = y_1,$$
$$3x_1 + 4x_2 + x_3 = y_2,$$
$$-2x_1 - 2x_2 + 4x_3 = y_3.$$

A matrix containing *all* the coefficients of this system is

$$\begin{bmatrix} 4 & -1 & 2 & 1 & 0 & 0 \\ 3 & 4 & 1 & 0 & 1 & 0 \\ -2 & -2 & 4 & 0 & 0 & 1 \end{bmatrix}.$$

Note that a separate column is provided for the coefficients of each of the six variables appearing in the problem. The identity submatrix on the right in this array corresponds to the fact that the equations give the y's explicitly. The inversion is accomplished by using the synthetic elimination process developed in the preceding section to obtain a new coefficient array with an identity submatrix on the left. Since synthetic elimination amounts to solving for the x's, this new array will have the inverse of the given matrix on the right. Although, to facilitate checking by the reader, the example to follow in Table 3.5.1 contains only rational fractions, in most applications the elements of the given matrix will be decimal approximations based on data obtained by observation. In such a case, the computations illustrated here could be performed conveniently with a desk calculator.

Table 3.5.1

	Key							*S*
1	(1)	4	−1	2	1	0	0	6
2	(2)	3	4	1	0	1	0	9
3	(3)	−2	−2	4	0	0	1	1
4	(1′)	1	−1/4	1/2	1/4	0	0	3/2
5	(2′)	1	4/3	1/3	0	1/3	0	3
6	(3′)	1	1	−2	0	0	−1/2	−1/2
7	(2′) − (1′)	0	19/12	−1/6	−1/4	1/3	0	3/2
8	(3′) − (1′)	0	5/4	−5/2	−1/4	0	−1/2	−2
9	(2″)	0	1	−2/19	−3/19	4/19	0	18/19
10	(3″)	0	1	−2	−1/5	0	−2/5	−8/5
11	(3″) − (2″)	0	0	−36/19	−4/95	−4/19	−2/5	−242/95
12	(1‴) = (3′) − (2‴) + 2(3‴)	1	0	0	1/5	0	−1/10	11/10
13	(2‴) = (3″) + 2(3‴)	0	1	0	−7/45	2/9	1/45	49/45
14	(3‴)	0	0	1	1/45	1/9	19/90	121/90
15	−1 · (2‴)	0	−1	0	7/45	−2/9	−1/45	−49/45
16	2 · (3‴)	0	0	2	2/45	2/9	19/45	121/45

In Table 3.5.1, the first eleven lines are computed in exactly the same way as the corresponding lines of Table 3.4.1. Dividing line 11 by $-36/19$, we obtain line 14. Line 14 is then combined with line 10 to give line 13, after which lines 14 and 13 are combined with line 6 to give line 12. In lines 12 to 14, the desired inverse immediately precedes the checking column. Lines 15 and 16 record the multiples of lines 14 and 13 which were added to lines 10 and 6 to yield lines 13 and 12.

In the case of this example, the formula for the inverse would have given the inverse more quickly. However, if decimal entries and higher order matrices are involved, the method of synthetic elimination is more efficient.

If one wishes to solve the system $AX = B$ and at the same time obtain A^{-1}, one can apply the sweep-out process to the matrix

$$[A, B, I].$$

3.6 Linear Computations

The evaluation of a determinant, the inversion of a matrix, and the solution of a system of equations are all examples of what may be called *linear computations*. The tabular forms we have given for the three mentioned linear computations are not necessarily the most efficient for a given problem. They are, however, easy to remember, and they require the memorization of no special formulas. For one who rarely performs such computations, these forms will prove sufficient. On the other hand, there are many other procedures known, some of which are particularly designed for use with special types of matrices, such as symmetric matrices, for example. (See Section 3.8.) The person who has a great many linear computations to perform with a desk calculator would do well to investigate these methods in detail. The most comprehensive treatment thereof is found in P. S. Dwyer, *Linear Computations*, New York, John Wiley, 1951.

It should also be pointed out that, in our brief discussions of computational procedures, we have largely ignored certain difficulties that may be involved, such as the loss of significant figures and the effect of rounding-off errors. These are by no means trivial matters. The reference already cited and the article by J. von Neumann and H. H. Goldstine entitled "Numerical Inverting of Matrices of High Order," *Bulletin of the American Mathematical Society*, Vol. 53, 1947, pp. 1021–1099, are recommended to the interested reader. Further references will be found in the bibliography under the heading "Numerical Analysis and Computation," where many helpful titles are listed.

3.7 Exercises

1. Solve by Cramer's rule:

(a)
$$\begin{aligned} x + 2y + z &= 4, \\ x - y + z &= 5, \\ 2x + 3y - z &= 1. \end{aligned}$$

What is the familiar, three-dimensional, geometrical interpretation of the result?

$$x_1 + 2x_2 - 3x_3 + 4x_4 = 1,$$
$$2x_1 + 2x_2 - 2x_3 + 3x_4 = 0,$$
(b)
$$x_2 + x_3 = -1,$$
$$x_1 - x_2 + x_3 - 2x_4 = 2.$$

2. Solve for x_1 and x_2 by Cramer's rule:

$$rx_1 - (1 - r)x_2 = 2,$$
$$(1 - r)x_1 + rx_2 = 5.$$

What assumption must be made about r for this solution to be valid?

3. Solve for x, y, z in terms of x', y', z':

$$x + 2y - 3z = x',$$
$$x - y + 2z = y',$$
$$3x + y + z = z'.$$

What is the inverse of the coefficient matrix?

4. If the coefficients a, b, c, d in the equation $y = ax_1 + bx_2 + cx_3 + dx_4$ are determined by the system of equations,

$$8a - 6b + 8c - 4d = 1,$$
$$-6a + 9b - 9c + 4d = 2,$$
$$8a - 9b + 18c - 2d = -1,$$
$$-4a + 4b - 2c + 4d = -2,$$

find them. (Systems like this, with symmetric coefficient matrices, are obtained in solving the statistical problem of finding the linear function which best fits a series of observations.)

5. Suppose a particle has the origin as its equilibrium position, but when displaced from the origin it is subject to a restoring force with components X, Y, Z related to the coordinates x, y, z of the particle by the linear equations

$$X = 4x - y - 2z,$$
$$Y = x + 4y - z,$$
$$Z = 2x + y + 4z.$$

Express the coordinates x, y, z of the particle as functions of the components X, Y, Z of the restoring force. (A particle properly suspended by three massless, perfect springs and set in motion would lead to a system of equations of this kind. See T. von Kàrmàn and M. A. Biot, *Mathematical Methods in Engineering*, New York, McGraw-Hill, 1940, p. 174.)

6. By evaluating the determinant

$$
\begin{vmatrix}
0 & a_{i1} & a_{i2} & \cdots & a_{in} \\
-b_1 & a_{11} & a_{12} & \cdots & a_{1n} \\
\vdots & & & & \\
-b_i & a_{i1} & a_{i2} & \cdots & a_{in} \\
\vdots & & & & \\
-b_n & a_{n1} & a_{n2} & \cdots & a_{nn}
\end{vmatrix}
$$

in terms of the elements of the first row and then in terms of the elements of the first column, show that, in the notation of Section 3.3,

$$ a_{i1} \det A_1 + a_{i2} \det A_2 + \cdots + a_{in} \det A_n = b_i \det A. $$

Then use this result to prove Theorem 3.3.1.

7. Let α, β, γ denote the angles of a triangle and let a, b, c denote the corresponding opposite sides. By solving the equations

$$ b \cos \gamma + c \cos \beta = a, $$

$$ c \cos \alpha + a \cos \gamma = b, $$

$$ a \cos \beta + b \cos \alpha = c, $$

for $\cos \alpha$, $\cos \beta$, and $\cos \gamma$, obtain the cosine laws

$$ \cos \alpha = \frac{b^2 + c^2 - a^2}{2bc}, \text{ etc.} $$

8. Suppose we are given the matrices A and B of order n, A being nonsingular. Suppose furthermore that we wish to evaluate $A^{-1}B$, but that we do not need to know A^{-1}. Devise a variation of the process of Section 3.5 which will enable us to evaluate this product directly.

9. Solve by the method of Section 3.4, using a desk calculator if possible:

$$ 0.703x_1 + 0.200x_2 + 0.104x_3 = 11.246, $$

$$ 0.200x_1 + 0.854x_2 + 0.256x_3 = 14.159, $$

$$ 0.104x_1 + 0.256x_2 + 0.989x_3 = 9.443. $$

10. In a four-pole electric network, the input and output quantities E_1, I_1 and E_2, I_2 respectively are related by equations

$$ E_1 = aE_2 + bI_2, $$

$$ I_1 = cE_2 + dI_2. $$

By assuming the necessary matrices to be nonsingular, solve for various pairs of E's and I's in terms of the remaining two.

11. Find the inverses of the following matrices:

(a) $\begin{bmatrix} 1 & 2 & 3 \\ 0 & 1 & 2 \\ 0 & 0 & 1 \end{bmatrix}$,   (b) $\begin{bmatrix} 7.322 & 2.141 & 0.166 \\ 2.141 & 8.053 & 1.345 \\ 0.166 & 1.345 & 9.659 \end{bmatrix}$.

Use the method outlined in Section 3.5.

12. Under what conditions can the system

$$A_{(n,n)}X_{(n,p)} + B_{(n,m)}Y_{(m,p)} = C_{(n,p)},$$
$$D_{(m,n)}X_{(n,p)} + E_{(m,m)}Y_{(m,p)} = G_{(m,p)},$$

be solved uniquely for the matrices X and Y? What is the solution?

3.8 Matrix Inversion by Partitioning

In this section, we show how partitioning may be used to compute the inverse of a symmetric matrix in a particularly effective way. The importance of the process lies in the fact that many of the matrices which arise in practice are symmetric. Even when a matrix is not symmetric, finding its inverse can be reduced to the inversion of a symmetric matrix, if that is desired. (See Exercise 2, Section 3.9.)

Let A be the symmetric matrix of order n whose inverse is to be computed. As before, the inverse will be obtained by solving the system of n equations in n unknowns,

$$(3.8.1) \qquad\qquad\qquad AX = Y,$$

for X, but the technique will be different. We begin by writing (3.8.1) in partitioned form thus:

$$\begin{array}{c} k \\ n-k \end{array} \begin{bmatrix} A_{11} & A_{12} \\ \hline A_{21} & A_{22} \end{bmatrix} \cdot \begin{bmatrix} X_1 \\ \hline X_2 \end{bmatrix} \begin{array}{c} k \\ n-k \end{array} = \begin{bmatrix} Y_1 \\ \hline Y_2 \end{bmatrix} \begin{array}{c} k \\ n-k \end{array}$$
$$\quad\; k \quad\; n-k$$

[Here the A_{ij} denote submatrices, not cofactors.]
This is equivalent to replacing (3.8.1) by the equations

$$(3.8.2) \qquad\qquad \begin{aligned} A_{11}X_1 + A_{12}X_2 &= Y_1, \\ A_{21}X_1 + A_{22}X_2 &= Y_2. \end{aligned}$$

In any particular case, we choose k, if possible, so that inverses exist for A_{11} and for other matrices which appear later. Then the first of these equations yields

$$(3.8.3) \qquad\qquad X_1 = A_{11}^{-1}Y_1 - A_{11}^{-1}A_{12}X_2.$$

Substituting this into the second equation, we find

(3.8.4) $(A_{22} - A_{21}A_{11}{}^{-1}A_{12})X_2 = Y_2 - A_{21}A_{11}{}^{-1}Y_1.$

To keep the notation in hand, let us put

$$B = A_{11}{}^{-1}A_{12} \quad \text{so that} \quad B^{\mathsf{T}} = A_{21}A_{11}{}^{-1}$$

since A is symmetric. We write also

$$C = A_{22} - A_{21}A_{11}{}^{-1}A_{12} = A_{22} - A_{21}B$$

and C is symmetric. Using these abbreviations and now assuming that C^{-1} exists, we rewrite (3.8.3) and (3.8.4), introducing B and C where possible. Then replacing X_2 in equation (3.8.3) by its value from equation (3.8.4), we finally obtain

(3.8.5)
$$X_1 = (A_{11}{}^{-1} + BC^{-1}B^{\mathsf{T}})Y_1 + (-BC^{-1})Y_2,$$
$$X_2 = (-BC^{-1})^{\mathsf{T}}Y_1 + C^{-1}Y_2.$$

Hence we must have

(3.8.6)
$$A^{-1} = \begin{bmatrix} A_{11}{}^{-1} + BC^{-1}B^{\mathsf{T}} & -BC^{-1} \\ (-BC^{-1})^{\mathsf{T}} & C^{-1} \end{bmatrix}.$$

Here A^{-1} and its upper left and lower right submatrices are symmetric, a fact which saves much work in the computation of an inverse.

When a symmetric matrix is inverted in this manner, we usually take $k = n - 1$. Then A_{22} reduces to the scalar a_{nn}, C likewise reduces to a scalar, and the computation becomes particularly simple. For example, let

$$A = \left[\begin{array}{cc:c} 5 & -2 & 4 \\ -2 & 1 & 1 \\ \hdashline 4 & 1 & 0 \end{array} \right].$$

We have

$$A_{11} = \begin{bmatrix} 5 & -2 \\ -2 & 1 \end{bmatrix}, \quad A_{11}{}^{-1} = \begin{bmatrix} 1 & 2 \\ 2 & 5 \end{bmatrix}, \quad A_{12} = \begin{bmatrix} 4 \\ 1 \end{bmatrix},$$

$$B = \begin{bmatrix} 1 & 2 \\ 2 & 5 \end{bmatrix} \cdot \begin{bmatrix} 4 \\ 1 \end{bmatrix} = \begin{bmatrix} 6 \\ 13 \end{bmatrix}, \quad A_{21} = [4 \;\; 1], \quad A_{22} = 0,$$

$$C = 0 - [4 \;\; 1] \cdot \begin{bmatrix} 6 \\ 13 \end{bmatrix} = -37, \quad C^{-1} = -\frac{1}{37}, \quad -BC^{-1} = \begin{bmatrix} \dfrac{6}{37} \\ \dfrac{13}{37} \end{bmatrix},$$

$$(BC^{-1})B^{\mathsf{T}} = \begin{bmatrix} \dfrac{-6}{37} \\[2mm] \dfrac{-13}{37} \end{bmatrix} \cdot [6 \quad 13] = \begin{bmatrix} \dfrac{-36}{37} & \dfrac{-78}{37} \\[3mm] \dfrac{-78}{37} & \dfrac{-169}{37} \end{bmatrix},$$

$$A_{11}^{-1} + BC^{-1}B^{\mathsf{T}} = \begin{bmatrix} \dfrac{1}{37} & \dfrac{-4}{37} \\[3mm] \dfrac{-4}{37} & \dfrac{16}{37} \end{bmatrix}.$$

Substituting into (3.8.6) we have, then,

$$A^{-1} = \left[\begin{array}{cc:c} \dfrac{1}{37} & \dfrac{-4}{37} & \dfrac{6}{37} \\[3mm] \dfrac{-4}{37} & \dfrac{16}{37} & \dfrac{13}{37} \\[3mm] \hdashline \dfrac{6}{37} & \dfrac{13}{37} & \dfrac{-1}{37} \end{array} \right].$$

The computations detailed above may be arranged compactly in the following array from which A^{-1} is easy to write down:

	A_{11}^{-1}	A_{12}	B	$BC^{-1}B^{\mathsf{T}}$	
	1 2	4	6	$\dfrac{-36}{37}$	$\dfrac{-78}{37}$
(3.8.7)	2 5	1	13	$\dfrac{-78}{37}$	$\dfrac{-169}{37}$
		0	-37		
		A_{22}	C		

In this table the matrix product of the first and second blocks gives the third block of the upper two rows. Then the scalar $A_{12}^{\mathsf{T}}B$, subtracted from the A_{22} entry, gives the value of C. Next BB^{T}, divided by C, gives the entry $BC^{-1}B^{\mathsf{T}}$ of the final block. This last block, added to the first, gives the upper left block of A^{-1}, B divided by $-C$ gives the upper right block, C^{-1} gives the lower right block, and the rest is found by symmetry.

By using the previous example as a starting point and by using the same steps as those employed to construct (3.8.7), we compute the inverse of

$$S = \begin{bmatrix} 5 & -2 & 4 & \vdots & 1 \\ -2 & 1 & 1 & \vdots & -1 \\ 4 & 1 & 0 & \vdots & 0 \\ \cdots & \cdots & \cdots & & \cdots \\ 1 & -1 & 0 & \vdots & 1 \end{bmatrix}$$

by means of the following array:

$S_{11}{}^{-1}$			S_{12}	B	$BC^{-1}B^{\mathsf{T}}$		
$\dfrac{1}{37}$	$\dfrac{-4}{37}$	$\dfrac{6}{37}$	1	$\dfrac{5}{37}$	$\dfrac{25}{444}$	$\dfrac{-100}{444}$	$\dfrac{-35}{444}$
$\dfrac{-4}{37}$	$\dfrac{16}{37}$	$\dfrac{13}{37}$	-1	$\dfrac{-20}{37}$	$\dfrac{-100}{444}$	$\dfrac{400}{444}$	$\dfrac{140}{444}$
$\dfrac{6}{37}$	$\dfrac{13}{37}$	$\dfrac{-1}{37}$	0	$\dfrac{-7}{37}$	$\dfrac{-35}{444}$	$\dfrac{140}{444}$	$\dfrac{49}{444}$
			1	$\dfrac{12}{37}$			
			S_{22}	C			

.

From this array we then have

$$S^{-1} = \begin{bmatrix} \dfrac{1}{12} & \dfrac{-1}{3} & \dfrac{1}{12} & \vdots & \dfrac{-5}{12} \\ \dfrac{-1}{3} & \dfrac{4}{3} & \dfrac{2}{3} & \vdots & \dfrac{5}{3} \\ \dfrac{1}{12} & \dfrac{2}{3} & \dfrac{1}{12} & \vdots & \dfrac{7}{12} \\ \cdots & \cdots & \cdots & & \cdots \\ \dfrac{-5}{12} & \dfrac{5}{3} & \dfrac{7}{12} & \vdots & \dfrac{37}{12} \end{bmatrix}.$$

The reader should check the details. These two examples show how one could invert, by successive steps, a symmetric matrix of arbitrary order. In the examples we have used rational numbers to make it easier for the reader to follow and check the various steps. However, when observational data are involved, one usually has decimal entries, and the computations may be performed by machine. In this connection, an important characteristic of this method is that it permits control of the rounding-off error. (For details see M. Lotkin and R. Remage, "Scaling and Error Analysis for Matrix Inversion by Partitioning," *The Annals of Mathematical Statistics,*

Vol. 24, 1953, pp. 428–439.) Finally, in the case of observational data, the matrices A_{11} and C are almost always nonsingular, so that the assumptions on which the process rests are well justified. The nonsymmetric case is treated in R. A. Frazer, W. J. Duncan, A. R. Collar, *Elementary Matrices*, New York, Cambridge University Press, 1950, pp. 112–118.

3.9 Exercises

1. Invert by the method of Section 3.8 and check the result:

$$\begin{bmatrix} 0 & 1 & 2 & 3 \\ 1 & 1 & 2 & 3 \\ 2 & 2 & 2 & 3 \\ 3 & 3 & 3 & 3 \end{bmatrix}.$$

*2. If A is any square matrix, show that $A^{\mathsf{T}}A$ is symmetric and that, if A is nonsingular, $A^{-1} = (A^{\mathsf{T}}A)^{-1}A^{\mathsf{T}}$. This shows how the inversion of an arbitrary matrix A may be reduced to the inversion of a symmetric matrix.

3. Apply Exercise 2 to the matrix

$$\begin{bmatrix} 1 & -1 & 0 \\ -1 & -2 & 1 \\ 1 & -1 & 1 \end{bmatrix}.$$

CHAPTER FOUR

Rank and Equivalence

RANK

4.1 The Concept of Rank

We begin by recalling that a **submatrix** of a given matrix A is defined to be either A itself or any array remaining after certain lines are deleted from A. For example, the matrix

$$\begin{bmatrix} 2 & 1 & -1 \\ 0 & 3 & -2 \end{bmatrix}$$

has as submatrices first itself, next the matrices

$$\begin{bmatrix} 2 & 1 \\ 0 & 3 \end{bmatrix}, \quad \begin{bmatrix} 2 & -1 \\ 0 & -2 \end{bmatrix}, \quad \begin{bmatrix} 1 & -1 \\ 3 & -2 \end{bmatrix},$$

$$\begin{bmatrix} 2 \\ 0 \end{bmatrix}, \quad \begin{bmatrix} 1 \\ 3 \end{bmatrix}, \quad \begin{bmatrix} -1 \\ -2 \end{bmatrix},$$

$$[2 \quad 1 \quad -1], \quad [0 \quad 3 \quad -2],$$

$$[2 \quad 1], \quad [0 \quad 3], \quad [2 \quad -1],$$

$$[0 \quad -2], \quad [1 \quad -1], \quad [3 \quad -2],$$

and finally its individual elements. The square submatrices of a given matrix are of particular usefulness. The determinant of a submatrix of order r of a given matrix is often called a **determinant of order r of the matrix.**

A matrix is said to be of **rank r** if and only if it has at least one non-singular submatrix of order r, but has no nonsingular submatrix of order more than r. A matrix is said to be of **rank zero** if and only if all its elements are zero.

We illustrate the definition by some examples. First, the matrix

$$A = \begin{bmatrix} 2 & 1 & -1 \\ 0 & 3 & -2 \\ 2 & 4 & -3 \end{bmatrix}$$

has rank 2 because

$$\det \begin{bmatrix} 2 & 1 \\ 0 & 3 \end{bmatrix} \neq 0,$$

but

$$\det A = 0.$$

The matrix

$$\begin{bmatrix} 1 & a & b & 0 \\ 0 & c & d & 1 \\ 1 & a & b & 0 \\ 0 & c & d & 1 \end{bmatrix}$$

also has rank 2 since the matrix itself and all submatrices of order 3 are singular (because of identical rows), whereas the second-order submatrix

$$\begin{bmatrix} 1 & 0 \\ 0 & 1 \end{bmatrix}$$

obtained by deleting the middle two rows and the middle two columns is nonsingular.

In the example just given, although the elements of the given matrix include the indeterminates a, b, c, d, its rank is nevertheless uniquely defined. The rank is, of course, always uniquely defined when the elements are all explicitly given numbers, but not necessarily otherwise. For example, the matrix

$$\begin{bmatrix} 4-x & 2\sqrt{5} & 0 \\ 2\sqrt{5} & 4-x & \sqrt{5} \\ 0 & \sqrt{5} & 4-x \end{bmatrix}$$

has rank less than 3 if and only if its determinant, which is the polynomial

$$(4-x)^3 - 25(4-x),$$

is zero. This polynomial vanishes when $x = 9$, 4, or -1. When $x = 9$, we have the singular matrix

$$\begin{bmatrix} -5 & 2\sqrt{5} & 0 \\ 2\sqrt{5} & -5 & \sqrt{5} \\ 0 & \sqrt{5} & -5 \end{bmatrix},$$

which has, among others, the nonsingular submatrix

$$\begin{bmatrix} -5 & \sqrt{5} \\ \sqrt{5} & -5 \end{bmatrix},$$

so that its rank is 2. It is easy to verify that the rank is 2 also when $x = 4$ or -1. For any other value of x, the rank is, of course, 3.

4.2 Elementary Transformations

From the expansion of the determinant of a matrix in terms of the cofactors of the elements of a line, we see that *if all submatrices of order r of a given matrix are singular, then so are all submatrices of order r + 1 or higher.* Hence, in examining a matrix to determine its rank, if we find that all the square submatrices of a given order are singular, there is no need to examine submatrices of any higher order.

Despite the observation just made, the determination of the rank of a given matrix by a direct application of the definition would be hopelessly tedious except in the simplest cases. We therefore investigate some methods of altering a matrix in such a way that the rank remains the same but is simpler to determine. These methods are based on the following three types of operations, which are called **elementary transformations of a matrix**:

(a) The interchange of any two parallel lines of a matrix.

(b) The multiplication of all the elements of any line by the same nonzero constant.

(c) The addition to any line of an arbitrary multiple of any other parallel line.

The **inverse of an elementary transformation** is defined to be the operation which undoes the effect of the given transformation, thereby restoring the matrix to its original condition. If we interchange two parallel lines and then interchange them again, the matrix suffers no net change. Thus an elementary transformation (a) is its own inverse. The inverse of a transformation (b) is the multiplication of the line in question by the reciprocal constant. The inverse of a transformation (c) is the addition to the same line of the corresponding negative multiple of the other line. From these observations we have

Theorem 4.2.1: *The inverse of an elementary transformation is an elementary transformation of the same type.*

We are now ready to prove the following basic theorem:

Theorem 4.2.2: *When an elementary transformation is applied to a matrix, there results a matrix of the same order and the same rank.*

In the case of transformations of types (a) and (b), the result follows at once from familiar properties of determinants and from the definition of rank. The reader may supply the details. For the case of transformations of type (c), we shall supply proof. We begin by showing that such a transformation cannot *raise* the rank of a matrix. If the rank of the given matrix is the maximum possible for a matrix of its order, this result is obvious. Hence suppose that it has a rank r less than the maximum possible rank, so that the determinants of all submatrices of order $r + 1$ are zero. Now let a transformation of type (c) be applied to the matrix and consider in the new matrix any submatrix of order $r + 1$. Either this submatrix is identical to the corresponding submatrix of the original matrix, in which case its determinant is zero, or else it shows the effects of the transformation (c) which has been applied. In the latter case, it has a line which may be regarded as a sum of two parallel lines. Hence by Theorems 2.7.6 and 2.7.7, its determinant may be written in the form $d_1 + kd_2$. Here d_1 is the determinant of a submatrix of order $r + 1$ of the original matrix, and hence is zero; d_2 is the determinant of a matrix which either is a submatrix of order $r + 1$ of the original matrix, with one line possibly not in the natural position, or else has two identical lines. In either case, $d_2 = 0$. It follows, then, that every submatrix of order $r + 1$ of the new matrix is singular so that the new matrix has rank $\leqslant r$. Thus a transformation of type (c) cannot raise the rank of a matrix. Neither can it lower the rank, for, if it could, then the inverse transformation, which is a transformation of the same type, would raise the rank. This is, of course, impossible by what has just been proved. The theorem follows.

From the theorem it next follows that *no finite sequence of elementary transformations can alter the rank of a matrix.* Using this fact, we are frequently able to determine the rank of a matrix more efficiently than might otherwise be possible. Let us use the symbol $\sim$ to mean "has the same order and rank as." Then, using transformation (c) repeatedly, we have

$$\begin{bmatrix} 1 & 2 & -1 & 3 \\ 2 & 4 & -4 & 7 \\ -1 & -2 & -1 & -2 \end{bmatrix} \sim \begin{bmatrix} 1 & 2 & -1 & 3 \\ 0 & 0 & -2 & 1 \\ 0 & 0 & -2 & 1 \end{bmatrix} \sim \begin{bmatrix} 1 & 2 & -1 & 3 \\ 0 & 0 & -2 & 1 \\ 0 & 0 & 0 & 0 \end{bmatrix}.$$

Here we subtracted twice the first row from the second and added the first row to the third row to obtain the second matrix, after which we subtracted the second row from the third row to obtain the third matrix.

All third-order submatrices of the last matrix written are singular, but since

$$\det \begin{bmatrix} 2 & -1 \\ 0 & -2 \end{bmatrix} \neq 0,$$

the rank is seen to be 2. It is much more efficient to proceed in this way than it would be to compute at once the determinants of all the third-order submatrices of the given matrix.

4.3 The Normal Form

The elementary transformations may be employed, in a manner suggested by the preceding example, to obtain a matrix having the same order and rank as a given matrix whose elements are explicitly given numbers, but having the simplest possible form. This may be accomplished by the following systematic procedure (the sweep-out process):

(1) Use transformations of type (a), if necessary, to obtain a nonzero element (preferably a 1) in the first row and the first column of the given matrix.

(2) Divide the first row by this element, if it is not 1.

(3) Subtract appropriate multiples of the first row from the other rows so as to obtain zeros in the remainder of the first column.

(4) Subtract appropriate multiples of the first column from the other columns so as to obtain zeros in the remainder of the first row.

(5) Repeat steps (1) through (4) starting with the element in the second row and the second column.

(6) Continue thus down the "main diagonal," either until the end of the diagonal is reached or until all the remaining elements in the matrix are zero. The final matrix then has one of the forms

$$(4.3.1) \qquad \begin{bmatrix} I_r \\ -- \\ 0 \end{bmatrix}, \qquad [I_r \mid 0], \qquad \begin{bmatrix} I_r & 0 \\ \hline 0 & 0 \end{bmatrix} \qquad \text{or} \qquad I_r,$$

where r is its rank and I_r is an identity matrix of order r.

Treating the example of the last section in this fashion, we have

$$\begin{bmatrix} 1 & 2 & -1 & 3 \\ 2 & 4 & -4 & 7 \\ -1 & -2 & -1 & -2 \end{bmatrix} \sim \begin{bmatrix} 1 & 2 & -1 & 3 \\ 0 & 0 & -2 & 1 \\ 0 & 0 & -2 & 1 \end{bmatrix} \sim \begin{bmatrix} 1 & 0 & 0 & 0 \\ 0 & 0 & -2 & 1 \\ 0 & 0 & -2 & 1 \end{bmatrix}$$

$$\sim \begin{bmatrix} 1 & 0 & 0 & 0 \\ 0 & 1 & -2 & 0 \\ 0 & 1 & -2 & 0 \end{bmatrix} \sim \begin{bmatrix} 1 & 0 & 0 & 0 \\ 0 & 1 & -2 & 0 \\ 0 & 0 & 0 & 0 \end{bmatrix} \sim \begin{bmatrix} 1 & 0 & 0 & 0 \\ 0 & 1 & 0 & 0 \\ \hline 0 & 0 & 0 & 0 \end{bmatrix}.$$

The reader should verify in detail that the above outline was followed in this illustration.

When a matrix has been reduced to a form (4.3.1) by elementary transformations, we say it has been reduced to **normal form**. To reduce a matrix to this form, it is often more convenient in specific cases to use different sequences of elementary transformations than those called for by steps (1) through (6) above. However, since elementary transformations do not alter rank or order, for a given matrix the end result must always be the same. Suppose now we know a sequence of elementary transformations which will reduce a given matrix to normal form. Then the inverses of these transformations, applied in the reverse order to the normal form, will lead us back to the original matrix. We summarize these observations in

Theorem 4.3.1:   *Every matrix whose elements are explicitly given numbers has a unique normal form to which it may be reduced, and from which it may be obtained, by elementary transformations.*

Theorem 4.3.2:   *Two matrices whose elements are explicitly given numbers have the same normal form if and only if they have the same rank and the same order.*

An immediate consequence of the two preceding theorems is

Theorem 4.3.3:   *Two matrices whose elements are explicitly given numbers can be transformed each into the other by elementary transformations if and only if they have the same rank and the same order.*

In fact, either of the two matrices may first be reduced to their common normal form, which then may be transformed into the other.

Fortunately, the principal application of the normal form is in the proof of certain theorems, and merely the fact that it exists is used. Thus it is only rarely necessary to perform the actual reduction to normal form. The technique outlined above is nevertheless useful when the rank of a given matrix is to be found and there is no obviously appropriate way to proceed. Then steps (1) through (6), employed to whatever extent may be necessary, provide a systematic method for solving the problem. Note that it is not necessary to obtain the normal form to decide the rank. Thus, in the example on p. 116, one step shows the rank to be 2.

4.4 Equivalence of Matrices

It is convenient to summarize the results of the last section by introducing a new term. Two matrices whose elements are real or complex numbers are said to be **equivalent** if and only if each can be transformed into the other by means of elementary transformations. From Theorem 4.3.3, we then have at once

Theorem 4.4.1:   *Two matrices whose elements are explicitly given numbers are equivalent if and only if they have the same rank and the same order.*

In what follows, the symbol $\sim$, defined earlier to mean "has the same rank and order as," may now be read "is equivalent to."

It should be emphasized that equivalence as defined here is *equivalence with respect to elementary transformations.* Later we will define equivalence with respect to other types of transformations. Each such type of equivalence has its own particular uses. The type defined here is the most general, and each of the other types implies equivalence with respect to elementary transformations, but not conversely.

4.5 Exercises

1. Find the rank of each matrix:

(a) $\begin{bmatrix} 3 & 2 & 3 & 1 \\ 4 & 3 & 5 & 2 \\ 2 & 1 & 1 & 0 \end{bmatrix}$,   (b) $\begin{bmatrix} 0 & 6 & 6 & 1 \\ -8 & 7 & 2 & 3 \\ -2 & 3 & 0 & 1 \\ -3 & 2 & 1 & 1 \end{bmatrix}$,   (c) $\begin{bmatrix} 0 & i & -i \\ -i & 0 & i \\ i & -i & 0 \end{bmatrix}$.

2. Reduce to normal form by elementary transformations:

(a) $\begin{bmatrix} 1 & 4 & 3 & 2 \\ 2 & 2 & 1 & 1 \\ 1 & -2 & -2 & -1 \end{bmatrix}$,   (b) $\begin{bmatrix} 0 & 1 & 2 & 3 & 4 \\ 1 & 1 & 2 & 3 & 3 \\ 2 & 2 & 0 & 2 & 2 \\ 3 & 3 & 2 & 1 & 1 \\ 4 & 3 & 2 & 1 & 0 \end{bmatrix}$.

3. Is I_3 equivalent to the following matrix?

$$\begin{bmatrix} 1 & 0 & 2 \\ 0 & 1 & 0 \\ 2 & 0 & 1 \end{bmatrix}.$$

4. Write the normal forms for matrices of rank 3 and orders (4, 3), (3, 6), (4, 5), (3, 3), respectively.

5. Prove that every elementary transformation of type (a) may be accomplished by a succession of transformations of types (b) and (c).

*6. Show that the equivalence of matrices is indeed an "equivalence relation" as defined in Chapter One.

7. Given that A has rank r, prove that not all submatrices of any order s less than r can be singular.

8. Give an example to show that the normal form of a product of two matrices is not necessarily the product of their normal forms.

9. Give an example to show that the rank of a product of matrices may be less than the rank of any factor.

10. Under what conditions, if any, will the rank of the matrix

$$\begin{bmatrix} 1 & 0 & 0 \\ 0 & h-2 & 2 \\ 0 & k-1 & h+2 \\ 0 & 0 & 3 \end{bmatrix}$$

be less than 3, and what will that rank be?

11. Determine the ranks of the $n \times n$ matrices of the form

$$\begin{bmatrix} (n-1) & 1 & \cdots & 1 \\ 1 & (n-1) & \cdots & 1 \\ \vdots & & & \\ 1 & 1 & \cdots & (n-1) \end{bmatrix}, \begin{bmatrix} (1-n) & 1 & \cdots & 1 \\ 1 & (1-n) & \cdots & 1 \\ \vdots & & & \\ 1 & 1 & \cdots & (1-n) \end{bmatrix}.$$

12. Show that the locus of points (x, y, z) in ordinary 3-space, such that the matrix

$$\begin{bmatrix} x & y & z \\ 1 & x & y \end{bmatrix}$$

has rank 1, is the cubic space curve with parametric equations $x = t$, $y = t^2$, $z = t^3$.

13. Prove that three points (x_1, y_1), (x_2, y_2), (x_3, y_3) in the plane are collinear if and only if the rank of the matrix

$$\begin{bmatrix} x_1 & y_1 & 1 \\ x_2 & y_2 & 1 \\ x_3 & y_3 & 1 \end{bmatrix}$$

is less than 3.

14. Suppose that A has rank r and that the leading principal minor of order r is not zero. Then show that, if the first r elements in any row or column with index $\geq r + 1$ are all 0, so are all the remaining elements in that row or column.

*15. Show that it is possible, by using only row transformations, to reduce a matrix A to an equivalent matrix $[\alpha_{ij}]$ such that $\alpha_{ij} = 0$ if $i > j$, and, by using only column transformations, to an equivalent matrix $[\beta_{ij}]$ such that $\beta_{ij} = 0$ if $i < j$. Moreover, if $\alpha_{jj} \neq 0$, row transformations will also yield $\alpha_{ij} = 0$ for $i < j$ and if $\beta_{ii} \neq 0$, column transformations will also yield $\beta_{ij} = 0$ for $i > j$. Finally, if A has rank r, then no more than r of the elements α_{jj} and no more than r of the elements β_{ii} may differ from zero.

16. Show that the rank of a decomposable matrix $D[A_1, A_2, \ldots, A_k]$ (see Exercise 5, Section 1.20) is equal to the sum of the ranks of the A's.

17. Prove that, if A, of order n, and $(A + A^{\mathsf{T}})/2$ both have rank 1, then

$$a_{ii}a_{jj} - a_{ij}a_{ji} = a_{ii}a_{jj} - \frac{(a_{ij} + a_{ji})^2}{4} = 0,$$

and hence that A is symmetric.

18. Reduce this matrix to triangular form in such a way that the determinant is invariant:

$$\begin{bmatrix} 2 & -1 & 4 \\ 3 & \frac{1}{2} & 7 \\ 4 & 2 & 8 \end{bmatrix}.$$

ELEMENTARY MATRICES

4.6 Elementary Transformations in Matrix Form

In this section we shall show that the elementary transformations of a given matrix can all be accomplished by pre- or postmultiplying it by suitably chosen square matrices of very simple types.

Suppose first that we wish to interchange the second and third rows of a given 3×4 matrix. This can be accomplished as follows:

$$\begin{bmatrix} 1 & 0 & 0 \\ 0 & 0 & 1 \\ 0 & 1 & 0 \end{bmatrix} \cdot \begin{bmatrix} a_{11} & a_{12} & a_{13} & a_{14} \\ a_{21} & a_{22} & a_{23} & a_{24} \\ a_{31} & a_{32} & a_{33} & a_{34} \end{bmatrix} = \begin{bmatrix} a_{11} & a_{12} & a_{13} & a_{14} \\ a_{31} & a_{32} & a_{33} & a_{34} \\ a_{21} & a_{22} & a_{23} & a_{24} \end{bmatrix}.$$

On the other hand, the interchange of the second and third columns is effected thus:

$$\begin{bmatrix} a_{11} & a_{12} & a_{13} & a_{14} \\ a_{21} & a_{22} & a_{23} & a_{24} \\ a_{31} & a_{32} & a_{33} & a_{34} \end{bmatrix} \cdot \begin{bmatrix} 1 & 0 & 0 & 0 \\ 0 & 0 & 1 & 0 \\ 0 & 1 & 0 & 0 \\ 0 & 0 & 0 & 1 \end{bmatrix} = \begin{bmatrix} a_{11} & a_{13} & a_{12} & a_{14} \\ a_{21} & a_{23} & a_{22} & a_{24} \\ a_{31} & a_{33} & a_{32} & a_{34} \end{bmatrix}.$$

Note carefully how the position of the 1's in the pre- and postmultipliers respectively accomplishes the desired effect: a 1 on the diagonal leaves the corresponding row (column) unaltered, but an off-diagonal 1 selects the elements of the row (column) corresponding to the column (row) in which that 1 is situated.

Next suppose we wish to multiply a row or a column by a constant k:

$$\begin{bmatrix} 1 & 0 & 0 \\ 0 & k & 0 \\ 0 & 0 & 1 \end{bmatrix} \cdot \begin{bmatrix} a_1 & a_2 & a_3 \\ b_1 & b_2 & b_3 \\ c_1 & c_2 & c_3 \end{bmatrix} = \begin{bmatrix} a_1 & a_2 & a_3 \\ kb_1 & kb_2 & kb_3 \\ c_1 & c_2 & c_3 \end{bmatrix},$$

and

$$\begin{bmatrix} 2 & 1 & -2 \\ 0 & -1 & 1 \end{bmatrix} \cdot \begin{bmatrix} 1 & 0 & 0 \\ 0 & 1 & 0 \\ 0 & 0 & k \end{bmatrix} = \begin{bmatrix} 2 & 1 & -2k \\ 0 & -1 & k \end{bmatrix}.$$

Here we pre- or postmultiply by a diagonal matrix whose diagonal entries are all 1's, except for a k in the position corresponding to the row or column to be altered.

Finally, to add, say, a third row k times to a second, or a third column k times to a second, we could proceed as in these examples:

$$\begin{bmatrix} 1 & 0 & 0 \\ 0 & 1 & k \\ 0 & 0 & 1 \end{bmatrix} \cdot \begin{bmatrix} a_1 & a_2 & a_3 \\ b_1 & b_2 & b_3 \\ c_1 & c_2 & c_3 \end{bmatrix} = \begin{bmatrix} a_1 & a_2 & a_3 \\ b_1 + kc_1 & b_2 + kc_2 & b_3 + kc_3 \\ c_1 & c_2 & c_3 \end{bmatrix},$$

and

$$\begin{bmatrix} a_1 & a_2 & a_3 & a_4 \\ b_1 & b_2 & b_3 & b_4 \end{bmatrix} \cdot \begin{bmatrix} 1 & 0 & 0 & 0 \\ 0 & 1 & 0 & 0 \\ 0 & k & 1 & 0 \\ 0 & 0 & 0 & 1 \end{bmatrix} = \begin{bmatrix} a_1 & a_2 + ka_3 & a_3 & a_4 \\ b_1 & b_2 + kb_3 & b_3 & b_4 \end{bmatrix}.$$

Here an off-diagonal k in the ij-position of the pre- or postmultiplier adds to the ith row (jth column) of the multiplicand k times its jth row (ith column).

All these procedures may be summarized in a single, simple result:

Theorem 4.6.1: *To effect any elementary transformation on a given matrix A, one may first perform the same elementary transformation on an identity matrix of appropriate order, then premultiply A by the result if the operation is on rows, postmultiply if it is on columns.*

It is left to the reader to write a proof of this theorem with the aid of Exercise 31, Section 1.18.

The matrices which are formed from identity matrices as in Theorem 4.6.1 in order to effect elementary transformations by matrix multiplication are called **elementary matrices.** Conversely, every matrix so formed from an identity matrix may be interpreted as the elementary matrix corresponding to some elementary transformation. It is convenient to include the identity matrix among the elementary matrices. This is reasonable since the identity matrix corresponds, for example, to an elementary transformation of type (b), p. 115, in which the multiplier is 1.

We have already seen that the inverse transformation of an elementary transformation is another of the same kind. From this observation it is not difficult to conclude

Theorem 4.6.2:   *The inverse matrix of an elementary matrix is the matrix of the corresponding inverse elementary transformation.*

Thus, for example,

$$\begin{bmatrix} 1 & 0 & 0 \\ 0 & 0 & 1 \\ 0 & 1 & 0 \end{bmatrix}, \quad \begin{bmatrix} 1 & 0 & 0 \\ 0 & k & 0 \\ 0 & 0 & 1 \end{bmatrix}, \quad \text{and} \quad \begin{bmatrix} 1 & 0 & 0 \\ 0 & 1 & k \\ 0 & 0 & 1 \end{bmatrix}$$

have as inverses

$$\begin{bmatrix} 1 & 0 & 0 \\ 0 & 0 & 1 \\ 0 & 1 & 0 \end{bmatrix}, \quad \begin{bmatrix} 1 & 0 & 0 \\ 0 & \dfrac{1}{k} & 0 \\ 0 & 0 & 1 \end{bmatrix}, \quad \text{and} \quad \begin{bmatrix} 1 & 0 & 0 \\ 0 & 1 & -k \\ 0 & 0 & 1 \end{bmatrix}$$

respectively.

4.7 Properties of Equivalent Matrices

Suppose now that matrices A and B are equivalent. Then, by the results of the preceding section, there exist elementary matrices $C_1, C_2, \ldots, C_p$ and $D_1, D_2, \ldots, D_s$ such that

$$(C_p \cdots C_2 C_1) A (D_1 D_2 \cdots D_s) = B.$$

Here the C's represent operations affecting rows, and the D's represent operations affecting columns. (The associative law of multiplication was used in arriving at this conclusion. Explain.) Since the individual C's and D's are all nonsingular, so are the products $C = C_p \cdots C_2 C_1$ and $D = D_1 D_2 \cdots D_s$. We have thus established

Theorem 4.7.1:   *If two matrices A and B are equivalent, then there exist nonsingular matrices C and D such that $CAD = B$.*

The case when B is the normal form of A is of particular importance. This latter case is illustrated by the following example. The matrix

$$A = \begin{bmatrix} 1 & 0 & -2 \\ 2 & 3 & -4 \\ 3 & 3 & -6 \end{bmatrix}$$

may be reduced to normal form by:

(a) subtracting the first row from the third,

(b) subtracting the second row from the third,

(c) adding twice the first column to the third,

(d) dividing the second column by 3, and finally,

(e) subtracting twice the second column from the first.

Hence we have

$$
\overset{\text{(b)}}{\begin{bmatrix} 1 & 0 & 0 \\ 0 & 1 & 0 \\ 0 & -1 & 1 \end{bmatrix}} \cdot \overset{\text{(a)}}{\begin{bmatrix} 1 & 0 & 0 \\ 0 & 1 & 0 \\ -1 & 0 & 1 \end{bmatrix}} \cdot A \cdot \overset{\text{(c)}}{\begin{bmatrix} 1 & 0 & 2 \\ 0 & 1 & 0 \\ 0 & 0 & 1 \end{bmatrix}} \cdot \overset{\text{(d)}}{\begin{bmatrix} 1 & 0 & 0 \\ 0 & \frac{1}{3} & 0 \\ 0 & 0 & 1 \end{bmatrix}} \cdot \overset{\text{(e)}}{\begin{bmatrix} 1 & 0 & 0 \\ -2 & 1 & 0 \\ 0 & 0 & 1 \end{bmatrix}}
$$

$$
= \begin{bmatrix} 1 & 0 & 0 \\ 0 & 1 & 0 \\ 0 & 0 & 0 \end{bmatrix},
$$

or

$$
\begin{bmatrix} 1 & 0 & 0 \\ 0 & 1 & 0 \\ -1 & -1 & 1 \end{bmatrix} \cdot A \cdot \begin{bmatrix} 1 & 0 & 2 \\ -\frac{2}{3} & \frac{1}{3} & 0 \\ 0 & 0 & 1 \end{bmatrix} = \begin{bmatrix} 1 & 0 & 0 \\ 0 & 1 & 0 \\ 0 & 0 & 0 \end{bmatrix}.
$$

The reader should check the details.

Next we consider a special case of equivalent matrices. Any nonsingular matrix A_n and the identity matrix I_n have the same order and the same rank and, hence, are equivalent. Therefore there exist elementary matrices C_j, D_j such that

$$
A_n = (C_p \cdots C_2 C_1) I_n (D_1 D_2 \cdots D_s).
$$

This proves

Theorem 4.7.2: *Any nonsingular matrix of explicitly given numbers may be factored into a product of elementary matrices.*

This factorization can, of course, be performed in many ways since there are many sequences of elementary transformations that will reduce a given matrix to normal form. In particular, when A is nonsingular, it can be reduced to normal form by using only row operations or only column operations, so we need use only the C's or only the D's in the preceding formula. An important consequence of this theorem and Theorem 4.2.2 is

Theorem 4.7.3:   *The matrices A, BA, AC, and BAC, where B and C are nonsingular, all have the same rank.*

4.8 Exercises

1. Factor into a product of elementary matrices by first reducing to normal form

$$\begin{bmatrix} 1 & -1 & 0 \\ -1 & 2 & 0 \\ 0 & 0 & 1 \end{bmatrix}.$$

2. Prove that the determinant of an elementary matrix corresponding to the interchange of two rows or two columns is equal to -1.

3. Find matrices A and B such that

$$A \begin{bmatrix} 2 & 2 & -6 \\ -1 & 2 & 2 \end{bmatrix} B$$

is in the normal form.

4. Show that if $A_1 \sim A_2$ and $B_1 \sim B_2$, then

$$\begin{bmatrix} A_1 & 0 \\ 0 & B_1 \end{bmatrix} \sim \begin{bmatrix} A_2 & 0 \\ 0 & B_2 \end{bmatrix}.$$

*5. Show that, if a matrix R of order n effects a given elementary transformation on the rows (columns) of *every* $n \times n$ matrix A, then R *must be* the corresponding elementary matrix defined in Theorem 4.6.1.

6. Write out formal proofs of Theorems 4.6.1 and 4.6.2. The E_j's of Exercise 31, Section 1.18, will help.

7. Compute the inverse of the product

$$\begin{bmatrix} 1 & 0 & k \\ 0 & 1 & 0 \\ 0 & 0 & 1 \end{bmatrix} \cdot \begin{bmatrix} 1 & 0 & 0 \\ 0 & 1 & m \\ 0 & 0 & 1 \end{bmatrix} \cdot \begin{bmatrix} 1 & 0 & 0 \\ 0 & p & 0 \\ 0 & 0 & 1 \end{bmatrix}$$

without first evaluating the product.

8. Write the inverse *by inspection*, that is, interpret first as a product of elementary matrices:

$$\begin{bmatrix} 1 & 0 & 0 & 0 \\ 0 & 1 & 0 & 0 \\ 0 & 0 & 1 & 0 \\ a & b & c & 1 \end{bmatrix}.$$

9. Let N be the normal form of an $n \times m$ matrix A. Determine matrices C and D such that

$$\begin{bmatrix} A & I_n \\ \hline I_m & 0 \end{bmatrix} \sim \begin{bmatrix} N & C \\ \hline D & 0 \end{bmatrix}.$$

10. Prove that $[E_{\alpha_1}, E_{\alpha_2}, \ldots, E_{\alpha_n}] = [\delta_{i\alpha_j}]$.

11. Show that every matrix A of rank r may be expressed as a sum of r matrices of rank 1. (*Hint:* Express

$$\left[\begin{array}{c|c} I_r & 0 \\ \hline 0 & 0 \end{array}\right]$$

as such a sum in the obvious way, etc.)

12. Prove by direct computation that $\det AE = \det A \det E$, where E is any elementary matrix. Hence show that, if B is nonsingular and A is square, $\det AB = \det A \det B$.

13. Show that any finite sequence of elementary row transformations of the first r rows of an $m \times p$ matrix A, $r \leqslant m$, can be effected by premultiplication of A by a nonsingular matrix of the form

$$\left[\begin{array}{c|c} R & 0 \\ \hline 0 & I \end{array}\right],$$

where R is nonsingular and of order r. (Similarly for column transformations.)

14. Use the preceding exercise to prove that, if A_r is nonsingular of order r, then the matrix

$$\left[\begin{array}{c|c} A_r & I_r \\ \hline I_r & 0_r \end{array}\right]$$

may be reduced to the form

$$\left[\begin{array}{c|c} I_r & B_r \\ \hline C_r & 0_r \end{array}\right]$$

by operations on the first r rows and first r columns only, and that $CB = A^{-1}$.

15. Consider the partitioned matrix

$$A = \begin{bmatrix} A_{11} & A_{12} & \cdots & A_{1q} \\ A_{21} & A_{22} & \cdots & A_{2q} \\ \vdots & & & \\ A_{p1} & A_{p2} & \cdots & A_{pq} \end{bmatrix},$$

where the A_{ij}'s are submatrices of orders (m_i, n_j) respectively. Let

$$\begin{bmatrix} I_{m_1} & & & \\ & I_{m_2} & & 0 \\ & & \ddots & \\ & 0 & & I_{m_p} \end{bmatrix}, \qquad \begin{bmatrix} I_{n_1} & & & \\ & I_{n_2} & & 0 \\ & & \ddots & \\ & 0 & & I_{n_q} \end{bmatrix},$$

be partitioned identity matrices of orders $\sum m_i$ and $\sum n_j$ respectively. Show that elementary transformations of the rows and columns of submatrices of A may be effected by first applying these transformations to the rows or columns of submatrices of the partitioned identity matrices given above, then pre- or postmultiplying as before. Illustrate with examples.

16. Prove that the elementary transformations of partitioned matrices described in Exercise 15 do not alter rank.

*17. To which elementary transformations of a square matrix is one restricted if the determinant is to remain invariant?

18. By using block elementary transformations as in Exercise 15, prove that if P is $m \times m$, Q is $m \times n$, R is $n \times m$, and S is $n \times n$ and nonsingular, then

$$\det \begin{bmatrix} P & Q \\ R & S \end{bmatrix} = \det S \cdot \det [P - QS^{-1}R].$$

19. Let S be symmetric and nonsingular. Prove that there exists a nonsingular matrix C such that

$$S^{-1} = C^{\mathsf{T}}C.$$

(*Hint:* There exist nonsingular matrices C and D such that $CSD = I$.)

*20. Prove that, if A is nonsingular, it can be reduced to normal form by row operations only and also by column operations only.

4.9 The Rank of the Product of Two Matrices

We have already seen (Theorem 4.7.3) that, if B and C are nonsingular, then BA, AC, and BAC all have the same rank as A. In other cases, one cannot be so specific. Consider, for example, the following products in which each *factor* has rank 2, but the products have, respectively, ranks 2 and 1:

$$\begin{bmatrix} 1 & 0 & 0 \\ 0 & 1 & 0 \\ 0 & 0 & 0 \end{bmatrix} \cdot \begin{bmatrix} 1 & 0 & 0 \\ 0 & 1 & 0 \\ 0 & 0 & 0 \end{bmatrix} = \begin{bmatrix} 1 & 0 & 0 \\ 0 & 1 & 0 \\ 0 & 0 & 0 \end{bmatrix},$$

but

$$\begin{bmatrix} 1 & 0 & 0 \\ 0 & 1 & 0 \\ 0 & 0 & 0 \end{bmatrix} \cdot \begin{bmatrix} 0 & 0 & 0 \\ 0 & 1 & 0 \\ 0 & 0 & 1 \end{bmatrix} = \begin{bmatrix} 0 & 0 & 0 \\ 0 & 1 & 0 \\ 0 & 0 & 0 \end{bmatrix}.$$

We have, however:

Theorem 4.9.1:   *The rank of the product of two matrices cannot exceed the rank of either factor.*

Let the product be denoted by $A_{p \times m} B_{m \times q}$, where A has rank r_A and B has rank r_B. Then there exist nonsingular matrices C and D of orders p and m, respectively, such that

$$CAD = N_A,$$

where N_A denotes the normal form of A. Hence,

$$A = C^{-1}N_A D^{-1},$$

so that

$$AB = (C^{-1}N_A D^{-1})B = C^{-1}(N_A(D^{-1}B)),$$

By Theorem 4.7.3, AB has the same rank as $N_A(D^{-1}B)$. Now N_A has only 0's in the last $p - r_A$ rows and hence $N_A(D^{-1}B)$ also has only 0's in the last $p - r_A$ rows. Hence the rank of $N_A(D^{-1}B)$ is at most r_A, that is, the rank of AB is at most r_A.

Also, rank $(AB) = $ rank $(AB)^\mathsf{T} = $ rank $(B^\mathsf{T}A^\mathsf{T})$. But, by what has just been proved, rank $(B^\mathsf{T}A^\mathsf{T}) \leqslant$ rank $(B^\mathsf{T}) = $ rank B. That is, the rank of AB is at most r_B. This completes the proof of the theorem.

The theorem may also be deduced from Theorem 2.11.1. This alternative proof is important because it shows how the determinant of a submatrix of a product is related to determinants of submatrices of the factors.

We write $A = \{A_1, A_2, \ldots, A_p\}$ and $B = [B_1, B_2, \ldots, B_q]$, where the A_i's are row matrices and the B_j's are column matrices. Then

$$AB = \begin{bmatrix} A_1 \\ A_2 \\ \vdots \\ A_p \end{bmatrix} \cdot [B_1, B_2, \ldots, B_q] = \begin{bmatrix} A_1B_1 & A_1B_2 & \cdots & A_1B_q \\ A_2B_1 & A_2B_2 & \cdots & A_2B_q \\ \vdots & & & \\ A_pB_1 & A_pB_2 & \cdots & A_pB_q \end{bmatrix}.$$

Now let

$$\det \begin{bmatrix} A_{i_1}B_{j_1} & A_{i_1}B_{j_2} & \cdots & A_{i_1}B_{j_r} \\ A_{i_2}B_{j_1} & A_{i_2}B_{j_2} & \cdots & A_{i_2}B_{j_r} \\ \vdots & & & \\ A_{i_r}B_{j_1} & A_{i_r}B_{j_2} & \cdots & A_{i_r}B_{j_r} \end{bmatrix}$$

be any determinant of order r of AB. This determinant is the determinant of the product

$$\begin{bmatrix} A_{i_1} \\ A_{i_2} \\ \vdots \\ A_{i_r} \end{bmatrix}_{(r,m)} \cdot [B_{j_1}, B_{j_2}, \ldots, B_{j_r}]_{(m,r)},$$

and is zero if $r > m$, as was shown in Section 2.11. Hence assume in what follows that $r \leqslant m$. Then this determinant is equal to the sum of the products of corresponding majors, by Corollary 2.11.2. But the majors of the first matrix are minors of order r of A; those of the second are minors of order r of B. *Hence any minor of order r in AB is a sum of products of minors of order r from A with minors of order r of B.* Thus, if the rank of A is $r - 1$, so that all its minors of order r are zero, then all the minors of order r of AB are zero also, and the rank of AB necessarily is $\leqslant r - 1$. The same is true if B has rank $r - 1$. In short, the rank of AB cannot exceed the rank of either factor.

4.10 Exercises

  *1. Show that A^*, A^*A, and AA^* all have the same rank as A.

  *2. Show that, if A is a real m by n matrix ($m \leqslant n$) which has rank m, then the rank of AA^T is also m, so that AA^T is, in fact, a nonsingular, symmetric matrix of order m. Show also that the elements on the main diagonal of AA^T are non-negative and, finally, that, if A has rank $< m$, AA^T is singular. (This result is useful in statistical applications.)

  *3. Prove with the aid of Theorem 4.9.1 that, if A is of order (m, n) and if B is a nonsingular matrix of order n, then the product $P = AB$ has the same rank as A. Prove similarly that, if C is nonsingular of order m, the product $Q = CA$ has the same rank as A. (*Hint:* Apply Theorem 4.9.1 to each of $P = AB$ and $A = PB^{-1}$. This gives another proof of Theorem 4.7.3.)

MATRICES AND THE CONCEPT OF A FIELD

4.11 Number Fields

    A nonempty collection or set $\mathscr{F}$ of real or complex numbers which does not consist of the number zero alone will be called a **number field** if and only if the sum, difference, product, and quotient of any two numbers of $\mathscr{F}$ are again numbers of $\mathscr{F}$, division by zero being excepted. According to this definition, each of the following familiar sets of numbers constitutes a field:

    (a) The set of all rational numbers, that is, the set of all quotients of the form a/b where a and b are integers but $b \neq 0$.

    (b) The set of all real numbers.

    (c) The set of all complex numbers, that is, the set of all numbers of the form $a + bi$ where a and b are real and $i^2 = -1$.

    These fields are called respectively the **rational field**, the **real field**, and the **complex field**. They are the most important number fields as far as applications are concerned. Most statistical work is done in the real or rational fields whereas much work in physics and engineering is done in the complex field.

    Whenever the numbers of one field are all members of another field, the first field is called a **subfield** of the second. In the case of the three fields just listed, the rational field is a subfield of the real field, and the real field is a subfield of the field of complex numbers. It is customary to regard any field as a subfield of itself.

The operations of addition, subtraction, multiplication, and division involved in the definition of a field are known as the **four rational operations**.

It is worthwhile to note that there are number fields other than the three familiar ones just mentioned. For example, the set of all numbers of the form $a + b\sqrt{2}$, where a and b are rational numbers, is a field. In fact, if $\alpha + \beta\sqrt{2}$ and $\gamma + \delta\sqrt{2}$ are any two numbers of this kind, we have

$$(\alpha + \beta\sqrt{2}) \pm (\gamma + \delta\sqrt{2}) = (\alpha \pm \gamma) + (\beta \pm \delta)\sqrt{2},$$

$$(\alpha + \beta\sqrt{2}) \cdot (\gamma + \delta\sqrt{2}) = (\alpha\gamma + 2\beta\delta) + (\beta\gamma + \alpha\delta)\sqrt{2},$$

and, if $\gamma + \delta\sqrt{2} \neq 0$,

$$\frac{\alpha + \beta\sqrt{2}}{\gamma + \delta\sqrt{2}} = \frac{(\alpha + \beta\sqrt{2})(\gamma - \delta\sqrt{2})}{(\gamma + \delta\sqrt{2})(\gamma - \delta\sqrt{2})} = \frac{(\alpha\gamma - 2\beta\delta)}{(\gamma^2 - 2\delta^2)} + \frac{(\beta\gamma - \alpha\delta)}{(\gamma^2 - 2\delta^2)}\sqrt{2}.$$

(Because $\sqrt{2}$ is not rational and $\gamma + \delta\sqrt{2} \neq 0$, $\gamma^2 - 2\delta^2 \neq 0$ here.)

Since the set of rational numbers itself forms a field, each of the expressions on the right is of the form $a + b\sqrt{2}$ with a and b rational numbers. We have thus shown that, when the four rational operations are applied to any two numbers of the form $a + b\sqrt{2}$ with a and b rational, the result is a number of the same kind. Hence the set of all such numbers constitutes a field. There are, of course, infinitely many other number fields of various types, but our attention is directed almost exclusively to the three fields mentioned earlier in this section.

It is also worthwhile to look at some familiar sets of numbers which are not fields:

(a) The set of all positive real numbers.

(b) The set of all integers.

(c) The set of all complex numbers of the form bi where b is real.

In set (a), the difference of two members of the set is not in all cases in the set. In (b) the quotient of two members of the set is not in all cases in the set. In (c) the product of two members of the set is not in all cases in the set.

4.12 Exercises

1. Prove that every number field contains the integers 0 and 1.

2. Prove that every number field contains the rational number field as a subfield.

3. Prove that if $\alpha (\neq 0)$ belongs to a number field $\mathscr{F}$, then so do $-\alpha$ and α^k, where k is any positive or negative integer. Need $\sqrt{\alpha}$ also belong to $\mathscr{F}$? What about α^0?

4. Show that the set of all complex numbers $a + bi$ where $i^2 = -1$ and a and b are real actually constitutes a field, as stated in the text.

5. Show that the set of all numbers of the form $a + b\sqrt{p}$, where a and b are arbitrary rational numbers and p is a fixed rational number, constitutes a field. Discuss the interesting special cases.

6. Show that all numbers of the form $\alpha + \beta\sqrt[3]{2} + \gamma\sqrt[3]{4}$, where α, β, γ are rational, constitute a field. (See Weisner, *The Theory of Equations*, New York, Macmillan, 1938, p. 21, for some help.)

7. Same as Exercise 6 for $\alpha + \beta\sqrt{2} + \gamma\sqrt{3} + \delta\sqrt{6}$.

4.13 Matrices Over a Number Field

If all the elements of a matrix A belong to a number field $\mathscr{F}$, we say briefly that "A is over $\mathscr{F}$." For example, the matrix

$$\begin{bmatrix} 0 & -\frac{1}{2} \\ \frac{4}{3} & 6 \end{bmatrix}$$

is over the rational number field. (It is, of course, also over the real field and the complex field.) Many examples in preceding sections have involved, purely for the sake of simplicity, matrices over the rational number field. However, the matrix algebra and the determinant theory we have developed so far are valid over any number field. In the following, whenever the results depend on the number field used, we shall point this out explicitly.

To investigate the relation between the concept of a field and the concept of equivalence, we note first that, in finding sums, differences, products, scalar multiples, and inverses of matrices, we use only the four rational operations in the computations. Hence we have

Theorem 4.13.1: *A sum, difference, or product of matrices over a number field $\mathscr{F}$ is a matrix over $\mathscr{F}$; so is the inverse of any nonsingular matrix over $\mathscr{F}$ and the product of any matrix over $\mathscr{F}$ by a scalar from $\mathscr{F}$.*

When an elementary matrix is over a field $\mathscr{F}$, we say that the corresponding elementary transformation is over $\mathscr{F}$. By the foregoing, the inverse transformation must also be over $\mathscr{F}$. From Section 4.3 we now recall that a matrix A over a number field $\mathscr{F}$ can be reduced to normal form by repeated use of elementary transformations of the following nature:

(a) The interchange of two rows or two columns.

(b) The division of the elements of a line of a matrix by an element of the matrix.

(c) The subtraction from one line of a matrix of a multiple of another parallel line, where the multiplier is an element of that matrix.

Since these transformations involve the use only of 0's, 1's, and numbers obtained from the elements of A by the rational operations, they are over the same field $\mathscr{F}$ as A is, and so are the corresponding elementary matrices. (See Exercise 1, Section 4.12.) We have then

Theorem 4.13.2:   *A matrix A over a number field $\mathscr{F}$ may be reduced to normal form by elementary transformations all of which are over $\mathscr{F}$.*

A consequence of this, corresponding to Theorem 4.7.1, is

Theorem 4.13.3:   *If A and B are equivalent matrices over the same number field $\mathscr{F}$, there exist nonsingular matrices C and D also over $\mathscr{F}$, such that $B = CAD$.*

In fact, C and D are simply products of elementary matrices over $\mathscr{F}$, by what we observed above.

The point of these theorems is that, for the investigation of normal forms and equivalence as defined above, it is never necessary to operate in any more inclusive field than the simplest one in which the elements of the given matrices lie. For example, to discuss the equivalence of matrices which are over the rational field, there is never any need to use irrational or complex numbers.

A final observation is in order. A matrix may, at times, be regarded as being over any of several number fields. (The first example of this section is a case in point since it is over each of the rational number field, the real number field, and the complex number field.) One might suppose offhand that the rank of such a matrix could vary with the choice of field. That this is not the case follows from the definition of rank, for the value of a determinant does not depend on the number field to which its elements may be regarded as belonging.

4.14 Fields in General

We have seen that the set of all complex numbers constitutes a number field. We have also seen that the set of all scalar matrices of a given order whose elements come from the field of complex numbers is isomorphic to the field of complex numbers (Chapter One). That is, this set of scalar matrices has all the formal properties of a number field without being one. A similar situation holds with respect to the set of all scalar matrices of given order whose elements come from any other number field. Again, the set of all matrices

$$\begin{bmatrix} a & -b \\ b & a \end{bmatrix},$$

where a and b are real numbers, is isomorphic to the field of complex numbers $a + bi$. These examples suggest that we enlarge our definition of what constitutes a field so that, in particular, we may apply the name "field" to collections of matrices such as we have just described, as well as to certain collections of numbers.

In the generalized definition of a field, we shall want to keep all the basic properties of a number field without requiring the objects in the field to be numbers. We therefore proceed as follows:

Any collection $\mathscr{F}$ of at least two mathematical objects will be called a **commutative field** if and only if for the objects of $\mathscr{F}$ *equality* and operations of *addition* and *multiplication* are defined subject to the following requirements:

Equality means identity. It is therefore an equivalence relation, that is, it is definitive, reflexive, symmetric, and transitive.

Addition has the following properties:

(a_1) If α and β belong to $\mathscr{F}$, $\alpha + \beta$ is a uniquely defined element of $\mathscr{F}$.

(b_1) $\mathscr{F}$ contains an object 0 (**the zero element**) such that for each object α of $\mathscr{F}$, $\alpha + 0 = \alpha$.

(c_1) If α belongs to $\mathscr{F}$, there exists an object $-\alpha$ (the **negative** of α) also in $\mathscr{F}$ such that $\alpha + (-\alpha) = 0$.

(d_1) Addition is commutative: $\alpha + \beta = \beta + \alpha$ for any two elements α and β of $\mathscr{F}$.

(e_1) Addition is associative: $\alpha + (\beta + \gamma) = (\alpha + \beta) + \gamma$ for any three elements α, β, γ of $\mathscr{F}$.

Multiplication has the following properties:

(a_2) If α and β belong to $\mathscr{F}$, $\alpha\beta$ is a uniquely defined element of $\mathscr{F}$.

(b_2) $\mathscr{F}$ contains an object 1 (**the unit element**) such that $\alpha \cdot 1 = \alpha$ for any α in $\mathscr{F}$. Moreover, $1 \neq 0$.

(c_2) If α belongs to $\mathscr{F}$ and $\alpha \neq 0$, there exists an object α^{-1} (the **reciprocal** or **inverse** of α) also in $\mathscr{F}$ such that $\alpha \cdot \alpha^{-1} = 1$.

(d_2) Multiplication is commutative: $\alpha\beta = \beta\alpha$ for any two elements α, β of $\mathscr{F}$.

(e_2) Multiplication is associative: $\alpha(\beta\gamma) = (\alpha\beta)\gamma$ for any three elements α, β, γ of $\mathscr{F}$.

Finally, addition and multiplication are related by

(f) The distributive law: $(\alpha + \beta)\gamma = \alpha\gamma + \beta\gamma$, for any three elements α, β, γ of $\mathscr{F}$.

Because of isomorphisms already pointed out, we have

Theorem 4.14.1:   *The set of all scalar matrices of given order over a number field $\mathscr{F}$ is itself a field.*

Theorem 4.14.2:   *The set of all matrices*

$$\begin{bmatrix} a & -b \\ b & a \end{bmatrix},$$

where a and b are real numbers, is a field.

There are, of course, other kinds of fields than number fields and fields of matrices. Some fields have only a finite number of elements, but these too have important mathematical and practical applications. (For a more detailed treatment of the subject, the reader may consult G. Birkhoff and S. MacLane: *A Survey of Modern Algebra*, Revised Edition, New York, Macmillan, 1953.)

The concept of a field, like that of an isomorphism, reveals the fundamental likeness of a great variety of collections of mathematical objects. Similarly, the concept of an equivalence relation reveals the basic likeness of various different relationships existing among mathematical objects. These examples show how abstract concepts enable us to understand mathematics better by revealing its structure, thereby permitting us to organize mathematical information compactly and systematically. They also suggest ways of extending our present knowledge to new areas, and they often enable us to reduce the proofs of many theorems to the proof of one. For example, if— starting with the abstract definition of a field given above—we can prove a result about fields in general, this result will hold true for the rational number field, the complex field, a field of matrices, and, in fact, for every field that exists. Abstract concepts are thus seen to be powerful tools in mathematical research. Indeed, they have largely made possible the phenomenal expansion of mathematical knowledge in recent decades. Without this knowledge, a major part of our modern scientific development would not have been possible. Thus abstract mathematics, despite its ivory-tower flavor, is "practical" in the fullest sense of the word.

4.15 Exercises

1. Show that the set of all quotients $P(x)/Q(x)$, where $P(x)$ and $Q(x)$ are polynomials in a single indeterminate x with coefficients in a field $\mathscr{F}$, and where $Q(x) \neq 0$, constitutes a field. Here we define $P(x)/Q(x) = R(x)/S(x)$ if and only if $P(x)S(x) = Q(x)R(x)$. We also define

$$P(x)/Q(x) + R(x)/S(x) = (P(x)S(x) + Q(x)R(x))/Q(x)S(x)$$

and

$$P(x)/Q(x) \cdot R(x)/S(x) = P(x)R(x)/Q(x)S(x).$$

This is called the **rational function field** in one variable over the field $\mathscr{F}$.

*2. Show that the zero element and the unit element in a field are unique. Show also that, if α and β belong to a field $\mathscr{F}$, the equation $\alpha\beta = 0$ implies that at least one of α and β equals zero.

*3. Prove that, if α, β, and γ belong to a field $\mathscr{F}$, then $\alpha = \beta$ if and only if $\alpha + \gamma = \beta + \gamma$.

*4. Prove that, if α, β, and γ belong to a field $\mathscr{F}$, then, if $\alpha = \beta$, $\alpha\gamma = \beta\gamma$ also, and if $\alpha\gamma = \beta\gamma$ and $\gamma \neq 0$, then $\alpha = \beta$.

5. Does the set of all matrices of order n over a field $\mathscr{F}$ also constitute a field? Why?

6. Show that, if p is a fixed integer which is *not* a perfect square, the set of all matrices

$$\begin{bmatrix} a & pb \\ b & a \end{bmatrix},$$

where a and b are rational numbers, constitutes a field. To what number field is it isomorphic?

7. Show that the set of all matrices

$$\begin{bmatrix} a & 2c & 2b \\ b & a & 2c \\ c & b & a \end{bmatrix},$$

where a, b, c are arbitrary rational numbers, is isomorphic to the number field $\{a + b\sqrt[3]{2} + c\sqrt[3]{4}\}$ of Exercise 6, Section 4.12, and hence is also a field. (The isomorphisms defined in Exercises 6 and 7 can be developed by a general procedure that will be explained in Chapter 6.)

8. Prove that every number field is indeed a field in the more general sense defined above.

9. Prove that every set isomorphic to a field is itself a field.

10. If we have a set R of objects satisfying all the requirements of the definition of a field except possibly for (b_2), (c_2), and (d_2), and if also (f') $\alpha(\beta + \gamma) = \alpha\beta + \alpha\gamma$ for all elements α, β, γ of R, the set R is called a **ring**. If (d_2) is also satisfied, it is called a **commutative ring,** and (f') reduces to (f). Show that the set of all $n \times n$ matrices over an arbitrary ring R also constitutes a (noncommutative) ring.

11. Prove that the set of lower (upper) triangular matrices of order n over a field $\mathscr{F}$ constitutes a ring with identity over $\mathscr{F}$.

12. Is the set of all symmetric matrices of order n over $\mathscr{F}$ a ring over $\mathscr{F}$?

13. Prove that the set of all matrices over a field $\mathscr{F}$ which commute with a fixed matrix A over $\mathscr{F}$ is a ring.

14. Prove that the set of all matrices of order n of the form

$$\begin{bmatrix} a & b & b & \cdots & b \\ b & a & b & \cdots & b \\ \vdots & & & & \\ b & b & b & \cdots & a \end{bmatrix}$$

over a commutative ring R also constitutes a commutative ring. Which of these matrices are nonsingular?   (You will need to define *nonsingular* here.)

15. Prove that the set of all elements common to two fields is also a field.

16. An expression of the form $f(A)/g(A)$, where $f(A)$ and $g(A)$ are polynomials in an indeterminate square matrix A is called a rational function of the matrix A. Define equality, addition, and multiplication as in Exercise 1 above. Does the set of all such functions of A, with coefficients from the complex field, constitute a field? Why? (See Exercise 24, Section 1.18.)

CHAPTER FIVE

Linear Equations and Linear Dependence

THE FUNDAMENTAL THEOREM FOR LINEAR EQUATIONS

5.1 Definitions

Our study of matrix algebra has brought us to the point where we need to discuss the existence of solutions for a system of m linear equations in n unknowns, whether $m > n$, $m = n$, or $m < n$. Let such a system be

$$
\begin{aligned}
& a_{11}x_1 + a_{12}x_2 + \cdots + a_{1n}x_n + b_1 = 0, \\
(5.1.1) \quad & a_{21}x_1 + a_{22}x_2 + \cdots + a_{2n}x_n + b_2 = 0, \\
& \vdots \\
& a_{m1}x_1 + a_{m2}x_2 + \cdots + a_{mn}x_n + b_m = 0,
\end{aligned}
$$

or, in matrix form, as in Section 1.10,

$$(5.1.2) \qquad\qquad AX + B = 0.$$

When all the coefficients and constant terms of such a system of equations belong to a field $\mathscr{F}$, we call it **a system of equations over** $\mathscr{F}$. In most applications, the field $\mathscr{F}$ is either the field of real numbers or the field of complex numbers. In most of the following examples and exercises, $\mathscr{F}$ is the field of rational numbers. In the case of equation (5.1.2), the coefficient matrix A and the column of constants B are matrices over $\mathscr{F}$.

Any set of values of $x_1, x_2, \ldots, x_n$ from a field $\mathscr{F}$ which simultaneously satisfy (5.1.1) is called a **solution** over $\mathscr{F}$ of the system. When such a system has one or more solutions, it is said to be **consistent**; otherwise it is **inconsistent**. The matrix $A = [a_{ij}]_{(m,n)}$ is called the **coefficient matrix** of the system, and the matrix $[A, B]_{(m, n+1)}$, which is the same as the coefficient matrix except that a column consisting of the constant terms has been attached, will be called the **augmented matrix** of the system. When a system of equations is written in the form $AX = B$, the matrix $[A, B]$ is customarily called the augmented matrix. This augmented matrix is *equivalent* to ours, and since only rank is of concern here, it is equally useful.

5.2 An Example

To illustrate some of the points which will arise, let us consider as an example the system of equations

(5.2.1)
$$x_1 - x_2 + x_3 - 2 = 0,$$
$$3x_1 - x_2 + 2x_3 + 6 = 0,$$
$$3x_1 + x_2 + x_3 + 18 = 0.$$

Here an attempt to solve by Cramer's rule would fail because

$$\det \begin{bmatrix} 1 & -1 & 1 \\ 3 & -1 & 2 \\ 3 & 1 & 1 \end{bmatrix} = 0.$$

However, we can use the first equation to eliminate x_1 from the last two:

$$x_1 - x_2 + x_3 - 2 = 0,$$
$$0 + 2x_2 - x_3 + 12 = 0,$$
$$0 + 4x_2 - 2x_3 + 24 = 0.$$

Now we can use the second equation to eliminate x_2 from the first and the third. We also divide the second equation by 2, thus obtaining

$$x_1 + \tfrac{1}{2}x_3 + 4 = 0,$$
$$x_2 - \tfrac{1}{2}x_3 + 6 = 0,$$
$$0 = 0.$$

From this system of equations we conclude that

(5.2.2)
$$x_1 = -\tfrac{1}{2}x_3 - 4,$$
$$x_2 = \tfrac{1}{2}x_3 - 6.$$

If we substitute these expressions into each of the originally given equations, we find that each equation is identically satisfied. That is, the expressions (5.2.2) satisfy the given equations *independently of what value may be assigned to x_3*. The system (5.2.1) therefore actually has infinitely many solutions (5.2.2), one for each value of the variable x_3. Moreover, since the equations (5.2.2) follow from (5.2.1), every solution of (5.2.1) must satisfy (5.2.2). Hence equations (5.2.2) give *all* solutions and *only* solutions of (5.2.1) as x_3 varies. For this reason, we call (5.2.2) a **complete solution** of (5.2.1). The solution obtained by assigning a particular value to x_3 is called a **particular solution**.

If the third equation of (5.2.1) had been any equation $3x_1 + x_2 + x_3 + c = 0$, with $c \neq 18$, the solution (5.2.2) of the first two equations would *not* have satisfied the third. This suggests that we could not ordinarily expect to find solutions to a problem of this kind. However, in the given problem, the coefficient and augmented matrices are respectively

$$\begin{bmatrix} 1 & -1 & 1 \\ 3 & -1 & 2 \\ 3 & 1 & 1 \end{bmatrix} \quad \text{and} \quad \begin{bmatrix} 1 & -1 & 1 & -2 \\ 3 & -1 & 2 & 6 \\ 3 & 1 & 1 & 18 \end{bmatrix}.$$

These have the same rank 2, and the problem has solutions. If now the entry 18 in the augmented matrix were changed to any number $c \neq 18$, the rank of the augmented matrix would rise to 3, the rank of the coefficient matrix would remain unchanged, and also there would be no solutions. On the other hand, if we were to change the coefficient of x_3 in the third equation to any number other than 1, the coefficient determinant would then be $\neq 0$, and there would be a unique solution by Cramer's rule. Also, the coefficient and augmented matrices would now both have rank 3. That the ranks of these two matrices are indeed the key to the problem will be proved presently. When, as in this example, the coefficient matrix and the augmented matrix have the same rank r, we call r **the rank of the system**.

We observe finally that equations (5.2.2) are over the rational field, just as is the case with the given equations (5.2.1). That such a relation is general will also appear in what follows.

5.3 Equivalent Systems of Equations

To make precise the results illustrated by the preceding example, we examine first certain operations which may be performed on a system of equations without altering its solutions.

We begin with a definition. Two systems of linear equations are called **equivalent systems of equations** if every particular solution of either one is also a solution of the other. Evidently *the process of "solving" a system of equations then amounts to deducing from the given system an equivalent system of a prescribed form.*

Throughout, we shall be discussing a system (5.1.2) of m equations in n unknowns $x_1, x_2, \ldots, x_n$. If we put

$$f_i \equiv a_{i1}x_1 + a_{i2}x_2 + \cdots + a_{in}x_n + b_i,$$

we can also write this system in the form

(5.3.1)
$$\begin{aligned} f_1 &= 0, \\ f_2 &= 0, \\ &\vdots \\ f_m &= 0. \end{aligned}$$

We prove first this basic result:

Theorem 5.3.1:   *The systems* (5.3.1) *and*

$$f_1 = 0,$$
$$\vdots$$
$$f_{i-1} = 0,$$

(5.3.2) $$c_1 f_1 + c_2 f_2 + \cdots + c_i f_i + \cdots + c_m f_m = 0,$$

$$f_{i+1} = 0,$$
$$\vdots$$
$$f_m = 0,$$

are equivalent, whatever may be the values of the constants $c_1, c_2, \ldots, c_m$, *provided only that* $c_i \neq 0$.

In fact, any solution of (5.3.1) satisfies (5.3.2) and, conversely, since $c_i \neq 0$, for any solution of (5.3.2), we must have $f_i = 0$ so that it is also a solution of (5.3.1). We have next

Theorem 5.3.2:   *If in a system of linear equations we* (a) *interchange any two of the equations,* (b) *multiply an equation by a nonzero constant, or* (c) *add a constant multiple of one equation to another equation, we obtain an equivalent system of equations.*

This is because operation (a) leaves us with the same set of equations as before whereas operations (b) and (c) are simple examples of the substitution used in Theorem 5.3.1. Operation (a) may also be accomplished by repeated use of Theorem 5.3.1, as the reader may show. (See also Exercise 5, Section 4.5.)

The three operations listed in this theorem are called **elementary operations** since they, in fact, result in elementary transformations of the rows of the augmented matrix of any system to which they are applied. From Section 4.6 we see that any sequence of these operations applied to (5.3.1) may be expressed as a single matrix multiplication

(5.3.3) $$\begin{bmatrix} c_{11} & \cdots & c_{1m} \\ \vdots & & \\ c_{m1} & \cdots & c_{mm} \end{bmatrix} \cdot \begin{bmatrix} f_1 \\ \vdots \\ f_m \end{bmatrix} = 0,$$

where the matrix $C = [c_{ij}]$ is an elementary matrix or a product of elementary matrices. Also, by Theorem 4.7.2, any nonsingular matrix can be factored into a product of elementary matrices. We therefore may state

Theorem 5.3.3:   *Every system equivalent under the elementary operations to the system of m equations in n unknowns (5.1.2) may be represented in the form*

$$(5.3.4) \qquad\qquad (CA)X + (CB) = 0,$$

where C is a nonsingular matrix of order m. Conversely, if C is any nonsingular matrix of order m, then (5.3.4) is equivalent to (5.1.2) under elementary operations.

Thus, except for a possible rearrangement of the order of terms or for a final transposition of terms, neither of which alters the solutions of an equation, the solving of a system of equations is equivalent to premultiplication by a suitable nonsingular matrix.

5.4 The Fundamental Theorem

We now use the elementary operations discussed in the previous section to establish this fundamental result:

Theorem 5.4.1:   *A system $AX + B = 0$ of m linear equations in n unknowns is consistent if and only if the coefficient matrix A and the augmented matrix $[A, B]$ have the same rank.*

The method of proof is to use the sweep-out process. In fact, the procedure outlined in the proof is effective for the actual solution of a system of equations or for the determination of the fact that it is inconsistent.

Let the system be represented by equations (5.1.1) and let the equations be numbered from 1 to m respectively.

First, let x_{i_1} be any convenient variable which actually appears in these equations. We rearrange the order of the variables, and of the equations, if necessary, so that the variable x_{i_1} appears with a nonzero coefficient in the first position of the first equation. Then we divide the first equation by the coefficient of x_{i_1} and eliminate x_{i_1} from equations 2 through m by the sweep-out process.

Now let x_{i_2} be any convenient variable actually appearing in equations 2 through m, and again rearrange the order of the variables and of the equations, if necessary, so that x_{i_2} appears in the second position of the second row. Then we divide the second equation by the coefficient of x_{i_2} and eliminate x_{i_2} from equations 1, 3, 4, ..., m.

Continuing in this fashion, *we eventually stop because we have used all m of the equations or because we have no more variables in the remaining equations.* Both cases may be represented by the following system of equations which, because of the nature of the operations performed to obtain it, is equivalent to the original system:

$$x_{i_1} \qquad + \alpha_{1,i_{k+1}} x_{i_{k+1}} + \alpha_{1,i_{k+2}} x_{i_{k+2}} + \cdots + \alpha_{1,i_n} x_{i_n} + \beta_1 = 0,$$

$$x_{i_2} \qquad + \alpha_{2,i_{k+1}} x_{i_{k+1}} + \alpha_{2,i_{k+2}} x_{i_{k+2}} + \cdots + \alpha_{2,i_n} x_{i_n} + \beta_2 = 0,$$

$$\ddots$$

(5.4.1) $$x_{i_k} + \alpha_{k,i_{k+1}} x_{i_{k+1}} + \alpha_{k,i_{k+2}} x_{i_{k+2}} + \cdots + \alpha_{k,i_n} x_{i_n} + \beta_k = 0,$$

$$\beta_{k+1} = 0,$$

$$\vdots$$

$$\beta_m = 0.$$

Here $k \leqslant m$ and $\beta_{k+1}, \ldots, \beta_m$ may or may not all be zero in the event that $k < m$. The significance of this will be indicated presently.

A system of equations of the form (5.4.1) is said to be in **echelon form**, and the process used here to obtain (5.4.1) is often called **Gaussian elimination**, after its inventor.

We note next that the operations we have performed on the given system of equations all imply only elementary transformations of the coefficient and augmented matrices. Therefore these matrices of the new system have respectively the same ranks as do the corresponding matrices A and $[A, B]$ of the original system. Hence, if at least one of $\beta_{k+1}, \ldots, \beta_m$ is unequal to zero, the coefficient and augmented matrices of the new system, and therefore of $AX + B = 0$, have unequal ranks. Also, the equations are inconsistent since at least one of the equations $\beta_j = 0. j = k + 1, \ldots, m$, is false. On the other hand, if $\beta_{k+1} = \beta_{k+2} = \cdots = \beta_m = 0$, the coefficient and augmented matrices here, and therefore A and $[A, B]$, have equal ranks, namely, k. Also, in this case, we may rewrite the system of equations (5.4.1) in the form:

(5.4.2) $$x_{i_j} = -\beta_j - \alpha_{j,i_{k+1}} x_{i_{k+1}} - \alpha_{j,i_{k+2}} x_{i_{k+2}} - \cdots - \alpha_{j,i_n} x_{i_n},$$

$$j = 1, 2, \ldots, k.$$

In these equations we may assign arbitrary values to $x_{i_{k+1}}, \ldots, x_{i_n}$. The corresponding values of $x_{i_1}, \ldots, x_{i_k}$ which satisfy (5.4.2) are then found by performing the operations indicated on the right. Thus equations (5.4.2) have one or more solutions (one solution, that is, a unique solution if $k = n$, infinitely many if $k < n$), and because equations (5.4.2) are equivalent to the given system $AX + B = 0$, it has these same solutions, and so is a consistent system. The theorem is therefore proved.

Since we may assign arbitrary values to $x_{i_{k+1}}, \ldots, x_{i_n}$ in (5.4.2) and thus obtain all solutions and only solutions of the original system of equations, we call (5.4.2) a **complete solution** thereof.

Suppose now that the system of equations $AX + B = 0$ is over the field $\mathscr{F}$. Since the operations employed to solve the system do not require the introduction of numbers not in $\mathscr{F}$, the complete solution (5.4.2) is also a system of equations over $\mathscr{F}$. Hence we may conclude

Theorem 5.4.2: *If a consistent system of equations* $AX + B = 0$ *is over a number field $\mathscr{F}$, and has a unique solution, that solution is over $\mathscr{F}$. If it has infinitely many solutions, then any complete solution obtained as in the proof of Theorem 5.4.1 is also over $\mathscr{F}$. In this case, the system has solutions over $\mathscr{F}$ as well as solutions not over $\mathscr{F}$ but over any given number field containing $\mathscr{F}$. If the system is inconsistent, it has no solution over any number field whatsoever.*

For example, the system

$$x_1 + 3x_2 - x_3 - 4 = 0,$$
$$2x_1 + x_2 + x_3 - 7 = 0,$$
$$2x_1 - 4x_2 + 4x_3 - 6 = 0,$$
$$3x_1 + 4x_2 \qquad - 11 = 0,$$

has the complete solution

$$x_1 = \tfrac{17}{5} - \tfrac{4}{5}x_3,$$
$$x_2 = \tfrac{1}{5} + \tfrac{3}{5}x_3,$$

easily obtained by the above sweep-out procedure. This solution, like the given system, is over the rational field. Hence rational solutions are obtained when rational values are assigned to x_3. However, if irrational or complex numbers are assigned to x_3, one obtains solutions over the real and the complex fields, respectively.

5.5 More Examples

As the proof of Theorem 5.4.1 suggests, there may be a great deal of choice in the selection of the r variables for which to solve. In some cases these variables may be chosen as the first r variables; in others not. Also, there are other methods than the one given for effecting a solution. The examples to follow illustrate how to proceed in various cases.

(1) The system

$$x_1 - 2x_2 + x_3 - x_4 + 1 = 0,$$
$$3x_1 \qquad - 2x_3 + 3x_4 + 4 = 0,$$
$$5x_1 - 4x_2 \qquad + x_4 + 3 = 0,$$

has the coefficient and augmented matrices

$$\begin{bmatrix} 1 & -2 & 1 & -1 \\ 3 & 0 & -2 & 3 \\ 5 & -4 & 0 & 1 \end{bmatrix} \quad \text{and} \quad \begin{bmatrix} 1 & -2 & 1 & -1 & 1 \\ 3 & 0 & -2 & 3 & 4 \\ 5 & -4 & 0 & 1 & 3 \end{bmatrix}.$$

The ranks of these matrices are respectively 2 and 3. Hence the system has no solution.

(2) The coefficient and augmented matrices of the system

(5.5.1)
$$x_1 - 2x_2 + x_3 - x_4 + 1 = 0,$$
$$3x_1 \qquad - 2x_3 + 3x_4 - 4 = 0,$$
$$5x_1 - 4x_2 \qquad + x_4 - 2 = 0,$$

both have rank 2. Hence the system is consistent and we can solve for at least one pair of unknowns in terms of the other two. Solving the first two equations for x_1 and x_2, we have easily

(5.5.2)
$$x_1 = \tfrac{2}{3}x_3 - x_4 + \tfrac{4}{3},$$
$$x_2 = \tfrac{5}{6}x_3 - x_4 + \tfrac{7}{6}.$$

We leave it to the reader to substitute these expressions into the third equation in order to verify that it actually is satisfied identically thereby.

Equations (5.5.2) constitute a complete solution of (5.5.1) in the sense described in Section 5.2. We could also have solved for x_3 and x_4 in terms of x_1 and x_2 if we had wished to do so, or for x_1 and x_3 in terms of x_2 and x_4, etc., thus obtaining other complete solutions. In fact, *given any consistent system of rank r, the result of solving for r of the variables in terms of the remaining n − r variables is a* **complete solution** *of the system because, from it, one can obtain* all *solutions, and* only *solutions, of the given system by assigning values to the n − r variables in terms of which the others are expressed.*

As a practical procedure, in a problem such as the preceding one, one can simply start the process of solution without first looking at the ranks of the coefficient and augmented matrices. If a solution is obtained, then these matrices must have the same rank. If a contradiction is obtained, then their ranks are unequal and no solution exists. The principal difficulty with this approach is that it is not always easy to decide for which variables to solve. This is illustrated in the next example.

(3) In the system

$$x_1 - x_2 + x_3 = 1,$$
$$2x_1 - 2x_2 + 4x_3 = 4,$$
$$x_1 - x_2 + 3x_3 = 3,$$

the coefficient and augmented matrices both have rank 2. In this case we cannot solve any two equations for x_1 and x_2 in terms of x_3, but we can solve for x_1 and x_3 in terms of x_2:

(5.5.3)
$$x_1 = x_2,$$
$$x_3 = 1.$$

Here, no matter what value we assign to x_2, if x_1 has the same value and if $x_3 = 1$, the three values will satisfy the system of equations. Hence, if t denotes an arbitrary parameter, we could express the complete solution (5.5.3) in the alternative parametric form:

(5.5.4)
$$x_1 = t,$$
$$x_2 = t,$$
$$x_3 = 1.$$

Equations (5.5.4) represent exactly the same infinite collection of particular solutions as do (5.5.3), each solution being obtainable by assigning a value to the parameter t. *When a parametric solution such as* (5.5.4) *gives all the solutions, and only solutions, by specialization of the parameters, it too will be called a* **complete solution** *of the system.*

The above examples suggest:

Theorem 5.5.1:   *One can solve a consistent system of rank r for the variables $x_{i_1}, x_{i_2}, \ldots, x_{i_r}$ in terms of the remaining $n - r$ variables if and only if the submatrix of coefficients of the variables $x_{i_1}, x_{i_2}, \ldots, x_{i_r}$ also has rank r.*

The reader should supply a detailed proof.

(4) For a final, geometrical example, let

$$A_1 x + B_1 y + C_1 = 0$$

and

$$A_2 x + B_2 y + C_2 = 0$$

be the equations of lines in a rectangular coordinate system. Then A_1 and B_1 are not both zero, nor are A_2 and B_2 both 0. Suppose these equations represent the same line. Then they are consistent, and the rank of the system must be 1 since the number of solutions is infinite. That is, the matrix

$$\begin{bmatrix} A_1 & B_1 & C_1 \\ A_2 & B_2 & C_2 \end{bmatrix}$$

has rank 1. Conversely, if this matrix has rank 1, the equations are consistent and, since the number of solutions is infinite, they must represent the same line.

5.6 Homogeneous Linear Equations

The system of m equations in n unknowns

$$\sum_{j=1}^{n} a_{ij} x_j = 0, \qquad i = 1, 2, \ldots, m,$$

or, in matrix notation,

$$AX = 0$$

is called a **system of homogeneous linear equations** since all its terms are of degree 1 in the x's, the constant terms being all zero. The coefficient and augmented matrices have the same rank, for they differ only by a column of zeros. A system of homogeneous linear equations is thus always consistent. In fact, $x_1 = x_2 = \cdots = x_n = 0$ is always a solution. However, in the applications this solution is often of no significance, so that we call it the **trivial solution**. We are then concerned to know whether or not there are other solutions which do not consist of zeros only, that is, whether or not there are nontrivial solutions.

Let us consider first the case in which the coefficient matrix has rank n.

Then there exists some set of n of the equations whose coefficient matrix is nonsingular. We can solve this set of equations for $x_1, x_2, \ldots, x_n$ by the sweep-out process. In this case the complete solution (5.4.2) becomes simply

$$x_{i_j} = 0, \qquad j = 1, 2, \ldots, n,$$

that is,

$$x_p = 0, \qquad p = 1, 2, \ldots, n.$$

Moreover, this solution is unique since $n - r = 0$ here. Thus there can be no nontrivial solutions in this case.

If the rank is $r < n$, then by Theorem 5.4.1 we can solve for some r of the variables in terms of the remaining $n - r$ variables, and this solution will reduce each equation of the system identically to zero. It is clear that there are infinitely many nontrivial solutions in this case. We summarize this specialization of Theorem 5.4.1 thus:

Theorem 5.6.1: *A necessary and sufficient condition that the system of m homogeneous linear equations in n unknowns,*

$$\sum_{j=1}^{n} a_{ij}x_j = 0, \qquad i = 1, 2, \ldots, m,$$

have nontrivial solutions is that its coefficient matrix have a rank less than the number of unknowns.

Two frequently useful particular cases are these:

Corollary 5.6.2: *A necessary and sufficient condition that a system of n homogeneous linear equations in n unknowns have nontrivial solutions is that the coefficient matrix be singular.*

Corollary 5.6.3: *If $m < n$, a system of m homogeneous linear equations in n unknowns always has nontrivial solutions.*

5.7 Examples

(1) The system

$$\begin{aligned}
x_1 - x_2 + x_3 &= 0, \\
x_1 + 2x_2 - x_3 &= 0, \\
2x_1 + x_2 + 3x_3 &= 0,
\end{aligned}$$

has a coefficient matrix of rank 3 and, hence, possesses only the trivial solution.

(2) The system

$$\begin{aligned}
x_1 - 2x_2 + x_3 &= 0, \\
x_1 - 2x_2 - x_3 &= 0, \\
2x_1 - 4x_2 - 5x_3 &= 0,
\end{aligned}$$

has a coefficient matrix of rank 2. Hence it possesses nontrivial solutions. We find readily from the first two equations that

$$x_1 = 2x_2,$$

$$x_3 = 0,$$

and these expressions satisfy the third equation identically. Again, since x_2 is arbitrary, we could put $x_2 = t$ and rewrite this complete solution in the parametric form

$$x_1 = 2t,$$

$$x_2 = t,$$

$$x_3 = 0.$$

A parametric solution is often useful because the parameters—rather than some of the x's—play the role of the independent variables.

In the homogeneous case, just as previously, one can simply attempt to solve the system, by, say, the sweep-out process. This determines the rank, and also completes much of the work of finding the solution if a nontrivial one exists.

(3) Corollary 5.6.2 may be used to solve a certain class of geometric problems. For example, suppose we wish to find an equation for the straight line determined by two distinct points (x_1, y_1) and (x_2, y_2). We use the fact that the line has an equation of the form

$$A_0 x + B_0 y + C_0 = 0 \qquad (A_0, B_0 \text{ not both } 0),$$

which is satisfied by x and y if and only if (x, y) is a point on the line. From this it follows that

$$A_0 x_1 + B_0 y_1 + C_0 = 0,$$

$$A_0 x_2 + B_0 y_2 + C_0 = 0,$$

and, hence, that the three equations

$$Ax \;+\; By \;+\; C = 0,$$

$$Ax_1 + By_1 + C = 0,$$

$$Ax_2 + By_2 + C = 0,$$

in the three unknowns A, B, C have the nontrivial solution A_0, B_0, C_0 if and only if (x, y) is a point on the line in question. However, by Corollary 5.6.2, these equations have a nontrivial solution if and only if the coefficient matrix is singular. Hence the equation in x and y

$$\begin{vmatrix} x & y & 1 \\ x_1 & y_1 & 1 \\ x_2 & y_2 & 1 \end{vmatrix} = 0$$

is satisfied by specific values of x and y if and only if the corresponding point (x, y) is a point on the line. Expanding, we see that this equation is linear in x and y and, hence, must be an equation of the line. From it values for A_0, B_0, C_0 may be obtained.

5.8 Exercises

1. Obtain complete solutions for such of the following systems of equations as are consistent:

(a)
$$x_1 - x_2 + x_3 + x_4 + 2 = 0,$$
$$x_1 + x_2 - x_3 + 2x_4 - 6 = 0,$$
$$3x_1 - x_2 + x_3 + 2x_4 - 2 = 0.$$

(b)
$$x_1 - x_2 + x_3 + x_4 + 2 = 0,$$
$$x_1 + x_2 - x_3 + 2x_4 - 1 = 0,$$
$$3x_1 - x_2 + x_3 + 4x_4 + 4 = 0.$$

(c)
$$5x_1 - x_2 + 2x_3 + 5 = 0,$$
$$-x_1 - x_2 - x_3 + 7 = 0,$$
$$9x_1 - 3x_2 + 3x_3 + 17 = 0,$$
$$11x_1 - x_2 + 3x_3 + 3 = 0.$$

(d)
$$x_1 + x_2 + x_3 + x_4 = 1,$$
$$x_1 + x_2 + x_3 - x_4 = 2,$$
$$x_1 + x_2 - x_3 - x_4 = 3,$$
$$x_1 - x_2 - x_3 - x_4 = 4.$$

(e)
$$x_1 - x_2 + x_3 - x_4 = 1.$$

2. For what values of the parameters t and r respectively will the systems

(a)
$$tx + 3y - z = 1,$$
$$x + 2y + z = 2,$$
$$-tx + y + 2z = -1,$$

(b)
$$rx + y + z = 1,$$
$$x + ry + z = 1,$$
$$x + y + rz = -2,$$

fail to have *unique* solutions? Will they have *any* solutions for these values of the parameters?

3. Determine whether or not this system is consistent:

$$\begin{bmatrix} 0 & i & 1-i \\ -i & 0 & i \\ 1-i & -i & 0 \end{bmatrix} \cdot \begin{bmatrix} x_1 \\ x_2 \\ x_3 \end{bmatrix} = \begin{bmatrix} -1 \\ 0 \\ 1 \end{bmatrix}.$$

4. Explain why, when a consistent system of linear equations is solved for some of the variables in terms of the others, the variables solved for will always be *linear* functions of the others.

5. Interpret geometrically the solution of the system $\sum_{j=1}^{3} a_{ij}x_j = b_i$, $i = 1, 2,$ $\ldots, m$ in the cases when the coefficient and the augmented matrices have common rank 3, 2, and 1. What is the geometrical interpretation in each of the cases where the ranks of the coefficient and augmented matrices are *unequal*?

6. Find any nontrivial solutions which may exist:

(a)
$$
\begin{aligned}
2x_1 + 5x_2 + 6x_3 &= 0, \\
x_1 - 3x_2 - 8x_3 &= 0, \\
3x_1 + x_2 - 4x_3 &= 0.
\end{aligned}
$$

(b)
$$
\begin{aligned}
4x_1 - x_2 + 6x_3 &= 0, \\
2x_1 + 7x_2 + 12x_3 &= 0, \\
x_1 - 4x_2 - 3x_3 &= 0, \\
5x_1 - 5x_2 + 3x_3 &= 0.
\end{aligned}
$$

(c)
$$
\begin{aligned}
2x_0 + 3x_1 - x_2 + x_3 &= 0, \\
3x_0 + 2x_1 - 2x_2 + 2x_3 &= 0, \\
5x_0 \qquad - 4x_2 + 4x_3 &= 0.
\end{aligned}
$$

7. Show that, if $AX = 0$ for all n-vectors X, then $A = 0$.

8. Given a square matrix A, by considering a system of homogeneous, linear equations, show that if $\det A = 0$, then $\det \mathscr{A} = 0$ also, where $\mathscr{A}$ is the adjoint matrix of A. [*Hint:* Recall equations (2.7.4).]

9. Use Vandermonde's determinant (Exercise 26, Section 2.12) to show that a polynomial

$$
f(x) \equiv a_0 x^n + a_1 x^{n-1} + \cdots + a_{n-1}x + a_n
$$

vanishes at $n + 1$ distinct values $x_1, x_2, \ldots, x_n, x_{n+1}$ of x if and only if $f(x) \equiv 0$, that is, if and only if $a_0, a_1, \ldots, a_n$ are all zero.

10. Show that an equation of the circle through three distinct noncollinear points (x_1, y_1), (x_2, y_2), and (x_3, y_3) is

$$
\begin{vmatrix}
x^2 + y^2 & x & y & 1 \\
x_1^2 + y_1^2 & x_1 & y_1 & 1 \\
x_2^2 + y_2^2 & x_2 & y_2 & 1 \\
x_3^2 + y_3^2 & x_3 & y_3 & 1
\end{vmatrix} = 0.
$$

What does this reduce to if the three points are collinear but are not all coincident?

11. Show by means of an example that a complete solution in parametric form of a system of linear equations over a field $\mathscr{F}$ need not also be over $\mathscr{F}$.

12. Under what conditions will k planes

$$
a_j x + b_j y + c_j z + d_j = 0, \qquad j = 1, 2, \ldots, k,
$$

intersect in exactly one point P? Under what further conditions will each set of three of these planes intersect in P and in no other point?

13. The solution of a certain system of n equations in n unknowns $AX = B$ is of the form $x_j = a_j b / c$ where a_j, b, and c are integers such that b and c have no common factors other than ± 1. How may one alter the elements of A and B so as to get a system whose solution is $x_j = a_j$, $j = 1, 2, \ldots, n$?

14. Given that $AX = B$ is consistent and of rank r, for what sets of r unknowns can one solve?

15. Let X denote a $1 \times n$ row matrix, let A be an $n \times m$ matrix, and let B denote a $1 \times m$ row matrix. Show how the results of preceding sections may be adapted to the problem of solving the systems of equations $XA + B = 0$ and $XA = 0$.

*16. Denote by $Y_j, j = 1, 2, \ldots, n$, the solutions of the n systems of n equations in n unknowns,

$$AX = E_j, \qquad j = 1, 2, \ldots, n,$$

where $\det A \neq 0$, and E_j is the jth elementary n-vector. Identify the matrix

$$[Y_1, Y_2, \ldots, Y_n].$$

Also, show that the solution of

$$AX = \sum_{j=1}^{n} b_j E_j$$

is

$$Y = \sum_{j=1}^{n} b_j Y_j.$$

17. Let A denote any skew-symmetric matrix of order 3:

$$A = \begin{bmatrix} 0 & c & -b \\ -c & 0 & a \\ b & -a & 0 \end{bmatrix}.$$

Obtain in parametric form the solutions of the equation $AX = 0$ and, hence, show without computing the product that $AB = 0$, where

$$B = \begin{bmatrix} a^2 & ab & ac \\ ab & b^2 & bc \\ ac & bc & c^2 \end{bmatrix}.$$

THE LINEAR DEPENDENCE OF VECTORS

5.9 Definitions

We have already agreed to call a column matrix an n-vector, the number n denoting the number of rows or **components** of the vector. We have also agreed (Section 1.10) that to save space we will write an n-vector in the form $\{a_1, a_2, \ldots, a_n\}$, the curly braces denoting the fact that this is really a column matrix.

Let us begin with an example. The vectors $A_1 = \{3, 12, -15\}$ and $A_2 = \{-2, -8, 10\}$ may be called "proportional" since their corresponding elements are proportional. This proportionality may be expressed by the equation

$$A_1 = -\tfrac{3}{2} A_2$$

or by the equation

$$2A_1 + 3A_2 = 0.$$

This latter equation suggests that we might well define proportionality for two n-vectors A_1 and A_2 are proportional if and only if there exist constants c_1 and c_2, not both of which are zero, such that

$$c_1 A_1 + c_2 A_2 = 0.$$

If neither A_1 nor A_2 is the zero vector, this definition corresponds to the usual concept of proportionality. In this case, neither c_1 nor c_2 can be 0. However, if for example A_2 is zero, then, independently of what A_1 and c_2 may be, we have

$$0 \cdot A_1 + c_2 \cdot 0 = 0.$$

Thus the definition implies that the zero n-vector and any n-vector A_1 are proportional. This may seem a little peculiar at first, but it is really quite useful since it eliminates the need of mentioning special cases in certain theorems.

The purpose of this section is to generalize the notion of proportionality just presented. To this end we consider next the set of k n-vectors:

$$A_1 = \{a_{11}, a_{21}, \ldots, a_{n1}\},$$

$$A_2 = \{a_{12}, a_{22}, \ldots, a_{n2}\},$$

$$\vdots$$

$$A_k = \{a_{1k}, a_{2k}, \ldots, a_{nk}\}.$$

The n-vector

$$c_1 A_1 + c_2 A_2 + \cdots + c_k A_k,$$

where the c's are arbitrary scalars from a field $\mathscr{F}$, is called a **linear combination** over $\mathscr{F}$ of the n-vectors $A_1, A_2, \ldots, A_k$. The linear combinations

$$A_j = 0 \cdot A_1 + \cdots + 0 \cdot A_{j-1} + 1 \cdot A_j + 0 \cdot A_{j+1} + \cdots + 0 \cdot A_k,$$
$$j = 1, 2, \ldots, k,$$

which express each vector of the set as a linear combination of the whole set will be called **elementary combinations** of $A_1, \ldots, A_k$.

If for some set of constants $c_1, c_2, \ldots, c_k$ from $\mathscr{F}$, not all of which are zero, we have

$$c_1 A_1 + c_2 A_2 + \cdots + c_k A_k = 0,$$

then the vectors $A_1, A_2, \ldots, A_k$ are said to be **linearly dependent** over $\mathscr{F}$. If, however, $\sum_{i=1}^{k} c_i A_i = 0$ only when all the scalars c_i are zero, the vectors are said to be **linearly independent** over $\mathscr{F}$. This definition is intended to apply also in the case where $k = 1$, so that *a single vector A_1 is independent if $A_1 \neq 0$ but dependent if $A_1 = 0$*.

For example, the vectors $\{1, 2, 3\}$ and $\{3, 2, 1\}$ are linearly independent over the field of rational numbers, for the condition

$$c_1\{1, 2, 3\} + c_2\{3, 2, 1\} = 0$$

is equivalent to the three scalar equations

(5.9.1)
$$c_1 + 3c_2 = 0,$$
$$2c_1 + 2c_2 = 0,$$
$$3c_1 + c_2 = 0,$$

which have a nontrivial solution if and only if the rank of the matrix

$$\begin{bmatrix} 1 & 3 \\ 2 & 2 \\ 3 & 1 \end{bmatrix}$$

is less than 2, by Theorem 5.6.1. Since the rank is 2, there are no nontrivial solutions so that the vectors are linearly independent.

Again, the 2-vectors $\{(1 + 2i), (1 - i)\}$ and $\{(2 - i), (-1 - i)\}$ are linearly dependent over the complex field, for

$$c_1\{(1 + 2i), (1 - i)\} + c_2\{(2 - i), (-1 - i)\} = 0$$

if and only if

$$c_1(1 + 2i) + c_2(2 - i) = 0,$$
$$c_1(1 - i) + c_2(-1 - i) = 0,$$

which have the solution $c_1 = ic_2$. If we put $c_2 = -i$, then $c_1 = 1$, and we have

$$1 \cdot \{(1 + 2i), (1 - i)\} - i\{(2 - i), (-1 - i)\} = 0.$$

As in these examples, we usually consider the linear dependence of vectors over some specified field $\mathscr{F}$ in which their components are considered to lie. Indeed, to determine whether or not certain vectors over $\mathscr{F}$ are linearly dependent over $\mathscr{F}$, we have to decide whether or not there are nontrivial solutions over $\mathscr{F}$ of a system of homogeneous equations whose coefficients, being components of the given vectors, are in $\mathscr{F}$. Hence, by Theorem 5.4.2, if these vectors are independent over $\mathscr{F}$, they are also independent over every number field containing the components of the vectors. In the following, therefore, we drop the reference to the field, understanding this to be a field to which the components of the vectors in question belong unless explicitly stated otherwise.

As a final example we note that if X is any n-vector, we may write it in the form

$$X = x_1 \begin{bmatrix} 1 \\ 0 \\ 0 \\ \vdots \\ 0 \end{bmatrix} + x_2 \begin{bmatrix} 0 \\ 1 \\ 0 \\ \vdots \\ 0 \end{bmatrix} + \cdots + x_n \begin{bmatrix} 0 \\ \vdots \\ 0 \\ 0 \\ 1 \end{bmatrix}.$$

The n-vector $E_j = \{0, \ldots, 0, 1, 0, \ldots, 0\}$ with a 1 in the jth position, all other components being 0, will be called the **jth elementary n-vector**. The example shows that *every n-vector can be written as a linear combination of the elementary n-vectors, $E_1, E_2, \ldots, E_n$.* This conclusion does not depend on the field to which the elements of X belong, since 0 and 1, the elements of the E_j's, belong to every field.

5.10 Exercises

1. Apply the definition to show that the vectors $\{1, -1, 1\}$, $\{2, 1, 1\}$, and $\{3, 0, 2\}$ are linearly dependent.

2. Determine whether or not the vectors

$$\begin{bmatrix} 1 \\ -1 \\ 4 \\ 2 \end{bmatrix}, \quad \begin{bmatrix} 4 \\ 1 \\ 1 \\ 1 \end{bmatrix}, \quad \begin{bmatrix} 2 \\ -1 \\ 0 \\ 1 \end{bmatrix}, \quad \begin{bmatrix} 3 \\ 2 \\ 2 \\ 3 \end{bmatrix}, \quad \begin{bmatrix} 1 \\ 1 \\ 1 \\ 1 \end{bmatrix},$$

are linearly dependent.

3. Same as Exercise 2 for the vectors, $\{3, 2\sqrt{2}\}$, $\{5 + 4\sqrt{2}, 2\}$, $\{1 + 2\sqrt{2}, 1 - \sqrt{2}\}$.

4. Show by an example that a set of distinct vectors may be linearly dependent over a number field which is not extensive enough to contain all the components of these vectors.

5. Show by an example that a set of vectors linearly *independent* over the rational number field may be linearly *dependent* over the real number field.

6. Show that if $P_1, \ldots, P_k$ are linearly independent vectors and if $P = \sum_{i=1}^{k} a_i P_i$, then $P_1 - P, P_2 - P, \ldots, P_k - P$ are linearly independent if and only if $\sum \alpha_i \neq 1$.

*7. Show that, if any row (or column) of a square matrix A is a linear combination of the other rows (or columns) of A, then $\det A = 0$. State and prove a converse result.

*8. (a) Prove that in an upper triangular matrix, the columns with diagonal elements $\neq 0$ are linearly independent.

(b) Prove that the columns of

$$
\begin{bmatrix}
A_{m \times n} \\
\hline
T_{n \times n}
\end{bmatrix},
$$

where T is upper triangular with $t_{ii} \neq 0$, are linearly independent.

*9. Prove that the n-vectors $X_1, X_2, \ldots, X_p$ are linearly dependent if and only if for some $k \geqslant 2$, X_k is a linear combination of $X_1, X_2, \ldots, X_{k-1}$.

*10. Prove that the k n-vectors $A_1, A_2, \ldots, A_k$ are linearly independent if and only if the equation $[A_1, A_2, \ldots, A_k]X_{k \times 1} = 0$ has only the trivial solution.

11. Prove that, if columns $j_1, j_2, \ldots, j_r$ of B are dependent, then columns $j_1, j_2, \ldots, j_r$ of AB are also dependent. Hence show that, if columns $j_1, j_2, \ldots, j_r$ of AB are independent, so are those of B.

12. Show that the n-vectors $A_1, A_2, \ldots, A_k$ are linearly dependent if and only if the n-vectors $\alpha_1 A_1, \alpha_2 A_2, \ldots, \alpha_k A_k$, where no α_j is zero, are linearly dependent.

5.11 Basic Theorems

We now prove a collection of basic theorems about the linear dependence of vectors. In doing so, we make frequent use of the results of Sections 5.4 and 5.6. We begin with a very useful result:

Theorem 5.11.1: *The k n-vectors $A_1, A_2, \ldots, A_k$ are linearly dependent if and only if the rank of the matrix $A = [A_1, A_2, \ldots, A_k]$ with the given vectors as columns is less than k. They are independent if and only if the rank is equal to k.*

Using the same notation as in Section 5.9, we will have

$$c_1 A_1 + c_2 A_2 + \cdots + c_k A_k = 0,$$

where not all of the scalars $c_1, c_2, \ldots, c_k$ are zero, if and only if the system of linear equations

$$c_1 a_{11} + c_2 a_{12} + \cdots + c_k a_{1k} = 0,$$

$$c_1 a_{21} + c_2 a_{22} + \cdots + c_k a_{2k} = 0,$$

$$\vdots$$

$$c_1 a_{n1} + c_2 a_{n2} + \cdots + c_k a_{nk} = 0,$$

has at least one nontrivial solution for the c's. By Theorem 5.6.1, a necessary and sufficient condition that this be the case is that the coefficient matrix A have rank less than k. Since this coefficient matrix is precisely the matrix having the given vectors as columns, the theorem is proved. We ask the reader to prove the next result.

Corollary 5.11.2: *The k n-vectors $A_1, A_2, \ldots, A_k$ are necessarily linearly dependent if $k > n$.*

Theorem 5.11.3: *If p n-vectors from a set of k n-vectors $A_1, A_2, \ldots, A_k$, where $p < k$, are linearly dependent, then all k of the vectors are linearly dependent.*

To prove this, let, for example, $A_1, A_2, \ldots, A_p$ be the linearly dependent vectors. Then there exist constants $c_1, c_2, \ldots, c_p$, not all zero, such that

$$c_1 A_1 + c_2 A_2 + \cdots + c_p A_p = 0.$$

Then also

$$c_1 A_1 + c_2 A_2 + \cdots + c_p A_p + 0 \cdot A_{p+1} + \cdots + 0 \cdot A_k = 0,$$

and, since not all the c's are zero, the result is proved.

The reader may prove

Corollary 5.11.4: *If the vectors $A_1, A_2, \ldots, A_k$ are linearly independent, then the vectors of every nonempty subset of these are also linearly independent.*

Theorem 5.11.5: *If k n-vectors $A_1, A_2, \ldots, A_k$ are linearly dependent, then at least one of them may be written as a linear combination of the rest.*

To prove this, note that there exist constants $c_1, c_2, \ldots, c_k$ not all zero such that

$$c_1 A_1 + c_2 A_2 + \cdots + c_k A_k = 0.$$

If c_1, for example, is not zero, we have

$$A_1 = -\frac{c_2}{c_1} A_2 - \cdots - \frac{c_k}{c_1} A_k,$$

which expresses A_1 as a linear combination of the remaining vectors.

Theorem 5.11.6: *If one of the k n-vectors $A_1, A_2, \ldots, A_k$ can be expressed as a linear combination of the rest, then the k vectors are linearly dependent.*

This is the easily proved converse of the preceding theorem.

Theorem 5.11.7: *If the n-vectors $A_1, A_2, \ldots, A_k$ are linearly independent but the n-vectors $A_1, A_2, \ldots, A_k, B$ are linearly dependent, then B is a linear combination of $A_1, A_2, \ldots, A_k$.*

For, there exist constants $c_1, c_2, \ldots, c_k$, c, not all zero, such that

$$c_1 A_1 + c_2 A_2 + \cdots + c_k A_k + cB = 0.$$

If c were equal to zero, $A_1, A_2, \ldots, A_k$ would be linearly dependent, contrary to hypothesis. Hence $c \neq 0$, and therefore,

$$B = -\frac{c_1}{c} A_1 - \frac{c_2}{c} A_2 - \cdots - \frac{c_k}{c} A_k.$$

The reader should have no difficulty in proving the next result.

Corollary 5.11.8: *If the k n-vectors $A_1, A_2, \ldots, A_k$ are linearly independent, and if the n-vector B cannot be written as a linear combination of $A_1, A_2, \ldots, A_k$, then $A_1, A_2, \ldots, A_k, B$ are linearly independent.*

Theorem 5.11.9: *Whether or not the k n-vectors $A_1, A_2, \ldots, A_k$ are linearly independent, any $k + 1$ linear combinations of these n-vectors are linearly dependent.*

Let the $k + 1$ linear combinations be

$$B_1 \quad = c_{11}A_1 + c_{12}A_2 + \cdots + c_{1k}A_k,$$
$$B_2 \quad = c_{21}A_1 + c_{22}A_2 + \cdots + c_{2k}A_k,$$
$$\vdots$$
$$B_{k+1} = c_{k+1,1}A_1 + c_{k+1,2}A_2 + \cdots + c_{k+1,k}A_k.$$

We must show there exist constants $\alpha_1, \alpha_2, \ldots, \alpha_{k+1}$, not all zero, such that

$$\alpha_1 B_1 + \alpha_2 B_2 + \cdots + \alpha_{k+1}B_{k+1} = 0.$$

By substituting for the B's, we reduce this condition to the form

$$\sum_{i=1}^{k} (\alpha_1 c_{1i} + \alpha_2 c_{2i} + \cdots + \alpha_{k+1}c_{k+1,i})A_i = 0.$$

Such an equation will certainly hold if all the coefficients of the A's are zero:

$$\alpha_1 c_{11} + \alpha_2 c_{21} + \cdots + \alpha_{k+1}c_{k+1,1} = 0,$$
$$\alpha_1 c_{12} + \alpha_2 c_{22} + \cdots + \alpha_{k+1}c_{k+1,2} = 0,$$
$$\vdots$$
$$\alpha_1 c_{1k} + \alpha_2 c_{2k} + \cdots + \alpha_{k+1}c_{k+1,k} = 0.$$

Here we have k equations in $k + 1$ unknowns, $\alpha_1, \alpha_2, \ldots, \alpha_{k+1}$. By Corollary 5.6.3, for such a system there always exist nontrivial solutions, so that the theorem is proved.

The reader should note carefully that the problems of linear dependence treated in Theorem 5.11.1 and 5.11.9 reduce ultimately to questions of whether or not certain systems of homogeneous linear equations have a nontrivial solution. This type of proof will appear repeatedly in the following. In some proofs nonhomogeneous systems must be used.

This section contains the most basic theorems on the linear dependence of vectors. Later we shall return to the subject in the chapter on vector spaces, but first we shall investigate a number of applications of what we have already learned. We begin with two useful theorems.

Theorem 5.11.10: *A square matrix A is singular if and only if its columns (rows) are linearly dependent.*

If the columns are linearly dependent, then, by Theorem 5.11.5, at least one of them may be written as a linear combination of the others. Then by repeated use of Theorem 2.7.8, this column can be reduced to 0 without affecting the value of the determinant. Thus $\det A = 0$ and A is singular.

Conversely, if A is singular, $\det A = 0$, and hence the equation $AX = 0$ has nontrivial solutions. If one of these is $\{y_1, y_2, \ldots, y_n\}$, then

$$AY = y_1 A_1 + y_2 A_2 + \cdots + y_n A_n = 0,$$

so that the columns of A are linearly dependent. This completes the proof for columns. A similar proof holds for rows.

As a second application of the concept of linear dependence, we prove

Theorem 5.11.11: *A system of m linear equations in n unknowns, $AX + B = 0$, is consistent if and only if the vector B is a linear combination of the columns of A.*

The system $AX + B = 0$ is consistent if and only if there is a vector X such that $B = -AX = A(-X)$. But $A(-X)$ is a column which is a linear combination of the columns of A. Hence the system is consistent if and only if B is a linear combination of the columns of A.

Additional important theorems are included in the following exercises.

5.12 Exercises

1. Prove that two nonzero vectors A_1 and A_2 are linearly dependent if and only if there exists a constant c such that $A_1 = cA_2$.

*2. Prove that k n-vectors $A_1, A_2, \ldots, A_k$ are linearly dependent if two of these vectors are the same or have proportional components. Is the converse true?

*3. Prove that, if a set of n-vectors includes the zero n-vector, then the vectors of the set are linearly dependent.

*4. Prove that a necessary and sufficient condition that k linear combinations of k linearly independent n-vectors be also independent is that the matrix of the coefficients of combination be nonsingular.

*5. Prove that, excluding differences in arrangement, there cannot be more than one representation of a given vector as a linear combination of a given set of linearly independent vectors.

6. Suppose that the system of m equations in n unknowns $AX + B = 0$ is consistent and has rank m. Show that it has a unique solution X of the form

$$X = \sum_{j=1}^{m} c_j A^{(j)*},$$

where $A^{(j)}$ denotes the jth row of A. (*Hint:* Use Exercise 1, Section 4.10.)

7. Suppose that in the system of m equations in n unknowns $AX + B = 0$, the matrix A has rank r with

$$\det \begin{bmatrix} a_{11} & \cdots & a_{1r} \\ \vdots & & \\ a_{r1} & \cdots & a_{rr} \end{bmatrix} \neq 0.$$

Then the determinants

$$\begin{bmatrix} a_{11} & \cdots & a_{1r} & y_1 \\ a_{21} & \cdots & a_{2r} & y_2 \\ a_{r1} & \cdots & a_{rr} & y_r \\ a_{r+p,1} & \cdots & a_{r+p,r} & y_{r+p} \end{bmatrix}$$

are called the **characteristic determinants** of the system. Prove that the system is consistent if and only if the characteristic determinants are all reduced to 0 by substitution of the b's for the corresponding y's.

8. Find a proof of Theorem 5.11.9 that is based on Theorem 5.11.1 and the fact that rank $PQ \leqslant$ rank P.

THE LINEAR DEPENDENCE OF OTHER MATHEMATICAL OBJECTS

5.13 Linear Dependence of Equations

An important application of the concept of linear dependence is to systems of linear equations. The linear equations in n unknowns

$$(5.13.1) \qquad f_i = 0, \qquad i = 1, 2, \ldots, m,$$

are said to be linearly dependent if and only if their left members are linearly dependent.

For example, the equations

$$f_1 \equiv 2x - 3y + 4 = 0,$$
$$f_2 \equiv x + y - 1 = 0,$$
$$f_3 \equiv 6x + y = 0,$$

are linearly dependent since

$$f_1 + 4f_2 - f_3 \equiv 0.$$

This identity is equivalent to the equation

$$[2, -3, 4] + 4[1, 1, -1] - [6, 1, 0] = [0, 0, 0].$$

That is, the linear dependence of the three equations is equivalent to the linear dependence of the rows of the augmented matrix of the system. This fact is, of course, entirely general, which leads us to the following conclusion:

Theorem 5.13.1: *The equations of the system (5.13.1) are linearly dependent if and only if the rank r of the augmented matrix is less than the number m of equations.*

Suppose now that the equations (5.13.1) are linearly dependent:

$$(5.13.2) \qquad c_1 f_1 + c_2 f_2 + \cdots + c_i f_i + \cdots + c_m f_m \equiv 0.$$

Since at least one coefficient is not zero, assume $c_i \neq 0$. Then if we replace f_i in (5.13.1) by the linear combination (5.13.2), by Theorem 5.3.1 there results an equivalent system of equations. But (5.13.2) is identically zero, so that the number of equations has been in effect reduced by one. Since in this case f_i can be expressed as a linear combination of the other f's, we have the important result:

Theorem 5.13.2: *If from a system (5.13.1) we delete any equation which is linearly dependent on the remaining equations of the system, the result is an equivalent system of equations.*

Repeated application of this theorem yields the useful observation:

Theorem 5.13.3: *If the system (5.13.1) is consistent and of rank r, then any r linearly independent equations of the system form an equivalent system of equations.*

5.14 The Linear Dependence of Forms

The notion of linear dependence which we have developed for vectors extends naturally to many other mathematical objects. For example, if $P_1, P_2, \ldots, P_k$ are polynomials in n variables $x_1, x_2, \ldots, x_n$ and with coefficients in a field $\mathscr{F}$, and if $c_1, c_2, \ldots, c_k$ also belong to $\mathscr{F}$, then the polynomial

$$c_1 P_1 + c_2 P_2 + \cdots + c_k P_k$$

is a **linear combination** over $\mathscr{F}$ of $P_1, P_2, \ldots, P_k$. These polynomials are defined to be **linearly dependent** if for some set of c's, not all zero, the above linear combination is identically zero in the x's. Otherwise they are **linearly independent**. Thus, for example, the polynomials

$$2x_1 - x_2, \qquad x_1 + 2x_2, \qquad 5x_1 + 7x_2$$

are linearly dependent over the field of rational numbers since

$$3(2x_1 - x_2) + 19(x_1 + 2x_2) - 5(5x_1 + 7x_2) \equiv 0.$$

Among the polynomials most frequently encountered are the linear forms. A **linear form** in n variables $x_1, x_2, \ldots, x_n$ is a polynomial of the type

$$(5.14.1) \qquad \sum_{j=1}^{n} a_j x_j,$$

that is, it is a linear, homogeneous expression in the given variables. For example, $2x_1 - x_2 + \frac{1}{2}x_3$ is a linear form in x_1, x_2, x_3. Again, the arithmetic mean m_x of $x_1, x_2, \ldots, x_n$ is given by the formula

$$(5.14.2) \qquad m_x = \frac{1}{n} \sum_{j=1}^{n} x_j = \frac{1}{n} x_1 + \frac{1}{n} x_2 + \cdots + \frac{1}{n} x_n,$$

so that m_x is a linear form in $x_1, x_2, \ldots, x_n$ with all the coefficients equal to $1/n$. In statistics, m_x is an estimate of the mean of a variable x of which the observed values $x_1, \ldots, x_n$ constitute a "sample."

If we let

$$A = [a_1, a_2, \ldots, a_n]$$

and

$$X = \{x_1, x_2, \ldots, x_n\},$$

then we have

$$AX = a_1x_1 + a_2x_2 + \cdots + a_nx_n,$$

so that a linear form may be represented very compactly by using the matrix notation. The members of a system of linear forms in n unknowns

$$b_{11}x_1 + b_{12}x_2 + \cdots + b_{1n}x_n,$$
$$b_{21}x_1 + b_{22}x_2 + \cdots + b_{2n}x_n,$$
$$\vdots$$
$$b_{m1}x_1 + b_{m2}x_2 + \cdots + b_{mn}x_n,$$

may be taken as the components of an m-vector which may be written in the form BX, where $B = [b_{ij}]_{(m,n)}$ and $X = \{x_1, x_2, \ldots, x_n\}$. The matrix equation $BX = 0$ then represents the simultaneous vanishing of the corresponding linear forms.

Another kind of polynomial that is of frequent use is the bilinear form. A **bilinear form** in the two sets of variables $x_1, x_2, \ldots, x_n$ and $y_1, y_2, \ldots, y_m$ is a polynomial of the type

$$(5.14.3) \qquad \sum_{i=1}^{n} \sum_{j=1}^{m} a_{ij}x_iy_j,$$

that is, it is linear and homogeneous in each of the two sets of variables. Thus, for example,

$$2x_1y_1 + (1 - i)x_1y_2 + (1 + i)x_2y_1$$

is a bilinear form over the complex number field in the two sets of variables x_1, x_2 and y_1, y_2.

Another example is given by the expression

$$(5.14.4) \qquad \frac{1}{n - 1} \sum_{j=1}^{n} (x_j - m_x)(y_j - m_y).$$

Here m_x and m_y are the means of $x_1, \ldots, x_n$ and $y_1, \ldots, y_n$ respectively. The differences $x_j - m_x$ and $y_j - m_y$ are called the **deviations from the means** of the variables $x_1, \ldots, x_n$ and $y_1, \ldots, y_n$ respectively. When the means m_x and m_y in (5.14.4) are replaced by expressions of the form (5.14.2) and the result is expanded, the result is seen to be bilinear in $x_1, \ldots, x_n$ and $y_1, \ldots, y_n$. This bilinear form arises in the estimation of the coefficient of correlation of two variables x and y. The pairs of values $(x_1, y_1), \ldots, (x_n, y_n)$ are n sets of simultaneous observations of these two variables from which the estimate of the coefficient is to be computed. The form itself estimates the **covariance** of x and y.

A bilinear form may also be represented compactly with the aid of the matrix notation. If we let

$$X = \{x_1, x_2, \ldots, x_m\},$$
$$Y = \{y_1, y_2, \ldots, y_n\},$$

and

$$A = [a_{ij}]_{(m,n)},$$

we find that

$$X^{\mathsf{T}}{}_{(1,m)} A_{(m,n)} Y_{(n,1)} = X^{\mathsf{T}}(AY) = \sum_{i=1}^{m} \left(\sum_{j=1}^{n} a_{ij} y_j \right) x_i$$

$$= \sum_{i=1}^{m} \sum_{j=1}^{n} a_{ij} x_i y_j.$$

The matrix A is called **the matrix of the bilinear form.**

A third type of polynomial of basic importance is the quadratic form. A **quadratic form** in the variables $x_1, x_2, \ldots, x_n$ is a polynomial

$$(5.14.5) \qquad\qquad \sum_{i,j=1}^{n} a_{ij} x_i x_j,$$

that is, it is homogeneous and of the second degree in the n variables. A simple example is

$$3x_1{}^2 - x_1 x_2 + x_2{}^2 - 2x_2 x_3,$$

which is a quadratic form in x_1, x_2, x_3. The expression

$$(5.14.6) \qquad\qquad \frac{1}{n-1} \sum_{j=1}^{n} (x_j - m_x)^2,$$

where m_x is defined as before, may be seen by substitution for m_x in terms of $x_1, \ldots, x_n$, to be a quadratic form in $x_1, \ldots, x_n$. This quadratic form estimates the **variance** of a variable x of which $x_1, \ldots, x_n$ constitute a sample. [When the sample is large, the coefficient $1/n$ rather than $1/(n-1)$ is often used.]

A quadratic form (5.14.5) may likewise be written in matrix form. If

$$X = \{x_1, x_2, \ldots, x_n\},$$

and

$$A = [a_{ij}]_n,$$

we have

$$X^{\mathsf{T}}AX = X^{\mathsf{T}}(AX) = \sum_{i=1}^{n} \left(\sum_{j=1}^{n} a_{ij} x_j \right) x_i = \sum_{i,j=1}^{n} a_{ij} x_i x_j.$$

The matrix A is called the **matrix of the quadratic form.**

By the replacement of each of a_{ij} and a_{ji}, $i \neq j$, by their mean, $(a_{ij} + a_{ji})/2$, *the matrix of the quadratic form may always be made symmetric.* This is fair since

$$a_{ij} x_i x_j + a_{ji} x_j x_i \equiv \frac{(a_{ij} + a_{ji})}{2} x_i x_j + \frac{(a_{ij} + a_{ji})}{2} x_j x_i.$$

It will appear that *this is the most useful way of writing the coefficient matrix of a quadratic form, and in the remainder of this book we adhere to it exclusively.*

We shall make a detailed study of each of these three types of forms at a later time. For the present we are merely concerned with questions of linear dependence. The ideas are essentially the same in all three cases, as the first paragraph of this section indicates. For example, to investigate the linear dependence of the three linear forms given at the beginning of this section, we must determine whether or not there exist three constants c_1, c_2, c_3, not all zero, such that the identity in x_1 and x_2,

$$c_1(2x_1 - x_2) + c_2(x_1 + 2x_2) + c_3(5x_1 + 7x_2) \equiv 0,$$

holds, that is, such that

$$(2c_1 + c_2 + 5c_3)x_1 + (-c_1 + 2c_2 + 7c_3)x_2 \equiv 0$$

holds identically in x_1 and x_2. This will be true if and only if

(5.14.7)
$$2c_1 + c_2 + 5c_3 = 0,$$
$$-c_1 + 2c_2 + 7c_3 = 0.$$

A nontrivial solution of this system is

$$c_1 = 3, \qquad c_2 = 19, \qquad c_3 = -5,$$

which checks with the result given above.

It should be noted that equations (5.14.7) express the conditions for the dependence of the three vectors

$$\begin{bmatrix} 2 \\ -1 \end{bmatrix}, \quad \begin{bmatrix} 1 \\ 2 \end{bmatrix}, \quad \begin{bmatrix} 5 \\ 7 \end{bmatrix},$$

whose components are the coefficients of the three given forms. As a matter of fact, *the dependence of a set of linear forms is equivalent to the dependence of the vectors defined by their coefficients.* (See Exercise 3, Section 5.16.)

The three quadratic forms

$$x_1{}^2 + x_1 x_2 + x_2{}^2,$$
$$2x_1{}^2 - x_1 x_2 + 2x_2{}^2,$$
$$x_1{}^2 \qquad - x_2{}^2,$$

are, by definition, dependent polynomials if and only if there exist constants c_1, c_2, c_3, not all zero, such that

$$(c_1 + 2c_2 + c_3)x_1{}^2 + (c_1 - c_2)x_1 x_2 + (c_1 + 2c_2 - c_3)x_2{}^2 \equiv 0,$$

that is, such that

$$c_1 + 2c_2 + c_3 = 0,$$
$$c_1 - c_2 = 0,$$
$$c_1 + 2c_2 - c_3 = 0.$$

Since the determinant of the coefficient matrix of these equations is not zero, the system has only the trivial solution, and the three given forms are independent polynomials.

5.15 The Linear Dependence of Matrices

The definitions of linear combinations and linear dependence of matrices of order (m, n) are exactly analogous to those already given for vectors. Hence we do not restate them here. The subject is important in both higher mathematics and in applications in, for example, statistics and quantum mechanics. (See Exercises 7 through 12, Section 5.16.) Moreover, one can alternatively define the dependence of quadratic or bilinear forms to mean the dependence of their coefficient matrices. This is the point of view we shall take in Chapter Nine.

5.16 Exercises

1. Investigate the linear dependence or independence of the three linear forms

$$x_1 + 2x_2 - 3x_3,$$
$$x_1 + x_2 - x_3,$$
$$x_2 - 2x_3.$$

*2. Prove that the m linear forms in n variables

$$a_{i1}x_1 + a_{i2}x_2 + \cdots + a_{in}x_n, \qquad i = 1, 2, \ldots, m,$$

are linearly dependent if and only if the rank of the matrix $[a_{ij}]$ is less than m. In particular, if $m = n$, they are linearly dependent if and only if $\det [a_{ij}] = 0$, and if $m > n$, they are always linearly dependent.

*3. Show that if $A_1, A_2, \ldots, A_m$ and X are n-vectors, the linear forms $A_1{}^\mathsf{T}X$, $A_2{}^\mathsf{T}X, \ldots, A_m{}^\mathsf{T}X$ are linearly dependent if and only if $A_1, A_2, \ldots, A_m$ are dependent.

4. If the polynomials of either of the following sets are linearly dependent, find coefficients not all zero such that the corresponding linear combination is identically zero:

$$
\begin{array}{ll}
& x_1{}^2 + x_1x_2 + x_2{}^2, \qquad\qquad x_1y_1 - x_1y_2 + x_2y_1 - x_2y_2, \\
\text{(a)}\quad 2x_1{}^2 + 3x_1x_2 + x_2{}^2, \quad \text{(b)}\quad -x_1y_1 + x_1y_2 - x_2y_1 + x_2y_2, \\
& \quad - x_1x_2 + x_2{}^2. \qquad\qquad 2x_1y_1 + x_1y_2 - 2x_2y_1 - 2x_2y_2.
\end{array}
$$

5. Restate and prove the results of Exercise 2 for quadratic forms.

*6. Show that the concept of the linear dependence of polynomials of a given degree in a given set of n variables is essentially the same as the concept of the linear dependence of vectors.

*7. Define linear dependence for matrices of order (m, n) and show that here, as everywhere else, a problem in linear dependence reduces to a problem in linear equations.

8. Are the matrices

$$
\begin{bmatrix} 2 & -1 \\ 4 & 6 \end{bmatrix}, \quad
\begin{bmatrix} 3 & 2 \\ 8 & 3 \end{bmatrix}, \quad
\begin{bmatrix} -5 & -8 \\ -16 & 4 \end{bmatrix}
$$

linearly dependent?

9. Show that every matrix of order 2 can be expressed as a linear combination of the matrices

$$
\begin{bmatrix} 1 & 0 \\ 0 & 0 \end{bmatrix}, \quad
\begin{bmatrix} 0 & 1 \\ 0 & 0 \end{bmatrix}, \quad
\begin{bmatrix} 0 & 0 \\ 1 & 0 \end{bmatrix}, \quad
\begin{bmatrix} 0 & 0 \\ 0 & 1 \end{bmatrix}.
$$

Generalize this result.

10. What changes must be made in the theorems of Section 5.11 so that the results will apply to $m \times n$ matrices?

11. Show that the Pauli spin matrices σ_x, σ_y, σ_z (Exercise 19, Section 1.9) and the identity matrix I_2 are a linearly independent set and then show how an arbitrary matrix $A = [a_{ij}]$ of order 2 may be written as a linear combination of these four.

12. If $P = a_1\sigma_x + a_2\sigma_y + a_3\sigma_z + a_4 I_2$ and $Q = b_1\sigma_x + b_2\sigma_y + b_3\sigma_z + b_4 I_2$, where the a's and b's are scalars, express PQ as a linear combination of σ_x, σ_y, σ_z, and I_2.

13. Eliminate m_x and m_y from the covariance (5.14.4) and express the resulting bilinear form as a matrix product. What is the rank of the coefficient matrix?

14. Eliminate m_x from the variance (5.14.6) and express the resulting quadratic form as a matrix product with a symmetric coefficient matrix. Find the rank of the coefficient matrix.

15. Let A, B, X, Y all be matrices of the same order. Prove that, if A and B are independent and

$$X = \alpha A + \beta B,$$
$$Y = \gamma A + \delta B,$$

where α, β, γ, δ are scalars, then X and Y are linearly dependent if and only if

$$\det \begin{bmatrix} \alpha & \beta \\ \gamma & \delta \end{bmatrix} = 0.$$

(Use the definition you phrased in Exercise 7 above.)

16. Reduce to an equivalent system of independent equations:

$$\frac{x_1 - 1}{1} = \frac{x_2 - 2}{2} = \frac{x_3 - 3}{3} = \frac{x_4 - 4}{4}.$$

*17. Show that a system of m linear equations in n unknowns can contain at most $n + 1$ independent equations. When there are $n + 1$ independent equations, how many solutions does the system have?

18. How many independent quadratic equations of the form

$$Ax^2 + Bxy + Cy^2 + Dx + Ey + F = 0$$

may a simultaneous system of such equations contain? Could a system with this many independent equations have a simultaneous solution for x and y? (*Hint:* Write the system in question in matrix form.)

*19. Show that m linear equations in n unknowns are linearly independent if either (a) each equation contains, with nonzero coefficient, an unknown appearing in no other equation, or (b) each equation contains, with nonzero coefficient, an unknown appearing in no previous equation. These tests are often used in network theory.

20. Show by examples that the equations of a system may be (a) dependent and consistent, (b) dependent and inconsistent, (c) independent and consistent, or (d) independent and inconsistent.

COMPLETE SYSTEMS OF SOLUTIONS OF LINEAR EQUATIONS

5.17 Solutions of Homogeneous Systems

We shall now employ the theory of linear dependence to gain a fuller understanding of the nature of the families of solutions of systems of linear equations. We begin with

Theorem 5.17.1: *If the k n-vectors $R_1 = \{r_{11}, r_{21}, \ldots, r_{n1}\}$, $R_2 = \{r_{12}, r_{22}, \ldots, r_{n2}\}, \ldots, R_k = \{r_{1k}, r_{2k}, \ldots, r_{nk}\}$ are all solutions of the system of linear homogeneous equations in n variables, $AX = 0$, then every linear combination $c_1 R_1 + c_2 R_2 + \cdots + c_k R_k$ of these solutions is also a solution.*

In fact,

$$A(c_1 R_1 + c_2 R_2 + \cdots + c_k R_k) = c_1 A R_1 + c_2 A R_2 + \cdots + c_k A R_k$$
$$= c_1 \cdot 0 + c_2 \cdot 0 + \cdots + c_k \cdot 0 = 0.$$

Theorem 5.17.2: *If a homogeneous linear system of m equations in n unknowns, $AX = 0$, has rank $r < n$, then all solutions may be written as linear combinations of $n - r$ linearly independent solutions. When $r = n$, the only solution is the dependent vector 0.*

In the case $r < n$, we know we can solve this system of equations for some set of r unknowns in terms of the remaining $n - r$. Since it will not alter the basic nature of the argument, we assume that the notation is so chosen and that the equations are so arranged that we can solve for $x_1, x_2, \ldots, x_r$ in terms of $x_{r+1}, x_{r+2}, \ldots, x_n$, and hence that we can write the solution thus:

$$
\begin{aligned}
x_1 &= b_{1,r+1} x_{r+1} + b_{1,r+2} x_{r+2} + \cdots + b_{1n} x_n \\
x_2 &= b_{2,r+1} x_{r+1} + b_{2,r+2} x_{r+2} + \cdots + b_{2n} x_n \\
&\vdots \\
x_r &= b_{r,r+1} x_{r+1} + b_{r,r+2} x_{r+2} + \cdots + b_{rn} x_n \\
x_{r+1} &= x_{r+1} \\
x_{r+2} &= x_{r+2} \\
&\vdots \\
x_n &= x_n,
\end{aligned}
$$

(5.17.1)

where $x_{r+1}, x_{r+2}, \ldots, x_n$ are completely arbitrary, but $x_1, x_2, \ldots, x_r$ are uniquely determined in terms of these.

Now we substitute successively into (5.17.1) the following sets of values of $x_{r+1}, \ldots, x_n$:

(1) $\qquad x_{r+1} = 1, \qquad x_{r+2} = x_{r+3} = \cdots = x_n = 0,$

(2) $\qquad x_{r+1} = 0, \qquad x_{r+2} = 1, \qquad x_{r+3} = \cdots = x_n = 0,$

$\qquad \vdots$

$(n - r) \qquad x_{r+1} = x_{r+2} = \cdots = x_{n-1} = 0, \qquad x_n = 1.$

Corresponding to these sets of values of the independent variables, we have the particular solutions

$$
R_1 = \begin{bmatrix} b_{1,r+1} \\ b_{2,r+1} \\ \vdots \\ b_{r,r+1} \\ 1 \\ 0 \\ 0 \\ \vdots \\ 0 \end{bmatrix}, \quad
R_2 = \begin{bmatrix} b_{1,r+2} \\ b_{2,r+2} \\ \vdots \\ b_{r,r+2} \\ 0 \\ 1 \\ 0 \\ \vdots \\ 0 \end{bmatrix}, \ldots, \quad
R_{n-r} = \begin{bmatrix} b_{1n} \\ b_{2n} \\ \vdots \\ b_{rn} \\ 0 \\ 0 \\ \vdots \\ 0 \\ 1 \end{bmatrix}.
$$

From the nature of the last $n - r$ rows of these vectors, it follows that they are linearly independent. (See Exercise 8, Section 5.10.) Furthermore, equations (5.17.1), rewritten in matrix form, show that every solution X is a linear combination of these, the coefficients being $x_{r+1}, x_{r+2}, \ldots, x_n$:

$$X = x_{r+1} R_1 + x_{r+2} R_2 + \cdots + x_n R_{n-r}.$$

The result for $r = n$ is simply a restatement of Theorem 5.6.1. Thus the theorem is completely proved.

Corollary 5.17.3: *Any $n - r + 1$ solutions of the homogeneous linear system $AX = 0$ in which the matrix A is of rank r are linearly dependent.*

This follows at once from Theorem 5.11.9 and the preceding theorem.

Theorem 5.17.4: *If a homogeneous linear system of equations $AX = 0$ has rank r, then every solution may be expressed as a linear combination of any $n - r$ linearly independent solutions.*

Suppose $P_1, P_2, \ldots, P_{n-r}$ are any $n - r$ linearly independent solutions, and let P be any solution of the system. Then these $n - r + 1$ solutions are linearly dependent by the previous corollary. That there exist constants $c_1, c_2, \ldots, c_{n-r}$ such that $P = c_1 P_1 + c_2 P_2 + \cdots + c_{n-r} P_{n-r}$ now follows from Theorem 5.11.7. We may restate these results as follows:

Corollary 5.17.5: *If* $P_1, P_2, \ldots, P_{n-r}$ *are any* $n - r$ *linearly independent solutions of a homogeneous linear system of rank* r, *then a complete solution of the system is given by*

$$X = t_1 P_1 + t_2 P_2 + \cdots + t_{n-r} P_{n-r}.$$

For example, by inspection we see that the system

$$x_1 - x_2 + x_3 - x_4 = 0,$$

$$x_1 + x_2 - x_3 - x_4 = 0,$$

has the solutions $\{1, 1, 1, 1\}$ and $\{1, -1, -1, 1\}$ which are linearly independent. The complete solution is, therefore,

$$X = t_1\{1, 1, 1, 1\} + t_2\{1, -1, -1, 1\},$$

since here $n - r = 2$.

5.18 An Important Special Case

A particular case of Theorem 5.17.1 is that, if $R = \{r_1, r_2, \ldots, r_n\}$ is a solution of $AX = 0$, then so is $\{kr_1, kr_2, \ldots, kr_n\}$. This allows us to express the solution of a system of n equations in n unknowns in an especially simple way when the rank is $n - 1$. In this case we could solve for $n - 1$ of the variables in terms of the remaining one, so that there is one independent variable in the solution. The solution may, however, be expressed more simply thus:

Let us arrange the equations so that the submatrix formed from the coefficients of the first $n - 1$ rows has rank $n - 1$. Then the cofactors of the elements in the nth row of $A = [a_{ij}]$ are not all zero. Also, since $\det A$ is zero by hypothesis, we will have, by equations (2.7.4),

(5.18.1) $a_{i1} A_{n1} + a_{i2} A_{n2} + \cdots + a_{in} A_{nn} = \det A \cdot \delta_{in} = 0,$

$$i = 1, 2, \ldots, n.$$

Thus the n-vector $\{A_{n1}, A_{n2}, \ldots, A_{nn}\}$ is a nontrivial solution of the system. Hence the vector $\{t A_{n1}, t A_{n2}, \ldots, t A_{nn}\}$ is also a solution for every value of t. This solution contains a single parameter and, since $n - r = 1$ here, gives the complete solution of the system (Corollary 5.17.5).

If we have a system of $n - 1$ homogeneous equations in n unknowns and if the rank is $n - 1$, then by the device of appending an nth equation with coefficients all zero, we see that in this case also, the same formula will give the complete solution. For example, suppose we wish to determine direction numbers a, b, c for a line perpendicular to each of two lines with direction numbers $2, 3, -1$, and, $1, 1, 2$ respectively. This requires that we solve simultaneously the equations

$$2a + 3b - c = 0,$$

$$a + b + 2c = 0.$$

By the above observation, the complete solution is

$$\left\{ t \begin{vmatrix} 3 & -1 \\ 1 & 2 \end{vmatrix}, \quad -t \begin{vmatrix} 2 & -1 \\ 1 & 2 \end{vmatrix}, \quad t \begin{vmatrix} 2 & 3 \\ 1 & 1 \end{vmatrix} \right\} = \{7t, -5t, -t\},$$

where t is arbitrary. Thus, putting $t = 1$, we obtain $7, -5, -1$ as a set of direction numbers for the line in question. If we put $t = \pm 1/5\sqrt{3}$, the resulting direction numbers are also direction cosines.

5.19 Solutions of Nonhomogeneous Systems

We begin with a theorem that enables us to use our knowledge of homogeneous systems in the solution of nonhomogeneous ones:

Theorem 5.19.1:   If the linear system of m equations in n unknowns $AX + B = 0$ is consistent, then a complete solution thereof is given by a complete solution of the corresponding homogeneous system $AX = 0$ plus any particular solution of $AX + B = 0$.

Let Y_o designate any particular solution of $AX + B = 0$. Then if Y is any solution, from $AY + B = 0$ and $AY_o + B = 0$, we have by subtraction $A(Y - Y_o) = 0$. That is, if $W = Y - Y_o$, W is a solution of $AX = 0$. Then $Y = W + Y_o$, so that every solution Y of the given system can be expressed as *some* solution W of the corresponding homogeneous system plus the particular solution Y_o of the given system.

If now W is *any* solution of the homogeneous system and if $Y = W + Y_o$, then $AY + B = AW + (AY_o + B) = 0$, so that Y is a solution of $AX + B = 0$. Thus, as W ranges over the set of all solutions of $AX = 0$, $W + Y_o$ ranges over *all* and *only* the solutions of $AX + B = 0$.

The reader familiar with the theory of linear differential equations will not fail to notice that many of the results obtained there parallel the above results exactly. This is explained by the fact that the theories of linear algebraic equations and linear differential equations are both special cases of a more general theory of "linear operators."

To illustrate this result, consider the system

$$x_1 - x_2 + 2x_3 = 1,$$
$$2x_1 + x_2 - x_3 = 2.$$

Put $x_1 = 0$. Then $x_2 = 5$ and $x_3 = 3$. That is, $\{0, 5, 3\}$ is a particular solution. The corresponding homogeneous system

$$x_1 - x_2 + 2x_3 = 0,$$
$$2x_1 + x_2 - x_3 = 0,$$

now has the complete solution

$$\left\{ t \begin{vmatrix} -1 & 2 \\ 1 & -1 \end{vmatrix}, -t \begin{vmatrix} 1 & 2 \\ 2 & -1 \end{vmatrix}, t \begin{vmatrix} 1 & -1 \\ 2 & 1 \end{vmatrix} \right\},$$

or

$$\{-t, 5t, 3t\}.$$

A complete solution of the given nonhomogeneous system is therefore $\{-t, 5t + 5, 3t + 3\}$.

5.20 An Alternative Procedure

We can also obtain a sequence of theorems analogous to those in Section 5.17.

Theorem 5.20.1: *If the coefficient and augmented matrices of the nonhomogeneous linear system of m equations in n unknowns $AX + B = 0$, $B \neq 0$, have the same rank r, then every solution can be expressed as a linear combination of $n - r + 1$ linearly independent solutions and in this combination the sum of the coefficients will be 1.*

Again we assume the notation so chosen that we can solve for $x_1, x_2, \ldots, x_r$ in terms of $x_{r+1}, x_{r+2}, \ldots, x_n$

$$x_1 = b_{1,r+1}x_{r+1} + b_{1,r+2}x_{r+2} + \cdots + b_{1n}x_n + \beta_1$$
$$x_2 = b_{2,r+1}x_{r+1} + b_{2,r+2}x_{r+2} + \cdots + b_{2n}x_n + \beta_2$$
$$\vdots$$

(5.20.1)
$$x_r = b_{r,r+1}x_{r+1} + b_{r,r+2}x_{r+2} + \cdots + b_{rn}x_n + \beta_r$$
$$x_{r+1} = x_{r+1}$$
$$x_{r+2} = x_{r+2}$$
$$\vdots$$
$$x_n = x_n.$$

Here too $x_{r+1}, x_{r+2}, \ldots, x_n$ are arbitrary, and $x_1, x_2, \ldots, x_r$ are determined uniquely in terms of them. In these equations, not all the β_i can be zero, for if they were, the trivial solution would be a solution of the given system. This is impossible since $B \neq 0$, by hypothesis.

In (5.20.1) we now substitute successively the $n - r + 1$ sets of values

(1) $\qquad\qquad x_{r+1} = 1, \qquad x_{r+2} = x_{r+3} = \cdots = x_n = 0,$

(2) $\qquad\qquad x_{r+1} = 0, \qquad x_{r+2} = 1, \qquad x_{r+3} = \cdots = x_n = 0,$

$$\qquad\qquad\qquad \vdots$$

$(n - r) \qquad\qquad x_{r+1} = x_{r+2} = \cdots = x_{n-1} = 0, \qquad x_n = 1,$

$(n - r + 1) \qquad x_{r+1} = x_{r+2} = \cdots = x_n = 0,$

for the independent variables and obtain the linearly independent solutions
(5.20.2)

$$
R_1 = \begin{bmatrix} b_{1,r+1} + \beta_1 \\ b_{2,r+1} + \beta_2 \\ \vdots \\ b_{r,r+1} + \beta_r \\ 1 \\ 0 \\ 0 \\ \vdots \\ 0 \end{bmatrix}, \quad
R_2 = \begin{bmatrix} b_{1,r+2} + \beta_1 \\ b_{2,r+2} + \beta_2 \\ \vdots \\ b_{r,r+2} + \beta_r \\ 0 \\ 1 \\ 0 \\ \vdots \\ 0 \end{bmatrix}, \cdots,
$$

$$
R_{n-r} = \begin{bmatrix} b_{1n} + \beta_1 \\ b_{2n} + \beta_2 \\ \vdots \\ b_{rn} + \beta_r \\ 0 \\ 0 \\ \vdots \\ 0 \\ 1 \end{bmatrix}, \quad
R_{n-r+1} = \begin{bmatrix} \beta_1 \\ \beta_2 \\ \vdots \\ \beta_r \\ 0 \\ 0 \\ \vdots \\ 0 \\ 0 \end{bmatrix}.
$$

As in the proof of Theorem 5.17.2, the linear independence of these R's follows from the nature of the last $n - r$ entries in each column and from the fact that not all β_j's are zero.

We can now rewrite equations (5.20.1) in the form

$$X = x_{r+1}(R_1 - R_{n-r+1}) + x_{r+2}(R_2 - R_{n-r+1}) + \cdots$$
$$+ x_n(R_{n-r} - R_{n-r+1}) + R_{n-r+1},$$

so that

$$X = x_{r+1}R_1 + x_{r+2}R_2 + \cdots + x_n R_{n-r}$$
$$+ (1 - x_{r+1} - x_{r+2} - \cdots - x_n)R_{n-r+1},$$

from which the theorem follows.

Notice that although we have $n - r + 1$ linearly independent solutions, we cannot take *arbitrary* linear combinations of them to get other solutions as we could in the homogeneous case. Here, as there, there are just $n - r$ arbitrary quantities in the solution. We have, however, the following result:

Theorem 5.20.2: *If the coefficient and augmented matrices of the nonhomogeneous linear system of m equations in n unknowns $AX + B = 0$ have the same rank r, and if $P_1, P_2, \ldots, P_{n-r+1}$ are any $n - r + 1$ linearly independent solutions thereof, then the expression*

(5.20.3) $$X = t_1 P_1 + t_2 P_2 + \cdots + t_{n-r+1} P_{n-r+1},$$

where

(5.20.4) $$t_1 + t_2 + \cdots + t_{n-r+1} = 1,$$

but the t's are otherwise arbitrary, is a complete solution.

To prove this, we note first that, since $AP_j = -B$ for $j = 1, 2, \ldots, n - r + 1$ and since $\sum t_j = 1$, we have from (5.20.3),

$$AX + B = t_1 AP_1 + t_2 AP_2 + \cdots + t_{n-r+1} AP_{n-r+1} + B$$
$$= (-\sum t_j)B + B = 0.$$

This proves that (5.20.3) and (5.20.4) give *only* solutions of $AX + B = 0$.

Next let P be any solution of the system. Then $P, P_1, \ldots, P_{n-r+1}$ are $n - r + 2$ linear combinations of $R_1, R_2, \ldots, R_{n-r+1}$ as given in Theorem 5.20.1, and are therefore linearly dependent. Hence, since $P_1, \ldots, P_{n-r+1}$ are linearly independent, it follows from Theorem 5.11.7 that there exist constants $t_1, \ldots, t_{n-r+1}$ such that

$$P = t_1 P_1 + \cdots + t_{n-r+1} P_{n-r+1}.$$

Now, substituting P for X in $AX + B = 0$ and using the fact that all the P_j's are solutions of this equation, we find $(1 - \sum t)B = 0$, from which $\sum t = 1$, since $B \neq 0$. That is, *every* solution is included in (5.20.3) and (5.20.4), and this completes the proof of the theorem.

By way of illustration, consider the system

$$2x_1 + x_2 + x_3 + x_4 = 2,$$
$$3x_1 - x_2 + x_3 - x_4 = 2,$$
$$x_1 + 2x_2 - x_3 + x_4 = 1,$$
$$6x_1 + 2x_2 + x_3 + x_4 = 5.$$

The system is consistent, the ranks of the coefficient and augmented matrices both being 3. The first three equations may be used to obtain the solution.

Put $x_1 = 0$. Then from the first three equations we find $x_2 = 3$, $x_3 = 2$, $x_4 = -3$, so that a particular solution is $\{0, 3, 2, -3\}$. Then, putting $x_1 = 2$, we obtain the particular solution $\{2, -5, -3, 6\}$. Since $n - r + 1 = 2$ here, the complete solution of the system is

$$
\begin{bmatrix} x_1 \\ x_2 \\ x_3 \\ x_4 \end{bmatrix} = t_1 \begin{bmatrix} 0 \\ 3 \\ 2 \\ -3 \end{bmatrix} + t_2 \begin{bmatrix} 2 \\ -5 \\ -3 \\ 6 \end{bmatrix}, \qquad t_1 + t_2 = 1.
$$

For certain purposes, the form of solution obtained in this section is more useful than that obtained in Section 5.19.

5.21 Exercises

1. Do several problems from Exercise 1, Section 5.8, by the method used in the preceding section, also by the method of Section 5.19.

*2. Show that, if A is any singular matrix of order n, there always exist nonzero, singular matrices B of order n such that $AB = 0$.

3. Find a system of homogeneous linear equations in $x_1, \ldots, x_4$ with the complete solution

$$
t_1 \begin{bmatrix} 1 \\ 2 \\ 3 \\ 4 \end{bmatrix} + t_2 \begin{bmatrix} 2 \\ 1 \\ 0 \\ -1 \end{bmatrix}.
$$

Hint: Let

$$
P = \begin{bmatrix} 1 & 2 \\ 2 & 1 \\ 3 & 0 \\ 4 & -1 \end{bmatrix},
$$

and find a matrix A of rank 2 which satisfies the equation $AP = 0$. Then $AX = 0$ is the system required, where

$$
X = \{x_1, x_2, x_3, x_4\}.
$$

4. Generalize Exercise 3 into a theorem and prove it.

5. Find a system of nonhomogeneous linear equations in x_1, x_2, x_3, x_4 with the general solution

$$
t_1 \begin{bmatrix} 1 \\ 2 \\ 3 \\ 4 \end{bmatrix} + t_2 \begin{bmatrix} 2 \\ 1 \\ 0 \\ -1 \end{bmatrix} + \begin{bmatrix} -1 \\ 0 \\ 1 \\ -2 \end{bmatrix}.
$$

Hint: Use Exercise 3 and the idea of Theorem 5.19.1.

6. Generalize Exercise 5 into a theorem and prove it.

7. Let the rank of the system

$$AX = 0$$

be r, and let $P_1, \ldots, P_{n-r}$ be any $n - r$ linearly independent solutions. These are then called a **fundamental system of solutions**. Furthermore, the matrix

$$P = [P_1, P_2, \ldots, P_{n-r}]$$

determined by these solutions is called a **fundamental matrix of solutions**. It has the following properties: (a) its columns are linearly independent vectors and (b) every linear combination of its columns gives a solution of $AX = 0$. Show that if B is a nonsingular square matrix of order $n - r$, then the matrix PB also has the properties (a) and (b). Finally, show that, given P, every fundamental matrix of solutions is representable in the form PB with B nonsingular.

*8. If $A_{(m,n)}B_{(n,m)} = I_{(m,m)}$, A is called a **left inverse** of B, and B is called a **right inverse** of A. When may a matrix have a left inverse? A right inverse? A unique inverse? When are the left and right inverse the same? How may one determine all inverses of a given matrix?

*9. Show that if $AX + B = 0$ is consistent and of rank r, and if $P, P_1, \ldots, P_{n-r}$ are linearly independent solutions thereof, then a complete solution is

$$X = P + t_1(P_1 - P) + t_2(P_2 - P) + \cdots + t_{n-r}(P_{n-r} - P),$$

in which the t's are arbitrary.

10. Show that, if P_1 is a solution of $AX = B_1$ and P_2 is a solution of $AX = B_2$ then $\lambda_1 P_1 + \lambda_2 P_2$ is a solution of $AX = \lambda_1 B_1 + \lambda_2 B_2$. Then show how one may use this fact to write the complete solution of this last equation.

11. Show that, if P_j is a solution of $AX = E_j$, $j = 1, 2, \ldots, m$, then $\sum_{j=1}^{m} b_j P_j$ is a solution of $AX = B$. (Here we assume that we have m equations in n unknowns. Also, E_j is the jth elementary vector. See Section 5.9.) In the particular case when $m = n$ and $\det A \neq 0$, what is the matrix $[P_1, P_2, \ldots, P_n]$? (The first part of this problem is an algebraic form of the widely useful **principle of superposition**.)

*12. If r_A is the rank of $A_{(m,n)}$ and r_B is the rank of $B_{(n,p)}$, and if $AB = 0$, prove that $r_A + r_B \leqslant n$. (Use the fact that each column of B is a solution of the equation $AX = 0$.)

13. In the study of electric circuits, it is at times necessary to solve systems of equations of the form

$$\begin{bmatrix} a_{11} & a_{12} & \cdots & a_{1n} \\ a_{21} & a_{22} & \cdots & a_{2n} \\ \vdots & & & \\ a_{n1} & a_{n2} & \cdots & a_{nn} \end{bmatrix} \cdot \begin{bmatrix} I_1 \\ I_2 \\ \vdots \\ I_n \end{bmatrix} = \begin{bmatrix} E \\ 0 \\ 0 \\ \vdots \\ 0 \end{bmatrix},$$

where $[a_{ij}]_n$ is nonsingular, the I's are the "mesh currents," and E is a "source voltage." The "branch currents" are then expressions of the form

$$i_p = \sum_{j=1}^{n} \alpha_{pj} I_j, \qquad p = 1, 2, \ldots, b,$$

where each α is $+1$, 0, or -1. Show that the branch currents are proportional to E, that is,

$$\begin{bmatrix} i_1 \\ i_2 \\ \vdots \\ i_b \end{bmatrix} = E \begin{bmatrix} \beta_1 \\ \beta_2 \\ \vdots \\ \beta_b \end{bmatrix},$$

where the β's are constants depending on the a's and on the α's.

14. Show that, if $\det A = 0$, the system $AX = 0$ has the (possibly trivial) solution $\{A_{t1}, A_{t2}, \ldots, A_{tn}\}$. Then, if $X_1, X_2, \ldots, X_{n+1}$ are any $n + 1$ n-vectors, show that

$$\det [X_2, X_3, \ldots, X_{n+1}]X_1 - \det [X_1, X_3, \ldots, X_{n+1}]X_2 + \cdots$$
$$+ (-1)^n \det [X_1, X_2, \ldots, X_n]X_{n+1} = 0,$$

by noting that

$$\det \begin{bmatrix} X_1 & X_2 & \cdots & X_{n+1} \\ \hline 0 & 0 & \cdots & 0 \end{bmatrix} = 0.$$

15. Determine in each case the locus in three-dimensional Euclidean space of the endpoints of the vectors of the set:

(a) $X = t_1 A_1 + t_2 A_2,$ $t_1 + t_2 = 1,$ $t_1, t_2 > 0.$

(b) $X = t_1 A_1 + t_2 A_2 + t_3 A_3,$ $t_1 + t_2 + t_3 = 1,$ $t_1, t_2, t_3 > 0.$

MORE ABOUT THE RANK OF A MATRIX

5.22 Linear Dependence and Rank

Let $[A_1, A_2, \ldots, A_n]$ denote an $m \times n$ matrix A which has been partitioned into its columns. The columns may then be regarded as vectors. If A has rank r, then some submatrix of order r is nonsingular. Let $A_{j_1}, A_{j_2}, \ldots,$ A_{j_r} be the columns of A passing through this submatrix. Since the matrix $[A_{j_1}, A_{j_2}, \ldots, A_{j_r}]$ then has rank r, by Theorem 5.11.1, the vectors $A_{j_1},$ $A_{j_2}, \ldots, A_{j_r}$ are linearly *independent*. If now $A_{j_{r+1}}$ denotes any column of A, the matrix $[A_{j_1}, \ldots, A_{j_r}, A_{j_{r+1}}]$ still has rank r, and hence the columns $A_{j_1}, \ldots, A_{j_r}, A_{j_{r+1}}$ are linearly *dependent*. Hence, by Theorem 5.11.7, we can write $A_{j_{r+1}}$ as a linear combination of $A_{j_1}, A_{j_2}, \ldots, A_{j_r}$. Similar reasoning applies, of course, to the rows of A, which may be regarded as transposed vectors. We have therefore proved

Theorem 5.22.1: *If the rank of a matrix A of order (m, n) is r, then there is at least one set of r linearly independent columns (rows) of A, and every column (row) can be written as a linear combination of any such set.*

An immediate consequence is

Corollary 5.22.2:   *A square matrix is nonsingular if and only if its columns (rows) are linearly independent.*

These results may be illustrated by the matrix

$$[A_1, A_2, A_3] = \begin{bmatrix} 2 & 1 & -5 \\ 3 & 1 & 1 \\ 0 & -1 & 17 \end{bmatrix},$$

whose rank is 2. The first two columns are linearly independent. We have the relations

$$A_1 = 1 \cdot A_1 + 0 \cdot A_2,$$

$$A_2 = 0 \cdot A_1 + 1 \cdot A_2,$$

$$A_3 = 6 \cdot A_1 - 17 \cdot A_2,$$

in which, corresponding to the word "every" in the statement of the theorem, A_1 and A_2 are expressed as elementary combinations of themselves.

We are now ready to prove

Theorem 5.22.3:   *If a matrix A of order (m, n) has rank r, then the major determinants of a submatrix consisting of any r rows of A are proportional to the corresponding major determinants of any other such submatrix.*

We assume $r < m$ and $r < n$. (If $r = m$ or $r = n$, the theorem is trivially true.)

We illustrate the theorem by means of an example before proceeding to the proof. In the matrix of rank 2 given above, the submatrix of the first two rows has the major determinants

$$\begin{vmatrix} 2 & 1 \\ 3 & 1 \end{vmatrix} = -1, \qquad \begin{vmatrix} 2 & -5 \\ 3 & 1 \end{vmatrix} = 17, \qquad \begin{vmatrix} 1 & -5 \\ 1 & 1 \end{vmatrix} = 6.$$

The submatrix consisting of the last two rows has the corresponding majors,

$$\begin{vmatrix} 3 & 1 \\ 0 & -1 \end{vmatrix} = -3, \qquad \begin{vmatrix} 3 & 1 \\ 0 & 17 \end{vmatrix} = 51, \qquad \begin{vmatrix} 1 & 1 \\ -1 & 17 \end{vmatrix} = 18,$$

and from the first and last rows we obtain in the same way,

$$\begin{vmatrix} 2 & 1 \\ 0 & -1 \end{vmatrix} = -2, \qquad \begin{vmatrix} 2 & -5 \\ 0 & 17 \end{vmatrix} = 34, \qquad \begin{vmatrix} 1 & -5 \\ -1 & 17 \end{vmatrix} = 12.$$

The meaning of the theorem should now be clear. Sometimes, in applying the theorem, we have to remember that the zero n-vector and any other n-vector are "proportional." Now, the proof.

Let a set of r linearly independent columns of A be denoted by L_1, $L_2, \ldots, L_r$. Then, by Theorem 5.22.1, every column of A is a linear combination of these r columns, and hence we may write,

$$A = \left[\sum_{i=1}^{r} k_{i1} L_i, \ \sum_{i=1}^{r} k_{i2} L_i, \ \ldots, \ \sum_{i=1}^{r} k_{in} L_i \right]$$

$$= [L_1, L_2, \ldots, L_r] \cdot \begin{bmatrix} k_{11} & k_{12} & \cdots & k_{1n} \\ k_{21} & k_{22} & \cdots & k_{2n} \\ \vdots & & & \\ k_{r1} & k_{r2} & \cdots & k_{rn} \end{bmatrix}.$$

The factors of this product have rank *at most* r, but since A has rank r, they also have rank *at least* r (Theorem 4.9.1). Hence each factor has rank exactly r.

Let us now select a set of r rows from A. We can effect this by picking *the same rows* from $[L_1, L_2, \ldots, L_r]$. If we denote the result of this last step by $[L_1{'}, L_2{'}, \ldots, L_r{'}]$, then the matrix of the r rows selected from A is given by

$$[L_1{'}, L_2{'}, \ldots, L_r{'}] \cdot \begin{bmatrix} k_{11} & \cdots & k_{1n} \\ \vdots & & \\ k_{r1} & \cdots & k_{rn} \end{bmatrix}.$$

Similarly, let

$$[L_1{''}, L_2{''}, \ldots, L_r{''}] \cdot \begin{bmatrix} k_{11} & \cdots & k_{1n} \\ \vdots & & \\ k_{r1} & \cdots & k_{rn} \end{bmatrix}$$

represent any other set of r rows of A.

Corresponding major determinants of these two sets of r rows may now be formed by picking corresponding sets of r columns from $[k_{ij}]_{(r,n)}$. By the theorem on the determinant of the product of two square matrices, these majors are

$$|L_1{'}, L_2{'}, \ldots, L_r{'}| \cdot \begin{vmatrix} k_{1j_1} & \cdots & k_{1j_r} \\ \vdots & & \\ k_{rj_1} & \cdots & k_{rj_r} \end{vmatrix},$$

$$|L_1{'}, L_2{'}, \ldots, L_r{'}| \cdot \begin{vmatrix} k_{1p_1} & \cdots & k_{1p_r} \\ \vdots & & \\ k_{rp_1} & \cdots & k_{rp_r} \end{vmatrix}, \ldots,$$

and

$$|L_1'', L_2'', \ldots, L_r''| \cdot \begin{vmatrix} k_{1j_1} & \cdots & k_{1j_r} \\ \vdots & & \\ k_{rj_1} & \cdots & k_{rj_r} \end{vmatrix},$$

$$|L_1'', L_2'', \ldots, L_r''| \cdot \begin{vmatrix} k_{1p_1} & \cdots & k_{1p_r} \\ \vdots & & \\ k_{rp_1} & \cdots & k_{rp_r} \end{vmatrix}, \ldots,$$

the proportionality of which is evident.

A similar argument may be developed to prove the result for the majors of sets of r columns.

The previously given example of this theorem illustrates also the following special case:

Corollary 5.22.4:   *In a square matrix A of order n and rank $n - 1$, the cofactors of the elements of any two parallel lines are proportional.*

This result also follows at once from the fact that if $\det A = 0$, the cofactors of the elements of any row provide a solution of the system of equations $AX = 0$, whereas if A has rank $n - 1$, all solutions are multiples of any one nontrivial solution. Similarly, the cofactors of the elements of any column provide a solution of $A^T X = 0$.

An equivalent way to state the corollary is to say that the matrices of cofactors:

$$\begin{bmatrix} A_{i1} & A_{i2} & \cdots & A_{in} \\ A_{k1} & A_{k2} & \cdots & A_{kn} \end{bmatrix} \quad \text{and} \quad \begin{bmatrix} A_{1j} & A_{1p} \\ A_{2j} & A_{2p} \\ \vdots & \\ A_{nj} & A_{np} \end{bmatrix}$$

have rank < 2 for all choices of i, k, j, p. Hence all their second-order major determinants vanish. This gives us

Corollary 5.22.5:   *If A is a square matrix of order n and of rank $n - 1$, we have the identities among the cofactors,*

$$A_{ij}A_{kp} = A_{ip}A_{kj},$$

where the subscripts all range from 1 to n.

In particular, when $j = i$ and $p = k$, we have

$$A_{ii}A_{kk} = A_{ik}A_{ki}.$$

(The result still holds but is uninteresting if the rank of A is $< n - 1$.)

The next theorem is important in our study of quadratic forms, which follows in a later chapter.

Theorem 5.22.6: *If A is a Hermitian matrix of rank $r > 0$, then at least one principal minor of order r of A is not zero.*

Since A has rank r, suppose B is a submatrix of order r such that

$$\det B = \begin{vmatrix} a_{i_1 j_1} & \cdots & a_{i_1 j_r} \\ \vdots & & \\ a_{i_r j_1} & \cdots & a_{i_r j_r} \end{vmatrix} \neq 0.$$

If this is a principal minor, the theorem is proved for A. If it is not a principal minor, the fact that A is Hermitian and the fact that $\det B^* = \overline{\det B}$ imply that also

$$\det B^* = \begin{vmatrix} a_{j_1 i_1} & \cdots & a_{j_1 i_r} \\ \vdots & & \\ a_{j_r i_1} & \cdots & a_{j_r i_r} \end{vmatrix} \neq 0.$$

Now the determinants

$$\begin{vmatrix} a_{i_1 i_1} & \cdots & a_{i_1 i_r} \\ \vdots & & \\ a_{i_r i_1} & \cdots & a_{i_r i_r} \end{vmatrix}, \quad \begin{vmatrix} a_{i_1 j_1} & \cdots & a_{i_1 j_r} \\ \vdots & & \\ a_{i_r j_1} & \cdots & a_{i_r j_r} \end{vmatrix},$$

and

$$\begin{vmatrix} a_{j_1 i_1} & \cdots & a_{j_1 i_r} \\ \vdots & & \\ a_{j_r i_1} & \cdots & a_{j_r i_r} \end{vmatrix}, \quad \begin{vmatrix} a_{j_1 j_1} & \cdots & a_{j_1 j_r} \\ \vdots & & \\ a_{j_r j_1} & \cdots & a_{j_r j_r} \end{vmatrix},$$

are corresponding pairs of "majors" as in Theorem 5.22.3, and are, therefore, proportional. Hence, since $\det B^* = \overline{\det B}$,

$$(5.22.1) \quad \begin{vmatrix} a_{i_1 i_1} & \cdots & a_{i_1 i_r} \\ \vdots & & \\ a_{i_r i_1} & \cdots & a_{i_r i_r} \end{vmatrix} \cdot \begin{vmatrix} a_{j_1 j_1} & \cdots & a_{j_1 j_r} \\ \vdots & & \\ a_{j_r j_1} & \cdots & a_{j_r j_r} \end{vmatrix} = \begin{Vmatrix} a_{i_1 j_1} & \cdots & a_{i_1 j_r} \\ \vdots & & \\ a_{i_r j_1} & \cdots & a_{i_r j_r} \end{Vmatrix}^2.$$

The outer bars on the right denote absolute value. The principal minors on the left are necessarily real. (Why?) The right member is unequal to zero by hypothesis, so that neither of the two principal minors on the left can be zero and the proof of the theorem is complete.

For example, the symmetric and, therefore, Hermitian matrix

$$\begin{bmatrix} 0 & 0 & 1 & 2 \\ 0 & 0 & 2 & 4 \\ 1 & 2 & 0 & 0 \\ 2 & 4 & 0 & 0 \end{bmatrix}$$

of order 4 and rank 2 has four nonzero principal minors of order 2.

The reader should think through this theorem for the special case $r = 1$ and see that the reasoning still applies.

Corollary 5.22.7:   *The nonzero principal minors of order r of a Hermitian matrix A of rank r all have the same sign and their sum is unequal to zero.*

By Theorem 5.22.6, there exists at least one nonzero principal minor of order r. Suppose the corresponding submatrix contains rows and columns with indices $i_1, i_2, \ldots, i_r$. If the principal minor involving the indices $j_1, j_2, \ldots, j_r$ also is different from zero, then, by (5.22.1), we have

$$\begin{vmatrix} a_{i_1 i_1} & \cdots & a_{i_1 i_r} \\ \vdots & & \\ a_{i_r i_1} & \cdots & a_{i_r i_r} \end{vmatrix} \cdot \begin{vmatrix} a_{j_1 j_r} & \cdots & a_{j_1 j_r} \\ \vdots & & \\ a_{j_r j_1} & \cdots & a_{j_r j_r} \end{vmatrix} > 0,$$

so that the second principal minor has the same sign as the first. Thus all nonzero principal minors have the same sign and, hence, their sum is not zero.

5.23 Exercises

1. Prove that the rank of a matrix is r if and only if some r columns of the matrix are linearly independent but every set of $r + 1$ columns is linearly dependent.

2. Prove that not all determinants of order r in any set of r rows of a non-singular matrix may be zero.

3. Prove that, if $k > n/2$, this matrix is singular:

$$\begin{bmatrix} 0 & \cdots & 0 & a_{1,k+1} & \cdots & a_{1n} \\ \vdots & & & \vdots & & \\ 0 & \cdots & 0 & a_{k,k+1} & \cdots & a_{kn} \\ a_{k+1,1} & \cdots & a_{k+1,k} & a_{k+1,k+1} & \cdots & a_{k+1,n} \\ \vdots & & & \vdots & & \\ a_{n1} & \cdots & a_{nk} & a_{k+1,n} & \cdots & a_{nn} \end{bmatrix}.$$

*4. Show that, if a matrix A of order (m, n) has rank 1, then it can be written as a product of two matrices of rank 1:

$$A = \begin{bmatrix} \alpha_1 \\ \alpha_2 \\ \vdots \\ \alpha_m \end{bmatrix} \cdot [\beta_1, \beta_2, \ldots, \beta_n],$$

where the α's and β's are scalars. If it has rank 2, then it can be written in the form

$$A = \begin{bmatrix} \alpha_{11} & \alpha_{12} \\ \alpha_{21} & \alpha_{22} \\ \vdots & \\ \alpha_{m1} & \alpha_{m2} \end{bmatrix} \cdot \begin{bmatrix} \beta_{11} & \beta_{12} & \cdots & \beta_{1n} \\ \beta_{21} & \beta_{22} & \cdots & \beta_{2n} \end{bmatrix},$$

and so on. What are the possible factorizations when A is square and nonsingular?

*5. Show that the rank of $\mathscr{A}$, the adjoint matrix of a square matrix A of order n, is (a) n when A is nonsingular, (b) 1 when A is of rank $n - 1$, (c) 0 when A is of rank $< n - 1$.

*6. Show that if a matrix A of order n has rank $r < n$, there are exactly $n - r$ linearly independent equations relating the columns (rows) of A. (*Hint:* If $\sum \alpha_j A_j = 0$, where A_j are the columns of A, then $\{\alpha_1, \alpha_2, \ldots, \alpha_n\}$ is a solution of the equation $AX = 0$.) Illustrate with an example. What is the corresponding result when A is of order (m, n)? (The number $n - r$ is known as the **nullity** or the **degeneracy** of A when A is square.)

*7. Show that, if A has rank r, then there exist nonsingular matrices R and C such that RA and AC respectively have the forms

$$\begin{bmatrix} G_1 \\ G_2 \\ \vdots \\ G_r \\ 0 \\ \vdots \\ 0 \end{bmatrix}$$

and

$$[F_1, F_2, \ldots, F_r, 0, \ldots, 0],$$

where $G_1, \ldots, G_r$ are independent rows and $F_1, \ldots, F_r$ are independent columns. Use these results to prove again that the rank of a product $AB = P$ cannot exceed the rank of either factor.

8. Suppose $A_{n \times n}$ is of rank r. Moreover, suppose that the first r rows and the first r columns of A are independent so that A can be written in the form

$$A = \begin{bmatrix} A_{11} & A_{12} \\ \hline A_{21} & A_{22} \end{bmatrix},$$

where A_{11} is $r \times r$ and det $A_{11} \neq 0$. Prove there exist matrices B and C such that

$$A = \begin{bmatrix} A_{11} & A_{12} \\ \hline BA_{11} & BA_{12} \end{bmatrix} = \begin{bmatrix} A_{11} & A_{11}C \\ \hline BA_{11} & BA_{11}C \end{bmatrix}.$$

9. Let A be the matrix of Exercise 8. Show that the system of linear equations

$$AX = D$$

or

$$\begin{bmatrix} A_{11} & A_{12} \\ \hline A_{21} & A_{22} \end{bmatrix} \cdot \begin{bmatrix} X_1 \\ \hline X_2 \end{bmatrix} = \begin{bmatrix} D_1 \\ \hline D_2 \end{bmatrix},$$

has the complete solution

$$X_1 = A_{11}^{-1}D_1 - CX_2,$$

where X_1 and D_1 each have r components and where $D_2 = BD_1$.

10. Use Exercise 9 to solve the system

$$\begin{bmatrix} 2 & 1 & -2 \\ 1 & 2 & 2 \\ 3 & 3 & 0 \end{bmatrix} \cdot \begin{bmatrix} x_1 \\ x_2 \\ x_3 \end{bmatrix} = \begin{bmatrix} 4 \\ -1 \\ 5 \end{bmatrix}.$$

11. Show that a Hermitian matrix of rank 1 cannot have all its diagonal entries equal to zero.

12. Show that every Hermitian matrix of order n and rank 1 can be written in the form XX^* where X is a suitably chosen n-vector.

CHAPTER SIX

Vector Spaces and Linear Transformations

VECTOR SPACES

6.1 Examples and Definitions

Consider the set of all n-vectors X with components in a number field $\mathscr{F}$ which satisfy the equation $AX = 0$ where A is an $n \times n$ matrix over $\mathscr{F}$. By substitution we see at once that:

(a) If Y belongs to the set, then so does cY where c is any scalar from $\mathscr{F}$.

(b) If Y_1 and Y_2 belong to the set, so does the vector $Y_1 + Y_2$.

(c) Moreover, we have seen that all solutions are representable as linear combinations of a finite number of solutions

$$Y = \sum_{j=1}^{n-r} c_j Y_j,$$

where r is the rank of A, where $Y_1, Y_2, \ldots, Y_{n-r}$ are any $n - r$ linearly independent solutions of $AX = 0$, and where the c's are arbitrary scalars.

A closely related situation is the following: Let $A_1, A_2, \ldots, A_h$ be arbitrary n-vectors, not necessarily linearly independent, over a field $\mathscr{F}$. Consider the set of all linear combinations

$$\sum_{1}^{h} \alpha_j A_j,$$

where the α's are arbitrary scalars from $\mathscr{F}$. In this case:

(a) If X is a member of this set, then cX, where c is an arbitrary scalar from $\mathscr{F}$, is also a member of this set, for if $X = \sum \alpha_j A_j$, then $cX = \sum (c\alpha_j) A_j$.

(b) If X and Y are members of the set, then so is $X + Y$, for if $X = \sum \alpha_j A_j$ and $Y = \sum \beta_j A_j$, then $X + Y = \sum (\alpha_j + \beta_j) A_j$.

(c) All members of the set are expressed as linear combinations of $A_1, A_2, \ldots, A_h$.

Sets of n-vectors exhibiting properties (a) and (b) appear so frequently that it is helpful to assign them a special name. Hence we make the following definition: A nonempty set $\mathscr{V}_n$ of n-vectors with components from a number field $\mathscr{F}$ is a **linear vector space over** $\mathscr{F}$, more briefly a **vector space** or a **linear space** over $\mathscr{F}$, if and only if for all X and Y belonging to $\mathscr{V}_n$, (a) cX and (b) $X + Y$ also belong to $\mathscr{V}_n$, where c is an arbitrary scalar from $\mathscr{F}$.

In each of the above examples of vector spaces, all vectors of the space are expressible as linear combinations of a finite number of vectors of the space. For this reason, these vector spaces are called "finite dimensional." In addition, any set of n-vectors, independent or not, of which *all* vectors of the space are linear combinations, is said to **span** the space, and the space is said to be **spanned** by these vectors. We shall presently define dimension precisely and show that every vector space of n-vectors is finite dimensional for any positive integer n. Later we shall give a more general definition of a vector space and examples of infinite dimensional spaces. First, however, we turn to a geometric interpretation.

6.2 A Geometric Interpretation

Recall from the analytic geometry of three-dimensional Euclidean space (denoted here by $\mathscr{E}_3$) the concept of a directed line segment or, as we shall call it, a **geometric vector** $\overrightarrow{AB}$ *from* point A *to* point B. Any two such vectors which have the same length and the same direction are defined to be **equal**. It is convenient to include here the notion of a geometric vector of length zero from a point A to A itself. Such a vector is called a **zero-vector**. A zero-vector has no direction. Any two zero-vectors are defined to be equal.

The definition of equality just given divides the set of all vectors in $\mathscr{E}_3$ into **equivalence classes**: the set of all geometric vectors equal to any one vector constitutes such a class. Each specific vector of such a class is called a **representative** of that class.

Now let O denote a fixed point which is designated the **origin** of $\mathscr{E}_3$. Consider any class $\{V\}$ of equal nonzero-vectors. There is only one line through O in a given direction and there is only one point on this line at a given distance and in the given direction from O. Hence there is a unique point P such that $\overrightarrow{OP}$ has the length and the direction of the vectors of $\{V\}$, that is, is a representative of $\{V\}$. The definition of the zero-vector is intended to imply that there is only one zero-vector at a given point. Thus every class $\{V\}$ of equal vectors, including the class of zero-vectors, has a unique representative at O. The same is true at every other point in $\mathscr{E}_3$.

However, for the purpose of illustrating the algebra to follow, we use mostly vectors of the form $\overrightarrow{OP}$ where O is fixed.

Next we define certain operations with geometric vectors. If c is any real number and V is any vector $\overrightarrow{OP}$, then cV is defined to be a vector $\overrightarrow{OQ}$, $|c|$ times as long as $\overrightarrow{OP}$ and in the same direction if $c > 0$, but in the opposite direction if $c < 0$. (See Figure 6.2.1.) If $c = 0$, cV is the zero-vector at O.

The sum of any two geometric vectors $V_1 = \overrightarrow{OP_1}$ and $V_2 = \overrightarrow{OP_2}$ is by definition a vector found as follows: Using P_1 as an initial point, we construct a vector equal to $\overrightarrow{OP_2}$. Let the endpoint of this segment be the point P_3. Then $\overrightarrow{OP_3}$ is the sum $V_1 + V_2$. (Figure 6.2.2.) It is not difficult to show that

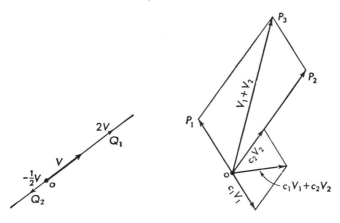

Figure 6.2.1   Figure 6.2.2

interchanging the roles of $\overrightarrow{OP_1}$ and $\overrightarrow{OP_2}$ in this process does not change the sum.

It is especially important to note that, if V_1 and V_2 lie on the same line through O, $V_1 + V_2$ is also *on this line* while if V_1 and V_2 are not collinear, they determine a plane through O and $V_1 + V_2$ *is in this plane*. Furthermore, if for arbitrary real numbers c_1 and c_2 we construct the vector $c_1 V_1 + c_2 V_2$ by adding vectors $c_1 V_1$ and $c_2 V_2$, we again obtain a vector which is in the same line as V_1 and V_2 if they are collinear but is otherwise in the same plane (Figure 6.2.2). We may therefore conclude the following result: If $\mathscr{V}$ is the set of all vectors of the form $\overrightarrow{OP}$ in a line (or plane) through O, then:

(a) If V belongs to $\mathscr{V}$, cV also belongs to $\mathscr{V}$ for any real number c.
(b) If V and W belong to $\mathscr{V}$, so does $V + W$.

The relation between these geometric properties and the algebraic concept of a vector space may be demonstrated by the introduction of a rectangular coordinate system with origin at O. In this coordinate system, let the coordinates of the endpoint P of a vector $V = \overrightarrow{OP}$ be taken as components of an **algebraic vector** $X = \{x_1, x_2, x_3\}$. In this way, to each geometric vector $V = \overrightarrow{OP}$ representing a class of equal vectors, there corresponds a unique algebraic vector, and conversely.

By the definition of equality of vectors, $\overrightarrow{AB} = \overrightarrow{OP}$, where $A = (y_1, y_2, y_3)$, $B = (z_1, z_2, z_3)$, and $P = (x_1, x_2, x_3)$, if and only if $z_1 - y_1 = x_1$, $z_2 - y_2 = x_2$, $z_3 - y_3 = x_3$ (Figure 6.2.3). Thus the point P and the algebraic vector X

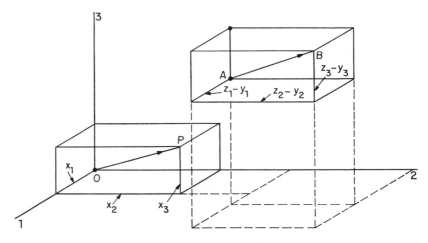

Figure 6.2.3

associated with a class of equal geometric vectors are readily determined as soon as the endpoints of one vector $\overrightarrow{AB}$ of the class are specified.

Now every vector on the line through O determined by a nonzero-vector $V = \overrightarrow{OP}$ is a multiple cV of V. If X is the algebraic vector corresponding to V, then by similar triangles, as is shown for the x_3 coordinate at the left

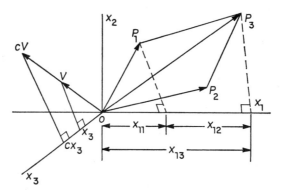

Figure 6.2.4

in Figure 6.2.4, we see that the geometric vector cV and the algebraic vector $cX = \{cx_1, cx_2, cx_3\}$ must also correspond. It is easy to check that the set of all multiples cX of a nonzero algebraic vector X, c and X real, is a vector space over the real number field. The corresponding geometric concept is therefore the set of all vectors cV on a line through O.

Next consider two vectors $V_1 = \overrightarrow{OP_1}$ and $V_2 = \overrightarrow{OP_2}$, and form the sum $V_1 + V_2$ as defined above. Then we know from analytic geometry (see Figure 6.2.4, right) that the projection on the x_1-axis of $\overrightarrow{OP_3}$ is the sum of the projections of $\overrightarrow{OP_1}$ and $\overrightarrow{P_1P_3}$. If P_j is the point (x_{1j}, x_{2j}, x_{3j}), $j = 1, 2, 3$, then these projections of $\overrightarrow{OP_1}$, $\overrightarrow{P_1P_3}$, and $\overrightarrow{OP_3}$ are respectively x_{11}, x_{12}, and x_{13} since $\overrightarrow{P_1P_3} = \overrightarrow{OP_2}$. Hence, $x_{13} = x_{11} + x_{12}$. Similar formulas hold for the other two axes. That is, if $V_3 = V_1 + V_2$, and if X_1, X_2, X_3 correspond respectively to V_1, V_2, V_3, then $X_3 = X_1 + X_2$. Thus the algebraic and geometric sums of corresponding algebraic and geometric vectors are again corresponding vectors. Moreover, since sums and scalar multiples correspond, it now follows that, if X_1 and X_2 correspond respectively to V_1 and V_2, then $c_1 X_1 + c_2 X_2$ corresponds to $c_1 V_1 + c_2 V_2$.

Now let V_1 and V_2 determine a plane π through O. Then the set of all vectors $c_1 V_1 + c_2 V_2$ is the set of all vectors $\overrightarrow{OP}$ in π. For let V denote any vector $\overrightarrow{OP}$ in π. Then (Figure 6.2.5) by drawing, through P, parallels to V_1 and V_2 intersecting the lines containing V_2 and V_1 respectively, we determine unique multiples $c_1 V_1$ and $c_2 V_2$ such that $V = c_1 V_1 + c_2 V_2$. Finally, since the geometric vectors V_1 and V_2 are not collinear, the corresponding algebraic vectors X_1 and X_2 are not proportional and, hence, are linearly independent. Thus, to the set of all vectors $\overrightarrow{OP}$ in a plane through O determined by two noncollinear vectors, there corresponds by the preceding paragraph the set of all linear combinations of two linearly independent algebraic vectors, and

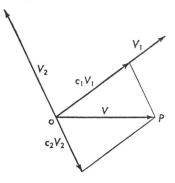

Figure 6.2.5

the converse is also true. But the set of all vectors $c_1 X_1 + c_2 X_2$ is a vector space over the real field. Thus *in $\mathscr{E}_3$ the set of all vectors $\overrightarrow{OP}$ in a plane through O and the vector space of all linear combinations of two independent algebraic vectors are corresponding concepts.*

What we have shown above is summarized by saying that there exists an "isomorphism" between certain sets of geometric and algebraic vectors when $n = 3$ (and hence, by specialization to subspaces, also when $n = 1$ or 2), with respect to the operations of vector addition and the multiplication of a vector by a scalar. That is, there is a one-to-one correspondence between algebraic and geometric vectors, such that algebraic and geometric sums of vectors correspond and algebraic and geometric scalar multiples correspond. This isomorphism is valuable in that it permits us to give our algebraic operations a simple and familiar geometric interpretation. The geometric language will be extended to higher dimensions in the next chapter. In this chapter we make free use of examples in $\mathscr{E}_3$ to help the reader grasp the algebraic concepts. We customarily drop the adjectives "algebraic" and "geometric" and refer simply to "vectors" since, in view of the above isomorphism, no further distinction is needed. Similarly, we shall refer to the sets of all vectors $\overrightarrow{OP}$ on a line or in a plane through O as vector spaces.

6.3 Exercises

*1. Show that the two conditions (a) and (b) in the definition of a vector space are equivalent to the single condition that, if X and Y belong to the set, then $c_1 X + c_2 Y$ also belong to the set, where c_1 and c_2 are arbitrary scalars from $\mathscr{F}$.

*2. Show that the zero-vector belongs to every vector space and that the zero-vector is itself a vector space over every field $\mathscr{F}$.

*3. Show that, if $A_1, A_2, \ldots, A_p$ belong to a vector space over a field $\mathscr{F}$, so does every linear combination over $\mathscr{F}$ of these vectors.

4. A single geometric vector is defined to be linearly dependent if and only if it is the zero-vector. Two geometric vectors $\overrightarrow{OP_1}$ and $\overrightarrow{OP_2}$ in $\mathscr{E}_3$ are defined to be linearly dependent if and only if they are collinear (that is, O, P_1, and P_2 are collinear), and three such vectors are defined to be linearly dependent if and only if they are coplanar (that is, if and only if O and P_1, P_2, P_3 all lie in the same plane). Show that in each case geometric vectors are linearly dependent if and only if the corresponding algebraic vectors are linearly dependent.

5. Show that the set of all polynomials $a_0 + a_1 x + \cdots + a_n x^n$, where n is a fixed positive integer, x is an indeterminate, and the a's are arbitrary complex numbers, is isomorphic to a vector space of $(n + 1)$-vectors. Indicate $n + 1$ such vectors of which all vectors of this vector space are linear combinations. What are the corresponding polynomials?

6. An arbitrary geometric vector $\overrightarrow{OP}$ in $\mathscr{E}_3$ can be represented in the form $a_1 i + a_2 j + a_3 k$, where i, j, and k denote vectors of unit length in the positive directions of the coordinate axes respectively. Give the geometric interpretation of a_1, a_2, a_3 and state the corresponding representation of $\overrightarrow{OP}$ in terms of algebraic vectors.

6.4 Basis and Dimension

In the previous section we saw that in $\mathscr{E}_3$ every vector $\overrightarrow{OP}$ in a plane π through O may be expressed as a linear combination of any two noncollinear vectors $\overrightarrow{OP_1}$, $\overrightarrow{OP_2}$ in π. Since not all vectors in π are multiples of any one vector, it is clear that at least two vectors are necessary for such a representation. On the other hand, two are sufficient. We call $\overrightarrow{OP_1}$ and $\overrightarrow{OP_2}$ a *basis* for the linear space of vectors $\overrightarrow{OP}$ in π and say that this space has *dimension* 2 since two vectors are required for a basis. The extension of these ideas to an arbitrary vector space $\mathscr{V}_n$ is begun in

Theorem 6.4.1: *Over an arbitrary number field $\mathscr{F}$, every vector space $\mathscr{V}_n$ not consisting of the zero-vector alone contains at least one set of linearly independent vectors $A_1, A_2, \ldots, A_k$ such that the collection of all linear combinations X of the form*

$$X = t_1 A_1 + t_2 A_2 + \cdots + t_k A_k,$$

where the t's are arbitrary scalars from $\mathscr{F}$, is precisely $\mathscr{V}_n$. Moreover, the integer k is uniquely determined for each $\mathscr{V}_n$.

Since $\mathscr{V}_n$ does not consist of the zero-vector alone, there exists at least one vector $A_1 \neq 0$ in $\mathscr{V}_n$. Then every vector $t_1 A_1$, where t_1 belongs to $\mathscr{F}$, belongs to $\mathscr{V}_n$. If every vector in $\mathscr{V}_n$ is of this form, then just A_1 will serve as the set of independent vectors mentioned in the theorem. If not every vector in $\mathscr{V}_n$ is of this form, let A_2 be one which is not. Then A_1 and A_2 are independent by Corollary 5.11.8 and every vector $t_1 A_1 + t_2 A_2$ belongs to $\mathscr{V}_n$. If $\mathscr{V}_n$ contains no vectors not of this form, A_1 and A_2 constitute the set of linearly independent vectors mentioned in the theorem. Otherwise, there exists in $\mathscr{V}_n$ a vector A_3 independent of A_1 and A_2 by Corollary 5.11.8, and so on. Since more than n n-vectors are always linearly dependent, this process cannot continue indefinitely but must terminate with some vector A_k, $k \leqslant n$, such that all vectors X of the form

(6.4.1) $$X = t_1 A_1 + t_2 A_2 + \cdots + t_k A_k$$

belong to $\mathscr{V}_n$, and such that all vectors X of $\mathscr{V}_n$ are of this form.

It remains to show that k is unique. Suppose that a different choice of vectors in the above process leads us to conclude that exactly all vectors X of $\mathscr{V}_n$ are also given by the combinations

$$X = s_1 B_1 + s_2 B_2 + \cdots + s_p B_p,$$

with the B's independent. Since these p independent B's all belong to $\mathscr{V}_n$, each must have a representation of the form (6.4.1). If we had $p > k$, we would thus have more than k linearly independent combinations of only k vectors, which is impossible by Theorem 5.11.9. Hence $p \leqslant k$. A similar argument shows that $k \leqslant p$. Hence $k = p$, and the proof of the theorem is complete.

Given a vector space, the unique integer k defined in the preceding theorem is called its **dimension**. Any set of independent vectors of a space of dimension k, for example, $A_1, A_2, \ldots, A_k$ in the above proof, such that all vectors of the space are linear combinations of these, are said to form a **basis** for the given space.

In what follows we shall denote a specific vector space of dimension k

by the symbol $\mathscr{V}_n{}^k$. It should be noted, however, that for a given integer k such that $0 < k < n$, there will be many such spaces over a given $\mathscr{F}$. In this new terminology, the proof of the preceding theorem yields also

Theorem 6.4.2:   *The dimension k of a given vector space $\mathscr{V}_n{}^k$ is the maximum number of independent vectors in the $\mathscr{V}_n{}^k$ and is also the minimum number of vectors needed to span the $\mathscr{V}_n{}^k$. Every basis for the $\mathscr{V}_n{}^k$ therefore contains exactly k independent vectors.*

Because of this theorem, we may henceforth regard a vector space $\mathscr{V}_n{}^k$ over a field $\mathscr{F}$ as the set of all vectors of the form (6.4.1), where the vectors $A_1, A_2, \ldots, A_k$ are linearly independent and the t's are arbitrary scalars from $\mathscr{F}$. Conversely, every set of vectors of the form (6.4.1), with the A's independent vectors over $\mathscr{F}$ and with the t's arbitrary scalars from $\mathscr{F}$, is a $\mathscr{V}_n{}^k$ over $\mathscr{F}$. An immediate consequence of these results is

Theorem 6.4.3:   *Let the matrix $C_{m \times n}$ over a number field $\mathscr{F}$ have rank $n - k$. Then the set of all n-vectors over $\mathscr{F}$ which satisfy the homogeneous system $CX = 0$ constitutes a $\mathscr{V}_n{}^k$ over $\mathscr{F}$.*

These vectors may, in fact, be written in the form (6.4.1) with the A's independent and with the t's arbitrary scalars of $\mathscr{F}$. The $\mathscr{V}_n{}^k$ defined by a homogeneous system of equations $CX = 0$ is sometimes called the **solution space** of the system.

To illustrate the first theorem, we give a simple but important example. Every n-vector X with components $x_1, x_2, \ldots, x_n$ in a number field $\mathscr{F}$ can be written in the form

$$(6.4.2) \qquad\qquad X = \sum_{j=1}^{n} x_j E_j,$$

where $E_1, E_2, \ldots, E_n$ are the elementary n-vectors

$$E_1 = \{1, 0, 0, \ldots, 0\},$$

$$E_2 = \{0, 1, 0, \ldots, 0\},$$

$$\vdots$$

$$E_n = \{0, 0, \ldots, 0, 1\}.$$

These vectors are linearly independent, so the set of all n-vectors over $\mathscr{F}$ constitutes the n-dimensional vector space $\mathscr{V}_n{}^n$ over $\mathscr{F}$. (Since $\mathscr{V}_n{}^n$ contains *all* n-vectors over $\mathscr{F}$, there is only one $\mathscr{V}_n{}^n$ over a given number field $\mathscr{F}$.)

At the other extreme, the scalar multiples $t_1 A_1$ of a nonzero-vector A_1 constitute a vector space $\mathscr{V}_n{}^1$ of one dimension for which A_1 is a basis. Such a $\mathscr{V}_n{}^1$ contains, of course, infinitely many elements. A different situation results if we take A_1 to be the zero-vector, for then every multiple of A_1 is still the zero-vector. Thus the zero-vector defines a vector space consisting of the zero-vector alone. Since the zero-vector is not independent, there are no independent vectors in a basis for this space. Hence we say it has dimension zero and designate it by $\mathscr{V}_n{}^0$. (Since $\mathscr{V}_n{}^0$ contains only the zero-vector, there is only one $\mathscr{V}_n{}^0$ over a given field $\mathscr{F}$.) In the case of $\mathscr{E}_3$, $\mathscr{V}_3{}^0$ is, as noted in the last section, represented by the origin O, a $\mathscr{V}_3{}^1$ by vectors $\overrightarrow{OP}$ on a line through O, and a $\mathscr{V}_3{}^2$ by vectors $\overrightarrow{OP}$ in a plane through O.

6.5 Equivalent Representations of a Vector Space

Let us consider now an example of a different kind. The vectors $\{1, 2, 3\}$ and $\{1, -2, 1\}$ span a $\mathscr{V}_3{}^2$ over the real field, any vector X of which is given by

(6.5.1)
$$\begin{bmatrix} x_1 \\ x_2 \\ x_3 \end{bmatrix} = t_1 \begin{bmatrix} 1 \\ 2 \\ 3 \end{bmatrix} + t_2 \begin{bmatrix} 1 \\ -2 \\ 1 \end{bmatrix},$$

where t_1 and t_2 are real, that is, the $\mathscr{V}_3{}^2$ is also defined by the scalar *parametric equations*

(6.5.2)
$$\begin{aligned} x_1 &= t_1 + t_2, \\ x_2 &= 2t_1 - 2t_2, \\ x_3 &= 3t_1 + t_2. \end{aligned}$$

We can define the $\mathscr{V}_3{}^2$ nonparametrically as follows: First we note that, since the two basis-vectors are linearly independent, the coefficient matrix of the t's in (6.5.2) has rank 2, so that we must be able to solve some two of equations (6.5.2) for t_1 and t_2. Using the first two, we obtain

$$t_1 = \frac{2x_1 + x_2}{4},$$

$$t_2 = \frac{2x_1 - x_2}{4},$$

and substituting into the third equation, we have finally

(6.5.3)
$$4x_1 + x_2 - 2x_3 = 0,$$

a single homogeneous equation with complete solution (6.5.1). Thus (6.5.3) serves to define the same $\mathscr{V}_3{}^2$ as do the given vectors. In $\mathscr{E}_3$ this is, of course, the equation of the plane through the origin containing the given $\mathscr{V}_3{}^2$.

Similarly, the 4-vectors $\{1, 1, 1, 1\}$ and $\{1, 0, 2, -1\}$ define a $\mathscr{V}_4{}^2$ over the real field. A nonparametric representation of this space may be obtained as in the preceding example or in the following more instructive fashion.

A real vector X belongs to the $\mathscr{V}_4{}^2$ if and only if it is a linear combination of the two given vectors, that is, if and only if the matrix

$$\begin{bmatrix} x_1 & 1 & 1 \\ x_2 & 1 & 0 \\ x_3 & 1 & 2 \\ x_4 & 1 & -1 \end{bmatrix}$$

has rank 2. The first two rows are independent since

$$\det \begin{bmatrix} 1 & 1 \\ 1 & 0 \end{bmatrix} \neq 0.$$

The third and fourth rows will be linearly dependent on the first two, that is, the matrix has rank 2 if and only if

$$\det \begin{bmatrix} x_1 & 1 & 1 \\ x_2 & 1 & 0 \\ x_3 & 1 & 2 \end{bmatrix} = 0 \quad \text{and} \quad \det \begin{bmatrix} x_1 & 1 & 1 \\ x_2 & 1 & 0 \\ x_4 & 1 & -1 \end{bmatrix} = 0,$$

that is, if and only if

$$2x_1 - x_2 - x_3 = 0,$$
$$x_1 - 2x_2 + x_4 = 0.$$

Thus X belongs to the $\mathscr{V}_4{}^2$ if and only if these last two equations are satisfied.

The two preceding examples are generalized in

Theorem 6.5.1:   *Every $\mathscr{V}_n{}^k$ over a number field $\mathscr{F}$ may be defined as the set of all solutions over $\mathscr{F}$ of a system, also over $\mathscr{F}$, of homogeneous linear equations of rank $n - k$ in n variables.*

If $k = n$, the trivial system represented by $AX = 0$, where A is an $m \times n$ zero matrix, will serve as the system mentioned in the theorem since every n-vector X is a solution of the equation and the rank of A is 0.

If $k = 0$, any system $AX = 0$, where A is over $\mathscr{F}$ and $\det A \neq 0$, will serve since the only solution of such a system is $X = 0$.

Suppose next that a given $\mathscr{V}_n{}^k$ over $\mathscr{F}$, $0 < k < n$, is spanned by the linearly independent n-vectors $A_1, A_2, \ldots, A_k$. Then it consists of all linear combinations over $\mathscr{F}$ of the form

(6.5.4) $$X = \sum_{j=1}^{k} t_j A_j.$$

For given X over $\mathscr{F}$, since the A's are independent, the matrix

(6.5.5) $$[X, A_1, A_2, \ldots, A_k]$$

has rank k if and only if X is a linear combination of the A's, that is, if and only if X belongs to the $\mathscr{V}_n{}^k$. Also, there exists in the matrix $[A_1, A_2 \ldots, A_k]$ some set of k independent rows, with indices $i_1, i_2, \ldots, i_k$, say. Therefore we can arrange (6.5.5) in the following form where the R_i's denote rows, the first k of which are linearly independent:

$$(6.5.6) \qquad
\begin{bmatrix}
R_{i_1} \\
\vdots \\
R_{i_k} \\
R_{i_{k+1}} \\
\vdots \\
R_{i_n}
\end{bmatrix}
\equiv
\begin{bmatrix}
x_{i_1} & a_{i_1 1} & a_{i_1 2} & \cdots & a_{i_1 k} \\
\vdots \\
x_{i_k} & a_{i_k 1} & a_{i_k 2} & \cdots & a_{i_k k} \\
x_{i_{k+1}} & a_{i_{k+1} 1} & a_{i_{k+1} 2} & \cdots & a_{i_{k+1} k} \\
\vdots \\
x_{i_n} & a_{i_n 1} & a_{i_n 2} & \cdots & a_{i_n k}
\end{bmatrix},
$$

$$
\det
\begin{bmatrix}
a_{i_1 1} & \cdots & a_{i_1 k} \\
\vdots \\
a_{i_k 1} & \cdots & a_{i_k k}
\end{bmatrix}
\neq 0.
$$

If X belongs to the $\mathscr{V}_n{}^k$, this matrix has rank k and any $k + 1$ rows are linearly dependent. Hence, since the first k rows are certainly linearly independent, all the other rows must be dependent on these. This is equivalent to saying that

$$(6.5.7) \qquad
\det
\begin{bmatrix}
R_{i_1} \\
\vdots \\
R_{i_k} \\
R_{i_{k+j}}
\end{bmatrix}
= 0, \qquad j = 1, 2, \ldots, n - k.
$$

Expanding these determinants, we find that the coefficient of $x_{i_{k+j}}$ is always $\pm$ the nonvanishing determinant of (6.5.6). Hence, if we divide equations (6.5.7) by this coefficient, we can write them in the form

$$(6.5.8) \qquad
\begin{aligned}
x_{i_{k+1}} &\qquad\qquad + f_1(x_{i_1}, \ldots, x_{i_k}) = 0, \\
x_{i_{k+2}} &\qquad\qquad + f_2(x_{i_1}, \ldots, x_{i_k}) = 0, \\
&\qquad \cdots \\
x_{i_n} &+ f_{n-k}(x_{i_1}, \ldots, x_{i_k}) = 0,
\end{aligned}
$$

where the f's are linear forms in the indicated x's. That is, every X of the $\mathscr{V}_n{}^k$ is a solution of this system, which has rank $n - k$ since each equation contains at least one variable appearing in no other equation. Thus the requirement that a vector X belong to the vector space spanned by the independent vectors $A_1, A_2, \ldots, A_k$ is expressible by $n - k$ linearly independent equations in the components of X.

Conversely, suppose (6.5.8) and hence (6.5.7) are satisfied by the components of some X over $\mathscr{F}$. Then (6.5.6) has rank k since exactly k rows are independent. Hence the columns of (6.5.6) are dependent also so that X belongs to the $\mathscr{V}_n{}^k$, by Theorem 5.11.7. Thus (6.5.8) has as solutions over $\mathscr{F}$ all those vectors X and only those vectors X over $\mathscr{F}$ which belong to the $\mathscr{V}_n{}^k$, so the theorem is proved. We add the final observation that, since each A_j belongs to the $\mathscr{V}_n{}^k$ and is therefore a solution of (6.5.8), and since the A's are independent, (6.5.4) is a complete solution over $\mathscr{F}$ of (6.5.8).

The system of equations representing a given $\mathscr{V}_n{}^k$ is not necessarily unique, but all systems so obtained will have the same complete solution (6.5.4) and hence define the same $\mathscr{V}_n{}^k$. They are therefore equivalent systems of equations.

We have now seen that, for a given field $\mathscr{F}$, the following are all equivalent concepts:

(a) A vector space $\mathscr{V}_n{}^k$ over $\mathscr{F}$.

(b) The set of all n-vectors X of the form $X = \sum_{j=1}^{k} t_j A_j$, where the A's are linearly independent n-vectors over $\mathscr{F}$ and the t's are arbitrary scalars of $\mathscr{F}$.

(c) The set of all solutions over $\mathscr{F}$ of a system (also over $\mathscr{F}$) of homogeneous equations $AX = 0$ in n variables and of rank $n - k$.

In what follows, we shall use whichever of these equivalent ideas is most convenient to the discussion at hand.

As in the above examples and theorems, we are typically concerned with equations, vector spaces, matrices, parameters, etc., all over a common number field $\mathscr{F}$. Hence, *in following sections, we will often drop the reference to the field $\mathscr{F}$ unless specific reference is needed to make the point clear. Otherwise an appropriate common field is to be understood.* In most applications, this is the real field.

To introduce the next theorem, we look at another kind of example. The $\mathscr{V}_2{}^2$ consisting of all 2-vectors may be represented by

$$\begin{bmatrix} x_1 \\ x_2 \end{bmatrix} = x_1 \begin{bmatrix} 1 \\ 0 \end{bmatrix} + x_2 \begin{bmatrix} 0 \\ 1 \end{bmatrix},$$

or by

$$\begin{bmatrix} x_1 \\ x_2 \end{bmatrix} = x_2 \begin{bmatrix} 1 \\ 1 \end{bmatrix} + (x_2 - x_1) \begin{bmatrix} -1 \\ 0 \end{bmatrix},$$

and the number of possible variations here is infinite. This example illustrates the next theorem:

Theorem 6.5.2:   *Any set of k linearly independent vectors of a $\mathscr{V}_n{}^k$ is a basis for that $\mathscr{V}_n{}^k$.*

Let $A_1, A_2, \ldots, A_k$ be a basis for the $\mathscr{V}_n{}^k$ (Theorem 6.4.1) and let $B_1, B_2, \ldots, B_k$ be any k linearly independent vectors of the $\mathscr{V}_n{}^k$. The theorem will be proved if we can show that for any vector X of the $\mathscr{V}_n{}^k$ there exist scalars $s_1, s_2, \ldots, s_k$ such that $X = \sum_{j=1}^{k} s_j B_j$. In scalar form, this is a system of n equations in k unknowns $s_1, \ldots, s_k$. The coefficient matrix $[B_1, B_2, \ldots, B_k]$ has rank k by hypothesis. Since each of the B's, and X as well, is a linear combination of the k independent A's, the $k + 1$ vectors $B_1, \ldots, B_k, X$ are dependent, the rank of the augmented matrix $[B_1, \ldots, B_k, X]$ is also k, the system is consistent, and the theorem follows.

This high degree of arbitrariness in the choice of a basis for a given $\mathscr{V}_n{}^k$ is in contrast to the uniqueness of the representation of a vector of $\mathscr{V}_n{}^k$ once the basis is chosen.

Theorem 6.5.3:   *If $A_1, A_2, \ldots, A_k$ are a basis for a $\mathscr{V}_n{}^k$, then a given vector X of the $\mathscr{V}_n{}^k$ can be represented in one and only one way in the form*

$$X = \sum_{j=1}^{k} t_j A_j.$$

For if also

$$X = \sum_{j=1}^{k} s_j A_j,$$

then

$$\sum_{j=1}^{k} (t_j - s_j) A_j = 0.$$

Since the A's are independent, the coefficients here must all vanish. That is, $t_j = s_j, j = 1, 2, \ldots, k$, and the two representations are identical.

These last two theorems illuminate the problem of solving a system $AX = B$ of n equations in n unknowns over a field $\mathscr{F}$. In the case when A is of rank n, the columns of A are independent and, hence, constitute a basis for $\mathscr{V}_n{}^n$, to which B necessarily belongs. Hence the vector B is representable as a unique linear combination of the columns of A:

$$x_1 A_1 + x_2 A_2 + \cdots + x_n A_n = B,$$

that is, there exists a unique solution to the system $AX = B$. In the case when A has rank $r < n$, there exists at least one subset of r columns $A_{j_1}, A_{j_2}, \ldots, A_{j_r}$ of A which constitute a basis for a $\mathscr{V}_n{}^r$ in $\mathscr{V}_n{}^n$ to which all columns of A, being representable as linear combinations of these r, belong. If now

$AX = B$ is a consistent system with solution Y, then, since $B = \sum_{j=1}^{n} y_j A_j$, B also belongs to the $\mathscr{V}_n^r$ determined by the columns of A. Hence B is expressible as a *unique* linear combination of $A_{j_1}, A_{j_2}, \ldots, A_{j_r}$. That is, for each set $A_{j_1}, A_{j_2}, \ldots, A_{j_r}$ of r independent columns of A, there exists in this case a unique solution of $AX = B$ in which all x_j's are 0 except for x_{j_1}, $x_{j_2}, \ldots, x_{j_r}$. Conversely, the system $AX = B$ is consistent if B belongs to the $\mathscr{V}_n^r$ since then a solution of the type just named exists.

6.6 Exercises

1. Find a nonparametric equation for the $\mathscr{V}_4^3$ over the real field spanned by $\{1, -1, 1, -1\}$, $\{1, 1, 1, 1\}$, and $\{1, 0, -1, 0\}$.

2. If $\begin{bmatrix} a \\ b \end{bmatrix}$ and $\begin{bmatrix} c \\ d \end{bmatrix}$ are independent so that they form a basis for a $\mathscr{V}_2^2$, find y_1 and y_2 such that

$$\begin{bmatrix} x_1 \\ x_2 \end{bmatrix} = y_1 \begin{bmatrix} a \\ b \end{bmatrix} + y_2 \begin{bmatrix} c \\ d \end{bmatrix}.$$

3. Find the dimension of the vector space over the rational field spanned by the columns of the matrix

$$\begin{bmatrix} 2 & 3 & -1 \\ -1 & 4 & -16 \\ 0 & -8 & 24 \end{bmatrix}.$$

4. Prove that the only k-dimensional subspace of a $\mathscr{V}_n^k$ is the $\mathscr{V}_n^k$ itself.

5. Prove that, if the rank of a matrix A of order (n, p) is $k \leqslant p$, then its columns span a $\mathscr{V}_n^k$ and the columns of A^{T} span a $\mathscr{V}_p^k$.

6. If E_j is the jth elementary p-vector and A is a matrix of order (n, p) over a number field $\mathscr{F}$, what is represented by the sum $\sum_{j=1}^{p} t_j(AE_j)$, where the t_j's are arbitrary scalars from $\mathscr{F}$?

7. Prove that the set of all m-vectors of the form $A_{m \times n} X_{n \times 1}$, where A and X are over a field $\mathscr{F}$, is a vector space whose dimension is equal to the rank of A. Here A is fixed and X is arbitrary.

*8. The vector space defined by the set of all linear combinations of the columns of a matrix A is called the **column space** of A, and the vector space defined by the columns of A^{T} is called the **row space** of A. Show that the columns of AB are in the column space of A and that the columns of $(AB)^{\mathsf{T}}$ are in the row space of B.

9. The vector space consisting of all vectors Y such that $Y^{\mathsf{T}} X = 0$ for all vectors X of a $\mathscr{V}_n^k$ is called the **annihilator** of the $\mathscr{V}_n^k$. Show that the annihilator is indeed a vector space. Show also how to find a basis for the annihilator of a given $\mathscr{V}_n{}^k$. Then find the annihilator of the $\mathscr{V}_3{}^2$ in $\mathscr{E}_3$ spanned by $\{1, 2, 3\}$ and $\{0, -1, 2\}$. Illustrate with a figure.

10. Show that Theorem 6.5.2 follows from Theorems 6.5.1 and 5.17.4.

11. Prove that, if A is over $\mathscr{F}$ and if $\mathscr{F}'$ is any subfield of $\mathscr{F}$, then the set of all solutions of $AX = 0$ which are over $\mathscr{F}'$ is a vector space over $\mathscr{F}'$.

12. Show that, if A_1, A_2, A_3 are linearly independent 3-vectors and if X is an arbitrary 3-vector, then

$$X = \frac{\det[X, A_2, A_3]}{\det A} A_1 + \frac{\det[A_1, X, A_3]}{\det A} A_2 + \frac{\det[A_1, A_2, X]}{\det A} A_3,$$

where $\det A = \det[A_1, A_2, A_3]$.

Extend this result to n-vectors and prove it.

*13. Prove that the columns of AB, where B is *nonsingular*, span the same vector space as do the columns of A. Given that $X = \sum c_j A_j$ is any member of this vector space, determine an expression for X as a linear combination of the columns of AB.

14. Does the vector space of vectors $\overrightarrow{OP}$ in $\mathscr{E}_3$ spanned by $\{1, -1, 1\}$ and $\{2, -3, 1\}$ contain any vectors in the first octant, that is, vectors which have all their components positive?

15. What linear combinations of the vectors $\{-1, 1, 1\}$ and $\{3, -2, 1\}$ in $\mathscr{E}_3$ yield vectors in the first octant?

16. Show that the set of all n-vectors $\{x_1, x_2, \ldots, x_n\}$ over a field $\mathscr{F}$, such that $x_{j_1} = x_{j_2} = \cdots = x_{j_k} = 0$ for fixed $j_1, j_2, \ldots, j_k$, constitutes a vector space. What is its dimension? Interpret geometrically in $\mathscr{E}_3$.

17. For what values of a, b, c do the vectors $\{1, 0, 0\}, \{1, a, 0\}, \{1, b, c\}$ span the $\mathscr{V}_3{}^3$ over a field $\mathscr{F}$?

18. Which subsets of the set of vectors

$$\begin{bmatrix} 1 \\ 1 \\ 3 \end{bmatrix}, \quad \begin{bmatrix} 2 \\ -1 \\ -4 \end{bmatrix}, \quad \begin{bmatrix} 4 \\ 1 \\ 2 \end{bmatrix}, \quad \begin{bmatrix} -2 \\ -2 \\ -6 \end{bmatrix}$$

constitute a basis for the vector space over the real field spanned by these vectors?

19. Under what conditions do the columns (rows) of a Vandermonde matrix determine a $\mathscr{V}_n{}^n$?

20. If elementary transformations on only the rows (columns) of a matrix A will transform it into a matrix B, A and B are called **row (column) equivalent**. Show that, if two matrices A and B over a number field $\mathscr{F}$ are row (column) equivalent, then their rows (columns) define the same vector space.

6.7 A Test for Independence and The Steinitz Replacement Theorem

It is useful in this and in later sections to have a special test for determining when any p given linear combinations $B_1, B_2, \ldots, B_p$ of k linearly independent vectors $A_1, A_2, \ldots, A_k$ are linearly dependent. Let

$$(6.7.1) \qquad\qquad B_j = \sum_{i=1}^{k} s_{ij} A_i, \qquad j = 1, 2, \ldots, p,$$

be these combinations. The B's are linearly dependent if and only if there exist scalars $\alpha_1, \alpha_2, \ldots, \alpha_p$, not all zero, such that

$$\sum_{j=1}^{p} \alpha_j B_j = 0,$$

that is, if and only if

$$\sum_{j=1}^{p} \alpha_j \left(\sum_{i=1}^{k} s_{ij} A_i \right) = \sum_{i=1}^{k} \left(\sum_{j=1}^{p} \alpha_j s_{ij} \right) A_i = 0.$$

This condition reduces to the system of equations

$$(6.7.2) \qquad \sum_{j=1}^{p} s_{ij}\alpha_j = 0, \qquad i = 1, 2, \ldots, k,$$

since the A's are linearly independent. The existence of nontrivial solutions for this system is a necessary and sufficient condition for the dependence of the B's. Hence we have

Theorem 6.7.1: *If $A_1, A_2, \ldots, A_k$ are linearly independent n-vectors, then the p n-vectors*

$$B_j = \sum_{i=1}^{k} s_{ij} A_i, \qquad j = 1, 2, \ldots, p,$$

are linearly dependent if and only if the matrix $[s_{ij}]_{(k,p)}$ has rank less than p, that is, if and only if the k-vectors

$$S_j = \{s_{1j}, s_{2j}, \ldots, s_{kj}\}, \qquad j = 1, 2, \ldots, p,$$

are linearly dependent.

Of course, if the rank of $[s_{ij}]$ is p, the B's are independent. Note that the matrix of coefficients in (6.7.1) is just the transpose of the matrix of coefficients in (6.7.2). We prove next

Theorem 6.7.2: *Given k linearly independent n-vectors $A_1, A_2, \ldots, A_k$, $k < n$, we can always find another n-vector A_{k+1} such that $A_1, \ldots, A_k, A_{k+1}$ are linearly independent.*

Indeed, if no vector A_{k+1} exists such that $A_1, \ldots, A_k, A_{k+1}$ are independent, then every vector of $\mathscr{V}_n^n$ is a linear combination of $A_1, \ldots, A_k$. Hence, by Theorem 6.4.1, $k = n$. This contradicts the assumption that $k < n$ and the theorem follows.

This theorem says in effect that every $\mathscr{V}_n^k$, $k < n$, can be **embedded**, as we say, in a $\mathscr{V}_n^{k+1}$, for the $\mathscr{V}_n^{k+1}$ spanned by $A_1, \ldots, A_k, A_{k+1}$ certainly contains all the vectors of the $\mathscr{V}_n^k$ spanned by $A_1, \ldots, A_k$.

A particularly simple vector A_{k+1} satisfying the requirements of the theorem is readily obtained. Let

$$A_j = \{a_{1j}, a_{2j}, \ldots, a_{nj}\}, \qquad j = 1, 2, \ldots, k.$$

Then the matrix $[A_1, A_2, \ldots, A_k]$ has rank k since the A's are linearly independent. Hence it contains some nonvanishing k-rowed determinant

$$\begin{vmatrix} a_{i_1 1} & \cdots & a_{i_1 k} \\ \vdots & & \\ a_{i_k 1} & \cdots & a_{i_k k} \end{vmatrix} \neq 0,$$

where $i_1, i_2, \ldots, i_k$ denote appropriately chosen rows. A simple choice for A_{k+1} is the elementary vector $E_i = \{0, \ldots, 0, 1, 0, \ldots, 0\}$, the 1 being placed in the ith row, where i is different from each of the row indices appearing above. Then in the matrix $[A_1, \ldots, A_k, A_{k+1}]$ we have the likewise nonvanishing determinant

$$\begin{vmatrix} a_{i_1 1} & \cdots & a_{i_1 k} & 0 \\ \vdots & & & \\ a_{i1} & \cdots & a_{ik} & 1 \\ \vdots & & & \\ a_{i_k 1} & \cdots & a_{i_k k} & 0 \end{vmatrix} \neq 0,$$

with a single 1 in the last column. Thus the matrix $[A_1, \ldots, A_k, A_{k+1}]$ has rank $k + 1$ so that the $k + 1$ A's are linearly independent.

Repeated application of the preceding results leads ultimately to

Theorem 6.7.3: *Given any set of k linearly independent n-vectors A_1, $A_2, \ldots, A_k$, $k < n$, we can always find $n - k$ additional n-vectors $A_{k+1}, \ldots$, A_n, such that the vectors $A_1, \ldots, A_k, A_{k+1}, \ldots, A_n$ are linearly independent and hence form a basis for $\mathscr{V}_n{}^n$. $A_{n+1}, \ldots, A_n$ may be chosen as elementary n-vectors.*

There are always infinitely many choices for each of $A_{k+1}, \ldots, A_n$ even though the above process suggests using only elementary vectors. Can you prove this?

It is, of course, clear that every $\mathscr{V}_n{}^k$ is embedded in $\mathscr{V}_n{}^n$, that is, it is a subspace of $\mathscr{V}_n{}^n$. The preceding paragraphs do more than corroborate this fact, however. They also give us a simple method of expressing this relationship in terms of a basis of a given $\mathscr{V}_n{}^k$ and suitable elementary vectors of $\mathscr{V}_n{}^n$. We shall make use of this technique shortly. Before continuing, however, we give a numerical example to illustrate the preceding theorem.

The vectors $\{1, 1, 3, 6\}$ and $\{1, 1, 1, 0\}$ are linearly independent and, hence, span a $\mathscr{V}_4{}^2$. In the matrix

$$\begin{bmatrix} 1 & 1 \\ 1 & 1 \\ 3 & 1 \\ 6 & 0 \end{bmatrix}$$

we have

$$\begin{bmatrix} 3 & 1 \\ 6 & 0 \end{bmatrix} \neq 0,$$

so that, by the procedure described in the theorem,

$$\begin{bmatrix} 1 & 1 & 0 \\ 1 & 1 & 1 \\ 3 & 1 & 0 \\ 6 & 0 & 0 \end{bmatrix} \quad \text{and} \quad \begin{bmatrix} 1 & 1 & 0 & 1 \\ 1 & 1 & 1 & 0 \\ 3 & 1 & 0 & 0 \\ 6 & 0 & 0 & 0 \end{bmatrix}$$

have ranks 3 and 4 respectively. Thus the vectors $\{1, 1, 3, 6\}$, $\{1, 1, 1, 0\}$, $\{0, 1, 0, 0\}$ span a $\mathscr{V}_4{}^3$ which contains the $\mathscr{V}_4{}^2$, and the vectors $\{1, 1, 3, 6\}$, $\{1, 1, 1, 0\}$, $\{0, 1, 0, 0\}$, $\{1, 0, 0, 0\}$ span $\mathscr{V}_4{}^4$ which contains both the $\mathscr{V}_4{}^2$ and the $\mathscr{V}_4{}^3$.

Suppose now that $A_1, A_2, \ldots, A_k$ are linearly independent n-vectors and that

$$B_j = \sum_{i=1}^k s_{ij} A_i, \qquad j = 1, 2, \ldots, p,$$

are any p linearly independent linear combinations thereof, where $p < k$. Then the k-vectors

$$S_j = \{s_{1j}, s_{2j}, \ldots, s_{kj}\}, \qquad j = 1, 2, \ldots, p,$$

are linearly independent by Theorem 6.7.1. By Theorem 6.7.3 we can now select $k - p$ elementary k-vectors $E_{i_1}, E_{i_2}, \ldots, E_{i_{k-p}}$ such that the k k-vectors

$$S_1, S_2, \ldots, S_p, E_{i_1}, E_{i_2}, \ldots, E_{i_{k-p}},$$

are linearly independent. The independence of these then implies, again by Theorem 6.7.1, that the corresponding linear combinations of the A's, namely,

$$B_1, B_2, \ldots, B_p, A_{i_1}, A_{i_2}, \ldots, A_{i_{k-p}},$$

are linearly independent and, hence, by Theorem 6.5.2, span the same $\mathscr{V}_n{}^k$ as do the A's themselves. We have thus proved what is known as the **exchange theorem** or the **Steinitz replacement theorem**:

Theorem 6.7.4: *Let $A_1, A_2, \ldots, A_k$ span a $\mathscr{V}_n{}^k$ and let $B_1, B_2, \ldots, B_p$ be any p linearly independent vectors of this $\mathscr{V}_n{}^k$. Then we can select from the A's $k - p$ vectors $A_{i_1}, A_{i_2}, \ldots, A_{i_{k-p}}$ such that $B_1, \ldots, B_p, A_{i_1}, \ldots, A_{i_{k-p}}$ are linearly independent and, hence, also span the $\mathscr{V}_n{}^k$.*

We establish a final theorem in this section. We have seen that every $\mathscr{V}_n{}^k$ can be defined as the set of all n-vectors X of the form $X = \sum_{j=1}^{k} s_j A_j$, where the A's are independent n-vectors and where distinct sets of scalars $s_1, \ldots, s_k$ yield distinct vectors X. In other words, there exists a one-to-one correspondence between the vectors X of the $\mathscr{V}_n{}^k$ and the vectors $\{s_1, \ldots, s_k\}$ of $\mathscr{V}_k{}^k$. This correspondence has a striking property. Let X_{S_1} and X_{S_2} be the n-vectors corresponding to the k-vectors $S_1 = \{s_{11}, s_{21}, \ldots, s_{k1}\}$ and $S_2 = \{s_{12}, s_{22}, \ldots, s_{k2}\}$:

$$X_{S_1} = \sum_{j=1}^{k} s_{j1} A_j \qquad \text{and} \qquad X_{S_2} = \sum_{j=1}^{k} s_{j2} A_j.$$

Then we have

$$c_1 X_{S_1} + c_2 X_{S_2} = \sum_{j=1}^{k} (c_1 s_{j1} + c_2 s_{j2}) A_j.$$

Since the right member here is the n-vector corresponding to the k-vector $c_1 S_1 + c_2 S_2$, we may write

$$c_1 X_{S_1} + c_2 X_{S_2} = X_{c_1 S_1 + c_2 S_2}.$$

Hence to any linear combination of k-vectors in $\mathscr{V}_k{}^k$ there corresponds in this way the *same* linear combination of the corresponding n-vectors in $\mathscr{V}_n{}^k$. We have thus proved

Theorem 6.7.5: *Over a given number field $\mathscr{F}$, every $\mathscr{V}_n{}^k$ is isomorphic to $\mathscr{V}_k{}^k$ with respect to the operation of forming linear combinations.*

6.8 The Intersection and the Sum of Two Vector Spaces

We begin by defining the set of all vectors common to two vector spaces $\mathscr{V}_n{}^k$ and $\mathscr{V}_n{}^h$ to be their **intersection**. In particular, since every $\mathscr{V}_n{}^k$ consisting of n-vectors is a subspace of $\mathscr{V}_n{}^n$, the intersection of a $\mathscr{V}_n{}^k$ with $\mathscr{V}_n{}^n$ is just the $\mathscr{V}_n{}^k$ itself. Similarly, the intersection of every $\mathscr{V}_n{}^k$ with $\mathscr{V}_n{}^0$ is $\mathscr{V}_n{}^0$. Next we define the set of all vectors $X + Y$, where X belongs to a $\mathscr{V}_n{}^k$ and Y belongs to a $\mathscr{V}_n{}^h$ to be the **sum** of the two vector spaces. We now prove

Theorem 6.8.1: *The intersection and the sum of two vector spaces $\mathscr{V}_n{}^k$ and $\mathscr{V}_n{}^h$ are again vector spaces.*

Let X and Y denote any two vectors of the intersection $\mathscr{K}$ of the $\mathscr{V}_n{}^k$ and the $\mathscr{V}_n{}^h$. Then X and Y each belong to both the $\mathscr{V}_n{}^k$ and the $\mathscr{V}_n{}^h$. Hence

$c_1 X + c_2 Y$ belongs to each of the $\mathscr{V}_n{}^k$ and the $\mathscr{V}_n{}^h$ and, hence, to $\mathscr{K}$. Therefore, by Exercise 1, Section 6.3, the intersection $\mathscr{K}$ is a vector space. It is possible for $\mathscr{K}$ to consist of the zero-vector alone.

Next let X and Y denote any two vectors of the sum $\mathscr{S}$ of the $\mathscr{V}_n{}^k$ and the $\mathscr{V}_n{}^h$. Then $X = U_1 + V_1$ and $Y = U_2 + V_2$, where U_1 and U_2 belong to the $\mathscr{V}_n{}^k$ and V_1 and V_2 belong to the $\mathscr{V}_n{}^h$. Hence

$$c_1 X + c_2 Y = (c_1 U_1 + c_2 U_2) + (c_1 V_1 + c_2 V_2),$$

which is a sum of a vector from the $\mathscr{V}_n{}^k$ and a vector from the $\mathscr{V}_n{}^h$ and hence is in $\mathscr{S}$. Thus $\mathscr{S}$ is also a vector space and the theorem is completely proved.

Suppose now that $A_1, A_2, \ldots, A_k$ form a basis for the $\mathscr{V}_n{}^k$ and that $B_1, B_2, \ldots, B_h$ form a basis for the $\mathscr{V}_n{}^h$. Then every linear combination

$$(6.8.1) \qquad \sum_{i=1}^{k} \alpha_i A_i + \sum_{j=1}^{h} \beta_j B_j$$

is a sum $X + Y$ of a vector X from the $\mathscr{V}_n{}^k$ and a vector Y from the $\mathscr{V}_n{}^h$, and every such sum $X + Y$ can be represented in the form (6.8.1). Thus the set consisting of the A's and the B's spans the sum $\mathscr{S}$. If the whole set of the $k + h$ A's and B's is a linearly independent set, then the dimension of the vector space (6.8.1) is $k + h$; otherwise it is less. We have, therefore,

Theorem 6.8.2: *The dimension of the sum of two vector spaces does not exceed the sum of their dimensions.*

The dimensions of the sum and of the intersection may now be related as follows:

Theorem 6.8.3: *If the given vector spaces $\mathscr{V}_n{}^k$ and $\mathscr{V}_n{}^h$ have vector spaces $\mathscr{V}_n{}^p$ and $\mathscr{V}_n{}^s$ as their intersection and sum respectively, then*

$$k + h = p + s.$$

We treat first the case where $p < k$ and $p < h$. Let $A_1, \ldots, A_p$ span the $\mathscr{V}_n{}^p$. Then, by Theorem 6.5.2, we can find vectors $A_{p+1}, \ldots, A_k$ and $B_{p+1}, \ldots, B_h$ such that $A_1, \ldots, A_p, A_{p+1}, \ldots, A_k$ span the $\mathscr{V}_n{}^k$ and such that $A_1, \ldots, A_p, B_{p+1}, \ldots, B_h$ span the $\mathscr{V}_n{}^h$. If we now can prove that $A_1, \ldots, A_p, A_{p+1}, \ldots, A_k, B_{p+1}, \ldots, B_h$ are independent, the theorem will follow, for these vectors are sufficient to span the $\mathscr{V}_n{}^s$. Suppose then there exist scalars α_j, β_j such that

$$\sum_{j=1}^{k} \alpha_j A_j + \sum_{j=p+1}^{h} \beta_j B_j = 0.$$

Then

$$\sum_{j=1}^{k} \alpha_j A_j = \sum_{j=p+1}^{h} (-\beta_j) B_j.$$

The vector on the left belongs to the $\mathscr{V}_n^k$. The right member shows that this vector also belongs to the $\mathscr{V}_n^h$. Hence it belongs to the $\mathscr{V}_n^p$, which shows that $\alpha_{p+1} = \cdots = \alpha_k = 0$, since $A_1, \ldots, A_p$ span the $\mathscr{V}_n^p$ and the whole set of A's is an independent set. Thus,

$$\sum_{j=1}^{p} \alpha_j A_j + \sum_{j=p+1}^{h} \beta_j B_j = 0,$$

which implies, since $A_1, \ldots, A_p, B_{p+1}, \ldots, B_h$ were chosen to be linearly independent, that also $\alpha_1 = \cdots = \alpha_p = \beta_{p+1} = \cdots = \beta_h = 0$. Thus all of $A_1, \ldots, A_p, A_{p+1}, \ldots, A_k, B_{p+1}, \ldots, B_h$ are linearly independent. Since these vectors span the $\mathscr{V}_n^s$, we have $s = k + h - p$, from which the desired result follows at once.

In the case where p is equal to k, every basis for the $\mathscr{V}_n^p$ is contained in the $\mathscr{V}_n^k$ and hence is also a basis for the $\mathscr{V}_n^k$, by Theorem 6.5.2. Thus the $\mathscr{V}_n^k$ and the $\mathscr{V}_n^p$ are the same space and, hence, the $\mathscr{V}_n^k$ is a subspace of the $\mathscr{V}_n^h$. Then the sum of the two spaces is just the $\mathscr{V}_n^h$ itself, and the relationship $k + h = p + s$ reduces to the identity $k + h = k + h$. The same is true if $p = h$.

Theorem 6.8.4:   *Let a $\mathscr{V}_n^h$ and a $\mathscr{V}_n^k$ intersect in a $\mathscr{V}_n^p$. Let $A_1, A_2, \ldots,$ A_p span the $\mathscr{V}_n^p$, $A_1, \ldots, A_p, B_{p+1}, \ldots, B_k$ span $\mathscr{V}_n^k$, and $A_1, \ldots, A_p,$ $C_{p+1}, \ldots, C_h$ span the $\mathscr{V}_n^h$. Then no two of the vector spaces $\mathscr{V}_n^p$, the $\mathscr{V}_n^{k-p}$ spanned by $B_{p+1}, \ldots, B_k$ and the $\mathscr{V}_n^{h-p}$ spanned by $C_{p+1}, \ldots, C_h$, have more than the zero-vector as their intersection.*

Suppose that a vector of the $\mathscr{V}_n^p$ belongs also to the $\mathscr{V}_n^{k-p}$ so that

$$\sum_{j=1}^{p} \lambda_j A_j = \sum_{j=p+1}^{k} \mu_j B_j.$$

This implies that all the λ's and μ's are zero since the A's and B's are linearly independent, that is, the zero-vector is the only vector common to the $\mathscr{V}_n^p$ and the $\mathscr{V}_n^{k-p}$. This is also true for the $\mathscr{V}_n^p$ and the $\mathscr{V}_n^{h-p}$. Finally, if the $\mathscr{V}_n^{k-p}$ and the $\mathscr{V}_n^{h-p}$ intersect, their intersection is in both the $\mathscr{V}_n^k$ and the $\mathscr{V}_n^h$, thus is in the $\mathscr{V}_n^p$. By what has just been proved, this must then be the zero-vector.

6.9 Exercises

    1. Consider two distinct planes through the origin in $\mathscr{E}_3$. What are the intersection and the sum of the associated linear spaces of vectors $\overrightarrow{OP}$?

    2. Prove that the dimension of the intersection of a $\mathscr{V}_n^k$ and a $\mathscr{V}_n^h$ over the same field is at least $k + h - n$. Give an example where it is exactly $k + h - n$.

    3. Under what conditions on k and h will a $\mathscr{V}_n^k$ and a $\mathscr{V}_n^h$ over the same field necessarily have an intersection of dimension > 0?

    4. Interpret Theorems 6.7.1, 6.7.2, and 6.7.3 geometrically in $\mathscr{E}_3$.

5. Determine the dimensions of the sum and of the intersection of the vector spaces defined by the columns of these matrices:

$$\begin{bmatrix} 1 & 0 & 0 & 1 \\ 0 & 1 & 0 & 1 \\ 0 & 0 & 1 & 1 \\ 0 & 0 & 0 & 1 \\ 0 & 0 & 0 & 1 \end{bmatrix}, \quad \begin{bmatrix} 1 & 1 & 1 & 1 \\ 0 & 1 & 1 & 1 \\ 0 & 0 & 1 & 1 \\ 0 & 0 & 0 & 1 \\ 0 & 0 & 0 & -1 \end{bmatrix}.$$

*6. The columns of a matrix of order (n, m) and rank r determine a vector space $\mathscr{V}_n{}^r$. Use this fact and Theorem 6.8.2 to prove that the rank of the sum of two matrices cannot exceed the sum of their ranks.

*7. Given two subspaces $\mathscr{V}_n{}^k$ and $\mathscr{V}_n{}^h$ of a $\mathscr{V}_n{}^n$ with the property that *every* vector of the $\mathscr{V}_n{}^n$ can be expressed uniquely as the sum of a vector from the $\mathscr{V}_n{}^k$ and a vector from the $\mathscr{V}_n{}^h$, prove that the $\mathscr{V}_n{}^k$ and the $\mathscr{V}_n{}^h$ have $\mathscr{V}_n{}^0$ as their intersection and $\mathscr{V}_n{}^n$ as their sum, so that $k + h = n$. Then state and prove the converse theorem. Two spaces with this property are called **complementary subspaces** of the $\mathscr{V}_n{}^n$. Given a $\mathscr{V}_n{}^k$, is a complementary $\mathscr{V}_n{}^{n-k}$ uniquely defined?

8. Show that, if in a $\mathscr{V}_n{}^n$ one n-vector has a unique representation as the sum of a vector from a $\mathscr{V}_n{}^k$ and a vector from a $\mathscr{V}_n{}^h$, then the sum of the $\mathscr{V}_n{}^k$ and the $\mathscr{V}_n{}^h$ is a $\mathscr{V}_n{}^{k+h}$, and their intersection is $\mathscr{V}_n{}^0$.

9. Prove that the intersection of a $\mathscr{V}_n{}^k$ over $\mathscr{F}_1$ and a $\mathscr{V}_n{}^h$ over $\mathscr{F}_2$ is a vector space over the intersection of $\mathscr{F}_1$ and $\mathscr{F}_2$.

10. Given that $A_{m \times n}$ has rank n and that $B_{n \times p} = [B'_{n \times r}, B''_{n \times (p-r)}]$, where the columns of B' are independent and B has rank r, what can be said about the columns of $AB = [AB', AB'']$? Similarly, if

$$A_{m \times n} = \begin{bmatrix} A'_{r \times n} \\ A''_{(m-r) \times n} \end{bmatrix}$$

has rank r with the rows of A' independent and if $B_{n \times p}$ has rank n, what can be said about the rows of

$$AB = \begin{bmatrix} A'B \\ A''B \end{bmatrix}?$$

LINEAR OPERATORS

6.10 Linear Vector Functions

The concept of function may be applied to vector as well as to scalar variables. A **vector function** f of a vector variable is a relation which associates, with each n-vector X of some set, a unique corresponding m-vector $f(X)$. The set of n-vectors to which X is restricted is called the **domain** of the function, and the set of corresponding m-vectors $f(X)$ is called the **range** of the function. As in the case of scalars, we often denote the vector corresponding to X by Y or by some other convenient symbol: $Y = f(X)$. A function is often called a **mapping**, and is said to map the vector X *onto* its unique **image vector** Y. It is also said to map its domain **onto** its range. In cases where the range is a subset of another set S, we say the function maps its domain **into** S.

If distinct vectors of the domain of a function always yield distinct image vectors, the function is said to define a **one-to-one correspondence** between its domain and its range because, for each vector of the domain, there is a unique corresponding vector of the range, and each vector of the range arises from a unique vector of the domain.

A simple but important example of a vector function is defined by the equation $Y = AX$ where A is an $n \times n$ matrix of scalars. A geometric interpretation of such a function when $n = 3$ is simply obtained. We regard the function as associating with each given vector X of $\mathscr{E}_3$ a certain vector Y of $\mathscr{E}_3$. Thus the function defined by

$$Y = \begin{bmatrix} 2 & 1 & 1 \\ 1 & 2 & 1 \\ 1 & 1 & 2 \end{bmatrix} X$$

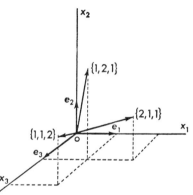

Figure 6.10.1

associates the vector $Y_1 = \{2, 1, 1\}$ with the vector $X_1 = E_1$, $Y_2 = \{1, 2, 1\}$ with E_2, $Y_3 = \{1, 1, 2\}$ with E_3, and so on. (See Figure 6.10.1.) It is important to notice that, if we know that the function has the form $Y = AX$, then as soon as we know the vectors Y_1, Y_2, Y_3 which correspond respectively to E_1, E_2, E_3, we can write the matrix which defines the function, for Y_1, Y_2, Y_3 are the columns of this matrix.

There are also vector functions of several vector variables. For example, the **cross product** $Z = X \times Y = \{(x_2 y_3 - x_3 y_2), (x_3 y_1 - x_1 y_3), (x_1 y_2 - x_2 y_1)\}$ will be familiar to the student of three-dimensional vector analysis. The reader should distinguish clearly between a *vector function* of vectors, which operates on vectors to produce vectors, and a *scalar function* of vectors, such as the scalar product $z = X^\mathsf{T} Y$, for example, which operates on vectors to produce scalars.

As an example of a vector function $Y = f(X)$, in which X and Y belong to spaces having different dimensions, consider the mapping

$$\begin{bmatrix} y_1 \\ y_2 \end{bmatrix} = \begin{bmatrix} 1 & 0 & 0 \\ 0 & 1 & 0 \end{bmatrix} \cdot \begin{bmatrix} x_1 \\ x_2 \\ x_3 \end{bmatrix},$$

where all vectors are over the real field. This function maps each vector X of $\mathscr{V}_3{}^3$ onto a unique vector Y of $\mathscr{V}_2{}^2$ in such a way that the components of the image vectors Y are the same as the first two components of the original vector X.

Let us interpret X as a vector $\overrightarrow{OP}$ in $\mathscr{E}_3$, and Y as a vector $\overrightarrow{OQ}$ in $\mathscr{E}_2$. Then this function amounts to projecting $\overrightarrow{OP}$ onto the x_1x_2-plane, thereafter plotting an "equal" vector in the y_1y_2-plane (Figure 6.10.2).

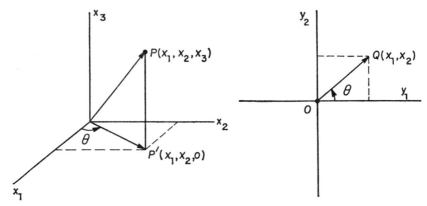

Figure 6.10.2

Although orthogonal axes are used in this figure, oblique axes could be used just as well. The same remark applies throughout this chapter. In Chapter 7, distance and angle will be defined and, for certain purposes, orthogonal reference systems will be essential.

As in the case of scalar functions of scalar variables, the concept of a linear function is of basic importance. We define a **linear homogeneous vector function**, also called a **linear vector function**, a **linear transformation**, or, as in what follows here, a **linear operator**, to be a vector function which maps the vectors of the $\mathscr{V}_n{}^n$ over a field $\mathscr{F}$ onto vectors of the $\mathscr{V}_m{}^m$ over $\mathscr{F}$, and which possesses the following properties:

(a) To each vector X of $\mathscr{V}_n{}^n$ it relates a unique vector Y of $\mathscr{V}_m{}^m$.
(b) $f(\lambda X) = \lambda f(X)$ for each scalar λ and for each vector X of $\mathscr{V}_n{}^n$.
(c) $f(X_1 + X_2) = f(X_1) + f(X_2)$ for all vectors X_1, X_2 of $\mathscr{V}_n{}^n$.

The analogous scalar properties are exhibited by the linear homogeneous function defined by the equation $f(x) = \alpha x$, where α belongs to $\mathscr{F}$.

Now let $E_1, E_2, \ldots, E_n$ denote the elementary n-vectors, and let $f(E_j) = A_j$ be the unique m-vectors corresponding to the E_j's by property (a). Then, since if $X = \{x_1, x_2, \ldots, x_n\}$, we can write

$$X = \sum_{j=1}^{n} x_j E_j,$$

and it follows by repeated use of (b) and (c) that

$$f(X) = \sum_{j=1}^{n} x_j f(E_j) = \sum_{j=1}^{n} x_j A_j,$$

or, if $[A_1, A_2, \ldots, A_n] = A$,

(6.10.1) $f(X) = AX.$

Moreover, since every function of the form (6.10.1) exhibits properties (a), (b), (c), every such function is a linear operator. We have therefore proved

Theorem 6.10.1: Every linear operator which maps vectors of the $\mathscr{V}_n^n$ over $\mathscr{F}$ onto vectors of the $\mathscr{V}_m^m$ over $\mathscr{F}$ can be represented in the form $f(X) = AX$, where A is the $m \times n$ matrix over $\mathscr{F}$, whose columns are the unique m-vectors $A_1, A_2, \ldots, A_n$ which the function relates to the elementary n-vectors $E_1, E_2, \ldots, E_n$ respectively. Conversely, every function representable in the form $f(X) = AX$ is a linear operator.

The above proof shows that a linear operator is uniquely defined as soon as the images of the elementary n-vectors $E_1, E_2, \ldots, E_n$, that is, the columns of A, are given. In this way there is established a one-to-one correspondence between the linear operators mapping the $\mathscr{V}_n^n$ over $\mathscr{F}$ into the $\mathscr{V}_m^m$ over $\mathscr{F}$, and the $m \times n$ matrices over $\mathscr{F}$. We shall see later that a one-to-one correspondence between these two sets can be established in other ways.

If the domain of a vector function $Y = f(X)$ is a certain set S, then the range of the function is called the **image of S by the function**. Using this terminology, we have

Theorem 6.10.2: The image of a vector space by a linear operator is again a vector space.

For if $Y_1 = AX_1$ and $Y_2 = AX_2$, then $c_1 Y_1 + c_2 Y_2 = A(c_1 X_1 + c_2 X_2)$. Thus if Y_1 and Y_2 are images of vectors X_1 and X_2 of a given vector space, then $c_1 Y_1 + c_2 Y_2$ is also an image of a vector of the same vector space. Hence the set of all these images constitutes a vector space. The set of all images of vectors of $\mathscr{V}_n^n$ is called the **image space** of the operator.

A particular case of the preceding theorem gives geometrical meaning to the rank of a matrix:

Theorem 6.10.3: Over a field $\mathscr{F}$, the image of a $\mathscr{V}_n^n$ by an operator $Y = A_{m \times n} X$ is a $\mathscr{V}_m^r$, where r is the rank of A.

Indeed, the image space is just the set of all linear combinations of the columns of A, that is, it is the vector space spanned by the columns of A, and this space has dimension r.

Theorem 6.10.4: The images of linearly dependent vectors by a linear operator are linearly dependent vectors.

Let the dependent vectors be $X_1, X_2, \ldots, X_k$ so that there exist scalars $\alpha_1, \alpha_2, \ldots, \alpha_k$, not all zero, such that

(6.10.2)
$$\sum_{j=1}^{k} \alpha_j X_j = 0.$$

Let the linear operator be represented by $Y = AX$, so that we have for images of the X's, $Y_j = AX_j, j = 1, 2, \ldots, k$. Multiplying (6.10.2) by A, we have

$$\sum_{j=1}^{k} \alpha_j (AX_j) = 0,$$

from which

$$\sum_{j=1}^{k} \alpha_j Y_j = 0,$$

and the theorem is proved.

An immediate consequence of the preceding two theorems is

Theorem 6.10.5:   *The dimension of the image, by a linear operator, of a given $\mathscr{V}_n{}^k$, is not greater than k.*

To determine when the rank of the image space is also k, we need

Theorem 6.10.6:   *If A is an $m \times n$ matrix of rank n, then the images of linearly independent n-vectors by the linear operator $Y = AX$ are also linearly independent vectors.*

Let $X_1, X_2, \ldots, X_k$ be independent, and let $Y_j = AX_j, j = 1, 2, \ldots, k$. Then if

(6.10.3)
$$\sum_{j=1}^{k} \alpha_j Y_j = 0,$$

we have by substitution

$$\sum_{j=1}^{k} \alpha_j (AX_j) = 0,$$

or

$$A \left(\sum_{j=1}^{k} \alpha_j X_j \right) = 0,$$

which, since A has rank n so that $AX = 0$ has no nontrivial solutions, implies that

$$\sum_{j=1}^{k} \alpha_j X_j = 0.$$

Now the vectors $X_1, X_2, \ldots, X_k$ are linearly independent by hypothesis, so that $\alpha_1 = \alpha_2 = \cdots = \alpha_k = 0$. Since this conclusion follows from the assumption (6.10.3), the Y's must also be independent.

This theorem enables us to prove

Theorem 6.10.7:   *Over a field* $\mathscr{F}$, *the image of a* $\mathscr{V}_n{}^k$ *by the linear operator* $Y = AX$, *where* A *is an* $m \times n$ *matrix of rank* n, *is a* $\mathscr{V}_m{}^k$.

First of all, the image is a vector space of dimension $\leqslant k$ by Theorems 6.10.2 and 6.10.5. But by Theorem 6.10.6, the image of any set of basis vectors of the $\mathscr{V}_n{}^k$ is a set of k linearly independent m-vectors. Hence the image space has dimension k.

It is important to note the nature of the image of a linear combination of vectors. If $Y = AX$, where A is $m \times n$, and if

$$X = \sum_{j=1}^{k} \alpha_j X_j,$$

where $X_1, X_2, \ldots, X_k$ are arbitrary n-vectors, then the image of this linear combination is given by

$$Y = AX = \sum_{j=1}^{k} \alpha_j (A X_j),$$

or, if we put

$$Y_j = AX_j, \qquad j = 1, 2, \ldots, k,$$

by

$$Y = \sum_{j=1}^{k} \alpha_j Y_j,$$

that is, *the image of a linear combination of vectors by a linear operator is the same linear combination of the image vectors.*

6.11 Operators on a $\mathscr{V}_n{}^n$

Of particular importance in many applications are the linear operators which map vectors of the $\mathscr{V}_n{}^n$ over a field $\mathscr{F}$ onto vectors of the same $\mathscr{V}_n{}^n$. In this case, the operator is called **an operator on the** $\mathscr{V}_n{}^n$. The matrix A associated with the operator is now square, and this fact gives rise to the following definition: A linear operator $Y = AX$ on a $\mathscr{V}_n{}^n$ is said to be **nonsingular** if and only if the associated matrix A is nonsingular, that is, if and only if A is square and $\det A \neq 0$. The geometrical meaning of nonsingularity is given in

Theorem 6.11.1:   *A linear operator* $Y = AX$ *is nonsingular if and only if distinct vectors* X_1, X_2 *always give rise to distinct image vectors* $Y_1 = AX_1$ *and* $Y_2 = AX_2$, *that is, if and only if the correspondence is one-to-one.*

Note first that $X_1 \neq X_2$ if and only if $X_1 - X_2 \neq 0$. Now $Y_1 = Y_2$ for $X_1 \neq X_2$ if and only if $AX_1 = AX_2$ for $X_1 \neq X_2$, that is, if and only if $A(X_1 - X_2) = 0$ for $X_1 - X_2 \neq 0$. But $AX = 0$ can have a nontrivial solution $X_1 - X_2$ if and only if A is singular (Corollary 5.6.2). Thus we can have $Y_1 = Y_2$ for $X_1 \neq X_2$ if and only if A is singular. The theorem follows.

Theorems 6.10.6 and 6.10.7 may now be specialized as follows:

Theorem 6.11.2:   *The images of linearly independent vectors by a non-singular linear operator are linearly independent vectors.*

Theorem 6.11.3:   *The image of a vector space by a nonsingular linear operator is a vector space of the same dimension.*

To provide a geometrical example in $\mathscr{E}_3$, let a given $\mathscr{V}_3{}^2$ be spanned by the vectors $\{-1, 1, 1\}$ and $\{0, 0, 1\}$, and let a given nonsingular operator be

$$Y = \begin{bmatrix} 0 & 1 & 0 \\ 1 & 0 & 0 \\ 1 & 1 & 1 \end{bmatrix} X.$$

This maps the given vectors into the vectors $\{1, -1, 1\}$ and $\{0, 0, 1\}$ respectively. If we represent all these vectors in the same reference system, we see that, in this particular case, both the first two and their images determine the same plane through the origin, that is, the same $\mathscr{V}_3{}^2$ (Figure 6.11.1).

Theorem 6.11.4:   *There is a unique linear operator which maps the elementary vectors $E_1, E_2, \ldots, E_n$ of $\mathscr{V}_n{}^n$ onto any set of n-vectors $A_1, A_2, \ldots, A_n$, in that order. The operator is nonsingular if and only if $A_1, A_2, \ldots, A_n$ are linearly independent. Its matrix is $A = [A_1, A_2, \ldots, A_n]$.*

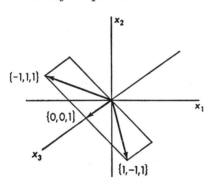

Figure 6.11.1

For the operator $Y = AX = [A_1, A_2, \ldots, A_n]X$ maps the elementary vectors onto the columns of the matrix A respectively. Given the n n-vectors $A_1, A_2, \ldots, A_n$ which are to be the images of the elementary vectors, we can write A at once, and this is the *only* matrix which will effect the required mapping. Moreover, A will be nonsingular if and only if the columns $A_1, A_2, \ldots, A_n$ are independent.

Theorem 6.11.5:   *Given any n linearly independent n-vectors of a $\mathscr{V}_n{}^n$, there exists a nonsingular linear operator by which their images are the elementary vectors.*

Let $A_1, A_2, \ldots, A_n$ denote the given vectors. Then the operator $Y = A^{-1}X$, where A is chosen as in the preceding theorem, will do it.

Theorem 6.11.6:   *Given any two sets of n linearly independent n-vectors of a $\mathscr{V}_n{}^n$, there exists a nonsingular linear operator which maps the vectors of one set respectively onto those of the other.*

Let $X_1, X_2, \ldots, X_n$ and $Z_1, Z_2, \ldots, Z_n$ be the two sets of independent n-vectors. Now suppose that the operator $Y = AX$ maps the vectors $X_1, X_2, \ldots, X_n$ onto the elementary vectors respectively, and suppose that the operator $Z = BY$ maps the elementary vectors onto the set of vectors $Z_1, Z_2, \ldots, Z_n$ respectively. Then the operator $Z = B(AX) = (BA)X$ maps the vectors $X_1, X_2, \ldots, X_n$ onto the vectors $Z_1, Z_2, \ldots, Z_n$ respectively. Since A and B are nonsingular, so is the matrix BA, and the proof is complete.

To illustrate the last theorem in $\mathscr{E}_2$, we find the linear operator which maps the vectors $\{1, 1\}, \{1, -1\}$ respectively onto the vectors $\{1, 2\}, \{2, -1\}$.

We first let $X = A^{-1}Y$ denote the operator which maps $\{1, 0\}$ and $\{0, 1\}$ respectively onto $\{1, 1\}, \{1 -1\}$. Then, by Theorem 6.11.4,

$$X = \begin{bmatrix} 1 & 1 \\ 1 & -1 \end{bmatrix} Y \quad \text{or} \quad Y = \begin{bmatrix} \frac{1}{2} & \frac{1}{2} \\ \frac{1}{2} & -\frac{1}{2} \end{bmatrix} X.$$

The operator $Z = BY$ which maps $\{1, 0\}$ and $\{0, 1\}$ respectively onto $\{1, 2\}, \{2, -1\}$ is, again by Theorem 6.11.4,

$$Z = \begin{bmatrix} 1 & 2 \\ 2 & -1 \end{bmatrix} Y.$$

Combining the two operators, we obtain

$$Z = \begin{bmatrix} 1 & 2 \\ 2 & -1 \end{bmatrix} \cdot \begin{bmatrix} \frac{1}{2} & \frac{1}{2} \\ \frac{1}{2} & -\frac{1}{2} \end{bmatrix} X = \begin{bmatrix} \frac{3}{2} & -\frac{1}{2} \\ \frac{1}{2} & \frac{3}{2} \end{bmatrix} X,$$

which maps $\{1, 1\}$ and $\{1, -1\}$ respectively onto $\{1, 2\}$ and $\{2, -1\}$.

Alternatively, we can write

$$\begin{bmatrix} z_1 \\ z_2 \end{bmatrix} = \begin{bmatrix} a & b \\ c & d \end{bmatrix} \cdot \begin{bmatrix} x_1 \\ x_2 \end{bmatrix},$$

from which, by substituting pairs of corresponding vectors, we obtain

$$\begin{bmatrix} 2 \\ 1 \end{bmatrix} = \begin{bmatrix} a & b \\ c & d \end{bmatrix} \cdot \begin{bmatrix} 1 \\ 1 \end{bmatrix}, \quad \begin{bmatrix} 1 \\ -2 \end{bmatrix} = \begin{bmatrix} a & b \\ c & d \end{bmatrix} \cdot \begin{bmatrix} 1 \\ -1 \end{bmatrix}.$$

These are equivalent to the two pairs of scalar equations

$$a + b = 2, \quad c + d = 1,$$
$$a - b = 1, \quad c - d = -2.$$

Solving these equations for a, b, c, d, we have, again,

$$Z = \begin{bmatrix} \frac{3}{2} & -\frac{1}{2} \\ \frac{1}{2} & \frac{3}{2} \end{bmatrix} X.$$

6.12 Exercises

1. Find the linear operator on a $\mathscr{V}_2{}^2$ which maps the vectors $\{1, 1\}$ and $\{3, -2\}$ onto the vectors $\{2, 1\}$ and $\{1, 2\}$ respectively.

2. Find the linear operator on a $\mathscr{V}_3{}^3$ which maps the elementary vectors onto the vectors $\{1, 1, 1\}$, $\{-1, 1, -1\}$, and $\{1, 1, 2\}$ respectively. Then find the linear operator that maps these last three vectors onto the elementary vectors.

3. A certain linear operator maps $\{1, 1, 0\}$ onto $\{0, 2, 1\}$, $\{1, 0, 0\}$ onto $\{1, -1, 2\}$, and $\{1, 1, 1\}$ onto $\{3, 4, 0\}$. Onto what vectors does it map E_1, E_2, E_3 respectively? Recall that, if a linear operator maps X_1 onto Y_1 and X_2 onto Y_2, then it maps $c_1X_1 + c_2X_2$ onto $c_1Y_1 + c_2Y_2$.

4. Determine the linear operator $Y = AX$ which maps the vectors E_1, E_2, E_3 of a $\mathscr{V}_3{}^3$ onto the vectors $\{1, 0\}$, $\{0, 1\}$, $\{1, 1\}$ of a $\mathscr{V}_2{}^2$ respectively. Show that every vector of the $\mathscr{V}_2{}^2$ is the image by this operator of infinitely many vectors of the $\mathscr{V}_3{}^3$. If each of the vectors of the $\mathscr{V}_3{}^3$ which have the same image $\{a, b\}$ is represented as a geometrical vector $\overrightarrow{OP}$, what is the locus of the endpoints P?

5. Determine the linear operator $Y = AX$ which maps the vectors $\{1, 2\}$ and $\{2, 1\}$ of a $\mathscr{V}_2{}^2$ respectively onto the vectors $\{7, 0, -8\}$ and $\{5, 3, 2\}$ of a $\mathscr{V}_3{}^3$. Onto what vectors does it map $\{1, 0\}$ and $\{0, 1\}$? Does any vector in the $\mathscr{V}_2{}^2$ map onto $\{1, 9, 22\}$? Onto $\{1, 0, 0\}$? Which vectors in the $\mathscr{V}_3{}^3$ are images by this operator of vectors in the $\mathscr{V}_2{}^2$?

*6. Prove that a system $AX = B$ of m equations in n unknowns is consistent if and only if the vector B belongs to the vector space defined by the columns of A.

7. Show that any $\mathscr{V}_n{}^k$ ($k < n$) in a $\mathscr{V}_n{}^n$ may be mapped onto the $\mathscr{V}_n{}^k$ represented by the equations $y_1 = y_2 = \cdots = y_{n-k} = 0$ by a nonsingular linear operator.

8. Show that any $\mathscr{V}_n{}^k$ in a $\mathscr{V}_n{}^n$ may be mapped onto any other $\mathscr{V}_n{}^k$ of the $\mathscr{V}_n{}^n$ by a nonsingular operator.

9. The basis vectors of a $\mathscr{V}_n{}^k$ may be used as the columns of a matrix of order (n, k) and rank k. To what results concerning matrices are Exercises 7 and 8 therefore equivalent?

10. Interpret each of the following linear operators geometrically in $\mathscr{E}_3$:

(a) $Y = 0 \cdot X$, where 0 denotes the zero matrix.

(b) $Y = IX$.

(c) $Y = \lambda X$, $\lambda \neq 0$.

(d) $Y = D[\lambda_1, \lambda_2, \lambda_3]X$.

*11. Show that each of the following vector functions is a linear operator, and represent it in the form $Y = AX$. In each case, the domain of the function is the $\mathscr{V}_n{}^n$ over a field $\mathscr{F}$.

(a) $Y(X) = (A^{\mathsf{T}}X)A$, where A is a fixed vector of $\mathscr{V}_n{}^n$.

(b) $Y(X) = \{x_1, \frac{1}{2}(x_1 + x_2), \frac{1}{3}(x_1 + x_2 + x_3), \ldots, 1/n(x_1 + x_2 + \cdots + x_n)\}$.

(c) $Y(X) = \{x_{j_1}, x_{j_2}, \ldots, x_{j_n}\}$, where $j_1, j_2, \ldots, j_n$ are a permutation of $1, 2, \ldots, n$.

(d) $Y(X) = \{x_1, x_2, \ldots, x_k, 0, 0, \ldots, 0\}$, where $k < n$.

(e) $Y(X) = BX + CX$, where B and C are $m \times n$ matrices over $\mathscr{F}$.

(f) $Y(X) = B(CX)$, where B is an $m \times r$ matrix and C is an $r \times n$ matrix over $\mathscr{F}$.

(g) $Y(X) = \alpha X$, where α is a scalar in $\mathscr{F}$.

(h) $Y(X) = \alpha(BX)$, where α is a scalar in $\mathscr{F}$ and B is an $m \times n$ matrix over $\mathscr{F}$.

12. Show that each of the following vector functions is *not* a linear operator:

(a) $f(X) = AX + B$, where A is an $n \times n$ matrix over $\mathscr{F}$ and B is a fixed nonzero n-vector over $\mathscr{F}$.

(b) $g(X) = \{\sqrt{x_1{}^2}, \sqrt{x_2{}^2}, \ldots, \sqrt{x_n{}^2}\}$, where $\mathscr{F}$ is the real field.

(c) $h(X) = (A^\mathsf{T}X)X$, where A is a fixed n-vector.

Interpret (a), (b), (c) geometrically in $\mathscr{E}_2$.

*13. Show that, if $Y = AX$ represents a nonsingular linear operator, then the y's are linearly independent functions of the x's.

14. Show that the operator in $\mathscr{E}_3$, $Y = A \times X$, where the cross product is as defined in Section 6.10 and A is a fixed 3-vector, is singular. Show also that the scalar triple product $(A \times B)^\mathsf{T}C$ is given by $\det [A, B, C]$.

15. Let $AX = B$ be a consistent system, and let $X = CY$ be a nonsingular linear operator. Show that the system $(AC)Y = B$ is also consistent, and that the solutions of the two systems are in one-to-one correspondence.

16. Let $AX = B$ be a consistent system, and let P and Q denote nonsingular matrices such that PAQ is in the normal form as defined in Chapter Four. Show that, if P and Q are known, the given system of equations may be solved readily with the aid of the substitution $X = QY$. What are the arbitrary parameters in the solution?

17. Let $AX = B$ be a consistent system of equations, and put $X = CY$. Here A is $m \times n$, C is $n \times p$, and Y is $p \times 1$. If the system $(AC)Y = B$ is consistent, then each solution Y leads to a solution $X = CY$ of the first system. Show that, vice versa, each solution X of the first system leads to a solution of the second if and only if the columns of C span the solution space of the first system. Comment on the significance of the nonsingularity of C in Exercise 15.

18. Find an operator which maps every vector of the $\mathscr{V}_3{}^3$ over the real field onto a vector of the subspace spanned by $\{1, 0, 1\}$ and $\{0, 1, 0\}$.

19. Given two sets of vectors $A_1, A_2, \ldots, A_n$ and $B_1, B_2, \ldots, B_n$, of the same $\mathscr{V}_n{}^n$, under what conditions does there exist a linear operator which maps the A's onto the B's respectively? When is this operator nonsingular?

*20. Prove that an operator $Y = AX$ on a $\mathscr{V}_n{}^n$ is nonsingular if and only if its range is the $\mathscr{V}_n{}^n$.

*21. Given a $\mathscr{V}_n{}^r$ and a $\mathscr{V}_n{}^k$ in $\mathscr{V}_n{}^n$, with $r \geqslant k$, show that there exists a linear operator which maps the $\mathscr{V}_n{}^r$ onto the $\mathscr{V}_n{}^k$. (This is a generalization of Theorem 6.11.6.)

6.13 Products of Linear Operators

Suppose that, as in Section 6.11, the operator $Y = AX$ maps a vector X onto a vector Y, and that an operator $Z = BY$ then maps Y onto Z. The mapping $Z = B(AX)$, which thus maps X via Y onto Z, is called the **product of the two given operators**. Such a product is defined whenever the matrices B and A associated with the operators are conformable for multiplication, that is, whenever the product BA is defined. Since we then may write $Z = (BA)X$, the product is also an operator, namely, one which maps X directly onto Z. In summary, we have

Theorem 6.13.1:   *The product of two linear operators is a linear operator whose matrix is the product of their matrices, the matrix of the second operator premultiplying that of the first.*

If we now multiply the above product by an operator $W = CZ$, we obtain the product $W = C(BA)X$. On the other hand, if we multiply the last two operators first, $W = (CB)Y$, and then combine with $Y = AX$, we obtain the product $W = (CB)AX$. Since matrix multiplication is associative, the two results are identical. We therefore have

Theorem 6.13.2:   *The multiplication of linear operators is associative.*

A linear operator as defined in this chapter is a particular example of a very general type of mapping called a "transformation." When one defines what is meant in general by a transformation and by the product of transformations, it may be shown that multiplication is always associative. Then the associativity just proved here, and hence the associativity of matrix multiplication, may be concluded as a special case of the more general result. (See G. Birkhoff and S. Mac Lane, *A Survey of Modern Algebra*, Revised Edition, New York, Macmillan, 1953, p. 120.)

The products of the operators $Z = BY, Y = AX$, and $Z = AY, Y = BX$ are respectively $Z = (BA)X$ and $Z = (AB)X$, if they both exist. Since matrix multiplication is not in general commutative, these products are not in general the same and possibly may not even both be defined. Hence we conclude

Theorem 6.13.3:   *The multiplication of linear operators is not in general commutative.*

It is important to recognize that the most essential aspect of the representation $Y = AX$ of an operator is the matrix A. The symbols Y and X are just convenient symbols for the vectors which correspond under the mapping, "dummy variables" as it were. If we have both $Y = AX$ and $W = AZ$, we therefore say that we apply the *same operator* to both X and Z. Indeed, the same operations are performed on both X and Z to obtain their images. The only occasion when the symbols for the vectors are of special significance is when we wish to form the product of operators. In this case, we use appropriate common symbols for certain vectors to indicate the order in which the multiplication is to be carried out, as the above proofs illustrate.

Because the operator is represented by a matrix A, the matrix itself is at times called an operator. It will appear in a following section that the same operator may be represented by different matrices in different reference systems, and that the same matrix A may represent different operators in different reference systems. Hence to refer to the matrix A as a linear operator is not, in fact, legitimate. However, if the reference system involved is fully understood, this usage may not cause confusion. These matters will be clarified in Sections 6.16 through 6.18.

To give more significance to the concept of the product of two operators, let us study again the rank of the product of two matrices. First we prove

Theorem 6.13.4:   *If $A_{m \times n}$ has rank n and $B_{n \times p}$ has rank r_B, then the product AB has rank r_B.*

Let $C = AB$. Then the columns of C are the images by the operator $Y = AX$ of the corresponding columns of B:

$$C_j = AB_j, \qquad j = 1, 2, \ldots, p.$$

By Theorems 6.10.4 and 6.10.6, since there are r_B independent columns in B, there will also be r_B independent columns in C, but not more. Thus C has rank r_B.

Looking at it another way, by Theorem 6.10.7, since A has rank n, the image of the column space of B has dimension r_B. But since the image of a linear combination of vectors is the same linear combination of their images, the image of the column space of B is just the column space of C. Thus C also has rank r_B.

We can use the operator concept to prove an important result established earlier in another way:

The image of a $\mathscr{V}_p^p$ by the operator $Y = (A_{m \times n} B_{n \times p})X = A(BX)$ is the image by $Y = AZ$ of the image by $Z = BX$ of $\mathscr{V}_p^p$. Since the image by $Z = BX$ of $\mathscr{V}_p^p$ is a subspace of $\mathscr{V}_n^n$, the image by $Y = (AB)X$ of $\mathscr{V}_p^p$ is a subspace of the image of $\mathscr{V}_n^n$ by $Y = AZ$ (Figure 6.13.1). This last-named image space has dimension r_A by Theorem 6.10.3. By the same theorem, the image of $\mathscr{V}_p^p$ by the operator $Y = (AB)X$ has dimension r_{AB}. Hence $r_{AB} \leqslant r_A$.

Also, the image by $Y = AZ$ of the $\mathscr{V}_n^{r_B}$ which is the image by $Z = BX$ of $\mathscr{V}_p^p$ is of dimension not greater than r_B, by Theorem 6.10.4. But the

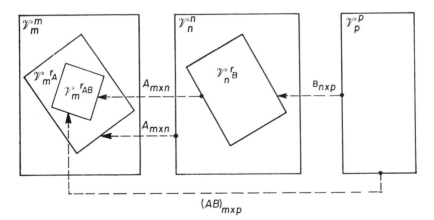

Figure 6.13.1

image by $Y = AZ$ of this $\mathcal{V}_n^{r_B}$ is just the image by $Y = (AB)X$ of $\mathcal{V}_p^p$. Hence $r_{AB} \leqslant r_B$. Thus we have another proof of the following result:

Theorem 6.13.5: *The rank of the product of two matrices cannot exceed the rank of either factor.*

The geometrical reasoning used in the proof of this theorem is useful in many applications. The relations between the various spaces and subspaces are shown in Figure 6.13.1.

6.14 The Null Space of a Linear Operator

Let $Y = B_{n \times p}X$ represent a linear operator mapping the vectors of a $\mathcal{V}_p^p$ onto vectors of a $\mathcal{V}_n^n$. Then the **null space** of the operator is defined to be the set of all p-vectors X whose images are the zero n-vector, that is, the set of all p-vectors X such that $BX = 0$. By Theorem 5.17.4, the dimension N_B of this null space is given by

$$N_B = p - r_B.$$

This dimension is called the **nullity of the operator**. It is also called the **nullity** or the **deficiency of the matrix** B.

Now let $Z = A_{m \times n}Y$ represent a linear operator mapping the $\mathcal{V}_n^n$ into a $\mathcal{V}_m^m$. Then the product operator $Z = (AB)X$ is defined. Moreover, if $BX = 0$, then $A(BX) = (AB)X = 0$ also. Hence we have

Theorem 6.14.1: *The null space of $Y = BX$ is a subspace of the null space of $Z = ABX$. The nullity of the operator $Z = (AB)X$ is at least as great as the nullity of the operator $Y = BX$.*

The dimension of the null space of $Z = ABX$ bears no general relation to that of A. Consider the following examples:

$$A = \begin{bmatrix} 1 & 0 & 0 & 0 \\ 0 & 1 & 0 & 0 \end{bmatrix}, \quad B = \begin{bmatrix} 1 & 0 \\ 0 & 1 \\ 0 & 0 \\ 0 & 0 \end{bmatrix}, \quad AB = \begin{bmatrix} 1 & 0 \\ 0 & 1 \end{bmatrix}, \quad \begin{cases} N_{AB} = 0, \\ N_A = 2, \\ N_{AB} < N_A. \end{cases}$$

$$A = \begin{bmatrix} 0 & 0 & 1 & 0 \\ 0 & 0 & 0 & 1 \end{bmatrix}, \quad B = \begin{bmatrix} 1 & 0 \\ 0 & 1 \\ 0 & 0 \\ 0 & 0 \end{bmatrix}, \quad AB = \begin{bmatrix} 0 & 0 \\ 0 & 0 \end{bmatrix}, \quad \begin{cases} N_{AB} = 2, \\ N_A = 2, \\ N_{AB} = N_A. \end{cases}$$

$$A = \begin{bmatrix} 0 & 0 & 1 & 0 \\ 0 & 0 & 0 & 1 \end{bmatrix}, \quad B = \begin{bmatrix} 1 & 0 & 0 \\ 0 & 1 & 0 \\ 0 & 0 & 0 \\ 0 & 0 & 0 \end{bmatrix}, \quad AB = \begin{bmatrix} 0 & 0 & 0 \\ 0 & 0 & 0 \end{bmatrix}, \quad \begin{cases} N_{AB} = 3, \\ N_A = 2, \\ N_{AB} > N_A. \end{cases}$$

However, in the event that A and B are both square and of order n, then we have, again by Theorem 6.13.5,

$$r_{AB} \leqslant r_A, \qquad r_{AB} \leqslant r_B,$$

so that, subtracting each member from n, we have

$$N_{AB} \geqslant N_A, \qquad N_{AB} \geqslant N_B.$$

Thus we have:

Theorem 6.14.2: *The nullity of the product of two square matrices is at least as great as the nullity of either factor.*

Once again, let A be an $m \times n$ matrix, B an $n \times p$ matrix. Let $\mathscr{V}_p{}^{N_B}$ be the null space of B, and let $\mathscr{V}_p{}^{N_{AB}}$ be that of AB. Then $\mathscr{V}_p{}^{N_B}$ is a subspace of $\mathscr{V}_p{}^{N_{AB}}$ by Theorem 6.14.1. By Theorem 6.5.2, we can therefore choose vectors $X_1, X_2, \ldots,$ $X_{N_B}, X_{N_B+1}, \ldots, X_{N_{AB}}$ so that $X_1, X_2, \ldots, X_{N_B}$ span $\mathscr{V}_p{}^{N_B}$ and the entire set spans $\mathscr{V}_p{}^{N_{AB}}$. The vectors $BX_{N_B+1}, \ldots, BX_{N_{AB}}$ then all belong to the null space of A. Moreover, they are independent, for $\sum_{j=N_B+1}^{N_{AB}} \lambda_j B X_j = 0$ implies

$$B \left(\sum_{j=N_B+1}^{N_{AB}} \lambda_j X_j \right) = 0,$$

that is, the vector $\sum_{j=N_B+1}^{N_{AB}} \lambda_j X_j$ belongs to $\mathscr{V}_p{}^{N_B}$. This means that for suitable scalars μ_i,

$$\sum_{j=N_B+1}^{N_{AB}} \lambda_j X_j = \sum_{i=1}^{N_B} \mu_i X_i.$$

Since the X's are linearly independent, this implies that all λ's (and μ's) are 0. Thus $BX_{N_B+1}, \ldots, BX_{N_{AB}}$ are independent, and so span a subspace of dimension $N_{AB} - N_B$ of the null space of A. Hence $N_A \geqslant N_{AB} - N_B$. Since $N_{AB} = p - r_{AB}$, $N_A = n - r_A, N_B = p - r_B$, we may conclude the following result:

Theorem 6.14.3: *The nullity of the product of two matrices $A_{m \times n}$ and $B_{n \times p}$ is not greater than the sum of their nullities, that is, $N_{AB} \leqslant N_A + N_B$, and the rank of the product satisfies the inequality $r_{AB} \geqslant r_A + r_B - n$.*

The fact that, in the case when A and B are both square,

$$\max [N_A, N_B] \leqslant N_{AB} \leqslant N_A + N_B,$$

is what is known in the literature as **Sylvester's law of nullity.**

6.15 Projections

A linear operator $X' = AX$ on a $\mathscr{V}_n{}^n$, such that $A^2 = A$, is called a **projection.** As an example, consider the operator defined by

$$X' = \begin{bmatrix} 1 & 0 & 0 \\ 0 & 1 & 0 \\ 0 & 0 & 0 \end{bmatrix} X.$$

Here the image of the vector $\{x_1, x_2, x_3\}$ is the vector $\{x_1, x_2, 0\}$, so that in $\mathscr{E}_3$ the geometric interpretation of this operator is exactly what is meant by projection in the geometric sense (Figure 6.15.1).

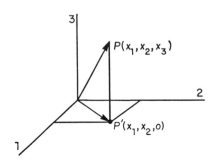

The set of all vectors which project onto the zero-vector is the null space of the projection. The set of all vectors which are images of vectors of $\mathscr{V}_n{}^n$ is the *image space* or *range* of the projection. In the given example, the null space consists of all vectors $k\{0, 0, 1\}$, that is, all vectors on the x_3-axis. The image space is the set of all vectors $\overrightarrow{OP'}$ in the x_1x_2-plane.

Theorem 6.15.1:   *Every projection except the identity is singular.*

Figure 6.15.1

Since $A^2 = A$, we have $A(I - A) = 0$. This holds true if $A = I$. Otherwise, since only a singular matrix is a divisor of zero (Exercise 18, Section 3.2), both A and $I - A$ are singular.

Suppose now that $X' = AX$ is any projection. Then the dimension of its null space is $n - r_A$, and the dimension of its image space (that is, of the column space of A) is r_A.

Suppose next that a vector P belongs to the image space of the projection. This means that there exists a vector X such that $AX = P$. Hence we have

$$A(AX) = A^2X = AX,$$

that is,

$$AP = P.$$

Thus every vector of the image space remains invariant under the projection.

Moreover, if X is any vector such that $AX = X$, then X is its own image and, hence, X is in the image space. We therefore have proved

Theorem 6.15.2:   *The vectors of $\mathscr{V}_n{}^n$ which are invariant under a projection are the vectors of the image space of the projection.*

Now if $P \neq 0$ and $AP = P$, then $AP \neq 0$ also. Hence no nonzero vector of the image space belongs to the null space. Since the dimension of the intersection of these two spaces is thus zero, the dimension of their sum is given by the sum of their dimensions (Theorem 6.8.3), that is, by $(n - r_A) + r_A$. Hence we have

Theorem 6.15.3:   *The intersection of the null space and the image space of a projection is the zero-vector alone. The sum of the null space and the image space is $\mathscr{V}_n{}^n$.*

An important property of projections is the fact that every vector P of the image space is left fixed by the operator, that is, $AP = P$ (Theorem 6.15.2). We shall define, *for an arbitrary operator*, the **fixed space** to be the set of all vectors left fixed by that operator. (The reader may show that the fixed space is indeed a vector space and is a subspace of the image space of the operator. In the case of a projection, the fixed space *is* the image space, by Theorem 6.15.2.) This definition permits us to obtain a converse to the preceding theorem.

Suppose $X' = AX$ represents any operator such that the sum of the null space and the fixed space is $\mathscr{V}_n{}^n$. Then every vector X of $\mathscr{V}_n{}^n$ can be written in the form

$$X = P + Z,$$

where P belongs to the fixed space and Z belongs to the null space. Moreover, since $AP = P$ and $AZ = 0$,

$$AX = AP + AZ = P.$$

Hence,

$$A^2X = AP = AP + AZ = A(P + Z) = AX.$$

Since $A^2X = AX$ for *all* X of the $\mathscr{V}_n{}^n$, we must have

$$A^2 = A.$$

The operator $X' = AX$ is therefore a projection. Thus we have proved

Theorem 6.15.4:   *Every operator on $\mathscr{V}_n{}^n$, such that the sum of the null space and the fixed space of the operator is $\mathscr{V}_n{}^n$, is a projection.*

The two preceding theorems show that the projections on a $\mathscr{V}_n{}^n$ are exactly those linear operators for which the sum of the fixed space and the null space is the $\mathscr{V}_n{}^n$.

We prove finally:

Theorem 6.15.5:   *If a $\mathscr{V}_n{}^n$ is the sum of two of its subspaces $\mathscr{V}_n{}^k$ and $\mathscr{V}_n{}^{n-k}$, then there is a unique projection having the $\mathscr{V}_n{}^k$ as its fixed space and the $\mathscr{V}_n{}^{n-k}$ as its null space.*

First we note that the dimension of the intersection of the $\mathscr{V}_n{}^k$ and the $\mathscr{V}_n{}^{n-k}$ is 0 since the sum is $\mathscr{V}_n{}^n$. Hence, if $B_1, B_2, \ldots, B_k$ is a basis for the $\mathscr{V}_n{}^k$, and $B_{k+1}, B_{k+2}, \ldots, B_n$ is a basis for the $\mathscr{V}_n{}^{n-k}$, these vectors are independent so that $B = [B_1, B_2, \ldots, B_n]$ is nonsingular. We now seek all matrices A for which $\mathscr{V}_n{}^k$ is the fixed space and $\mathscr{V}_n{}^{n-k}$ is the null space, that is, such that

$$A[B_1, B_2, \ldots, B_k, B_{k+1}, B_{k+2}, \ldots, B_n] = [B_1, B_2, \ldots, B_k, 0, 0, \ldots, 0].$$

Since B is nonsingular, this implies

(6.15.1) $A = [B_1, B_2, \ldots, B_k, 0, 0, \ldots, 0]B^{-1},$

which is independent of the choice of basic vectors B_j, so the operator is unique. By Theorem 6.15.4, it is a projection, so the theorem is proved.

The importance of the proof here is that (6.15.1) shows how to write the matrix of a projection when the fixed space and the null space are given.

Projections are important not only in geometry but also in the study of quantum mechanics, statistics, etc. Further properties of projections are given in the exercises of Section 6.20.

TRANSFORMATIONS OF COORDINATES

6.16 Reference Systems in Vector Spaces

Consider a $\mathscr{V}_n^{\ k}$ with basis $A_1, A_2, \ldots, A_k$ so that an arbitrary X of the $\mathscr{V}_n^{\ k}$ has a unique representation

$$(6.16.1) \qquad X = \sum_{i=1}^{k} u_i A_i.$$

The vectors $A_1, A_2, \ldots, A_k$ are called a **reference system** or **coordinate system** in the $\mathscr{V}_n^{\ k}$, and $u_1, u_2, \ldots, u_k$ are the **coordinates** of X with respect to this reference system. In particular, the components of an n-vector X are its coordinates with respect to the **natural reference system** $E_1, E_2, \ldots, E_n$, and all the analysis thus far has been carried out with respect to this reference system. Moreover, in the following, *whenever no reference system is specified, the natural reference system is to be assumed.*

This is the natural generalization of the familiar situation in $\mathscr{E}_3$ where all vectors are expressible as linear combinations of the three elementary vectors:

$$X = x_1 E_1 + x_2 E_2 + x_3 E_3,$$

and the E's are in effect the i, j, k of vector analysis.

6.17 Transformations of Coordinates

Now let $A_1, A_2, \ldots, A_k$ and $B_1, B_2, \ldots, B_k$ be two bases for the same $\mathscr{V}_n^{\ k}$. Then we have a set of relations of the form

$$(6.17.1) \qquad B_j = \sum_{i=1}^{k} s_{ij} A_i, \qquad j = 1, 2, \ldots, k,$$

defining the B's in terms of the A's. By Theorem 6.7.1, since the B's are independent, we have $\det [s_{ij}]_k \neq 0$.

Let X be any vector of the $\mathscr{V}_n^{\ k}$. Then there exist scalars $u_1, u_2, \ldots, u_k$ and $v_1, v_2, \ldots, v_k$ such that

$$(6.17.2) \qquad X = \sum_{i=1}^{k} u_i A_i \qquad \text{and} \qquad X = \sum_{j=1}^{k} v_j B_j.$$

From the second of these equations and (6.17.1), we have

$$X = \sum_{j=1}^{k} v_j \left(\sum_{i=1}^{k} s_{ij} A_i \right) = \sum_{i=1}^{k} \left(\sum_{j=1}^{k} s_{ij} v_j \right) A_i.$$

By Theorem 6.5.3, we then conclude that

$$(6.17.3) \qquad u_i = \sum_{j=1}^{k} s_{ij} v_j, \qquad i = 1, 2, \ldots, k.$$

If we put $U = \{u_1, \ldots, u_k\}$, $V = \{v_1, \ldots, v_k\}$, $S = [s_{ij}]_k$, this becomes

(6.17.4) $$U = SV,$$

or, since S is nonsingular,

(6.17.5) $$V = S^{-1}U.$$

These last two equations define a **linear transformation of coordinates** relating the u's and the v's. By combining equations (6.17.1) into a single matrix equation, we may restate these results as follows:

Theorem 6.17.1: *Let two bases $A_1, A_2, \ldots, A_k$ and $B_1, B_2, \ldots, B_k$ of a $\mathscr{V}_n{}^k$ be related by the equation*

$$[B_1, B_2, \ldots, B_k] = [A_1, A_2, \ldots, A_k]S,$$

and let the k-vectors U, V give the coordinates of an arbitrary vector X of the $\mathscr{V}_n{}^k$ with respect to these two bases respectively. Then U and V are related by the nonsingular linear transformation $U = SV$.

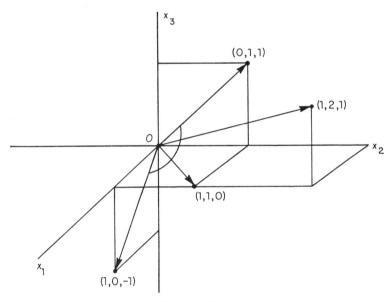

Figure 6.17.1

For example, in $\mathscr{E}_3$ consider the $\mathscr{V}_3{}^2$ with basis $\{1, 1, 0\}$ and $\{0, 1, 1\}$. The vectors $\{1, 2, 1\}$ and $\{1, 0, -1\}$ are also in this space and, being independent, form a basis for it (Figure 6.17.1). Moreover

$$\begin{bmatrix} 1 \\ 2 \\ 1 \end{bmatrix} = \begin{bmatrix} 1 \\ 1 \\ 0 \end{bmatrix} + \begin{bmatrix} 0 \\ 1 \\ 1 \end{bmatrix} \qquad \text{and} \qquad \begin{bmatrix} 1 \\ 0 \\ -1 \end{bmatrix} = \begin{bmatrix} 1 \\ 1 \\ 0 \end{bmatrix} - \begin{bmatrix} 0 \\ 1 \\ 1 \end{bmatrix}.$$

Now if

$$X = u_1 \cdot \begin{bmatrix} 1 \\ 1 \\ 0 \end{bmatrix} + u_2 \cdot \begin{bmatrix} 0 \\ 1 \\ 1 \end{bmatrix} = v_1 \cdot \begin{bmatrix} 1 \\ 2 \\ 1 \end{bmatrix} + v_2 \cdot \begin{bmatrix} 1 \\ 0 \\ -1 \end{bmatrix},$$

we obtain by substitution on the right,

$$u_1 \cdot \begin{bmatrix} 1 \\ 1 \\ 0 \end{bmatrix} + u_2 \cdot \begin{bmatrix} 0 \\ 1 \\ 1 \end{bmatrix} = (v_1 + v_2) \cdot \begin{bmatrix} 1 \\ 1 \\ 0 \end{bmatrix} + (v_1 - v_2) \cdot \begin{bmatrix} 0 \\ 1 \\ 1 \end{bmatrix},$$

from which, since the coefficients are unique,

$$u_1 = v_1 + v_2,$$

$$u_2 = v_1 - v_2,$$

or

$$\begin{bmatrix} u_1 \\ u_2 \end{bmatrix} = \begin{bmatrix} 1 & 1 \\ 1 & -1 \end{bmatrix} \cdot \begin{bmatrix} v_1 \\ v_2 \end{bmatrix},$$

which is in agreement with (6.17.4).

The most important special case of Theorem 6.17.1 occurs when $k = n$. Here we may write the first of (6.17.2) in the form $X = AU$, where $A = [A_1, A_2, \ldots, A_n]$, or

(6.17.6) $U = A^{-1}X,$

which shows how to obtain the u-coordinates directly from the x-coordinates when the latter are coordinates with respect to the natural basis. Suppose now that $B_1, B_2, \ldots, B_n$ also span the $\mathscr{V}_n^{\,n}$ and that

$$X = \sum_{j=1}^{n} v_j B_j = BV, \qquad V = B^{-1}X.$$

Then, substituting for X, we have

(6.17.7) $V = (B^{-1}A)U,$

which is the linear transformation expressing the coordinates of X with respect to the B's directly in terms of the coordinates of X with respect to the A's. That is, the matrix $B^{-1}A$ of (6.17.7) is, for this case, the matrix S^{-1} of (6.17.5).

We illustrate again with an example from $\mathscr{E}_3$. Suppose we wish to express the coordinates v_1, v_2, v_3 of a vector X with respect to the coordinate system

{1, 1, 0}, {1, 1, 1}, {1, 0, 0} in terms of its coordinates u_1, u_2, u_3 with respect to the coordinate system {1, 0, 1}, {0, 1, 0}, {0, 0, 1}. We have

$$X = \begin{bmatrix} 1 & 1 & 1 \\ 1 & 1 & 0 \\ 0 & 1 & 0 \end{bmatrix} V \quad \text{or} \quad V = \begin{bmatrix} 0 & 1 & -1 \\ 0 & 0 & 1 \\ 1 & -1 & 0 \end{bmatrix} X,$$

and

$$X = \begin{bmatrix} 1 & 0 & 0 \\ 0 & 1 & 0 \\ 1 & 0 & 1 \end{bmatrix} U.$$

Hence

$$V = \begin{bmatrix} 0 & 1 & -1 \\ 0 & 0 & 1 \\ 1 & -1 & 0 \end{bmatrix} \cdot \begin{bmatrix} 1 & 0 & 0 \\ 0 & 1 & 0 \\ 1 & 0 & 1 \end{bmatrix} U = \begin{bmatrix} -1 & 1 & -1 \\ 1 & 0 & 1 \\ 1 & -1 & 0 \end{bmatrix} U.$$

6.18 Transformation of a Linear Operator

Let the equation

(6.18.1) $X_2 = AX_1$

represent a linear operator which maps a vector X_1 onto the vector X_2 of the same $\mathscr{V}_n{}^n$, the reference system being the natural one. In $\mathscr{E}_2$ and $\mathscr{E}_3$, such a mapping is readily visualized geometrically. Now consider the linear transformation of coordinates

(6.18.2) $X = BU, \quad U = B^{-1}X,$

which defines the coordinates $u_1, u_2, \ldots, u_n$ of X with respect to a reference system defined by the columns of B.

What is the representation of the function (6.18.1) in this new reference system? From (6.18.2) we have

$$X_1 = BU_1 \quad \text{and} \quad X_2 = BU_2.$$

Substituting into (6.18.1), we obtain

$$BU_2 = ABU_1$$

or

(6.18.3) $U_2 = (B^{-1}AB)U_1,$

which represents the same linear operator as (6.18.1) but in the new reference system. If we recall that X_1 and U_1 are two representations of the same geometric vector, and similarly for X_2 and U_2, we conclude that, if multiplication by the matrix A maps one vector onto another in the natural reference system, then multiplication by the matrix $B^{-1}AB$ maps the *same* first vector onto the *same* second vector in the new reference system. Putting it another way, the equations $X_2 = AX_1$ and $U_2 = (B^{-1}AB)U_1$ are *different arithmetic descriptions of the same geometric operation*. In summary we have

   Theorem 6.18.1:   *The linear operator on a $\mathscr{V}_n{}^n$ which is represented by the matrix A in the natural reference system is represented by the matrix $B^{-1}AB$ in the reference system whose basis vectors are defined by the columns of B.*

   Thus not only does every vector have a particular set of coordinates in each reference system but also every linear operator on a vector space has a particular representation in each reference system for that vector space.

   The formation of a matrix $B^{-1}AB$ is called a **similarity transformation** of A. An important problem of matrix algebra is the determination of the canonical forms to which a matrix may be reduced by similarity transformations. This problem is left to more advanced texts.

   The same procedure may be applied to an operator which maps vectors of a $\mathscr{V}_n{}^n$ onto vectors of a $\mathscr{V}_m{}^m$. Let

(6.18.4) $$Y = A_{m \times n}X$$

represent such an operator, where X and Y are each referred to the natural reference systems in their respective spaces.

   Suppose now we introduce new reference systems in the $\mathscr{V}_n{}^n$ and in the $\mathscr{V}_m{}^m$, the resulting linear transformations of coordinates being respectively

$$X = BU, \qquad Y = CV.$$

Then the operator $Y = AX$ is represented by

$$CV = A(BU)$$

or

(6.18.5) $$V = (C^{-1}AB)U$$

in the new reference systems.

   A geometric implication of this result is as follows: Since C^{-1} and B are nonsingular, $C^{-1}AB$ is an $m \times n$ matrix which has the same rank as A. Hence the null space of the operator (6.18.5) has dimension $n - r_A$, the same as that of the operator (6.18.4). Thus we have

   Theorem 6.18.2:   *The dimension of the null space of a linear operator is independent of the reference systems employed in its representation.*

   A final remark is in order. Theorem 6.10.1 establishes a one-to-one correspondence between linear operators $Y = AX$, mapping the $\mathscr{V}_n{}^n$ over $\mathscr{F}$ into the $\mathscr{V}_m{}^m$ over $\mathscr{F}$, and the $m \times n$ matrices over $\mathscr{F}$, all vectors being referred to the natural reference systems. If, however, reference systems $B_1, B_2, \ldots, B_n$ and $C_1, C_2, \ldots, C_m$ are employed, the representation of the operator becomes $V = (C^{-1}AB)U$. Thus the one-to-one correspondence in question also varies with the reference systems. A consequence is that not only does a given operator have infinitely many matrix representations but also a given matrix can represent infinitely many distinct operators, depending on which reference systems are chosen.

6.19 Linear Forms

As was pointed out in Section 6.10, there are both vector-valued functions of vector arguments and scalar-valued functions of vector arguments. Among the scalar-valued functions of vector arguments, those that have the characteristic properties of linearity are of particular importance. We define a **linear form** or **linear functional** by the following properties:

(a) To each vector X of the $\mathscr{V}_n{}^n$ over a field $\mathscr{F}$, it relates a unique *scalar* $f(X)$.
(b) For each scalar λ of $\mathscr{F}$, and each X of $\mathscr{V}_n{}^n$, $f(\lambda X) = \lambda f(X)$.
(c) For all vectors X_1 and X_2 of $\mathscr{V}_n{}^n$, $f(X_1 + X_2) = f(X_1) + f(X_2)$.

Note that these are precisely the same properties as were used to define a linear vector function or operator (Section 6.10), except that the function relates a scalar rather than a vector to a given vector.

Let $f(E_j) = a_j$, $j = 1, 2, \ldots, n$, where $E_1, E_2, \ldots, E_n$ are the elementary vectors. Then, since

$$X = \sum_{j=1}^{n} x_j E_j,$$

we have, by repeated use of (b) and (c),

$$f(X) = \sum_{j=1}^{n} x_j a_j = \sum_{j=1}^{n} a_j x_j.$$

or, if $A = \{a_1, a_2, \ldots, a_n\}$,

$$f(X) = A^{\mathsf{T}}X.$$

Thus, we have

Theorem 6.19.1: *A linear form is representable as the scalar product of a fixed n-vector A and the variable n-vector X.*

(Note that the proof of this theorem parallels the corresponding proof in Section 6.10 exactly. Indeed, if we observe that the set of scalars is a $\mathscr{V}_1{}^1$, the present result appears as a special case of the earlier one.)

Now suppose we apply a *nonsingular* operator defined by $X' = BX$ or $X = B^{-1}X'$ to the vectors of $\mathscr{V}_n{}^n$. We have

$$A^{\mathsf{T}}X = A^{\mathsf{T}}(B^{-1}X') = (A^{\mathsf{T}}B^{-1})X'.$$

Hence we can state

Theorem 6.19.2: *A nonsingular operator with matrix B associates the image form $(A^{\mathsf{T}}B^{-1})X'$ with the form $A^{\mathsf{T}}X$. The value of $A^{\mathsf{T}}X$ at a given X is the same as the value of $(A^{\mathsf{T}}B^{-1})X'$ at the image of X by the given operator.*

As an example in $\mathscr{E}_2$, consider the linear form

$$2x_1 + 3x_2 = [2, 3] \cdot \begin{bmatrix} x_1 \\ x_2 \end{bmatrix}$$

and the operator

$$\begin{bmatrix} x_1 \\ x_2 \end{bmatrix} = \begin{bmatrix} 0 & -1 \\ 1 & 0 \end{bmatrix} \cdot \begin{bmatrix} x_1' \\ x_2' \end{bmatrix}.$$

Substituting for $\{x_1, x_2\}$, we obtain the new form

$$[2, 3] \cdot \begin{bmatrix} 0 & -1 \\ 1 & 0 \end{bmatrix} \cdot \begin{bmatrix} x_1' \\ x_2' \end{bmatrix} = [3, -2] \cdot \begin{bmatrix} x_1' \\ x_2' \end{bmatrix} = 3x_1' - 2x_2'.$$

Thus $2x_1 + 3x_2$ has the image $3x_1' - 2x_2'$ by the given operator. Moreover, the vector $\{a, b\}$ has the image $\{b, -a\}$. Substituting the corresponding vectors into the corresponding forms, we find that

$$2a + 3b = 3b - 2(-a),$$

as the theorem asserts.

So far in this section, the analysis has been with respect to the natural reference system. If we now subject the space $\mathscr{V}°{}_n{}^n$ to a linear transformation of coordinates

$$X = CY,$$

where the columns of C are the new basis vectors, then we have

$$A\mathsf{T}X = A\mathsf{T}(CY) = (A\mathsf{T}C)Y.$$

Here Y is the representation of X in the new reference system, and $(A\mathsf{T}C)Y$ is the representation of the form $A\mathsf{T}X$ in the new reference system. Thus we have

Theorem 6.19.3:   *The representation of the linear form $A\mathsf{T}X$ in the reference system defined by the linear transformation $X = CY$ is $(A\mathsf{T}C)Y$. Moreover the two forms assume the same value at the two representations of the same vector.*

Thus a linear form, like a vector and like a linear operator, has a particular representation in each reference system.

6.20 Exercises

1. Show that a product of nonsingular linear operators is a nonsingular linear operator.

2. Interpret geometrically in $\mathscr{E}_2$:

(a) the *operator* $X' = \begin{bmatrix} 0 & -1 \\ 1 & 0 \end{bmatrix} X$;

(b) the linear transformation of coordinates

$$Y = \begin{bmatrix} 0 & -1 \\ 1 & 0 \end{bmatrix} X.$$

3. Compute the product of the operators

$$Z = \begin{bmatrix} 4 & 1 & 1 \\ 5 & 2 & 0 \end{bmatrix} Y, \qquad Y = \begin{bmatrix} 2 & -1 \\ -5 & 3 \\ -2 & 1 \end{bmatrix} X.$$

Explain geometrically what has occurred.

4. Determine the null space of the transformation

$$Y = \begin{bmatrix} 1 & 2 & 1 \\ 2 & 2 & 0 \\ 1 & 0 & -1 \end{bmatrix} X.$$

5. Show that the set of all vectors X such that $AX = X$, where A is of order n, constitutes a vector space. How does one determine the dimension of this space?

6. Let $A = D[a_1, a_2, \ldots, a_n]$ and $B = D[b_1, b_2, \ldots, b_n]$ have ranks r_A and r_B respectively. Under what circumstances would the product AB of these diagonal matrices illustrate the extreme cases of Sylvester's law of nullity?

7. Matrix products of the form $C^T A C$ arise in the analysis of electrical networks. Given that $A_{n \times n}$ and $C_{n \times m}$ both have rank n $(m \geqslant n)$, show that $C^T A C$ has rank n.

8. Given that $A_{n \times n}$ and $C_{n \times m}$ both have rank m $(m \leqslant n)$, show that the rank of $C^T A C$ is at least $3m - 2n$.

9. Given that $A_{n \times n}$ has rank n and that $C_{n \times m}$ has rank m $(m \leqslant n)$, show that the rank of $C^T A C$ is at least $2m - n$.

10. Give examples of Exercises 8 and 9, in which the product has the minimum possible rank.

11. Define the inverse of a given operator on a vector space. Then prove that an operator has an inverse if and only if its null space consists of the zero vector alone.

12. Let $X' = AX$ represent a linear operator on a $\mathscr{V}_n{}^n$ of which a $\mathscr{V}_n{}^p$ is a subspace. Show that the image of the $\mathscr{V}_n{}^p$ has dimension at least as great as $p - N_A$.

13. Suppose A is the matrix of a linear operator on a $\mathscr{V}_n{}^n$, and suppose $\mathscr{V}_n{}^k$ is a vector space such that, for each X of $\mathscr{V}_n{}^k$, AX is again a vector of $\mathscr{V}_n{}^k$. Then $\mathscr{V}_n{}^k$ is an **invariant subspace** of $\mathscr{V}_n{}^n$ with respect to the operator. Show that, if $\mathscr{V}_n{}^k$ is such an invariant subspace, then it is also invariant with respect to $f(A)$, where $f(A)$ is any polynomial function of A. Construct an example in $\mathscr{E}_3$. (Note that the definition does *not* require individual vectors to be invariant.)

14. Show that, if A is a matrix of a projection, then $I - A$ is also the matrix of a projection.

15. Show that the image space of a projection with matrix A is the null space of the projection with matrix $I - A$.

16. Show that, if A and B are matrices of projections and commute, then AB also represents a projection. Generalize.

17. Show that, if A and B are matrices of projections and $AB = BA = 0$, then $A + B$ is the matrix of a projection. Generalize.

18. Let V denote an arbitrary *unit vector* in $\mathscr{E}_3$, that is, a vector V such that $\sum_{j=1}^{3} v_j^2 = 1$. Define $P_V X = (V^\mathsf{T} X)V$ to be the **projection of** X **on** V. Prove that $P_{E_j} X = x_j$. Prove that $P_V X$ is a linear operator and find its matrix representation for an arbitrary unit vector V. Finally, prove that $P_V X$ is a projection in the sense defined in Section 6.15.

19. Given a linear operator defined by the equation

$$Y = \begin{bmatrix} 1 & 3 \\ 3 & 2 \end{bmatrix} X$$

with respect to the natural reference system of a $\mathscr{V}_2^2$, find an equation representing the same operator with respect to the basis $\{2, 1\}$, $\{1, 2\}$.

*20. Show that the determinant and the trace of a linear operator on a $\mathscr{V}_n^n$ are invariant with respect to nonsingular linear transformations of coordinates.

21. Suppose that in $\mathscr{E}_2$

$$X = u_1 \begin{bmatrix} 1 \\ 1 \end{bmatrix} + u_2 \begin{bmatrix} -1 \\ 1 \end{bmatrix},$$

and also

$$X = v_1 \begin{bmatrix} 2 \\ 1 \end{bmatrix} + v_2 \begin{bmatrix} -1 \\ 2 \end{bmatrix}.$$

What is the relation between

$$U = \begin{bmatrix} u_1 \\ u_2 \end{bmatrix} \quad \text{and} \quad V = \begin{bmatrix} v_1 \\ v_2 \end{bmatrix} ?$$

22. Given the linear transformation of coordinates

$$Y = \begin{bmatrix} 1 & 2 & 3 \\ 2 & 0 & 2 \\ 3 & 2 & 1 \end{bmatrix} X,$$

find the new coordinates (y's) of the old basis vectors (E's) and the old coordinates (x's) of the new elementary vectors.

23. Interpret the linear transformation of coordinates

$$X = D[d_1, d_2, \ldots, d_n]Y, \qquad d_1 d_2 \cdots d_n \neq 0,$$

geometrically if $n = 3$. What vector X is represented by $Y = \{1, 1, \ldots, 1\}$?

24. Prove that the identity operator $Y = IX$ has the same representation in every reference system.

25. If $U = AV$ represents a linear operator on a $\mathscr{V}_n^n$ in the reference system $B_1, B_2, \ldots, B_n$, what is its representation in the natural reference system? In the reference system $C_1, C_2, \ldots, C_n$?

26. Given a nonsingular operator on a $\mathscr{V}_n{}^n$ and with matrix A, what will be the matrix of the operator in the reference system defined by the columns of A? By the columns of A^{-1}? In what reference systems will the matrix of the operator still be A?

27. Let $A_1, A_2, \ldots, A_n$ be a basis for a $\mathscr{V}_n{}^n$. Define

$$A = [A_1, A_2, \ldots, A_n], \qquad A^{-1} = [B_1, B_2, \ldots, B_n].$$

Prove that, if X is any n-vector, then

$$X = \sum (X^\mathsf{T} B_j) A_j,$$

that is, $X^\mathsf{T} B_1, X^\mathsf{T} B_2, \ldots, X^\mathsf{T} B_n$ are the coordinates of X with respect to $A_1, A_2, \ldots, A_n$ respectively.

28. Show that, if A is the matrix of an operator with respect to the natural reference system and A is idempotent, then in every reference system the matrix of the operator is idempotent, that is, the property of being a projection does not depend on the reference system.

29. Let $f(A_1, A_2, \ldots, A_m)$ denote a polynomial function of matrices A_1, $A_2, \ldots, A_m$ of order n. If $A_j' = B^{-1} A_j B$, $j = 1, 2, \ldots, m$, and $f' = B^{-1} f B$, prove that

$$f(A_1, A_2, \ldots, A_m)' = f(A_1', A_2', \ldots, A_m').$$

30. Using the notation of Theorem 6.17.1, show that, if also

$$[C_1, C_2, \ldots, C_k] = [B_1, B_2, \ldots, B_k] Q,$$

then the coordinate vector $W = \{w_1, w_2, \ldots, w_k\}$ of a vector X with respect to the C's is related to the vectors U and V of the theorem by the transformations $V = QW$ and $U = SQW$.

31. Given that F is a differentiable function of $x_1, x_2, \ldots, x_n$ and that $Y = AX$, where $\det A \neq 0$, show that

$$\left\{ \frac{\partial F}{\partial y_1}, \frac{\partial F}{\partial y_2}, \ldots, \frac{\partial F}{\partial y_n} \right\} = (A^{-1})^\mathsf{T} \left\{ \frac{\partial F}{\partial x_1}, \frac{\partial F}{\partial x_2}, \ldots, \frac{\partial F}{\partial x_n} \right\}.$$

32. The system of forms

$$a_{11} x_1 + a_{12} x_2 + \cdots + a_{1n} x_n,$$

(6.20.1) $\vdots$

$$a_{m1} x_1 + a_{m2} x_2 + \cdots + a_{mn} x_n$$

may be represented as the product

$$AX,$$

where A is the $m \times n$ coefficient matrix of the system. The rank of the system is defined to be the number of linearly independent forms in the system.

(a) Show that the rank of the system is the same as the rank of A. (See Exercises 2 and 3, Section 5.16.)

(b) Show that a nonsingular linear operator transforms the system into an image system of the same rank.

(c) Show that, in a suitable reference system, a system of nonzero linear forms represented by AX can be represented by

$$c_{11}y_1$$

$$c_{12}y_1 + c_{22}y_2$$

$$\vdots$$

$$c_{m1}y_1 + c_{m2}y_2 + \cdots + c_{mn}y_n,$$

where some of the c's may be 0.

33. In vector analysis the cross product $X \times Y$ of two vectors X and Y in $\mathscr{E}_3$ is often defined to be the vector obtained by expanding a symbolic determinant

$$X \times Y = \begin{vmatrix} i & j & k \\ x_1 & x_2 & x_3 \\ y_1 & y_2 & y_3 \end{vmatrix} = \begin{vmatrix} x_2 & x_3 \\ y_2 & y_3 \end{vmatrix} i - \begin{vmatrix} x_1 & x_3 \\ y_1 & y_3 \end{vmatrix} j + \begin{vmatrix} x_1 & x_2 \\ y_1 & y_2 \end{vmatrix} k,$$

where the "unit vectors" i, j, k are the same as the elementary vectors E_1, E_2, E_3. Using a similar determinantal notation, show how the cross product generalizes to a vector product of $n - 1$ n-vectors $X_1, X_2, \ldots, X_{n-1}$. How is this latter product affected by permutations of the X's?

34. Show that, as X sweeps out a $\mathscr{V}_3{}^3$ but Y remains fixed, the cross product $Z = X \times Y$ sweeps out a $\mathscr{V}_3{}^2$. Identify this $\mathscr{V}_3{}^2$, and show that the relationship between Z and X is a singular linear operator. Generalize to a $\mathscr{V}_n{}^n$ with the aid of the preceding exercise.

35. The volume of the parallelepiped in $\mathscr{E}_3$ determined by three vectors $X_j = \overrightarrow{OP_j}$, $j = 1, 2, 3$, is given by $X_1{}^\mathsf{T}(X_2 \times X_3)$, where the cross product has been defined above. If $Y_j = AX_j$, where A is a nonsingular operator, how is the volume $Y_1{}^\mathsf{T}(Y_2 \times Y_3)$ related to that determined by the X's? (See Exercise **14**, Section 6.12). Generalize to n dimensions if you can.

36. Let P_1, P_2 denote Hermitian projection matrices. Prove that $P_1 P_2$ is a Hermitian projection matrix if and only if $P_1 P_2 = P_2 P_1$.

37. Let $P_1, P_2, \ldots, P_k$ denote Hermitian projection matrices. Prove that $\sum P_j$ is a Hermitian projection matrix if and only if $P_i P_j = 0$ when $i \neq j$.

38. Let P and Q be matrices of projections of a $\mathscr{V}_n{}^n$. We define $P \subseteq Q$ (P included in Q) if and only if $PQ = P$. Prove that in $\mathscr{E}_3$

$$\begin{bmatrix} 1 & 0 & 0 \\ 0 & 0 & 0 \\ 0 & 0 & 0 \end{bmatrix} \subseteq \begin{bmatrix} 1 & 0 & 0 \\ 0 & 1 & 0 \\ 0 & 0 & 0 \end{bmatrix},$$

and discuss geometrically.

39. Prove that the inclusion relation for matrices of projections has these properties:

(a) $P \subseteq P$ (the reflexive property);

(b) $P \subseteq Q, Q \subseteq P$ imply $P = Q$ (the antisymmetric property);

(c) $P \subseteq Q, Q \subseteq R$ imply $P \subseteq R$ (the transitive property).

40. Show that, if P_1 is the matrix of the projection which has the fixed space $\mathscr{V}_n^{\,k}$ and the null space $\mathscr{V}_n^{\,n-k}$, and if P_2 is the matrix of a projection which has the $\mathscr{V}_n^{\,n-k}$ as fixed space and the $\mathscr{V}_n^{\,k}$ as null space, then $P_1 P_2^{\mathsf{T}} = 0$.

41. Show that $Y = AX$ is a projection if and only if there is a reference system $B_1, B_2, \ldots, B_n$ such that for some $r < n$,

$$B^{-1}AB = \begin{bmatrix} I_r & \vdots & 0 \\ \cdots & \vdots & \cdots \\ 0 & \vdots & 0 \end{bmatrix}.$$

42. Let $\mathscr{V}_n^{\,k}$ be the fixed space of the projection $Y = PX$. Let $Y = AX$ denote any nonsingular operator on $\mathscr{V}_n^{\,n}$ which leaves the $\mathscr{V}_n^{\,k}$ invariant. Prove that $Y = AX$ also leaves the null space of the projection invariant. Then prove that a nonsingular operator $Y = BX$ on $\mathscr{V}_n^{\,n}$ leaves the $\mathscr{V}_n^{\,k}$ invariant if and only if $BP = PB$.

GROUPS OF OPERATORS

6.21 Groups of Operators

An important aspect of mathematics is the classification of sets of mathematical objects according to important properties which they possess. The concepts "field" and "vector space" which we have already introduced are examples of this. We now introduce another important concept of this type. A set G of mathematical objects, for which equality means identity, and each ordered pair (a, b) of which can be combined by an operation (denoted here by $\circ$) to give a unique "product" $a \circ b$, is called a **group** if and only if the following properties hold:

(a) G is *closed* with respect to the operation $\circ$, that is, if a and b are arbitrary elements of G, $a \circ b$ is also an element of G.

(b) The *associative law* holds, that is, for all a, b, c of G, $a \circ (b \circ c) = (a \circ b) \circ c$.

(c) G contains an *identity element*, that is, an element e such that for all a of G, $a \circ e = e \circ a = a$.

(d) For each element a of G, G contains an element a^{-1}, called the *inverse* of a, such that $a \circ a^{-1} = a^{-1} \circ a = e$.

If the commutative law also holds, that is, if $a \circ b = b \circ a$ for all a and b of G, then G is called a **commutative** or **Abelian group**.

If two groups G_1 and G_2 have the same operation $\circ$, and if every element of G_1 is also an element of G_2, G_1 is called a **subgroup** of G_2. If a group G contains only a finite number n of elements, it is called a **finite group** and is said to be of order n. Our principal concern here is with certain infinite groups of linear operators or linear transformations of coordinates.

There are many familiar examples of groups. The set of all complex numbers, the operation $\circ$ being ordinary addition, is an example. Indeed, the sum of two complex numbers is again a complex number, addition is associative, $a + 0 = 0 + a = a$, so that 0 is the identity element, and for each complex number a, $-a$ is its inverse. Thus all four requirements are satisfied.

Another example is provided by the set of four complex numbers 1, -1, i, $-i$, the operation now being multiplication. It is easy to check the closure property, multiplication is associative, 1 is the identity element, and the inverses of these numbers are respectively their reciprocals 1, -1, $-i$, i, all of which are in the set.

The vectors of a vector space $\mathscr{V}_n^{\,k}$ form a group with respect to the operation of addition. The closure property follows from the definition of a vector space, the addition of matrices is associative, the identity element is the zero-vector, which is in every vector space, and the inverse of a vector X of the space is the vector $-X$ which, again by the definition of a vector space, is also in the $\mathscr{V}_n^{\,k}$.

In the case of linear operators on a $\mathscr{V}_n^{\,n}$, the operation $\circ$ is taken to be multiplication as defined in a previous section. This operation is associative because matrix multiplication is associative. The identity operator $X' = I_n X$ is the identity element, since the product of this operator with another whose matrix is A has the matrix $I_n A$ or $A I_n$, that is, A. Finally, if A is nonsingular, operators with matrices A and A^{-1} are inverses in the group sense, since the matrix of their product is either $A A^{-1}$ or $A^{-1} A$, that is, I_n, the matrix of the identity operator. In view of these observations, a set of linear operators on a $\mathscr{V}_n^{\,n}$ is a group of linear operators if and only if

    (a) the product of any two operators of the set is an operator of the set,

    (b) the identity operator belongs to the set, and

    (c) the inverse of every operator of the set is also in the set.

This last requirement implies that *a group of linear operators may contain no singular operators*.

We now turn to some examples, noting first that the set of all nonsingular linear operators on a $\mathscr{V}_n^{\,n}$, the elements of whose matrices belong to a number field $\mathscr{F}$, constitutes a group with respect to the operation of multiplication:

    (a) If $Y = AX$ and $Z = BY$ are two such operators, their product $Z = (BA)X$ is also a nonsingular operator by Theorem 6.13.1.

    (b) The identity operator $Y = I_n X$ is nonsingular and, hence, belongs to the set.

    (c) If $Y = AX$ is in the set, A^{-1} exists and is nonsingular so that the inverse operator $Z = A^{-1} Y$ is also in the set.

This group of operators is called the **full linear group** over $\mathscr{F}$. The basic property of this group of operators is given in Theorem 6.11.3: Any operator of the full linear group takes a $\mathscr{V}_n^{\,k}$ again into a $\mathscr{V}_n^{\,k}$, that is, the property of being a vector space and the dimension of a vector space are *invariant* under operators of this group.

Among the infinitely many operators of the full linear group are the finitely many operators which simply permute the n variables. These permutations constitute what is known as the **symmetric group**. Since there are just $n!$ such permutations, the symmetric group has order $n!$ To prove that we actually have a group, we proceed as follows: Any such operator may be written in the form

$$x_1' = x_{i_1},$$

$$x_2' = x_{i_2},$$

$$\vdots$$

$$x_n' = x_{i_n},$$

where the x_{i_j}'s are $x_1, x_2, \ldots, x_n$ in some order. This may be written in matrix form thus:

$$X' = PX,$$

where the matrix P, a **permutation matrix**, has a single entry 1 in each row and in each column, all other entries being zero. Among these operators is the identity operator $X' = IX$ corresponding to the identical permutation which leaves the variables in the natural order. If we permute n variables and then permute them again, we still have a permutation of these variables. Hence the product of two permutations $X'' = P_2X'$, $X' = P_1X$, is a permutation $X'' = (P_2P_1)X$. (This may also be shown by examining the elements of P_2P_1.) Finally we observe that, if P is a permutation matrix, so is P^T, for it must have a single entry 1 in each *column* and in each *row*. Moreover, we have

$$P^\mathsf{T}P = I_n$$

for, if the ith row of P^T has its 1 in the kth column, then the ith column of P has its 1 in the kth row, and the product of the ith row of P^T and the ith column of P will be 1. On the other hand, no other column of P has a 1 in the kth row, and hence the product of the ith row of P^T and any *other* column of P must be 0. Thus $P^\mathsf{T}P$ is indeed the identity matrix, and hence the inverse of the operator $X' = PX$ is the operator $X'' = P^\mathsf{T}X'$, which is also a permutation. Thus the set of all $n!$ permutations is indeed a group of operators. This group is of great usefulness in a variety of applications.

The above discussion concerning groups of operators applies equally well to groups of linear transformations of coordinates since in this case, too, a product of transformations corresponds to a product of matrices. In either case, therefore, we are fundamentally concerned with groups of matrices, but different geometrical interpretations are given to matrix multiplication.

It would be difficult to overemphasize the importance of the group concept in modern mathematics, for it enters in some form into nearly every branch of the subject. However, we shall use it here in only the most elementary fashion. In the next chapter, we shall study the set of all n-vectors over a number field $\mathscr{F}$ with the special requirement that other properties in addition to dimension and linearity be invariant under the operators or linear transformations of coordinates which are used. It will appear then that the allowable operators or coordinate transformations form in each case a subgroup of the full linear group over $\mathscr{F}$.

6.22 Exercises

1. Show that, in a given group, there exists only one identity element and only one inverse for a given element.

2. Show that each of the following sets of linear operators on a vector space is a group:

(a) The set of all real nonsingular operators $X' = DX$, where D is a diagonal matrix.

(b) The set of all real operators $X' = AX$ with $\det A = \pm 1$.

(c) The set of all real operators $X' = AX$ with $\det A = 1$.

(d) The set of all complex operators $X' = AX$ with $|\det A| = 1$.

3. Show that, with respect to the operation of matrix multiplication, the set of all real matrices

$$\begin{bmatrix} a & -b \\ b & a \end{bmatrix}, \qquad a^2 + b^2 \neq 0,$$

constitutes a group.

4. Show that the set of matrices

$$\begin{bmatrix} 1 & 0 \\ 0 & 1 \end{bmatrix}, \quad \begin{bmatrix} -1 & 0 \\ 0 & -1 \end{bmatrix}, \quad \begin{bmatrix} 0 & 1 \\ -1 & 0 \end{bmatrix}, \quad \begin{bmatrix} 0 & -1 \\ 1 & 0 \end{bmatrix},$$

$$\begin{bmatrix} 0 & 1 \\ 1 & 0 \end{bmatrix}, \quad \begin{bmatrix} 0 & -1 \\ -1 & 0 \end{bmatrix}, \quad \begin{bmatrix} 1 & 0 \\ 0 & -1 \end{bmatrix}, \quad \begin{bmatrix} -1 & 0 \\ 0 & 1 \end{bmatrix},$$

forms a group of which the first four form a subgroup. Can you find the other two subgroups of order 4 and the five subgroups of order 2?

5. Show that the set of all nonsingular upper triangular matrices of order n over a field $\mathscr{F}$ constitutes a group with respect to multiplication.

6. Show that the nonsingular matrices of order n which commute with a fixed matrix of order n form a group.

7. Do the elementary row transformations of a given matrix form a group?

8. By actual consideration of their elements, show that the product of two permutation matrices is again a permutation matrix.

9. Show that every permutation matrix can be factored into a product of certain of the elementary matrices $P_{12}, P_{23}, \ldots, P_{n-1,n}$, where P_{ij} is a permutation matrix which corresponds to the interchange of the ith and jth variables (columns). (Some of these matrices may have to be used more than once in the product.)

10. Prove that, for every permutation matrix P of order n, there exists a positive integer q such that $P^q = I_n$, and hence that $P^{q-1} = P^{-1}$. How can you find the smallest positive integer that will serve? [*Hint:* Every power of P is a permutation matrix (of which there are only $n!$). Hence there must exist integers $r > s > 0$ such that $P^r = P^s$, etc.]

11. Show that the determinant of a permutation matrix is $+1$ or -1 depending on whether the corresponding permutation is even or odd.

12. An arbitrary permutation matrix P may be written in the form $P = [E_{i_1}, E_{i_2}, \ldots, E_{i_n}]$, where the E's are elementary n-vectors and $i_1, i_2, \ldots, i_n$ is a permutation of $1, 2, \ldots, n$. Establish a general rule for writing P^{-1} in terms of the E's. For example, if $P = [E_3, E_1, E_2]_3$, then $P^{-1} = [E_2, E_3, E_1]_3$, etc.

13. Prove that an $n \times n$ matrix commutes with every $n \times n$ permutation matrix if and only if it has the form $aI + bE$, where E is a matrix all of whose entries are 1's and a and b are scalars.

14. Determine under what conditions the matrix $aI + bE$ defined in Exercise 13 is nonsingular. Then compute the inverse. (*Hint:* Use the preceding exercise to show that the inverse has the same form. Then find scalars α and β such that $\alpha I + \beta E$ is the desired inverse.) Do the nonsingular matrices of this form constitute a group?

15. Let us call a matrix of the form $[E_i, E_{i+1}, \ldots, E_n, E_1, \ldots, E_{i-1}]$ a **cyclic permutation matrix**. Show that the set of cyclic permutation matrices of order n constitutes a subgroup of the set of all $n \times n$ permutation matrices. Show also that all the matrices of this group may be represented as powers of a single matrix.

16. The cyclic permutation matrices

$$I = \begin{bmatrix} 1 & 0 & 0 \\ 0 & 1 & 0 \\ 0 & 0 & 1 \end{bmatrix}, \qquad U = \begin{bmatrix} 0 & 1 & 0 \\ 0 & 0 & 1 \\ 1 & 0 & 0 \end{bmatrix}, \qquad U^2 = \begin{bmatrix} 0 & 0 & 1 \\ 1 & 0 & 0 \\ 0 & 1 & 0 \end{bmatrix}$$

are used in the study of 3-phase electric current. Show that the set of matrix polynomials $\alpha I + \beta U + \gamma U^2$, where α, β, γ are arbitrary complex numbers, constitutes a commutative ring with a unit element. Show that there exist divisors of zero in this ring.

17. Let us call a matrix of the form $[\alpha_1 E_{j_1}, \alpha_2 E_{j_2}, \ldots, \alpha_n E_{j_n}]$, where the α's are nonzero scalars from a field $\mathscr{F}$ a **weighted permutation matrix** over $\mathscr{F}$. Show that the set of all weighted permutation matrices over an arbitrary number field $\mathscr{F}$ constitutes a group with respect to multiplication.

A GENERALIZATION

6.23 A More General Definition of a Vector Space

There are many collections of mathematical objects other than sets of n-vectors with components from a number field $\mathscr{F}$ which display the characteristic properties (a) and (b) of Section 6.1. For example, the set of all polynomials in a single indeterminate x

$$a_0 + a_1 x + a_2 x^2 + \cdots + a_n x^n, \qquad 0 \leqslant n < \infty,$$

whose coefficients are in the real number field is a case in point. In fact, a scalar (real number) times any such polynomial is another of the same kind, as is also the sum of any two such polynomials. Since polynomials of all finite degrees appear, the set has no finite basis, for a finite number of polynomials can provide only a finite number of distinct powers of x. However, the infinite set of polynomials

$$1, x, x^2, \ldots$$

does constitute a "basis" in the sense that every polynomial in the set is a linear combination over the real field of a finite number of these, and every such combination is a member of the set.

Next consider the set of all formal power series over the real field, convergent or not, in a variable x:

$$S(x) = a_0 + a_1 x + a_2 x^2 + \cdots + a_n x^n + \cdots.$$

It is easy to check that properties (a) and (b) hold for the set of all these series if addition means the addition of coefficients of corresponding terms and multiplication by a scalar (real number) means the multiplication of every coefficient by this real number.

The most important subset of the preceding set is the set of all power series in x, each of which converges at least inside (and possibly at the endpoints of) an interval of convergence $-R < x < R$ with $R > 0$. (The interval need not be the same for all series.) From the theory of infinite series we know that:

(a) If $S(x) = \sum_0^\infty a_j x^j$ is a power series convergent in $-R < x < R$, $R > 0$, then $\alpha S(x)$, that is, $\sum_0^\infty (\alpha a_j) x^j$, also converges in $-R < x < R$.

(b) If $S_1(x) = \sum_0^\infty a_{1j} x^j$ converges in $-R_1 < x < R_1$ and $S_2(x) = \sum_0^\infty a_{2j} x^j$ converges in $-R_2 < x < R_2$, R_1 and R_2 both > 0, then $S_1(x) + S_2(x)$, that is, $\sum_0^\infty (a_{1j} + a_{2j}) x^j$, converges at least in the smaller of these two intervals of convergence. Thus once again properties (a) and (b) hold.

In neither of the two preceding sets, however, does there exist any sequence $S_1(x), S_2(x), \ldots, S_n(x), \ldots$ of finite or infinite series which may be regarded as constituting a basis for the set in the sense that every member of the set may be written as a linear combination of finitely many members of the sequence. The reader familiar with analysis may find it challenging to prove this.

As a final example of a different kind, we note that the set of all matrices of order n with elements from a complex number field enjoys properties (a) and (b):

(a) Any scalar (complex number) times a matrix of the set is a matrix of the set.

(b) The sum of two such matrices is again a matrix of the same kind.

In this case the set has what we could properly call a finite basis, for every matrix of the set is a linear combination over the field of complex numbers of the n^2 matrices E_{ij} where E_{ij} has a 1 in the ith row and jth column, all other entries being zero. For example, when $n = 2$,

$$\begin{bmatrix} a_{11} & a_{12} \\ a_{21} & a_{22} \end{bmatrix} = a_{11} \begin{bmatrix} 1 & 0 \\ 0 & 0 \end{bmatrix} + a_{12} \begin{bmatrix} 0 & 1 \\ 0 & 0 \end{bmatrix} + a_{21} \begin{bmatrix} 0 & 0 \\ 1 & 0 \end{bmatrix} + a_{22} \begin{bmatrix} 0 & 0 \\ 0 & 1 \end{bmatrix}.$$

To give a more general definition of a vector space which will include the preceding examples as well as our spaces of n-vectors, we proceed as follows. We assume first that we have a field $\mathscr{F}$ of "scalars" over which to work and a collection $\mathscr{V}$ of mathematical objects which we call "vectors" (even though they may not resemble geometric vectors). Equality of two vectors means they are identical. We call $\mathscr{V}$ a **vector space over** $\mathscr{F}$ if its members satisfy the following requirements:

(A) There is an operation called "addition" such that, corresponding to any two members V_1 and V_2 of $\mathscr{V}$, there exists a unique "sum" $V_1 + V_2$. Moreover, addition of vectors from $\mathscr{V}$ obeys these rules:

(1) $V_1 + V_2$ is always a member of $\mathscr{V}$ (closure).

(2) For all V_1, V_2, V_3 in $\mathscr{V}$, $V_1 + (V_2 + V_3) = (V_1 + V_2) + V_3$ (the associative law).

(3) For all V_1, V_2 in $\mathscr{V}$, $V_1 + V_2 = V_2 + V_1$ (the commutative law).

(4) There is a member of $\mathscr{V}$, called the *zero-vector* and denoted by 0, such that for each V of $\mathscr{V}$

$$V + 0 = V.$$

(5) To every member V of $\mathscr{V}$ there corresponds a *negative*, $-V$, which is also a member of $\mathscr{V}$, such that

$$V + (-V) = 0.$$

In brief, with respect to the operation of addition, the elements of $\mathscr{V}$ constitute a *commutative group*.

(S) There is an operation of multiplication of a vector by a scalar such that if α is any element of $\mathscr{F}$ and if V is any member of $\mathscr{V}$, there exists a uniquely defined product αV which also belongs to $\mathscr{V}$. Scalar multiplication is assumed to obey these rules, where α and β are in $\mathscr{F}$:

(1) $V\alpha = \alpha V$, that is, $V\alpha$ is defined to be the same vector as αV.

(2) $\alpha(V_1 + V_2) = \alpha V_1 + \alpha V_2$.

(3) $(\alpha + \beta)V = \alpha V + \beta V$.

(4) $\alpha(\beta V) = (\alpha\beta)V$.

(5) $0 \cdot V = 0, 1 \cdot V = V$.

Note that in (5), the left 0 denotes the *scalar* 0, whereas the right 0 denotes the *zero-vector*.

The properties (a) and (b) which were illustrated by our examples are incorporated in the postulates (S) and (A). It is not difficult to check that each of the three examples given above is a vector space in the sense of this definition.

A vector space $\mathscr{V}$ is called **finite dimensional** of **dimension** k if there exist k members $V_1, V_2, \ldots, V_k$ of $\mathscr{V}$ such that every member V of $\mathscr{V}$ can be written as a linear combination

$$(6.23.1) \qquad V = \alpha_1 V_1 + \alpha_2 V_2 + \cdots + \alpha_k V_k,$$

where the α's belong to $\mathscr{F}$, but there exists no set of fewer than k members of $\mathscr{V}$ with the same property. The vectors $V_1, V_2, \ldots, V_k$ are said to form a **basis** for $\mathscr{V}$. As before, any set of vectors $V_1, V_2, \ldots, V_m$, $m \geqslant k$, such that every vector of $\mathscr{V}$ can be written in at least one way as a linear combination of these V's, is said to **span** $\mathscr{V}$.

The set of all matrices of order n with elements in the complex field is thus an example of a vector space of dimension n^2, for it is not hard to show that a basis must contain exactly n^2 linearly independent matrices. In fact, the n^2 matrices E_{ij} mentioned above provide such a basis.

Another example is provided by the set of all polynomials of degree $\leqslant n$, including the polynomial 0 which has no degree, in an indeterminate x over a field $\mathscr{F}$. Here n is a fixed, positive integer, so that each polynomial of the set is a linear combination of the independent polynomials $1, x, x^2, \ldots, x^n$, and hence the space has dimension $n + 1$.

We now prove a sequence of theorems which show that our preceding work is general enough to include all finite dimensional vector spaces.

Theorem 6.23.1: *If $V_1, V_2, \ldots, V_k$ form a basis for a finite dimensional vector space $\mathscr{V}$ over a field $\mathscr{F}$, then for each V of $\mathscr{V}$ the representation*

$$V = \alpha_1 V_1 + \alpha_2 V_2 + \cdots + \alpha_k V_k$$

of V as a linear combination over $\mathscr{F}$ of $V_1, \ldots, V_k$ is unique.

In fact, if

$$V = \sum_{j=1}^{k} \alpha_j V_j = \sum_{j=1}^{k} \beta_j V_j,$$

then

$$\sum_{j=1}^{k} (\alpha_j - \beta_j) V_j = 0,$$

where 0 is the zero element of $\mathscr{V}$. If not every coefficient $\alpha_j - \beta_j$ is 0, then we can write some V_t in the form

$$V_t = \sum_{j \neq t} \gamma_j V_j, \qquad 1 \leqslant t \leqslant k.$$

Substituting this into (6.23.1), we see that every vector of $\mathscr{V}$ can be expressed as a linear combination of only $k - 1$ vectors $V_1, \ldots, V_{t-1}, V_{t+1}, \ldots, V_k$ of $\mathscr{V}$. Since by hypothesis this is not possible, we must have $\alpha_j - \beta_j = 0$, that is, $\alpha_j = \beta_j$, for each j, which proves the theorem.

Theorem 6.23.2:   *The members of a vector space $\mathscr{V}$ of dimension k over a field $\mathscr{F}$ and the set of all k-vectors over $\mathscr{F}$ are in one-to-one correspondence.*

Each member V of $\mathscr{V}$ determines a unique vector $\{\alpha_1, \alpha_2, \ldots, \alpha_k\}$ by the preceding theorem, and each such k-vector determines via (6.23.1) a unique member of $\mathscr{V}$, as follows from the definition of a vector space.

Theorem 6.23.3:   *If V and $\{\alpha_1, \alpha_2, \ldots, \alpha_k\}$ correspond as in the preceding theorem, then αV and $\alpha\{\alpha_1, \alpha_2, \ldots, \alpha_k\}$ correspond also.*

For if $V = \displaystyle\sum_{j=1}^{k} \alpha_j V_j$, then $\alpha V = \displaystyle\sum_{j=1}^{k} (\alpha \alpha_j) V_j$, by the definition of a vector space.

Theorem 6.23.4:   *If V_1 and $\{\alpha_{11}, \alpha_{21}, \ldots, \alpha_{k1}\}$, V_2 and $\{\alpha_{12}, \alpha_{22}, \ldots, \alpha_{k2}\}$ correspond as above, then $V_1 + V_2$ and $\{(\alpha_{11} + \alpha_{12}), (\alpha_{21} + \alpha_{22}), \ldots, (\alpha_{k1} + \alpha_{k2})\}$ also correspond.*

In fact, if

$$V_1 = \alpha_{11} V_1 + \alpha_{21} V_2 + \cdots + \alpha_{k1} V_k,$$

and

$$V_2 = \alpha_{12} V_1 + \alpha_{22} V_2 + \cdots + \alpha_{k2} V_k,$$

then, by the definition of a vector space,

$$V_1 + V_2 = (\alpha_{11} + \alpha_{12}) V_1 + (\alpha_{21} + \alpha_{22}) V_2 + \cdots + (\alpha_{k1} + \alpha_{k2}) V_k,$$

which proves the result. We can now state

Theorem 6.23.5:   *Every finite dimensional vector space of dimension k over a field $\mathscr{F}$ is isomorphic, with respect to addition and multiplication by a scalar, to the $\mathscr{V}_k{}^k$ over $\mathscr{F}$.*

This is the immediate consequence of the three preceding theorems. *Because of this theorem, every result of the preceding sections of this chapter may be applied in every finite dimensional vector space over a number field $\mathscr{F}$.* Thus the concept of isomorphism shows that we have in one stroke developed the linear algebra of all finite dimensional vector spaces over a given number field.

6.24 Fields of Matrices

In this section we show how operators can be used to study a specific type of vector space. We have seen earlier that there are infinitely many different number fields. Some of these can be constructed by a process of extending a given field in a systematic way. For example, let us assume the real number field to be given. The polynomial $x^2 + 1$, whose coefficients are in this field, contains no linear factor whose coefficients are real. This implies that the equation $x^2 + 1 = 0$ has no root in the *real* field. Denote a root by "*i*," that is, $i^2 + 1 = 0$, and consider the set of all symbols of the form $\alpha \cdot 1 + \beta \cdot i$, that is, the set of all linear combinations of the real unit 1 and the complex unit i. This set constitutes the complex number field (see Section 4.11; also Appendix II). The real number field is a subfield of the complex number field; the latter is called an extension of the real number field.

It is easy, and is left to the reader, to verify that the set of complex numbers $\alpha \cdot 1 + \beta \cdot i$ also constitutes a two-dimensional vector space over the real number field (Section 6.23). This vector space may be given a useful representation by letting the complex number $\alpha + \beta i$ correspond to the 2-vector $\{\alpha, \beta\}$. Since

$$\begin{bmatrix} \alpha \\ \beta \end{bmatrix} = \alpha \cdot \begin{bmatrix} 1 \\ 0 \end{bmatrix} + \beta \cdot \begin{bmatrix} 0 \\ 1 \end{bmatrix},$$

this correspondence may be represented geometrically with the aid of the familiar Argand diagram (Figure 6.24.1).

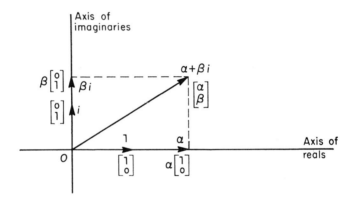

Figure 6.24.1

In this alternative representation of the vector $\alpha + \beta i$, the vector $\{1, 0\}$ corresponds to the real unit 1, and $\{0, 1\}$ corresponds to the complex unit i. The real numbers α and β are the components of the vector $\{\alpha, \beta\}$ with respect to the basis $\{1, 0\}$, $\{0, 1\}$, that is, of the vector $\alpha + \beta i$ with respect to the basis 1, i.

Now we can interpret the product

$$(a + bi)(\alpha + \beta i) = (a\alpha - b\beta) + (b\alpha + a\beta)i$$

as multiplication of the *vector* $\{\alpha, \beta\}$ by a 2×2 *matrix* which yields the vector $\{(a\alpha - b\beta), (b\alpha + a\beta)\}$ as the product, thus:

(6.24.1)
$$\begin{bmatrix} a & -b \\ b & a \end{bmatrix} \cdot \begin{bmatrix} \alpha \\ \beta \end{bmatrix} = \begin{bmatrix} (a\alpha - b\beta) \\ (b\alpha + a\beta) \end{bmatrix}.$$

Hence the operation of multiplying an arbitrary *vector* $\alpha + \beta i$ of the vector space of complex numbers by a fixed complex number $a + bi$ may be regarded as a *linear operator* which maps the given vector $\alpha + \beta i$ onto the vector $(a\alpha - b\beta) + (b\alpha + a\beta)i$ of the same space. Thus we are able to interpret a complex number in two ways—as a representation of a vector or as a representation of an operator on a vector. This is a fruitful circumstance.

Now, by the rules of matrix algebra, we have

$$(6.24.2) \qquad c \begin{bmatrix} a & -b \\ b & a \end{bmatrix} = \begin{bmatrix} ca & -cb \\ cb & ca \end{bmatrix},$$

$$(6.24.3) \qquad \begin{bmatrix} a & -b \\ b & a \end{bmatrix} + \begin{bmatrix} c & -d \\ d & c \end{bmatrix} = \begin{bmatrix} (a+c) & -(b+d) \\ (b+d) & (a+c) \end{bmatrix},$$

$$(6.24.4) \qquad \begin{bmatrix} a & -b \\ b & a \end{bmatrix} \cdot \begin{bmatrix} c & -d \\ d & c \end{bmatrix} = \begin{bmatrix} (ac-bd) & -(bc+ad) \\ (bc+ad) & (ac-bd) \end{bmatrix}.$$

If we multiply each of these equations on the right by $\{\alpha, \beta\}$ and then write the corresponding equations involving complex numbers, we obtain respectively

$$c(a + bi)(\alpha + \beta i) = (ca + cbi)(\alpha + \beta i),$$

$$(a + bi)(\alpha + \beta i) + (c + di)(\alpha + \beta i) = [(a + c) + (b + d)i](\alpha + \beta i),$$

and

$$(a + bi)(c + di)(\alpha + \beta i) = [(ac - bd) + (bc + ad)i](\alpha + \beta i),$$

each of which is true for *all* complex numbers $\alpha + \beta i$.

For the interpretation of complex numbers as operators, we have thus shown that a scalar times the matrix representing a complex number equals the matrix representing the scalar times the complex number. Also, the sum (product) of the matrices representing two complex numbers is the matrix representing the sum (product) of those numbers. That is, the matrix operations correspond exactly to the analogous operations performed on complex numbers interpreted as operators.

The conclusions of the preceding paragraph are the source of the isomorphism between complex numbers $a + bi$ and matrices

$$\begin{bmatrix} a & -b \\ b & a \end{bmatrix}$$

noted earlier (Section 4.14). Because of the isomorphism, we know that this set of matrices constitutes a field.

There remains this question: By what general principles could one deduce the *form* of the matrix which corresponds to a given complex number? {The matrix

$$\begin{bmatrix} a & -b \\ b & a \end{bmatrix}$$

was produced without explanation in (6.24.1).} To answer this, note first that

$$1(\alpha + \beta i) = \alpha + \beta i, \qquad i(\alpha + \beta i) = -\beta + \alpha i.$$

Hence, as is easy to determine by inspection, multiplications by 1 and i are representable by the following matrix operations:

$$\begin{bmatrix} 1 & 0 \\ 0 & 1 \end{bmatrix} \cdot \begin{bmatrix} \alpha \\ \beta \end{bmatrix} = \begin{bmatrix} \alpha \\ \beta \end{bmatrix}, \qquad \begin{bmatrix} 0 & -1 \\ 1 & 0 \end{bmatrix} \cdot \begin{bmatrix} \alpha \\ \beta \end{bmatrix} = \begin{bmatrix} -\beta \\ \alpha \end{bmatrix}.$$

Now, corresponding to the complex number $a \cdot 1 + b \cdot i$, we obtain, by (6.24.2) and (6.24.3), the matrix

$$a \cdot \begin{bmatrix} 1 & 0 \\ 0 & 1 \end{bmatrix} + b \cdot \begin{bmatrix} 0 & -1 \\ 1 & 0 \end{bmatrix} = \begin{bmatrix} a & -b \\ b & a \end{bmatrix},$$

where

$$\begin{bmatrix} 1 & 0 \\ 0 & 1 \end{bmatrix}$$

corresponds to 1, and

$$\begin{bmatrix} 0 & -1 \\ 1 & 0 \end{bmatrix}$$

corresponds to i. This kind of reasoning is readily generalized.

To illustrate further, consider the equation $x^3 - 2 = 0$, which has no rational root but has the real irrational root $\sqrt[3]{2}$. Consider the set of all real numbers of the form $\alpha + \beta\sqrt[3]{2} + \gamma\sqrt[3]{4}$ where α, β, γ are rational. It is not hard to show that this set is a field (Exercise 6, Section 4.12). To find the corresponding matrix field, we first interpret the given field as a vector space over the rational number field and establish the correspondence

$$\alpha + \beta\sqrt[3]{2} + \gamma\sqrt[3]{4} \leftrightarrow \{\alpha, \beta, \gamma\}.$$

Now

$$1(\alpha + \beta\sqrt[3]{2} + \gamma\sqrt[3]{4}) = \alpha + \beta\sqrt[3]{2} + \gamma\sqrt[3]{4},$$

$$\sqrt[3]{2}(\alpha + \beta\sqrt[3]{2} + \gamma\sqrt[3]{4}) = 2\gamma + \alpha\sqrt[3]{2} + \beta\sqrt[3]{4},$$

$$\sqrt[3]{4}(\alpha + \beta\sqrt[3]{2} + \gamma\sqrt[3]{4}) = 2\beta + 2\gamma\sqrt[3]{2} + \alpha\sqrt[3]{4}.$$

These multiplications correspond to the matrix operations:

$$\begin{bmatrix} 1 & 0 & 0 \\ 0 & 1 & 0 \\ 0 & 0 & 1 \end{bmatrix} \cdot \begin{bmatrix} \alpha \\ \beta \\ \gamma \end{bmatrix} = \begin{bmatrix} \alpha \\ \beta \\ \gamma \end{bmatrix}, \qquad \begin{bmatrix} 0 & 0 & 2 \\ 1 & 0 & 0 \\ 0 & 1 & 0 \end{bmatrix} \cdot \begin{bmatrix} \alpha \\ \beta \\ \gamma \end{bmatrix} = \begin{bmatrix} 2\gamma \\ \alpha \\ \beta \end{bmatrix},$$

$$\begin{bmatrix} 0 & 2 & 0 \\ 0 & 0 & 2 \\ 1 & 0 & 0 \end{bmatrix} \cdot \begin{bmatrix} \alpha \\ \beta \\ \gamma \end{bmatrix} = \begin{bmatrix} 2\beta \\ 2\gamma \\ \alpha \end{bmatrix},$$

in which the matrices are easy to determine by inspection. Hence multiplication by $a \cdot 1 + b\sqrt[3]{2} + c\sqrt[3]{4}$ corresponds to multiplication by the matrix

$$a \cdot \begin{bmatrix} 1 & 0 & 0 \\ 0 & 1 & 0 \\ 0 & 0 & 1 \end{bmatrix} + b \cdot \begin{bmatrix} 0 & 0 & 2 \\ 1 & 0 & 0 \\ 0 & 1 & 0 \end{bmatrix} + c \cdot \begin{bmatrix} 0 & 2 & 0 \\ 0 & 0 & 2 \\ 1 & 0 & 0 \end{bmatrix} = \begin{bmatrix} a & 2c & 2b \\ b & a & 2c \\ c & b & a \end{bmatrix},$$

and the set of all such matrices constitutes a field (Exercise 7, Section 4.15).

In general, let

$$f(x) = x^n + \alpha_{n-1}x^{n-1} + \alpha_{n-2}x^{n-2} + \cdots + \alpha_1 x + \alpha_0$$

denote a polynomial which has coefficients in a given number field $\mathscr{F}$, and which is irreducible over $\mathscr{F}$ (not factorable into factors with coefficients in $\mathscr{F}$). Let ω denote any zero of this polynomial. Then ω is not an element of $\mathscr{F}$. It can be shown that the set of all elements of the form

$$a_0 + a_1\omega + a_2\omega^2 + \cdots + a_{n-1}\omega^{n-1},$$

where $a_0, a_1, \ldots, a_{n-1}$ belong to $\mathscr{F}$, constitutes a field. Such a field is called an **extension field** of $\mathscr{F}$ and is denoted by the symbol $\mathscr{F}[\omega]$. To find a matrix representation of this field, one computes the coefficients on the right in each of the equations

(6.24.5)　$\omega^p(a_0 + a_1\omega + \cdots + a_{n-1}\omega^{n-1})$

$$= a_{0p} + a_{1p}\omega + a_{2p}\omega^2 + \cdots + a_{n-1,p}\omega^{n-1},$$

$$p = 0, 1, 2, \ldots, n-1,$$

by using the fact that

$$\omega^n + \alpha_{n-1}\omega^{n-1} + \cdots + \alpha_1\omega + \alpha_0 = 0,$$

to eliminate all powers of ω higher than ω^{n-1}. Now one writes equations (6.24.5) in operator form:

(6.24.6)　$$M_p \cdot \begin{bmatrix} a_0 \\ a_1 \\ \vdots \\ a_{n-1} \end{bmatrix} = \begin{bmatrix} a_{0p} \\ a_{1p} \\ \vdots \\ a_{n-1,p} \end{bmatrix}, \qquad p = 0, 1, 2, \ldots, n-1,$$

where, as in preceding examples, the matrices M_p are easily found by inspection. Then the matrix

(6.24.7)　$$M = \sum_{p=0}^{n-1} b_p M_p$$

represents the operator corresponding to the field element

(6.24.8)　$$b_0 + b_1\omega + b_2\omega^2 + \cdots + b_{n-1}\omega^{n-1}.$$

It may be shown that, under the stated hypotheses on $f(x)$, the correspondence between (6.24.7) and (6.24.8) is always an isomorphism so that the set of all such matrices constitutes a field. (See Birkhoff and MacLane: *A Survey of Modern*

Algebra, Revised Edition, New York, Macmillan, 1953, pp. 239–241.) Not all number fields can be represented in this way.

6.25 Exercises

1. Show that the set of all matrices of order (m, n) over a number field $\mathscr{F}$ is a vector space of dimension mn over $\mathscr{F}$.

2. Determine which of the following sets are vector spaces. State which of the spaces are finite dimensional.

(a) The set of all functions of t of the form $A \sin (\omega t + \alpha)$, where A and α are arbitrary real numbers, but ω is a fixed real number.

(b) The set of all n-vectors whose components are real polynomials of arbitrary degree in a single variable t.

(c) The set of all n-vectors whose components are real polynomials of degree $\leqslant n$ in a single variable t.

(d) The set of all real functions continuous on the closed interval $[0, 1]$.

(e) The set of real functions $f(x)$ of period $2L$ which may be represented as a Fourier series.

(f) The set of all real functions of three real variables continuous in the region $x_1{}^2 + x_2{}^2 + x_3{}^2 \leqslant 1$.

(g) The set of all solutions of an nth order homogeneous linear differential equation with constant coefficients.

(h) The set of all linear forms, in n variables, over a field $\mathscr{F}$.

3. Determine all bases for the vector space of complex numbers over the real-number field.

4. Let p_1 and p_2 denote arbitrary positive numbers (vectors). Define vector addition, "$\oplus$," and multiplication by a scalar, "$\odot$," in terms of ordinary multiplication by the equations

$$p_1 \oplus p_2 = p_1 p_2,$$

$$\alpha \odot p_1 = p_1{}^\alpha.$$

Show that, with respect to these operations, the set P of all positive real numbers is a finite dimensional vector space. Identify the zero-vector and write the expression for an arbitrary linear combination of $p_1, p_2, \ldots, p_n$ in terms of ordinary multiplication. Show that the isomorphism called for by Theorem 6.23.5 is given by the log function.

*5. Show that the following statements hold true for every vector space $\mathscr{V}$ over a field $\mathscr{F}$:

(a) There is only one zero vector in $\mathscr{V}$.

(b) There is only one negative of a given element in $\mathscr{V}$.

(c) For all V in $\mathscr{V}$, $(-1)V = -V$.

(d) For all α in $\mathscr{F}$ and all V in $\mathscr{V}$, if $\alpha V = 0$, then either $\alpha = 0$ (scalar) or $V = 0$ (vector).

(e) For all U, V, W in $\mathscr{V}$, $U + (V - W) = (U - W) + V$.

6. The concept of a linear operator extends at once to arbitrary vector spaces. Show that differentiation is a linear operator on the vector space of all polynomials of degree n or less in a single variable x over a given number field $\mathscr{F}$.

Represent the operator in matrix form and show that it is nilpotent. Identify the null space, the fixed space, and the image space of this operator.

7. Show that a translation of the variable, that is, replacement of x by $x + \alpha$, where α is a fixed element of $\mathscr{F}$, is also a linear operator on the vector space of Exercise 6. Represent this operator in matrix form. Find the inverse of the matrix of this operator by first finding the inverse of the operator.

8. Prove that the real polynomial *functions* $1, x, x^2, \ldots, x^n$ are linearly independent. (*Hint:* If there exist $c_0, c_1, \ldots, c_n$, not all zero such that $\sum_{j=0}^{n} c_j x^j = 0$, then, for $n + 1$ distinct values $x_1, x_2, \ldots, x_{n+1}$, we have $\sum_{j=0}^{n} c_j x_k^j = 0$, $k = 1, 2, \ldots, n + 1$. Now apply Corollary 5.6.2 and Exercise 26, Section 2.12. Alternatively, differentiate the identity repeatedly.)

9. Show that the set of all linear forms $A^{\mathsf{T}}X$, where A is a vector of a $\mathscr{V}_n^k$, is also a vector space of dimension k over the same number field. When $k = n$, this space is called the **dual space** of $\mathscr{V}_n^n$.

10. Show that every linear operator on the dual space of a $\mathscr{V}_n^n$ can be represented in matrix form.

11. Let U, W denote arbitrary subspaces of a vector space $\mathscr{V}$. Let $U + W$ and UW denote the sum and the intersection of U and W as defined in Section 6.8. Does the set of all subspaces of a $\mathscr{V}_n^n$ form a ring with respect to these operations? Why?

12. Obtain the matrix representation of the field $\{a + b\sqrt{2} \mid a, b \text{ rational}\}$.

13. Obtain the matrix representation of the field $\{a + b\sqrt{2} + c\sqrt{3} + d\sqrt{6} \mid a, b, c, d \text{ rational}\}$.

(*Hint:* Multiply this by 1, $\sqrt{2}$, $\sqrt{3}$, and $\sqrt{6}$, rewrite the resulting equations in operator form, then combine the results.)

14. Show that $f(M) = 0$, if $f(x) = 0$ is the irreducible equation defining ω and M is as defined in (6.24.7).

Special problem: Recall the definition of a ring $\mathscr{R}$ (Exercise 10, Section 4.15) and of a field $\mathscr{F}$ (Section 4.14). Review the results of Chapters 1 through 6 and determine which of them apply over $\mathscr{R}$ as well as over $\mathscr{F}$. Can any of them be revised to hold over $\mathscr{R}$ by means of a change in hypothesis or conclusion? The analog of a vector space, defined over a ring instead of over a field, is called a **module**.

CHAPTER SEVEN

Unitary and Orthogonal Transformations

LENGTH AND ORTHOGONALITY

7.1 The Length of a Vector

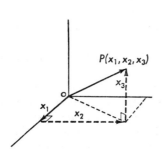

$P(x_1, x_2, x_3)$

x_3

x_1

x_2

Figure 7.1.1

In $\mathscr{E}_3$, by applying the Pythagorean theorem twice, one shows that the length of the segment $\overrightarrow{OP}$ is given by $\sqrt{x_1{}^2 + x_2{}^2 + x_3{}^2}$, where (x_1, x_2, x_3) is the endpoint of the segment (Figure 7.1.1). We write this in the form

$$|X| = (X^{\mathsf{T}}X)^{1/2} = \sqrt{x_1{}^2 + x_2{}^2 + x_3{}^2},$$

where $X = \{x_1, x_2, x_3\}$ and $|X|$ denotes the length of the vector X. More generally, if X is the vector $\{(b_1 - a_1), (b_2 - a_2), (b_3 - a_3)\}$ associated with the directed segment $\overrightarrow{AB}$, then $|X|$ is the **distance** $d(A, B)$ between A and B:

$$d(A, B) = \sqrt{(b_1 - a_1)^2 + (b_2 - a_2)^2 + (b_3 - a_3)^2}.$$

We can extend this to n dimensions by first defining a **point** A to be an ordered set of n real numbers $(a_1, a_2, \ldots, a_n)$. The real numbers $a_1, a_2, \ldots, a_n$ are called the **coordinates** of the point. The point $O(0, 0, \ldots, 0)$ is called the **origin**. If B is the point $(b_1, b_2, \ldots, b_n)$, then the set of all points

$$(a_1 + t(b_1 - a_1), a_2 + t(b_2 - a_2), \ldots, a_n + t(b_n - a_n)),$$

where $0 \leqslant t \leqslant 1$, is called the **line segment** AB. If we give to the points of this segment the order determined by increasing t continuously from 0 to 1

inclusive, we call the result the **directed line segment** $\overrightarrow{AB}$ of which A is the
initial point and B is the **terminal point**.

With each directed segment $\overrightarrow{AB}$ we associate a vector $\{(b_1 - a_1),$
$(b_2 - a_2), \ldots, (b_n - a_n)\}$ whose components are the differences of corresponding coordinates of the points B and A, *in that order*. Two directed
segments are defined to be equal if and only if their associated n-vectors are
equal. This definition of equality again divides all directed segments into
classes of equal segments. The class of all directed segments which have
associated with them the fixed vector $\{x_1, x_2, \ldots, x_n\}$ includes one representative with initial point $O(0, 0, \ldots, 0)$ and terminal point $P(x_1, x_2, \ldots, x_n)$,
that is, it includes a vector of the form $\overrightarrow{OP}$. As in $\mathscr{E}_3$, we are concerned
primarily with vectors of this kind.

To extend the idea of **length** to n-vectors, we employ the obvious generalization of our previous formula

$$(7.1.1) \qquad |X| = (X^{\mathsf{T}}X)^{1/2} = \sqrt{x_1{}^2 + x_2{}^2 + \cdots + x_n{}^2}.$$

This function is also commonly called the **norm** of the vector X. If X is the
vector associated with a directed segment $\overrightarrow{AB}$, then the **distance** $d(A, B)$
between A and B is defined to be $|X|$. Thus

$$(7.1.2) \quad d(A, B) = \sqrt{(b_1 - a_1)^2 + (b_2 - a_2)^2 + \cdots + (b_n - a_n)^2}.$$

The set of all points $(x_1, x_2, \ldots, x_n)$ with real coordinates and with distance
defined as in $(7.1.2)$ is called **Euclidean space of n dimensions** and is denoted
by $\mathscr{E}_n$. The vectors associated with ordered pairs of points, that is, with
directed segments, will be referred to as **vectors of $\mathscr{E}_n$**. One can develop in
$\mathscr{E}_n$ an analytic geometry which is the natural generalization of the analytic
geometry of $\mathscr{E}_3$. It is studied with the aid of transformations (operators or
transformations of coordinates) which leave distance—that is, the length of
a vector—invariant. In $\mathscr{E}_2$ and $\mathscr{E}_3$ these transformations are the familiar
translations, rotations, and reflections. We shall see presently what these
transformations are in $\mathscr{E}_n$.

The nonnegative scalar $X^{\mathsf{T}}X$ which appears in $(7.1.1)$ is a sum of squares
of real numbers. Since a sum of squares of real numbers is zero if and only if
each summand is zero, it follows that *a vector in $\mathscr{E}_n$ has length zero if and only
if it is the zero-vector; otherwise its length is a positive real number.*

It is useful to extend these ideas and definitions in yet another direction.
We shall call an ordered set of n numbers $(a_1, a_2, \ldots, a_n)$ a **point** even when
the a's are complex numbers. As before, with an ordered pair of points A, B,
we can associate a vector $\{(b_1 - a_1), (b_2 - a_2), \ldots, (b_n - a_n)\}$. In particular,
with the **origin** $O(0, 0, \ldots, 0)$ and the point $P(x_1, x_2, \ldots, x_n)$ we associate
the vector $X = \{x_1, x_2, \ldots, x_n\}$.

Suppose now we were to use the same formula for the length of a vector as we used in $\mathscr{E}_n$. Then we would have, for example, that the length of the nonzero-vector $X = \{i, 1\}$ would be zero, for $X^{\mathsf{T}}X = i^2 + 1^2 = 0$ in this case. Moreover, since $X^{\mathsf{T}}X$ could well be complex, length would not always be a real number if we used (7.1.1). To avoid such peculiarities as these, we use the tranjugate (see Chapter One) X^* instead of the transpose X^{T}, and define **length** or **norm** thus:

$$(7.1.3) \qquad |X| = (X^*X)^{1/2} = \sqrt{\sum_{j=1}^{n} \bar{x}_j x_j} = \sqrt{\sum |x_j|^2}.$$

Since for every complex number x_j, $\bar{x}_j x_j$ is the nonnegative real number $|x_j|^2$, it follows once again that *a vector has length zero if and only if it is the zero-vector.*

The **distance between two points** A and B is now defined to be

$$(7.1.4) \qquad d(A, B) = \sqrt{\sum \overline{(b_j - a_j)}(b_j - a_j)} = \sqrt{\sum |b_j - a_j|^2},$$

which is the length of the associated vector.

The set of all points $(a_1, a_2, \ldots, a_n)$ with coordinates from the complex field and with distance defined as in (7.1.4) is called **unitary n-space** $\mathscr{U}_n$. The vectors associated with ordered pairs of points of $\mathscr{U}_n$ we refer to as **vectors of** $\mathscr{U}_n$. As in the case of $\mathscr{E}_n$, we shall be especially concerned with linear transformations which leave the length of a vector invariant.

Since $\bar{\alpha} = \alpha$ if and only if α is real, the definitions of the preceding paragraph include $\mathscr{E}_n$ and its distances (7.1.1) and (7.1.2) as a special case. Hence, whatever results we establish for unitary n-space $\mathscr{U}_n$ hold also for Euclidean n-space $\mathscr{E}_n$ by specialization to the real case. In fact, the reader who is concerned only with real number applications may read X^* as "X-transpose" throughout, and all will be well. However, some proofs need minor changes if they are to apply only in $\mathscr{E}_n$.

7.2 Unit Vectors

Of particular importance in $\mathscr{U}_n$ and $\mathscr{E}_n$ are **unit vectors**, that is, vectors whose length is 1. For example, the vector $\{(1 + i)/2, i/2, 1/2\}$ is a unit vector in $\mathscr{U}_3$ because $(1 - i)/2 \cdot (1 + i)/2 + (-i/2)(i/2) + 1/2 \cdot 1/2 = 1$. The elementary vectors $E_1, E_2, \ldots, E_n$ are the simplest unit vectors.

We can associate a unique unit vector with any nonzero-vector X by dividing each component of X by the length of the vector. This process is called **normalization**. For example, to normalize the vector $\{1, -2, 3, 0\}$ of $\mathscr{E}_4$, we must divide each element by $\sqrt{1^2 + (-2)^2 + 3^2 + 0^2} = \sqrt{14}$. The resulting unit vector is then $\{1/\sqrt{14}, -2/\sqrt{14}, 3/\sqrt{14}, 0\}$. In $\mathscr{E}_3$, the unit vector obtained by normalizing a given vector X is a unit vector in the same direction as X. This fact generalizes to $\mathscr{E}_n$.

7.3 Orthogonality and the Inner Product

From analytic geometry we recall that, in $\mathscr{E}_3$, two lines with direction numbers a_1, b_1, c_1 and a_2, b_2, c_2 respectively are orthogonal (perpendicular) if and only if $a_1 a_2 + b_1 b_2 + c_1 c_2 = 0$. Now a convenient set of direction numbers for a directed segment $\overrightarrow{AB}$ is the set of components of the associated vector X. Applying these facts to two vectors $X = \overrightarrow{OP}$ and $Y = \overrightarrow{OQ}$ (Figure 7.3.1), we see that X and Y are orthogonal if and only if $X^{\mathsf{T}}Y \equiv x_1 y_1 + x_2 y_2 + x_3 y_3 = 0$.

How we should extend this to $\mathscr{E}_n$ is not hard to decide. We define two vectors X and Y of $\mathscr{E}_n$ to be **orthogonal** if and only if $X^{\mathsf{T}}Y \equiv \sum_1^n x_j y_j = 0$. For example, in $\mathscr{E}_4$, the vectors $X = \{1, 1, 1, 1\}$, $Y = \{1, -1, 1, -1\}$ are orthogonal.

A useful extension to $\mathscr{U}_n$ of the notion of orthogonality requires more consideration. Thus, if $X = \{i, 1\}$, then $X^{\mathsf{T}}X = 0$, so that the above definition would permit a nonzero-vector to be orthogonal to itself. It is convenient for our purposes to avoid this peculiarity. We therefore define two vectors X and Y of $\mathscr{U}_n$ to be **orthogonal** if and only if $X * Y = \sum_1^n \bar{x}_j y_j = 0$. With this definition, since $X * X > 0$ if $X \neq 0$, no nonzero-vector can be orthogonal to itself.

When each of k n-vectors is orthogonal to all the others, we say the k vectors are **mutually orthogonal**. The elementary vectors, $E_1, E_2 \ldots, E_n$ are a case in point.

The scalar $X * Y$ used in the definition of orthogonality will be called the **inner product** of X and Y *in that order*. If X and Y are real, then the inner product is the same as the scalar product $X^{\mathsf{T}}Y$.

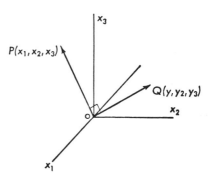

Figure 7.3.1

For the inner product of Y and X we have

$$Y * X = \sum \bar{y}_j x_j = \overline{\sum \bar{x}_j y_j} = \overline{X * Y}.$$

Hence $X * Y = 0$ if and only if $Y * X = 0$, so that *it does not matter which of two vectors we use first in testing for orthogonality.*

7.4 The Cauchy-Schwarz Inequality

The inner product appears in an important inequality which we now obtain. Let X and Y be any two given n-vectors with $X \neq 0$. Then consider the quadratic polynomial in t

$(7.4.1) \quad p(t) \equiv \sum (|x_j|t - |y_j|)^2 \equiv \sum |x_j|^2 t^2 - 2(\sum |x_j| |y_j|)t + \sum |y_j|^2.$

If this expression is zero for a real value t_0, then $\sum (|x_j|t_0 - |y_j|)^2$ is a vanishing sum of squares of real numbers, which implies that

$$|x_j|t_0 - |y_j| = 0, \quad j = 1, 2, \ldots, n.$$

Solving for $|y_j|$ and substituting in (7.4.1), we have

$$p(t) \equiv \sum (|x_j|t - |x_j|t_0)^2,$$

so that in this case

$$p(t) \equiv (t - t_0)^2 \sum |x_j|^2.$$

Since $X \neq 0$ by hypothesis, it follows that $\sum |x_j|^2 \neq 0$. Thus $p(t)$ cannot vanish for two *distinct* real values of t so that the discriminant must either vanish or be negative:

$$4(\sum |x_j| |y_j|)^2 - 4 \cdot \sum |x_j|^2 \cdot \sum |y_j|^2 \leqslant 0.$$

By the rules $|z| = |\bar{z}|$, $|z| |w| = |zw|$, and $|z + w| \leqslant |z| + |w|$ (see Appendix II), we have then

$(7.4.2) \quad (|\sum \bar{x}_j y_j|)^2 \leqslant (\sum |\bar{x}_j y_j|)^2 = (\sum |x_j| |y_j|)^2 \leqslant \sum |x_j|^2 \cdot \sum |y_j|^2.$

The extremes of this inequality may be written

$(7.4.3) \qquad\qquad |X^*Y|^2 \leqslant X^*X \cdot Y^*Y,$

so that

$(7.4.4) \qquad\qquad |X^*Y| \leqslant \sqrt{X^*X} \cdot \sqrt{Y^*Y} = |X| |Y|.$

Although the hypothesis $X \neq 0$ was necessary in this method of proof, it is clear that (7.4.2) and (7.4.3) still hold if $X = 0$, so that the restriction on X may now be lifted. In fact, when either X or Y is zero, the equality signs apply throughout.

When the components of X and Y are real, $X^* = X^\mathsf{T}$ and $|X^*Y|^2 = (X^\mathsf{T}Y)^2$. Thus (7.4.3) becomes, in the real case,

$(7.4.5) \qquad\qquad (X^\mathsf{T}Y)^2 \leqslant X^\mathsf{T}X \cdot Y^\mathsf{T}Y.$

The result (7.4.3) or (7.4.4) is the famous **Cauchy-Schwarz inequality.** One of the basic tools of analysis, it appears in a number of distinct but analogous forms. Restating (7.4.4) in words, we have

Theorem 7.4.1:   *The absolute value of the inner product of two vectors does not exceed the product of their lengths.*

7.5 Distance

We have defined the distance between two points A and B of $\mathscr{E}_n$ or $\mathscr{U}_n$ as the square root of the inner product of the vector $\{(b_1 - a_1), (b_2 - a_2), \ldots,$

$(b_n - a_n)\}$ with itself. There is a question whether or not this definition of distance is an acceptable one in a sense which we next define.

In mathematics many different collections of objects are at one time or another the subject of discussion. Any such collection is customarily called the **space** of the objects in question, and the objects themselves are called the **points** of the space. In such a space $\mathscr{S}$ one often finds it desirable to define a **distance** between two arbitrary points of $\mathscr{S}$. To be "acceptable," any such distance function is required to have the following four properties, in the statement of which $d(A, B)$ denotes the distance between points A and B of $\mathscr{S}$:

(1) $d(A, A) = 0$, for all points A of $\mathscr{S}$.
(2) $d(A, B) > 0$ if $A \neq B$, that is, distance is a positive real number if $A \neq B$.
(3) $d(A, B) = d(B, A)$, for all points A and B of $\mathscr{S}$.
(4) $d(A, B) + d(B, C) \geqslant d(A, C)$, for any three points of the space.

This last is known as **the triangle inequality**.

If the distance function satisfies requirements (1) through (4) above, the space $\mathscr{S}$ is called a **metric space** with respect to this definition of distance. Metric spaces of many kinds are employed in higher mathematics and in applications.

It is not hard to check that the first three of these properties hold for the distance formulas (7.1.2) and (7.1.4). That (4) holds may be demonstrated with the aid of the preceding section. It will suffice to prove this for $\mathscr{U}_n$ since $\mathscr{E}_n$ is contained in $\mathscr{U}_n$. We let

$$X = \{(b_1 - a_1), (b_2 - a_2), \ldots, (b_n - a_n)\}$$

and

$$Y = \{(c_1 - b_1), (c_2 - b_2), \ldots, (c_n - b_n)\},$$

so that $\sqrt{X*X} = d(A, B)$ and $\sqrt{Y*Y} = d(B, C)$. Then by (7.4.2), we have

$$X*X \cdot Y*Y \equiv \sum |b_j - a_j|^2 \cdot \sum |c_j - b_j|^2 \geqslant (\sum |b_j - a_j| \, |c_j - b_j|)^2.$$

Taking the square root on both sides, multiplying both members by 2, and then adding $\sum |b_j - a_j|^2 + \sum |c_j - b_j|^2$ to each, we have,

$$\sum |b_j - a_j|^2 + 2\sqrt{\sum |b_j - a_j|^2 \cdot \sum |c_j - b_j|^2} + \sum |c_j - b_j|^2$$
$$\geqslant \sum [|b_j - a_j|^2 + 2|b_j - a_j| \, |c_j - b_j| + |c_j - b_j|^2].$$

Thus

$$\left(\sqrt{\sum |b_j - a_j|^2} + \sqrt{\sum |c_j - b_j|^2}\right)^2 \geqslant \sum (|b_j - a_j| + |c_j - b_j|)^2,$$

or, since $|b_j - a_j| + |c_j - b_j| \geqslant |b_j - a_j + c_j - b_j| = |c_j - a_j|$, we have, by taking square roots on both sides once more,

$$\sqrt{\sum |b_j - a_j|^2} + \sqrt{\sum |c_j - b_j|^2} \geqslant \sqrt{\sum |c_j - a_j|^2},$$

that is,

$$d(A, B) + d(B, C) \geqslant d(A, C),$$

so that our definition of distance is indeed "acceptable."

7.6 Exercises

1. Find the length of the 4-vector $X = \{1 - i, 1 + i, 1, 0\}$; then normalize X.

2. Determine whether or not the vectors $\{i, -i, i, -i, 1\}$ and $\{i, i, i, i, 1\}$ in $\mathcal{U}_5$ are orthogonal.

3. The vectors $\{i, 1, 0\}$ and $\{0, 1, i\}$ are each orthogonal to a unit vector $\{x_1, x_2, x_3\}$. Find this last vector.

4. If X is a unit vector in $\mathcal{U}_n$, for what scalars α will αX still be a unit vector?

*5. Show that $E_i{}^* E_j = \delta_{ij}$, so that the unit vectors $E_1, E_2, \ldots, E_n$ constitute a basis of n mutually orthogonal unit vectors for the vectors of $\mathcal{U}_n$.

6. Prove that, for all scalars α and all n-vectors X in $\mathcal{U}_n$,

$$|\alpha X| = |\alpha| \cdot |X|.$$

7. Show that, if X and Y are nonzero-vectors in $\mathcal{E}_3$, then

$$|X - Y|^2 = |X|^2 + |Y|^2 - 2|X|\,|Y| \cos \theta,$$

where θ is the angle between X and Y such that $0 \leqslant \theta \leqslant \pi$.

8. Show that in $\mathcal{E}_n$ the angle between nonzero-vectors X and Y can be defined by

$$\cos \theta = \frac{X^\mathsf{T} Y}{|X| \cdot |Y|},$$

that is, $-1 \leqslant \cos \theta \leqslant 1$ for all X and Y different from zero.

9. Show that the inner product of X and AY is the same as the inner product of A^*X and Y, where A is a matrix of order n and X and Y are n-vectors.

10. Prove that A^*A is diagonal if and only if the columns of A are mutually orthogonal, and that $AA^* = I$ if and only if the rows of A are mutually orthogonal unit vectors. (A need not be square.)

*11. Show that, if $A_1, A_2, \ldots, A_k$ are mutually orthogonal nonzero-vectors, so are the unit vectors $N_1, N_2, \ldots, N_k$ obtained by normalizing the A's. Show also that, if the A's are linearly independent, so are the N's.

*12. Show that, if $A_1, A_2, \ldots, A_k$ are all orthogonal to a vector X, so is any linear combination of the A's.

13. Prove that, if $|X| \leqslant 1$ and $|Y| \leqslant 1$, where X and Y are in $\mathcal{U}_n$, then $|X^*Y| \leqslant 1$.

14. Show that in $\mathcal{E}_n$ the vectors $X = \overrightarrow{OP}$ and $Y = \overrightarrow{OQ}$ are orthogonal if and only if $d^2(P, Q) = d^2(O, P) + d^2(O, Q)$. Does the same theorem hold in $\mathcal{U}_n$?

15. Show that, if $P_{m \times n}$ has mutually orthogonal unit vectors $P_1, P_2, \ldots, P_n$ as columns, then

$$I_m - P_1 P_1{}^* - P_2 P_2{}^* - \cdots - P_n P_n{}^* = \prod_{j=1}^{n} (I_m - P_j P_j{}^*).$$

16. Let $A_1, A_2, \ldots, A_k$ be n-vectors over a field $\mathcal{F}$. Let $\mathcal{S}_1$ denote the set of all n-vectors over $\mathcal{F}$ that are orthogonal to each of $A_1, A_2, \ldots, A_k$, and let

$\mathscr{S}_2$ denote the set of all n-vectors over $\mathscr{F}$ that are orthogonal to at least one of $A_1, A_2, \ldots, A_k$. Are $\mathscr{S}_1$ and $\mathscr{S}_2$ vector spaces? If so, what can you say about their dimensions?

17. Show that, if P is Hermitian and the matrix of a projection, then for all n-vectors X, PX and $(I - P)X$ are orthogonal.

UNITARY AND ORTHOGONAL TRANSFORMATIONS

7.7 Unitary and Orthogonal Matrices

In Chapter One we made a number of definitions concerning matrices with complex elements. The transposed conjugate $(\overline{A})^\mathsf{T}$ of a matrix A was called the **tranjugate** and was denoted by A^*. A square matrix A was defined to be **Hermitian** if and only if $A = A^*$. It was pointed out that if A is real, $A^* \equiv A^\mathsf{T}$, so that a real Hermitian matrix is symmetric. A few simple properties of the tranjugate and of Hermitian matrices were given in the exercises in Section 1.18. More are given below. A careful study of all of these will shortly repay itself.

For use in coming sections, we define an $n \times n$ matrix U to be **unitary** if and only if it has the property that $U^*U = I_n$, that is, U is unitary if and only if its tranjugate U^* is its inverse. Since $U^* = U^{-1}$, we have also $UU^* = I_n$.

A *real* unitary matrix has the property that $U^\mathsf{T}U = UU^\mathsf{T} = I_n$. A real unitary matrix is said to be **orthogonal**.

From the condition

$$U^*U = \begin{bmatrix} U_1^* \\ U_2^* \\ \vdots \\ U_n^* \end{bmatrix} \cdot [U_1, U_2, \ldots, U_n] = [U_i^* U_j]_n = [\delta_{ij}]_n = I_n,$$

where $U_1, U_2, \ldots, U_n$ are the columns of U, and from a similar examination of UU^*, we obtain

Theorem 7.7.1: *A square matrix U is unitary if and only if its columns (rows) are mutually orthogonal unit vectors.*

Since $\det U^* = \det (\overline{U})^\mathsf{T} = \det \overline{U} = \overline{\det U}$, we see that, if U is unitary, then $\overline{\det U} \cdot \det U = |\det U|^2 = 1$. This yields

Theorem 7.7.2: *If U is unitary, the absolute value of $\det U$ is 1.*

If U is orthogonal, $\det U$ must therefore be ± 1. If $\det U$ is 1, the matrix U is said to be **unimodular**. The unimodular unitary matrices of order n are analogous to the matrices of rotations of axes in $\mathscr{E}_3$.

Any set of n linearly independent, mutually orthogonal, normalized (that is, unit) vectors of $\mathscr{U}_n$ is called an **orthonormal reference system** or an **orthonormal basis** for $\mathscr{U}_n$. We have then, from Theorem 7.7.1,

Theorem 7.7.3:   *The columns of a unitary matrix U constitute an orthonormal basis for $\mathscr{U}_n$. The same applies to the columns of U^*.*

7.8 Exercises

1. Under what conditions will the matrix

$$\begin{bmatrix} a+b & b-a \\ a-b & b+a \end{bmatrix},$$

where a and b represent real numbers, be orthogonal?

2. Show that, if U is orthogonal and det $U = +1$, then each element of U is equal to its cofactor in det U, and if det $U = -1$, then each element of U is equal to the negative of its cofactor in det U.

3. Prove that, if $X \neq 0$ is a real n-vector, then the matrix

$$I_n - \frac{2}{X^\mathsf{T} X} XX^\mathsf{T}$$

is orthogonal and symmetric.

4. Under what conditions are the matrices

$$\begin{bmatrix} 0 & \alpha & 0 & i\beta \\ \alpha & 0 & i\beta & 0 \\ 0 & i\beta & 0 & \alpha \\ i\beta & 0 & \alpha & 0 \end{bmatrix}, \quad \begin{bmatrix} 0 & 0 & \gamma & i\delta \\ 0 & 0 & i\delta & \gamma \\ \gamma & i\delta & 0 & 0 \\ i\delta & \gamma & 0 & 0 \end{bmatrix}, \quad \begin{bmatrix} 0 & \eta & 0 & \zeta \\ \eta & 0 & \zeta & 0 \\ 0 & \zeta & 0 & \eta \\ \zeta & 0 & \eta & 0 \end{bmatrix}$$

unitary if α, β, γ, δ, η, ζ, are real numbers? (The resulting unitary matrices are called "scattering matrices" in microwave circuit theory.)

5. Given that ω is a complex cube root of unity, for what values of α, β, γ will the matrix

$$\begin{bmatrix} \dfrac{\alpha}{\sqrt{3}} & \dfrac{\beta}{\sqrt{3}} & \dfrac{\gamma}{\sqrt{3}} \\[2mm] \dfrac{\alpha}{\sqrt{3}} & \dfrac{\beta\omega^2}{\sqrt{3}} & \dfrac{\gamma\omega}{\sqrt{3}} \\[2mm] \dfrac{\alpha}{\sqrt{3}} & \dfrac{\beta\omega}{\sqrt{3}} & \dfrac{\gamma\omega^2}{\sqrt{3}} \end{bmatrix}, \quad \left(\omega = \frac{-1 + i\sqrt{3}}{2}\right)$$

be both unitary and unimodular?

*6. Show that, if U is unitary, then so are $\bar{U}$, U^T and U^k for every integer k.

7. Given that V and W are $n \times n$ unitary matrices which commute, show that

$$\frac{1}{\sqrt{2}} \begin{bmatrix} V & -W \\ W^* & V^* \end{bmatrix}$$

is also unitary.

8. Show that, if U is both unitary and Hermitian, then $U^2 = I_n$, that is, U is involutory. In fact, any two of these properties imply the third.

*9. Show that any unitary matrix can be transformed into a unimodular, unitary matrix by multiplying any line thereof by a suitable scalar $\alpha + i\beta$.

*10. Prove in detail that $\det U^* = \overline{\det U}$.

*11. Show that a sum of Hermitian matrices is Hermitian.

12. Show that $A + \bar{A}$ has only real elements, and that $A - \bar{A}$ has only pure imaginary elements.

13. Show that k n-vectors $A_1, A_2, \ldots, A_k$ are linearly independent if and only if their conjugates $\bar{A}_1, \bar{A}_2, \ldots, \bar{A}_k$ are linearly independent.

*14. Show that a matrix A and its tranjugate A^* have the same rank.

*15. Show that, if H is Hermitian, $\det H$ is real.

16. Show that every permutation matrix is orthogonal.

17. Show that, if a matrix U of order 2 is both unitary and unimodular, it can be written in the form

$$\begin{bmatrix} \alpha & -\beta \\ \bar{\beta} & \bar{\alpha} \end{bmatrix},$$

where $\bar{\alpha}\alpha + \bar{\beta}\beta = 1$.

18. Show that, if X and Y are n-vectors, $XY^\mathsf{T} + YX^\mathsf{T}$ is symmetric and that $XY^* + YX^*$ is Hermitian.

19. Show that the Pauli spin matrices of Exercise 19, Section 1.9 are unitary, involutory, and Hermitian.

20. Show that, if U is unitary, so are U^* and $\bar{U}$.

21. Let $Z = X + iY$, $H = A + iB$, where X and Y are real n-vectors and A and B are real matrices of order n. Show that, if H is Hermitian, the scalar Z^*HZ is real for all Z. Show similarly that, if S is skew-Hermitian, the scalar Z^*SZ is a pure imaginary. (See Exercises 27 and 28, Section 1.18). Another proof of this will be given in Chapter Eight.

*22. Prove that, if U is unitary and U^*AU and U^*BU are both diagonal matrices, then A and B commute.

7.9 Unitary Transformations

If U is a unitary matrix, then the linear vector function defined by $Y = UX$, whose domain and range are $\mathcal{U}_n$, is called a **unitary operator** on $\mathcal{U}_n$. On the other hand, the same equation can be used to represent a **unitary transformation of coordinates**, that is, one in which the new reference vectors, just as $E_1, E_2, \ldots, E_n$, constitute an orthonormal basis for $\mathcal{U}_n$.

It is convenient at times to refer to the equation $Y = UX$ as representing a **linear transformation** which may then be interpreted either as an operator or as a transformation of coordinates. In this way, we can use one algebraic argument to prove two geometric theorems.

The unitary transformations play a role in $\mathcal{U}_n$ analogous to that of the distance-preserving rotations and reflections in $\mathscr{E}_3$. We have, in fact,

Theorem 7.9.1: *In $\mathcal{U}_n$, a linear transformation $Y = AX$ leaves the length of all vectors invariant if and only if it is a unitary transformation.*

Geometrically, this means that, if the transformation represents an operator, the image of a given vector always has the same length as the given vector. If the transformation is a linear transformation of coordinates, then the formula for the length of a given vector is the same in the new reference system as it is in the old reference system.

It will suffice to show that $X*X$ is invariant for all X if and only if A is unitary. The condition $Y*Y = X*X$, where $Y = AX$, is satisfied for every vector X if and only if $X*A*AX = X*X$ for all X.

Now if $A*A = I$, then $X*A*AX = X*X$ for all X. Conversely, suppose that $X*A*AX = X*X$ for all X. Then we may put $X = E_j$, which yields

$$E_j{}^\mathsf{T} A*A E_j = (A*A)_{jj} = E_j{}^\mathsf{T} E_j = 1,$$

where $(A*A)_{jj}$ denotes the jj-entry of $A*A$. Thus the diagonal entries of $A*A$ are all 1.

Next we put $X = E_j + E_k$, $j \neq k$, and obtain, since the length of X is invariant,

$$(E_j{}^\mathsf{T} + E_k{}^\mathsf{T}) A*A (E_j + E_k) = (E_j{}^\mathsf{T} + E_k{}^\mathsf{T})(E_j + E_k) = 2.$$

Recalling that $E_j{}^\mathsf{T} A*A E_k = (A*A)_{jk}$, we find with the aid of the previous step that

(7.9.1) $$(A*A)_{jk} + (A*A)_{kj} = 0.$$

Finally, we put $X = E_j + iE_k$, where $i^2 = -1$, and obtain

$$(E_j{}^\mathsf{T} - iE_k{}^\mathsf{T}) A*A (E_j + iE_k) = (E_j{}^\mathsf{T} - iE_k{}^\mathsf{T})(E_j + iE_k) = 2,$$

so that now

(7.9.2) $$(A*A)_{jk} - (A*A)_{kj} = 0.$$

The results (7.9.1) and (7.9.2) imply that, for all $j \neq k$,

$$(A*A)_{jk} = 0.$$

The off-diagonal entries of $A*A$ are thus all zero so that the proof that A is unitary is complete.

The proof clearly does not depend on whether the transformation represents a linear operator or a linear transformation of coordinates. A separate proof, not using the imaginary unit i, is required for $\mathscr{E}_n$.

The scalar $X*X = \sum \bar{x}_j x_j$ is also called the **Hermitian unit form** so that the previous theorem says that *a transformation is unitary if and only if it leaves the Hermitian unit form invariant.*

Theorem 7.9.2: *The unitary operators on $\mathscr{U}_n$ constitute a group; so do the unitary transformations of coordinates in $\mathscr{U}_n$.*

To prove this, we need only show that the unitary *matrices* of order n form a group with respect to multiplication:

(a) If A and B are unitary, then $A{*}A = I_n$, $B{*}B = I_n$, and hence $(AB){*}(AB) = B{*}(A{*}A)B = B{*}B = I_n$, so that AB is also unitary.

(b) If A is unitary, then $A{*}A = I_n$ so that $A{*} = A^{-1}$, and hence $(A^{-1}){*}A^{-1} = (A{*}){*}A^{-1} = AA^{-1} = I_n$ so that A^{-1} is also unitary.

(c) The identity matrix is unitary since $I{*}_n I_n = I_n$. These three properties establish the desired result.

The study of unitary n-space may be regarded as the study of those properties of vectors which are invariant under unitary transformations. The next two theorems illustrate this point.

Theorem 7.9.3: *In $\mathcal{U}_n$, the inner product $X{*}Y$ is invariant under a unitary transformation of coordinates.*

If U is unitary and $X = UW$, $Y = UZ$, then $X{*}Y = W{*}U{*}UZ = W{*}Z$, which proves the theorem.

An important consequence of this theorem is that the test for orthogonality of two vectors is independent of the choice of the orthonormal reference system for $\mathcal{U}_n$.

The same computations allow us also to conclude

Theorem 7.9.4: *In $\mathcal{U}_n$, a unitary operator maps orthogonal vectors onto orthogonal vectors and nonorthogonal vectors onto nonorthogonal vectors.*

7.10 Orthogonal Transformations

We have pointed out that, if U is unitary and real, then $U{*}U = I_n$ reduces to $U^{\mathsf{T}}U = I_n$ and U is called an orthogonal matrix. A transformation $Y = UX$ is then called an **orthogonal transformation**. The previous theorems have as special cases:

Theorem 7.10.1: *In $\mathscr{E}_n$ a linear transformation leaves the length of each vector invariant if and only if it is an orthogonal transformation.*

Theorem 7.10.2: *The orthogonal operators on $\mathscr{E}_n$ constitute a group; so do the orthogonal transformations of coordinates in $\mathscr{E}_n$.*

If we allow all the operators in question to have the vectors of $\mathcal{U}_n$ as their common domain, it now follows that the real orthogonal operators are a subgroup of the group of unitary operators and the latter, in turn, are a subgroup of the full linear group over the complex field (Section 6.21).

We have finally the special cases:

Theorem 7.10.3: *In $\mathscr{E}_n$, the inner product $X^{\mathsf{T}}Y$ is invariant under an orthogonal transformation of coordinates.*

Theorem 7.10.4: *In $\mathscr{E}_n$, an orthogonal operator maps orthogonal vectors onto orthogonal vectors and nonorthogonal vectors onto nonorthogonal vectors.*

The reader should write out proofs of each of these.

7.11 Orthogonal Transformations of Coordinates in $\mathscr{E}_2$

We have already pointed out that the determinant of an orthogonal matrix A is ± 1. When $\det A$ is 1, the transformation is called a **proper orthogonal transformation** and when $\det A$ is -1,

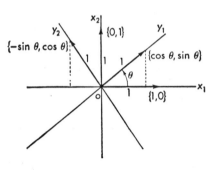

it is called an **improper orthogonal transformation**. We now examine the geometrical interpretation of these transformations in $\mathscr{E}_2$.

Consider any rotation of axes in $\mathscr{E}_2$ and let the angle of rotation be θ. Then the unit vectors E_1 and E_2 of the y-coordinate system are the unit vectors $\{\cos \theta, \sin \theta\}$ and $\{-\sin \theta, \cos \theta\}$ respectively in the x-coordinate system (Figure 7.11.1). These unit vectors

Figure 7.11.1

must constitute the columns of the orthogonal matrix A in the equation $X = AY$ representing the transformation (Section 6.11). Hence the transformation is defined by

$$(7.11.1) \qquad \begin{bmatrix} x_1 \\ x_2 \end{bmatrix} = \begin{bmatrix} \cos \theta & -\sin \theta \\ \sin \theta & \cos \theta \end{bmatrix} \cdot \begin{bmatrix} y_1 \\ y_2 \end{bmatrix},$$

the matrix of which is orthogonal and has determinant 1.

Conversely, let

$$(7.11.2) \qquad \begin{bmatrix} x_1 \\ x_2 \end{bmatrix} = \begin{bmatrix} a_{11} & a_{12} \\ a_{21} & a_{22} \end{bmatrix} \cdot \begin{bmatrix} y_1 \\ y_2 \end{bmatrix}$$

be any orthogonal transformation in $\mathscr{E}_2$. Here the unit vectors E_1 and E_2 of the y-coordinate system are the orthogonal unit vectors $\{a_{11}, a_{21}\}$ and $\{a_{12}, a_{22}\}$ respectively in the x-coordinate system. We may now choose θ in a transformation of type (7.11.1) in such a way that the unit vector $\{a_{11}, a_{21}\} = \{\cos \theta, \sin \theta\}$ defines the y_1-axis. Then the y_2-axis, being orthogonal to the y_1-axis, is defined either by the unit vector $\{-\sin \theta, \cos \theta\}$ or by the unit vector $\{\sin \theta, -\cos \theta\}$ in the opposite direction (Figure 7.11.2). That is, either $\{a_{12}, a_{22}\} = \{-\sin \theta, \cos \theta\}$,

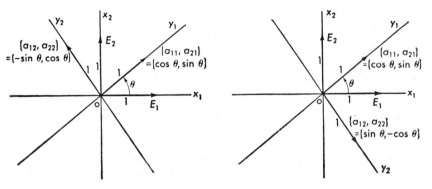

Figure 7.11.2

or $\{a_{12}, a_{22}\} = \{\sin \theta, -\cos \theta\}$. Our orthogonal transformation (7.11.2) is thus either a rotation (7.11.1) or a transformation of the form

(7.11.3)
$$\begin{bmatrix} x_1 \\ x_2 \end{bmatrix} = \begin{bmatrix} \cos \theta & \sin \theta \\ \sin \theta & -\cos \theta \end{bmatrix} \cdot \begin{bmatrix} y_1 \\ y_2 \end{bmatrix},$$

which is an improper orthogonal transformation since the determinant is -1. We can write (7.11.3) in the form

$$\begin{bmatrix} x_1 \\ x_2 \end{bmatrix} = \begin{bmatrix} \cos \theta & -\sin \theta \\ \sin \theta & \cos \theta \end{bmatrix} \cdot \begin{bmatrix} 1 & 0 \\ 0 & -1 \end{bmatrix} \cdot \begin{bmatrix} y_1 \\ y_2 \end{bmatrix},$$

and hence interpret it as the product of the proper orthogonal transformation

$$\begin{bmatrix} x_1 \\ x_2 \end{bmatrix} = \begin{bmatrix} \cos \theta & -\sin \theta \\ \sin \theta & \cos \theta \end{bmatrix} \cdot \begin{bmatrix} z_1 \\ z_2 \end{bmatrix},$$

and the transformation

$$\begin{bmatrix} z_1 \\ z_2 \end{bmatrix} = \begin{bmatrix} 1 & 0 \\ 0 & -1 \end{bmatrix} \cdot \begin{bmatrix} y_1 \\ y_2 \end{bmatrix},$$

which simply reverses the choice of positive direction on the y_2-axis. This latter transformation is called a **reflection in the y_1-axis**.

This argument may be extended to $\mathscr{E}_3$. That is, in $\mathscr{E}_3$ the proper orthogonal transformations represent rotations of axes and the improper orthogonal transformations represent rotations combined with a reflection in one of the coordinate planes. The proper orthogonal transformations in $\mathscr{E}_n$ and the unitary, unimodular transformations in $\mathscr{U}_n$ may thus be considered generalizations of the rotations of axes in $\mathscr{E}_2$ and $\mathscr{E}_3$.

7.12 The Eulerian Angles

If $X = AY$ represents an orthogonal transformation of coordinates in $\mathscr{E}_3$, then since the columns of A are *unit* vectors, and also represent the new reference vectors in the original reference system, *the columns of A are given by the direction cosines of the new reference axes with respect to the old reference system*. Similarly, in the equivalent equation $Y = A^{\mathsf{T}}X$, *the columns of A^{T} are given by the direction cosines of the old reference axes with respect to the new reference system*. For example, an orthogonal transformation of coordinates in which the new reference axes pass through the points $P_1(1, 1, 1)$, $P_2(0, 2, -2)$, $P_3(-2, 1, 1)$ respectively may be written in the form

$$X = \begin{bmatrix} \dfrac{1}{\sqrt{3}} & 0 & \dfrac{-2}{\sqrt{6}} \\[2ex] \dfrac{1}{\sqrt{3}} & \dfrac{1}{\sqrt{2}} & \dfrac{1}{\sqrt{6}} \\[2ex] \dfrac{1}{\sqrt{3}} & \dfrac{-1}{\sqrt{2}} & \dfrac{1}{\sqrt{6}} \end{bmatrix} Y,$$

where the columns are the normalized forms of $\overrightarrow{OP_1}$, $\overrightarrow{OP_2}$, $\overrightarrow{OP_3}$, that is, the direction cosines of these vectors in the x-reference system.

To illustrate how these observations are useful in a practical application, we discuss the Eulerian angles used in classical mechanics.

In many problems in mechanics, it is necessary to specify the instantaneous position of a rigid body which is free to rotate about a fixed point O, that is, free to move in such a way that every point in it remains always at the same distance from O.

We consider a line L passing through O and allow L to move with the body, but always require it to remain in the same position relative to the rigid body. If now the position of L relative to the reference system at O is fixed, the only further motion possible for the body is rotation about L.

The motion of the body may be described mathematically by using L as one axis of a reference system, centered also at O, the other two axes of which are, like L, fixed relative to the body and, therefore, move with it. When we specify the position of this reference system relative to the original reference system centered at O, we have then specified the position of the body. In this type of motion, every point of the body remains at a constant distance from O.

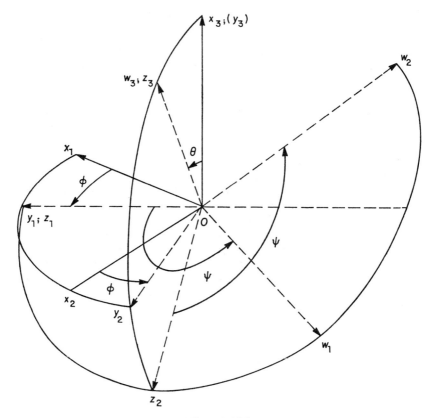

Figure 7.12.1

Let OX_1, OX_2, OX_3 denote the axes of the fixed reference system and let OW_1, OW_2, OW_3 denote the axes of the movable reference system. We wish to define the orthogonal transformation $W = AX$, which expresses the w-coordinates of an arbitrary point in terms of its x-coordinates.

First let new axes OY_1, OY_2, $OY_3 \equiv OX_3$ be obtained by a rotation about OX_3 through the angle φ in the $x_1 x_2$-plane, from OX_2 to the plane determined by OX_3 and OW_3 (Figure 7.12.1). Next we obtain new axes $OZ_1 \equiv OY_1$, OZ_2, OZ_3 by rotation about OY_1 through the angle θ from OX_3 to OW_3. Finally, we rotate about OZ_3 through the angle ψ between OZ_1 and OW_1. From the figure it is clear that this step brings us to the w-reference system. The angles φ, θ, ψ are to be chosen in the interval from 0 to π.

Writing the matrix representations of the above rotations according to the rules stated above, we obtain respectively,

$$(7.12.1) \qquad Y = \begin{bmatrix} \cos\varphi & \sin\varphi & 0 \\ -\sin\varphi & \cos\varphi & 0 \\ 0 & 0 & 1 \end{bmatrix} X,$$

$$(7.12.2) \qquad Z = \begin{bmatrix} 1 & 0 & 0 \\ 0 & \cos\theta & \sin\theta \\ 0 & -\sin\theta & \cos\theta \end{bmatrix} Y,$$

$$(7.12.3) \qquad W = \begin{bmatrix} \cos\psi & \sin\psi & 0 \\ -\sin\psi & \cos\psi & 0 \\ 0 & 0 & 1 \end{bmatrix} Z.$$

The reader should verify in detail the correctness of the entries in these matrices, and then should compute the product transformation $W = AX$.

The angles ψ, θ, φ used here are known as the *Eulerian angles*. There are other definitions of the Eulerian angles in the literature. Some authors use clockwise angles, some use left-handed reference systems, and some interchange the meaning of φ and ψ. (The usage here is the same as in Goldstein: *Classical Mechanics*, Addison-Wesley, Reading, Mass., 1950, and in Corben and Stehle: *Classical Mechanics*, John Wiley and Sons, New York, 1950.) Whatever notation the reader may encounter, he should be able to write correctly the matrices of the transformations simply by following the pattern established here and taking due account at each step of the differences in notation.

It should be pointed out that the Eulerian angles exhibit a certain defect. When the axes OX_3 and OW_3 coincide, the angle φ is undefined. If we assign it a value φ_0, we find at the next step that $\theta = 0$ and, at the last step, that $\psi = \alpha - \varphi_0$, where α is the angle from OX_1 to OW_1. The product A in this case reduces to

$$\begin{bmatrix} \cos\alpha & \sin\alpha & 0 \\ -\sin\alpha & \cos\alpha & 0 \\ 0 & 0 & 1 \end{bmatrix},$$

as one would expect.

7.13 The Triangularization of a Real Matrix

In the previous section we decomposed an orthogonal transformation of coordinates in $\mathscr{E}_3$ into the product of three plane rotations. The particular rotations chosen there were those most used in mechanics. There is a similar procedure in $\mathscr{E}_n$ which follows as a corollary of the next theorem. To make the process systematic, we define $P_{ik}(\theta)$, $i \neq k$, to be an $n \times n$ matrix such that in the

*i*th row and *i*th column appears $\cos \theta$;
*i*th row and *k*th column appears $-\sin \theta$;
*k*th row and *i*th column appears $\sin \theta$;
*k*th row and *k*th column appears $\cos \theta$.

The remaining elements are 0, except for the other elements on the principal diagonal, which are all 1.

It is readily seen that $P_{ik}(\theta)$ is orthogonal, that $\det P_{ik}(\theta) = 1$, and that

$$P_{ki}(\theta) = P_{ik}(-\theta) = P_{ik}{}^{\mathsf{T}}(\theta) = P_{ik}{}^{-1}(\theta).$$

In the previous section, we employed $P_{21}(\varphi)$, $P_{32}(\theta)$, and $P_{21}(\psi)$.

We now prove a theorem from which a number of important results are derived.

Theorem 7.13.1:   *Every square real matrix A may be written in the form*

(7.13.1) $$A = P_{21}P_{31} \cdots P_{n1}P_{32} \cdots P_{n2} \cdots P_{n,n-1}B,$$

where

$$P_{ik} = P_{ik}(\theta_{ik}),$$

the θ's depending on A, and where B is upper triangular with $b_{ii} \geqslant 0$ for $i < n$.

To prove this, let us write first of all

$$P_{21}{}^{-1}(\theta_{21})A = S,$$

and in the product require that $s_{21} = 0$, that is,

$$a_{11} \sin \theta_{21} + a_{21} \cos \theta_{21} = 0.$$

Hence, if $a_{11} \neq 0$, θ_{21} is defined by

$$\tan \theta_{21} = -\frac{a_{21}}{a_{11}}.$$

If $a_{11} = 0$, but $a_{21} \neq 0$, we take $\theta_{21} = \pi/2$ so that $-a_{21} \neq 0$ will appear in the 11-position. If $a_{11} = a_{21} = 0$, we take $\theta_{21} = 0$, and P_{21} is the identity matrix.

Next we put

$$P_{31}{}^{-1}(\theta_{31})S = T,$$

and require the vanishing of t_{31}:

$$t_{31} = s_{11} \sin \theta_{31} + s_{31} \cos \theta_{31} = 0.$$

Again, if $s_{11} \neq 0$, θ_{31} is defined by

$$\tan \theta_{31} = -\frac{s_{31}}{s_{11}}.$$

If $s_{11} = 0$ but $s_{31} \neq 0$, we take $\theta_{31} = \pi/2$. If $s_{11} = s_{31} = 0$, we take $\theta_{31} = 0$.
In the matrix T we have

$$t_{21} = 0 \cdot s_{11} + 1 \cdot s_{21} = 0,$$

so that the work of the previous step has not been undone.

We can continue this and obtain all zeros in the first column except possibly for the 11-entry, which is to be ≥ 0. If the last step in the first column is given by

$$P_{n1}{}^{-1}(\theta_{n1})R = Q,$$

then we require

$$q_{n1} = r_{11} \sin \theta_{n1} + r_{n1} \cos \theta_{n1} = 0,$$

$$q_{11} = r_{11} \cos \theta_{n1} - r_{n1} \sin \theta_{n1} \geq 0.$$

Here θ_{n1} is determined just as before, except that it may be necessary to add or subtract π in order to satisfy the inequality.

Now we operate on the second column in the same way, using

$$P_{32}{}^{-1}(\theta_{32}), \ldots, P_{n2}{}^{-1}(\theta_{n2})$$

to reduce to zero the elements of the second column below the main diagonal. The zeros in the first column are not destroyed by these operations.

Continuing thus with the first $n - 1$ columns, we have, finally,

(7.13.2) $$P_{n,n-1}^{-1}(\theta_{n,n-1}) \cdots P_{21}{}^{-1}(\theta_{21})A = B,$$

where B is triangular, and from which (7.13.1) follows at once, so the proof is complete. Since we do not work with the last column, there is no way to control the sign of b_{nn} in this process.

Since the P_{ij}'s are proper orthogonal and the product of proper orthogonal matrices is proper orthogonal, we have

Corollary 7.13.2:   *Every real matrix A can be expressed in the form*

$$A = PB,$$

where P is a proper orthogonal matrix and B is upper triangular, with $b_{ii} \geq 0$,
$i = 1, 2, \ldots, n - 1$.

If A itself is orthogonal, then more can be said about B. We have

Corollary 7.13.3:   *If A is orthogonal and if $\det A = 1$, then in (7.13.1), $B = I_n$. If $\det A = -1$, then in B, $b_{ij} = \delta_{ij}$, except that $b_{nn} = -1$.*

Indeed, from (7.13.2) it follows in either case that, since A is orthogonal, B is orthogonal. Hence, from the first column of B, we conclude $b_{11}{}^2 = 1$ so that, since $b_{11} \geq 0$, $b_{11} = 1$. Also, from the first row of B, we have

$$b_{11}{}^2 + b_{12}{}^2 + \cdots + b_{1n}{}^2 = 1,$$

from which now follows $b_{12} = b_{13} = \cdots = b_{1n} = 0$. Then, from column 2 and row 2 we have $b_{22} = 1$, $b_{23} = b_{24} = \cdots = b_{2n} = 0$. Similarly, for the first $n - 1$ rows and columns of B. Finally, $b_{nn}{}^2 = 1$. Since $\det A = \det B$ because $\det P_{ik} = 1$ in every case, we therefore have $b_{nn} = \pm 1$ according as $\det A = \pm 1$, and the proof of the corollary is complete.

An orthogonal transformation with matrix B in which $b_{ij} = \delta_{ij}$, except that $b_{ii} = -1$ for exactly one value of i, is called a **reflection** (in the ith coordinate hyperplane). An orthogonal transformation $P_{ij}(\theta)$ is called a **plane rotation**. Corollary 7.13.3 may therefore be restated thus:

Corollary 7.13.4: *Every orthogonal transformation of coordinates may be factored into a product of plane rotations and at most one reflection.*

Finally we prove

Corollary 7.13.5: *If A is nonsingular then the representation $A = PB$ of Corollary 7.13.2 is unique.*

If $A = PB = P'B'$, with P, P' both proper orthogonal and B, B' upper triangular, then $I = P^{\mathsf{T}}P'B'B^{-1}$. Thus the orthogonal matrix I is represented as the product of the proper orthogonal matrix PP' and the upper triangular matrix $B'B^{-1}$. Hence, by Corollary 7.13.3, $B'B^{-1} = I$, and, therefore, $P^{\mathsf{T}}P' = I$. Hence $B' = B$ and $P' = P$, and the corollary is proved.

7.14 Exercises

1. Show that these matrices are orthogonal:

$$
\begin{bmatrix}
\dfrac{1}{\sqrt{2}} & \dfrac{1}{\sqrt{2}} & 0 \\[2ex]
\dfrac{-1}{\sqrt{2}} & \dfrac{1}{\sqrt{2}} & 0 \\[2ex]
0 & 0 & 1
\end{bmatrix},
\qquad
\begin{bmatrix}
\dfrac{1}{\sqrt{14}} & \dfrac{2}{\sqrt{14}} & \dfrac{3}{\sqrt{14}} \\[2ex]
\dfrac{3}{\sqrt{10}} & 0 & -\dfrac{1}{\sqrt{10}} \\[2ex]
-\dfrac{1}{\sqrt{35}} & \dfrac{5}{\sqrt{35}} & -\dfrac{3}{\sqrt{35}}
\end{bmatrix}.
$$

2. Show that the product of two rotations in $\mathcal{E}_2$ is a rotation in $\mathcal{E}_2$.

3. Triangularize the matrix

$$
A = \begin{bmatrix}
1 & 2 & -1 \\[1ex]
1 & 3 & 0 \\[1ex]
-\sqrt{2} & 2\sqrt{2} & \dfrac{\sqrt{2}}{2}
\end{bmatrix}
$$

by the method of Theorem 7.13.1.

4. Compute the product of the three transformations (7.12.1) through (7.12.3).

5. Determine all $n \times n$ orthogonal matrices of 0's and 1's. Show that they form a group with respect to multiplication. What group is it?

6. Determine all $n \times n$ orthogonal matrices of 0's and 1's which are involutory, that is, whose squares are the identity.

7. Show that the unimodular, unitary transformations form a subgroup of the unitary group of transformations of n variables.

*8. Show in the manner of the proof of Theorem 7.9.1 that the inner product $X*Y$ is invariant under linear transformation if and only if the transformation is unitary and that the invariance of distance then follows as a corollary.

9. Given, in $\mathcal{E}_3$, a transformation of coordinates $Y = AX$, show that the Y-axes have the same orientation as the X-axes if and only if $\det A > 0$.

10. Write a proof of Theorem 7.10.1 which does not use the imaginary unit i but exploits the fact that $A^{\mathsf{T}}A$ is symmetric.

ORTHOGONALITY AND VECTOR SPACES

7.15 Some Tests for Independence

In the following we need some additional tests for the independence of vectors over a number field $\mathscr{F}$. We begin by defining the **Gramian matrix** G of k n-vectors $A_1, A_2, \ldots, A_k$ to be the matrix of inner products

$$(7.15.1) \qquad G = \begin{bmatrix} A_1{}^*A_1 & A_1{}^*A_2 & \cdots & A_1{}^*A_k \\ A_2{}^*A_1 & A_2{}^*A_2 & \cdots & A_2{}^*A_k \\ \vdots & & & \\ A_k{}^*A_1 & A_k{}^*A_2 & \cdots & A_k{}^*A_k \end{bmatrix} = A^*A.$$

We then define the **Gramian determinant** of these vectors to be det G. Note that G is Hermitian and that hence, by Exercise 15, Section 7.8, det G is real. We can, however, prove further:

Theorem 7.15.1:   *The Gramian determinant of k n-vectors is a nonnegative real number.*

We have, in fact,

$$(7.15.2) \qquad G = \begin{bmatrix} A_1{}^* \\ A_2{}^* \\ \vdots \\ A_k{}^* \end{bmatrix} \cdot [A_1, A_2, \ldots, A_k].$$

Since the rank of the product cannot exceed n here, det $G = 0$ if $k > n$. Hence we assume $k \leqslant n$ from now on. Then det G is a sum of products of corresponding majors of the first and second factors of this matrix product (Theorem 2.11.1). But any major, det M^*, of the first factor is the conjugate of the corresponding major, det M, of the second factor. Thus G is a sum of products of complex numbers and their conjugates, that is, a sum of nonnegative numbers, so that it is itself nonnegative.

Theorem 7.15.2:   *A necessary and sufficient condition that k n-vectors A_1, $A_2, \ldots, A_k$ be independent is that their Gramian determinant be positive.*

If the vectors are independent, each factor of (7.15.2) has rank k. For some pair of corresponding majors we have, therefore, det M^* det $M > 0$, so that det $G > 0$.

Conversely, suppose det $G > 0$. Then for some pair of corresponding majors we must have det M^* det $M > 0$ and, hence, det $M \neq 0$, so that $[A_1, A_2, \ldots, A_k]$ has rank k and the A's are independent.

An immediate consequence is

Theorem 7.15.3:   *A necessary and sufficient condition that k n-vectors be dependent is that their Gramian determinant be zero.*

The usefulness of this test is primarily in the proof of other theorems rather than in actual computation, as the next two results illustrate.

Theorem 7.15.4:   *If k nonzero n-vectors $A_1, A_2, \ldots, A_k$ are mutually orthogonal, they are linearly independent and hence span a $\mathscr{V}_n{}^k$.*

In this case $A_i{}^*A_j = 0$ if $i \neq j$, so that G is diagonal:

$$G = \begin{bmatrix} A_1{}^*A_1 & 0 & \cdots & 0 \\ 0 & A_2{}^*A_2 & \cdots & 0 \\ \vdots & & & \\ 0 & 0 & \cdots & A_k{}^*A_k \end{bmatrix}.$$

Since no A is a zero-vector, each diagonal entry here is positive. Hence det $G > 0$ so that the A's are linearly independent and therefore span a $\mathscr{V}_n{}^k$.

Theorem 7.15.5:   *If a nonzero-vector X is orthogonal to each of k linearly independent vectors $A_1, A_2, \ldots, A_k$, then $X, A_1, \ldots, A_k$ are linearly independent.*

The Gramian determinant of $X, A_1, A_2, \ldots, A_k$ is

$$\det \begin{bmatrix} X^*X & 0 & \cdots & 0 \\ \hline 0 & A_1{}^*A_1 & \cdots & A_1{}^*A_k \\ \vdots & \vdots & & \\ 0 & A_k{}^*A_1 & \cdots & A_k{}^*A_k \end{bmatrix},$$

which is not zero since X^*X is not zero and since its cofactor, the Gramian determinant of $A_1, A_2, \ldots, A_k$ is not zero by Theorem 7.15.2. Thus, again by Theorem 7.15.2, the $k + 1$ vectors $X, A_1, A_2, \ldots, A_k$ are independent.

7.16 The Gram-Schmidt Process

There are times when it is desirable or necessary to have a set of mutually orthogonal unit vectors as the basis for a vector space $\mathscr{V}_n{}^k$ in $\mathscr{U}_n$. Such a basis is called an **orthonormal basis** for the $\mathscr{V}_n{}^k$. It is always possible to obtain an orthonormal basis for a $\mathscr{V}_n{}^k$ by what is known as the **Gram-Schmidt process**. One form of this process is outlined in the proof of

Theorem 7.16.1:   *Every vector space $\mathscr{V}_n{}^k$ has an orthonormal basis.*

Let $A_1, A_2, \ldots, A_k$ be any basis for the $\mathscr{V}_n{}^k$. If it is not orthonormal, we construct an orthonormal basis $B_1, B_2, \ldots, B_k$ as follows. First we take

$$B_1 = A_1.$$

Then we put

$$B_2 = c_{12}B_1 + c_{22}A_2,$$

and determine c_{12}, c_{22} so that $B_1{}^*B_2 = 0$, that is, so that

$$c_{12}B_1{}^*B_1 + c_{22}B_1{}^*A_2 = 0.$$

The complete solution of this homogeneous equation in two unknowns is

$$c_{12} = -(B_1{}^*A_2)t,$$

$$c_{22} = \quad (B_1{}^*B_1)t,$$

where t is an arbitrary parameter. Since $A_1, \ldots, A_k$ span the $\mathscr{V}_n{}^k$, they are linearly independent. Hence $A_1 \neq 0$ so that $B_1 \neq 0$ and, therefore, $B_1{}^*B_1 \neq 0$. Thus there always exists a solution (c_{12}, c_{22}) with $c_{22} \neq 0$. (Note that, if B_1 and A_2 are by chance orthogonal, $B_1{}^*A_2 = 0$ so that $c_{12} = 0$, and we may as well take $c_{22} = 1$, that is, $B_2 = A_2$.) Furthermore, since the A's are linearly independent, B_2, which is a nontrivial linear combination of the A's, cannot be the zero-vector.

For B_3, we now write

$$B_3 = c_{13}B_1 + c_{23}B_2 + c_{33}A_3,$$

and determine the constants so that B_3 will be orthogonal to each of B_1 and B_2, that is, so that

$$B_1{}^*B_3 = c_{13}B_1{}^*B_1 + c_{23}B_1{}^*B_2 + c_{33}B_1{}^*A_3 = 0,$$

$$B_2{}^*B_3 = c_{13}B_2{}^*B_1 + c_{23}B_2{}^*B_2 + c_{33}B_2{}^*A_3 = 0.$$

Since $B_1{}^*B_2 = B_2{}^*B_1 = 0$ by the previous step, we see by Section 5.18 that c_{33} is a multiple of

$$\begin{vmatrix} B_1{}^*B_1 & 0 \\ 0 & B_2{}^*B_2 \end{vmatrix} \neq 0,$$

so that, again, we have nontrivial solutions, this time with $c_{33} \neq 0$. Also, since the A's are linearly independent, B_3, which is actually a nontrivial linear combination of the A's, cannot be the zero-vector.

Next we put

$$B_4 = c_{14}B_1 + c_{24}B_2 + c_{34}B_3 + c_{44}A_4$$

and continue as before, repeating the procedure until all the A's have been used. The resulting nonzero mutually orthogonal vectors $B_1, B_2, \ldots, B_k$ are linearly independent by Theorem 7.15.4. Since they are all, in fact, linear combinations of the A's, they are all in the $\mathscr{V}_n{}^k$.

We now normalize each of $B_1, B_2, \ldots, B_k$—which does not alter their mutually orthogonal character or, therefore, their linear independence—

and thus obtain the orthonormal basis for the $\mathcal{V}_n^k$, as announced in the theorem.

7.17 An Alternative Procedure

One can also normalize each vector B as it is obtained. This yields neat formulas for the coefficients c_{ij}, that is, for the B's, but it involves more difficult computation if the problem is being done by hand. Indeed, in the method of the preceding section, a wise choice of the c_{ij}'s at one step can often simplify the later computations a great deal. On the other hand, normalizing the B's at each step is useful from the computer point of view because of the iterative character of the formulas involved.

Again, let $A_1, A_2, \ldots, A_k$ denote independent vectors. In this method we choose

$$B_1 = \frac{A_1}{|A_1|}, \qquad B_1^*B_1 = 1,$$

and then choose c_{11} and c_{12} in

$$B_2 = c_{11}B_1 + c_{12}A_2,$$

so that

$$B_1^*B_2 = c_{11} + c_{12}B_1^*A_2 = 0,$$

which requires

$$c_{11} = -c_{12}B_1^*A_2,$$

so that, if we choose

$$c_{12} = \frac{1}{|A_2 - (B_1^*A_2)B_1|},$$

we obtain the unit vector

$$B_2 = \frac{A_2 - (B_1^*A_2)B_1}{|A_2 - (B_1^*A_2)B_1|}.$$

Now assume

$$B_1 = \frac{A_1}{|A_1|}, \qquad B_p = \frac{A_p - \sum\limits_{j=1}^{p-1} (B_j^*A_p)B_j}{|A_p - \sum\limits_{j=1}^{p-1} (B_j^*A_p)B_j|}, \qquad p = 2, 3, \ldots, r-1,$$

are mutually orthogonal unit vectors. Then B_r is determined from

$$B_r = c_{r1}B_1 + c_{r2}B_2 + \cdots + c_{r,r-1}B_{r-1} + c_{rr}A_r.$$

The requirements that $B_j^*B_r = 0$ yield the equations

$$c_{rj} = -c_{rr}(B_j^*A_r), \qquad j = 1, 2, \ldots, r-1.$$

Choosing

$$c_{rr} = \frac{1}{\left|A_r - \sum\limits_{j=1}^{r-1} (B_j*A_r)B_j\right|},$$

and substituting for the c's, we obtain the unit vector

(7.17.1) $$B_r = \frac{A_r - \sum\limits_{j=1}^{r-1} (B_j*A_r)B_j}{\left|A_r - \sum\limits_{j=1}^{r-1} (B_j*A_r)B_j\right|}.$$

Hence, by induction, the formula holds for all values of r such that $2 \leqslant r \leqslant k$.

7.18 Exercises

1. Apply the Gram-Schmidt process to the 4-vectors $\{1, 2, 1, 1\}$, $\{1, -1, 0, 2\}$, $\{2, 0, 1, 1\}$.

2. Nonzero-vectors $A_1, A_2, \ldots, A_k$ are mutually orthogonal if and only if their Gramian matrix is diagonal. Prove this.

3. Use the result of Theorem 7.15.1 for $r = 2$ to prove the Cauchy-Schwarz inequality.

*4. Given that $A_1, A_2, \ldots, A_n$ constitute an orthonormal reference system in $\mathscr{U}_n$, show that the coordinates y_j of a vector X with respect to this system are given by $y_j = A_j*X, j = 1, 2, \ldots, n$.

5. Prove that, if $A_1, A_2, \ldots, A_r$ are an orthonormal basis for a $\mathscr{V}_n{}^r$ in $\mathscr{U}_n$, then it is always possible to find $A_{r+1}, \ldots, A_n$ such that $A_1, A_2, \ldots, A_n$ constitute an orthonormal basis for $\mathscr{U}_n$.

6. Prove that, if tr $(A*A) = 0$, then $A = 0$.

7. Let $U_1, U_2, \ldots, U_k$ denote a set of orthonormal vectors. Show that

$$P = \sum_{j=1}^{k} U_j U_j*$$

is the matrix of a projection and determine its image space.

8. Show how to replace a system of m independent linear equations in n unknowns $AX = B$ by an equivalent system $CX = D$ such that the rows of C are mutually orthogonal unit vectors. (This operation is useful in the theory of statistics.)

9. Apply Exercise 8 to the system

$$x_1 + x_2 + x_3 + x_4 = -1,$$
$$x_1 - x_2 + x_3 \quad\quad = 2,$$
$$x_2 + x_3 - x_4 = -5.$$

10. The B's obtained in the proof of Theorem 7.13.1 are all linear combinations of the A's. Determine the coefficients of these combinations and show directly that the matrix of these coefficients is nonsingular.

11. Prove Theorem 7.15.5 without using the Gramian determinant.

12. If A is an $n \times k$ matrix whose columns are an orthonormal basis for a $\mathscr{V}_n{}^k$ in $\mathscr{U}_n$, then the columns of another matrix $B_{n \times k}$ are an orthonormal basis for the same $\mathscr{V}_n{}^k$ if and only if there exists a unitary matrix U of order k such that $B = AU$.

7.19 Orthogonality of Vector Spaces

In this section we study some of the geometry of the subspaces of the $\mathscr{V}_n{}^n$ over a number field $\mathscr{F}$. We begin with

Theorem 7.19.1:   *A vector V is orthogonal to every vector of a $\mathscr{V}_n{}^k$ if and only if it is orthogonal to every vector of a basis for the $\mathscr{V}_n{}^k$.*

Such a vector V is said to be **orthogonal to the** $\mathscr{V}_n{}^k$.

If $A_1, A_2, \ldots, A_k$ is a basis for $\mathscr{V}_n{}^k$, then every vector X thereof is of the form

$$X = \sum_{j=1}^{k} t_j A_j.$$

If now $V*A_j = 0$ for $j = 1, 2, \ldots, k$, then $V*X = \sum t_j V*A_j = 0$ also. Conversely, if $V*X = 0$ for every X of the $\mathscr{V}_n{}^k$, then, in particular, $V*A_j = 0$ for each j from 1 to k, so that the theorem is proved. We have next

Theorem 7.19.2:   *The set of all vectors V orthogonal to every vector X of a $\mathscr{V}_n{}^k$ constitutes a vector space $\mathscr{V}_n{}^{n-k}$. In particular, the only vector orthogonal to all n-vectors is the zero-vector.*

By the previous theorem, the vectors V in question are the solutions of the system of equations

$$V*A_1 = 0, \quad V*A_2 = 0, \quad \ldots, \quad V*A_k = 0,$$

where the A's form a basis for the $\mathscr{V}_n{}^k$. Since these A's are independent, the coefficient matrix has rank k so that there are $n - k$ linearly independent solutions and the theorem follows. In particular, when $k = n$, the coefficient matrix is a nonsingular matrix of order n, and $V = 0$ is the only solution.

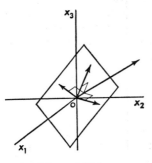

Figure 7.19.1

Two vector spaces which have the property that every vector of one is orthogonal to every vector of the other, as is the case in the preceding theorem, are said to be **orthogonal** to each other. When two orthogonal vector spaces have dimensions k and $n - k$ respectively, as is also the case in the preceding theorem, we call them **complementary orthogonal vector spaces.** Each is also called the **orthocomplement** of the other.

In $\mathscr{E}_3$ an example of complementary orthogonal spaces is given by the $\mathscr{V}_3{}^2$ of a plane on O and the $\mathscr{V}_3{}^1$ of a line perpendicular to this plane (Figure 7.19.1).

The fundamental result concerning complementary orthogonal vector spaces is

Theorem 7.19.3: *The sum of two complementary orthogonal vector spaces $\mathscr{V}_n{}^k$ and $\mathscr{V}_n{}^{n-k}$ is $\mathscr{V}_n{}^n$.*

To prove this, suppose $A_1, A_2, \ldots, A_k$ are an orthonormal basis for the $\mathscr{V}_n{}^k$ and $A_{k+1}, \ldots, A_n$ are an orthonormal basis for the complementary orthogonal space $\mathscr{V}_n{}^{n-k}$. Now if there exist $t_1, t_2, \ldots, t_n$ such that $\sum_{j=1}^{n} t_j A_j = 0$, then by multiplying this equation by each of $A_1{}^*, A_2{}^*, \ldots, A_n{}^*$ and noting that the n-vectors A_j are all mutually orthogonal, we obtain the equations

$$t_1 A_1{}^* A_1 = 0, \quad t_2 A_2{}^* A_2 = 0, \quad \ldots, \quad t_n A_n{}^* A_n = 0.$$

Since no A_j is a zero-vector, we must therefore have $t_j = 0, j = 1, 2, \ldots, n$, so that the A_j's are independent and hence span $\mathscr{V}_n{}^n$.

The result also follows from applying Theorem 7.15.4 to $A_1, A_2, \ldots, A_n$.

Theorem 7.19.4: *If $A_{(m,n)}$ has rank k so that the solutions of $AX = 0$ determine a $\mathscr{V}_n{}^{n-k}$, then the columns of A^* determine the complementary orthogonal $\mathscr{V}_n{}^k$.*

Since A^* has rank k also, the columns of A^* determine a $\mathscr{V}_n{}^k$. Let C_j denote the jth column of A^*. Then $C_j{}^*$ is the jth row of A. But then $C_j{}^* X = 0$, $j = 1, 2, \ldots, m$, whenever X is a solution of $AX = 0$. Hence by Theorem 7.19.1, every solution of $AX = 0$ is orthogonal to every vector in the $\mathscr{V}_n{}^k$ spanned by the columns of A^*, so that the $\mathscr{V}_n{}^k$ and the $\mathscr{V}_n{}^{n-k}$ are orthocomplements and the theorem is proved.

When A is real, so that $A^* = A^\mathsf{T}$, the orthocomplement of the space defined by $AX = 0$ is spanned by the columns of A^T.

Suppose now that we have given two subspaces $\mathscr{V}_n{}^{k_1}$ and $\mathscr{V}_n{}^{k_2}$ whose intersection has dimension r and whose sum has dimension s. Let orthonormal bases for the intersection, for $\mathscr{V}_n{}^{k_1}$, and for $\mathscr{V}_n{}^{k_2}$ be respectively

$$A_1, A_2, \ldots, A_r,$$

$$A_1, A_2, \ldots, A_r, B_1, \ldots, B_{k_1-r},$$

$$A_1, A_2, \ldots, A_r, C_1, \ldots, C_{k_2-r}.$$

Then a basis for the sum of the two spaces is, by Section 6.8,

$$A_1, A_2, \ldots, A_r, B_1, \ldots, B_{k_1-r}, C_1, \ldots, C_{k_2-r}.$$

Let these vectors constitute the columns of a matrix S. Then, by Theorem 7.19.1, the orthocomplement of the sum space is the set of all solutions X of the equation $S^*X = 0$. These vectors are precisely **the** ones which satisfy *both* equations

$$[A_1, \ldots, A_r, B_1, \ldots, B_{k_1-r}]^*X = 0,$$

$$[A_1, \ldots, A_r, C_1, \ldots, C_{k_2-r}]^*X = 0,$$

that is, which constitute the intersection of the orthocomplements of $\mathscr{V}_n^{\circ k_1}$ and $\mathscr{V}_n^{\circ k_2}$. Hence we have

Theorem 7.19.5:   *The orthocomplement of the sum of two vector spaces is the intersection of their orthocomplements.*

Since only the zero-vector is orthogonal to itself, the intersection of two orthogonal vector spaces is the zero-vector alone. Let $\mathscr{V}_n^{\circ k_1}$ have a basis $A_1, A_2, \ldots, A_{k_1}$ and let an orthogonal $\mathscr{V}_n^{\circ k_2}$ have a basis $B_1, B_2, \ldots, B_{k_2}$. Then the A's and B's together form an independent set, for $\sum \lambda_j A_j + \sum \mu_j B_j = 0$ implies $\sum \lambda_j A_j = -\sum \mu_j B_j$, so that, since the spaces intersect only in the zero-vector, $\sum \lambda_j A_j = 0$ and $\sum \mu_j B_j = 0$. Now the independence of the A's and of the B's implies that each λ and each μ is 0, that is, the A's and B's together form an independent set.

If $\mathscr{V}_n^{\circ k_1}$ and $\mathscr{V}_n^{\circ k_2}$ are orthocomplements, so that $k_1 + k_2 = n$, it now follows that $A_1, A_2, \ldots, A_{k_1}, B_1, B_2, \ldots, B_{k_2}$ is a basis for $\mathscr{V}_n^{\circ n}$. If X is any vector of $\mathscr{V}_n^{\circ n}$, then X has a unique representation of the form

$$X = \sum \lambda_j A_j + \sum \mu_j B_j,$$

that is, of the form

$$X = X_1 + X_2,$$

where X_1 belongs to the $\mathscr{V}_n^{\circ k_1}$ and X_2 belongs to the $\mathscr{V}_n^{\circ k_2}$. We have therefore proved

Theorem 7.19.6:   *Let $\mathscr{V}_n^{\circ k_1}$ and $\mathscr{V}_n^{\circ k_2}$ be orthocomplements in a $\mathscr{V}_n^{\circ n}$. Then each vector X of the $\mathscr{V}_n^{\circ n}$ has a unique representation of the form $X = X_1 + X_2$, where X_1 belongs to the $\mathscr{V}_n^{\circ k_1}$ and X_2 belongs to the $\mathscr{V}_n^{\circ k_2}$.*

We define X_1 to be the **projection** of X on the $\mathscr{V}_n^{\circ k_1}$ and X_2 to be the projection of X on the $\mathscr{V}_n^{\circ k_2}$. Using this definition, we conclude this section with a theorem that is important in applications:

Theorem 7.19.7:   *Let X denote a fixed vector of $\mathscr{V}_n^{\circ n}$ and let Y denote an arbitrary vector of a fixed $\mathscr{V}_n^{\circ r}$ in $\mathscr{V}_n^{\circ n}$. Then the length of $X - Y$ has a minimum value which is attained when Y is the projection of X on the $\mathscr{V}_n^{\circ r}$.*

The geometric significance of the theorem in $\mathscr{E}_3$ is indicated in Figure 7.19.2.

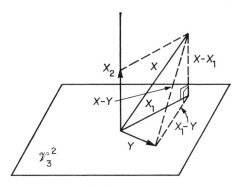

Figure 7.19.2

Let $X = X_1 + X_2$ represent the unique decomposition of X into the sum of a vector X_1 from the $\mathscr{V}_n{}^r$ and X_2 from its orthocomplement. Then X_1 denotes the projection of X on the $\mathscr{V}_n{}^r$. We write

$$X - Y = (X - X_1) + (X_1 - Y),$$

and observe that, because X_1 and Y belong to the $\mathscr{V}_n{}^r$, so does $X_1 - Y$. Also $X - X_1 = X_2$, which is in the orthocomplement of the $\mathscr{V}_n{}^r$. Hence $X - X_1$ and $X_1 - Y$ are orthogonal, that is,

$$(X - X_1)^*(X_1 - Y) = 0.$$

Therefore

$$|X - Y| = \sqrt{(X - Y)^*(X - Y)} = \sqrt{|X - X_1|^2 + |X_1 - Y|^2},$$

and, since X, X_1 are fixed, this will be a minimum when $|X_1 - Y| = 0$, that is, when $Y = X_1$.

7.20 Orthogonality and Systems of Linear Equations

The concept of orthogonality appears in a useful theorem concerning the consistency of a system of linear equations, $AX = B$.

Theorem 7.20.1: *In the complex field, a system $AX = B$ of m equations in n unknowns is consistent if and only if $B^*Y_0 = 0$ for every solution Y_0 of the homogeneous system $A^*Y = 0$.*

Suppose in fact that $AX = B$ is consistent and let X_0 be any solution. Then if $A^*Y_0 = 0$,

$$B^*Y_0 = (AX_0)^*Y_0 = X^*_0(A^*Y_0) = 0.$$

Conversely, suppose that $B^*Y = 0$ for all Y such that $A^*Y = 0$. This means that B belongs to the complementary orthogonal space of the vector space defined by $A * Y = 0$. Hence, by Theorem 7.19.4, B belongs to the vector space spanned by the columns of $(A*)* = A$. Hence the last column of $[A, B]$ is a linear combination of the earlier columns. Thus A and $[A, B]$ must have the same rank, and the system $AX = B$ is consistent.

In the real field, $AX = B$ is consistent if and only if B is orthogonal to every solution of $A^{\mathsf{T}} Y = 0$. This last system of equations is called the **transposed homogeneous system** corresponding to the system $AX = B$.

7.21 Exercises

1. Show that, if $k_1 + k_2 < n$, there exist vectors $X \neq 0$ orthogonal to each of any given $\mathscr{V}_n{}^{k_1}$, and any given $\mathscr{V}_n{}^{k_2}$ in $\mathscr{V}_n{}^n$.

2. If $k_1 < k_2$ and the intersection of a given $\mathscr{V}_n{}^{k_1}$ and a given $\mathscr{V}_n{}^{k_2}$ is a $\mathscr{V}_n{}^h$, then there exist vectors $X \neq 0$ in the $\mathscr{V}_n{}^{k_2}$ orthogonal to the $\mathscr{V}_n{}^h$.

3. Show that Theorem 7.19.3 also follows from Theorem 6.8.3.

4. Show that, if $A_1, A_2, \ldots, A_{k_1}$ and $B_1, B_2, \ldots, B_{k_2}$ are bases for orthogonal vector spaces in a $\mathscr{V}_n{}^n$, then all $k_1 + k_2$ A's and B's are linearly independent.

5. If $A(I_n - A) = 0$ and $A*(I_n - A) = 0$, where A is of order n, then the sum of the ranks of A and $I_n - A$ is n. (*Hint:* Apply Exercise 4, the observation that $I - A = [E_1 - A_1, E_2 - A_2, \ldots, E_n - A_n]$, where $A_1, A_2, \ldots, A_n$ are the columns of A, and Theorem 6.8.3.)

6. Outline the definitions, theorems, and processes of this chapter which still apply in the rational number field.

7. Let X_1 denote the projection of X on a $\mathscr{V}_n{}^k$, a basis for which is $A_1, A_2, \ldots, A_k$. Prove that

$$X_1 = \sum_{j=1}^{k} \left(\frac{A_j * X}{|A_j|^2} \right) A_j.$$

8. In Exercise 7, prove that $X_1 = PX$, where P is the matrix of a projection in the sense of Section 6.15.

9. Find an orthonormal basis for the orthocomplement of the $\mathscr{V}_4{}^3$ spanned by

$$\begin{bmatrix} 1 \\ 1 \\ 0 \\ 1 \end{bmatrix}, \begin{bmatrix} 1 \\ 0 \\ 1 \\ 0 \end{bmatrix}, \begin{bmatrix} 1 \\ 1 \\ 1 \\ 1 \end{bmatrix}.$$

10. Given that $X = \{1, 0, 1, 1\}$, find X_1 and X_2 such that $X = X_1 + X_2$, where X_1 and X_2 belong to the orthocomplementary spaces of Exercise 9.

11. If Y is an arbitrary vector of the $\mathscr{V}_4{}^3$ of Exercise 9 and if X is as given in Exercise 10, find the minimum value of $|X - Y|$.

12. Prove that, if $P*Q = 0$, then the image spaces of the operators with matrices P and Q are orthogonal.

CHAPTER EIGHT

The Characteristic Equation of a Matrix

CHARACTERISTIC ROOTS AND VECTORS

8.1 The Characteristic Value Problem

In many important applications of matrices in mathematics, in the physical sciences, and in the social sciences, the following problem arises: Given a matrix A of order n, determine the scalars λ and the nonzero-vectors X which simultaneously satisfy the equation

$$(8.1.1) \qquad AX = \lambda X.$$

This is known as the **characteristic value problem**. We assume in following proofs that A and X are over the complex field and that λ is a complex number. However, specializations to the real field will be pointed out as we go along. For example, in $\mathcal{E}_3$, solving this problem amounts to finding what vectors $\overrightarrow{OP}$ are transformed by the linear operator with matrix A into vectors lying along the same line.

Equation (8.1.1) may be written in the form

$$(8.1.2) \qquad (A - \lambda I_n)X = 0.$$

The corresponding system of n homogeneous linear equations in n unknowns has nontrivial solutions if and only if the determinant of the coefficient matrix vanishes:

$$(8.1.3) \quad \det (A - \lambda I_n) = \begin{vmatrix} a_{11} - \lambda & a_{12} & \cdots & a_{1n} \\ a_{21} & a_{22} - \lambda & \cdots & a_{2n} \\ \vdots & & & \\ a_{n1} & a_{n2} & \cdots & a_{nn} - \lambda \end{vmatrix} = 0.$$

The expansion of this determinant yields a polynomial of degree n in λ, which we denote by $\varphi(\lambda)$ and which is called the **characteristic polynomial** of A. The equation $\varphi(\lambda) = 0$ is called the **characteristic** or **secular equation** of A. Its n roots are the n **characteristic values** or **roots** of A.

Let λ_1 be any characteristic root of A. Then, for this value of λ, (8.1.3) is satisfied and, hence, the equation

$$(8.1.4) \qquad\qquad (A - \lambda_1 I_n)X = 0$$

has nontrivial solutions for X. Every such solution X is called a **characteristic vector** of A. The set of all solutions of this equation constitutes the vector space of characteristic vectors associated with the given root λ_1. Since $\varphi(\lambda) = 0$ may have only one distinct root λ_1, and the corresponding equation (8.1.4) may have only one independent solution, it is possible that only a one-dimensional space of characteristic vectors exists. An example of this is given in the following section.

In principle then, our problem is solved, for we have proved

Theorem 8.1.1:   *The equation $AX = \lambda X$ has nontrivial solutions X if and only if λ is a characteristic root of A. There exists at least one value of λ and an associated, nonzero X such that this equation is satisfied.*

There still remain basic problems, of course. The actual computation of the characteristic roots and vectors is normally no mean task, and the study of their natures and properties is most rewarding.

Before proceeding to these matters we should point out that other words are also used where we have used the word "characteristic." Physicists commonly prefer to use the terms **eigenvalue**, **eigenvector**, and **eigenvalue problem**, derived from the German *Eigenwert*. Some books refer to **proper values** and **proper vectors**. Social scientists generally prefer to speak of **latent roots** and **latent vectors**. Our terminology is the most common mathematical usage.

8.2 Examples and a Basic Theorem

As a first example, consider the matrix

$$A = \begin{bmatrix} 1 & 2 \\ 2 & 1 \end{bmatrix},$$

for which

$$\varphi(\lambda) = \begin{vmatrix} 1 - \lambda & 2 \\ 2 & 1 - \lambda \end{vmatrix} = \lambda^2 - 2\lambda - 3.$$

The equation $\varphi(\lambda) = 0$ has the solutions $\lambda_1 = -1$, $\lambda_2 = 3$. For each of these values of λ, the system (8.1.2) reduces to a single independent equation:

$$x_1 + x_2 = 0, \qquad (\lambda_1 = -1),$$

and

$$x_1 - x_2 = 0, \qquad (\lambda_2 = 3).$$

These equations have respectively the complete solutions

$$\begin{bmatrix} x_1 \\ x_2 \end{bmatrix} = k_1 \begin{bmatrix} 1 \\ -1 \end{bmatrix} \quad \text{and} \quad \begin{bmatrix} x_1 \\ x_2 \end{bmatrix} = k_2 \begin{bmatrix} 1 \\ 1 \end{bmatrix}.$$

With each characteristic root there is thus associated a one-dimensional vector space of characteristic vectors.

Geometrically, this example means that in $\mathscr{E}_2$ the one-dimensional vector spaces determined by the vectors $\{1, -1\}$ and $\{1, 1\}$ are left invariant by the linear operator with matrix A, that is, every vector of either of these spaces is transformed into a vector of the same space by A. See Figure 8.2.1.

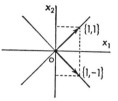

Figure 8.2.1

Consider next the identity matrix of order 2. Its characteristic equation, $(1 - \lambda)^2 = 0$, has the double root $\lambda = 1$. Equation (8.1.1) now becomes simply $0 \cdot X = 0$ of which every 2-vector X is a solution. In this case, therefore, with the double root of the characteristic equation there is associated the two-dimensional vector space consisting of all 2-vectors.

In contrast to the preceding example, let

$$A = \begin{bmatrix} 1 & -2 \\ 0 & 1 \end{bmatrix}.$$

The characteristic equation is again $(1 - \lambda)^2 = 0$. The characteristic vectors are now determined by the equation

$$\begin{bmatrix} 0 & -2 \\ 0 & 0 \end{bmatrix} \cdot \begin{bmatrix} x_1 \\ x_2 \end{bmatrix} = \begin{bmatrix} 0 \\ 0 \end{bmatrix},$$

that is, by the single equation $x_2 = 0$, the complete solution of which is

$$\begin{bmatrix} x_1 \\ x_2 \end{bmatrix} = k \begin{bmatrix} 1 \\ 0 \end{bmatrix}.$$

In this case there is only a one-dimensional vector space of characteristic vectors associated with the double root.

These last two examples illustrate the fact, to be proved later, that the dimension ρ of the vector space of characteristic vectors associated with a characteristic root of multiplicity r is bounded by the relation $1 \leqslant \rho \leqslant r$. The reader should recall here that "λ_0 is a characteristic root of multiplicity r" means that "$(\lambda - \lambda_0)^r$ divides the characteristic polynomial but $(\lambda - \lambda_0)^{r+1}$ does not."

The first example given above illustrates the following basic result:

Theorem 8.2.1: Let $\lambda_1, \lambda_2, \ldots, \lambda_k$ be distinct characteristic roots of a matrix A, and let $X_1, X_2, \ldots, X_k$ be any nonzero characteristic vectors associated with these roots respectively. Then $X_1, X_2, \ldots, X_k$ are linearly independent.

To prove this, suppose the contrary, that is, suppose there exist constants $c_1, c_2, \ldots, c_k$ such that

$$(8.2.1) \qquad c_1 X_1 + c_2 X_2 + \cdots + c_k X_k = 0.$$

Multiplying through by A, and using the fact that $A X_j = \lambda_j X_j$, we have

$$(8.2.2) \qquad c_1 \lambda_1 X_1 + c_2 \lambda_2 X_2 + \cdots + c_k \lambda_k X_k = 0.$$

Repeating the process, we obtain successively the equations

$$c_1 \lambda_1{}^2 X_1 + c_2 \lambda_2{}^2 X_2 + \cdots + c_k \lambda_k{}^2 X_k = 0,$$

$$(8.2.3) \qquad \vdots$$

$$c_1 \lambda_1{}^{k-1} X_1 + c_2 \lambda_2{}^{k-1} X_2 + \cdots + c_k \lambda_k{}^{k-1} X_k = 0.$$

The k equations (8.2.1) through (8.2.3) in the vector unknowns $X_1, X_2, \ldots, X_k$ may be written in the form

$$[c_1 X_1, c_2 X_2, \ldots, c_k X_k] \cdot \begin{bmatrix} 1 & \lambda_1 & \lambda_1{}^2 & \cdots & \lambda_1{}^{k-1} \\ 1 & \lambda_2 & \lambda_2{}^2 & \cdots & \lambda_2{}^{k-1} \\ \vdots & & & & \\ 1 & \lambda_k & \lambda_k{}^2 & \cdots & \lambda_k{}^{k-1} \end{bmatrix} = 0.$$

Since the λ's are all unequal, the right factor here is a nonsingular Vandermonde matrix (see Exercise 26, Section 2.12). If we multiply on the right by its inverse, we have

$$[c_1 X_1, c_2 X_2, \ldots, c_k X_k] = 0,$$

which, since no X is zero, implies that every c is zero. Hence the X's are independent.

This theorem may also be proved by induction, which is left as an exercise for the reader.

8.3 Exercises

1. Determine the characteristic roots and the associated spaces of characteristic vectors for the matrices

$$(a) \begin{bmatrix} 1 & 1 & 1 \\ 0 & 1 & 0 \\ 1 & 1 & 1 \end{bmatrix}, \quad (b) \begin{bmatrix} 1 & 0 & 0 \\ 0 & 1 & 0 \\ 0 & 0 & 2 \end{bmatrix}, \quad (c) \begin{bmatrix} 0 & 1 & 2 \\ 1 & 0 & -1 \\ 2 & -1 & 0 \end{bmatrix},$$

$$(d) \begin{bmatrix} 1 & 2 & 3 \\ 0 & 1 & 2 \\ 0 & 0 & 1 \end{bmatrix}, \quad (e) \begin{bmatrix} 0 & i & i \\ i & 0 & i \\ i & i & 0 \end{bmatrix}, \quad (f) \begin{bmatrix} 0 & 1 & 0 \\ 0 & 0 & 1 \\ -1 & -3 & -3 \end{bmatrix}.$$

*2. Show that $\lambda = 0$ is a characteristic root of a matrix A if and only if A is singular.

*3. Show that the characteristic roots of A^* are the conjugates of those of A.

*4. Show that the matrices A and $P^{-1}AP$ have the same characteristic equation and that, if $AX = \lambda X$, $X \neq 0$, then $P^{-1}X$ is a characteristic vector of $P^{-1}AP$ corresponding to λ.

*5. Show that, if A is real and λ is a real characteristic root of A, then the associated space of characteristic vectors may always be spanned by real vectors.

*6. Show that, if X is a unit vector such that $AX = \lambda X$, then $X^*AX = \lambda$.

*7. Show that the characteristic roots of a triangular matrix are just the diagonal elements of that matrix. The particular case when A is diagonal occurs frequently in what follows.

8. Show that, if $AB = BA$, $AX_0 = \lambda X_0$, and $BX_0 \neq 0$, then BX_0 is a characteristic vector of A associated with the characteristic root λ. Then show that, if the vector space of characteristic vectors of A associated with λ is *one-dimensional*, X_0 must also be a characteristic vector of B associated with an appropriate characteristic root μ of B.

9. Show that, if A has distinct characteristic roots $\lambda_1, \lambda_2, \ldots, \lambda_n$, and if λ_1^p, $\lambda_2^p, \ldots, \lambda_n^p$ are distinct, the characteristic roots of A^p, where p is any positive integer, are $\lambda_1^p, \lambda_2^p, \ldots, \lambda_n^p$. (*Hint:* If $AX = \lambda X$, then $A^2X = \lambda AX$, etc.) The requirement of distinctness will be removed in Exercise 3, Section 8.9.

10. By using the matrix

$$\begin{bmatrix} 0 & 1 & 0 & \cdots & 0 \\ 0 & 0 & 1 & \cdots & 0 \\ \vdots & & & & \\ 0 & 0 & 0 & \cdots & 1 \\ \dfrac{-a_n}{a_0} & \dfrac{-a_{n-1}}{a_0} & \dfrac{-a_{n-2}}{a_0} & \cdots & \dfrac{-a_1}{a_0} \end{bmatrix},$$

show that any given polynomial $a_0\lambda^n + a_1\lambda^{n-1} + \cdots + a_{n-1}\lambda + a_n$, $a_0 \neq 0$, of degree n may be regarded as the characteristic polynomial of a matrix of order n. This matrix is called the **companion matrix** of the given polynomial.

*11. If $AX_j = \lambda_j X_j$, $j = 1, 2, \ldots, n$, and if the X_j's are linearly independent, show that $\lambda_1, \lambda_2, \ldots, \lambda_n$ are the characteristic roots of A. Exercise 4 will be helpful here.

12. Show that, if $A^*X = \lambda X$, $AY = \mu Y$, and $\bar{\lambda} \neq \mu$, then $X^*Y = 0$.

13. Show that, if $AX = \lambda X$, $X \neq 0$, then

$$\lambda = \frac{X^*AX}{X^*X}.$$

*14. Show that the characteristic vectors of A^{-1} are the same as those of A. Show also that $\det (A^{-1} - \mu I) = (-\mu)^n \det A^{-1} \det (A - (1/\mu)I)$ and hence that, if the characteristic roots of A are $\lambda_1, \lambda_2, \ldots, \lambda_n$, distinct or not, those of A^{-1} are $(1/\lambda_1), (1/\lambda_2), \ldots, (1/\lambda_n)$.

15. Show that the characteristic roots of kA are $k\lambda_1, k\lambda_2, \ldots, k\lambda_n$, where λ_1, $\lambda_2, \ldots, \lambda_n$, are those of A.

16. Show that, if the characteristic roots of A are distinct and those of B are distinct, then $AB = BA$ if and only if A and B have the same characteristic vectors.

*17. If U is a unitary matrix and $U^*AU = D[d_1, d_2, \ldots, d_n]$, where D is a diagonal matrix whose diagonal elements are the d_j's, show that the d_j's are the characteristic roots of A and that the columns of U are characteristic vectors corresponding to the d's respectively. (*Hint:* Subtract λI from each member of the equation.)

18. Calculate the characteristic polynomial of the matrix $W_{n \times n} - I_{n \times n}$, where all the elements of W are 1's.

19. For what values of k do the matrices

$$\begin{bmatrix} 1 & 4k \\ 4 & 3 \end{bmatrix}, \quad \begin{bmatrix} 1 & 2 \\ 2 & k \end{bmatrix}$$

have (a) real and distinct, (b) real and equal, (c) complex characteristic roots?

20. Find the characteristic roots of the matrix

$$\begin{bmatrix} h & 1 & 0 \\ 1 & h & 0 \\ 0 & 0 & 1 \end{bmatrix}.$$

For what values of h will the matrix have multiple characteristic roots?

21. Given an example to show that, if $AX = \lambda_1 X$ and $AY = \lambda_2 Y$ with $\lambda_1 \neq \lambda_2$, then $\alpha X + \beta Y$ is *not*, in general, a characteristic vector of A.

22. Find the characteristic roots and characteristic vectors of the real matrix

$$A = \begin{bmatrix} a & -b \\ b & a \end{bmatrix}.$$

Normalize the characteristic vectors, and in each case compute X^*AX.

23. Given that P is the matrix of a projection, show that its characteristic roots are all 0 or 1. Then show that the characteristic vectors associated with the root 1 span the image space of P. What vectors correspond to the roots 0?

24. Prove that, if there exist n independent vectors $X_1, X_2, \ldots, X_n$ and

corresponding scalars $\lambda_1, \lambda_2, \ldots, \lambda_n$ such that $AX_j = \lambda_j X_j$ and $BX_j = \lambda_j X_j$, $j = 1, 2, \ldots, n$, then $A = B$.

25. Under what conditions on the elements will the matrix

$$\begin{bmatrix} a & b \\ c & d \end{bmatrix}$$

have equal characteristic roots?

26. Determine the characteristic roots of the matrix

$$\begin{bmatrix} a_1 & a_2 & \cdots & a_n \\ a_1 & a_2 & \cdots & a_n \\ \vdots & & & \\ a_1 & a_2 & \cdots & a_n \end{bmatrix}.$$

27. Let

$$I = \begin{bmatrix} 1 & 0 & 0 & 0 \\ 0 & 1 & 0 & 0 \\ 0 & 0 & 1 & 0 \\ 0 & 0 & 0 & 1 \end{bmatrix}, \quad \mathscr{I} = \begin{bmatrix} 0 & 1 & 0 & 0 \\ -1 & 0 & 0 & 0 \\ 0 & 0 & 0 & -1 \\ 0 & 0 & 1 & 0 \end{bmatrix},$$

$$\mathscr{J} = \begin{bmatrix} 0 & 0 & 1 & 0 \\ 0 & 0 & 0 & 1 \\ -1 & 0 & 0 & 0 \\ 0 & -1 & 0 & 0 \end{bmatrix}, \quad \mathscr{K} = \begin{bmatrix} 0 & 0 & 0 & 1 \\ 0 & 0 & -1 & 0 \\ 0 & 1 & 0 & 0 \\ -1 & 0 & 0 & 0 \end{bmatrix}.$$

Complete the multiplication table

$\times$	I	$\mathscr{I}$	$\mathscr{J}$	$\mathscr{K}$
I				
$\mathscr{I}$				
$\mathscr{J}$				
$\mathscr{K}$				

and then show that:

(a) The set of all matrices of the form

$$Q = aI + b\mathscr{I} + c\mathscr{J} + d\mathscr{K},$$

where a, b, c, d are arbitrary real numbers is a ring (see Exercise 10, Section 4.15).

(b) $QQ^{\mathsf{T}} = (a^2 + b^2 + c^2 + d^2)I$ and $Q + Q^{\mathsf{T}} = 2aI$.

(c) $(Q - \lambda I)(Q - \lambda I)^{\mathsf{T}} = ((a^2 + b^2 + c^2 + d^2) - 2a\lambda + \lambda^2)I$ and, hence, the characteristic roots of Q are $a \pm i\sqrt{b^2 + c^2 + d^2}$, each counted twice.

(d) $Q^{-1} = (a^2 + b^2 + c^2 + d^2)^{-1}(aI - b\mathscr{I} - c\mathscr{J} - d\mathscr{K})$ if $Q \neq 0$.

28. Show that, if

$$I = \begin{bmatrix} 1 & 0 \\ 0 & 1 \end{bmatrix}, \qquad R = \begin{bmatrix} i & 0 \\ 0 & -i \end{bmatrix}, \qquad S = \begin{bmatrix} 0 & 1 \\ -1 & 0 \end{bmatrix}, \qquad T = \begin{bmatrix} 0 & i \\ i & 0 \end{bmatrix},$$

then the set of all matrices P defined by

$$P = aI + bR + cS + dT,$$

where a, b, c, d are arbitrary real numbers, is a ring isomorphic to the ring of matrices defined in the preceding exercise.

The rings of matrices in the two preceding exercises are called **quaternion rings of matrices** since they are isomorphic to the ring of quaternions (see G. Birkhoff and S. Mac Lane: *A Survey of Modern Algebra*, Revised Edition, New York, Macmillan, 1953, pp. 236 ff.).

8.4 Properties of the Characteristic Polynomial

For the proof of certain important theorems, it is necessary to have explicit formulas for the coefficients of the characteristic polynomial, $\varphi(\lambda)$.

Let us look first at the special cases. If we put $\lambda = 0$ into $\varphi(\lambda) = a_0\lambda^n + a_1\lambda^{n-1} + \cdots + a_{n-1}\lambda + a_n$, we obtain the constant term a_n. If we put $\lambda = 0$ in $\det (A - \lambda I)$, we obtain $\det A$. Hence $a_n = \det A$. The diagonal term of $\det (A - \lambda I)$ is $(a_{11} - \lambda)(a_{22} - \lambda) \cdots (a_{nn} - \lambda)$, and this is the only product yielding λ^n and λ^{n-1}. Expanding the product, we obtain $(-1)^n\lambda^n$ and $(-1)^{n-1} \sum a_{jj}\lambda^{n-1}$ as the first two terms of $\varphi(\lambda)$. Hence $a_0 = (-1)^n$, $a_1 = (-1)^{n-1} \sum a_{jj}$.

To obtain a general formula for the coefficients of $\varphi(\lambda)$, we note that $A - \lambda I = [A_1 - \lambda E_1, A_2 - \lambda E_2, \ldots, A_n - \lambda E_n]$, where A_j is the jth column of A, and E_j is the jth elementary vector. Hence, by repeated use of Theorem 2.7.7, we see that $\det (A - \lambda I)$ is the sum of 2^n determinants, the jth column in each of which is either A_j or $-\lambda E_j$:

$$\begin{aligned}
\det (A - \lambda I) = {} & \det [-\lambda E_1, -\lambda E_2, \ldots, -\lambda E_n] \\
& + \det [A_1, -\lambda E_2, \ldots, -\lambda E_n] + \cdots \\
& + \det [-\lambda E_1, \ldots, -\lambda E_{n-1}, A_n] \\
& + \det [A_1, A_2, -\lambda E_3, \ldots, -\lambda E_n] + \cdots \\
& + \det [-\lambda E_1, \ldots, -\lambda E_{n-2}, A_{n-1}, A_n] + \cdots \\
& + \det [A_1, A_2, \ldots, A_{n-r}, -\lambda E_{n-r+1}, \ldots, -\lambda E_n] + \cdots \\
& + \det [-\lambda E_1, \ldots, -\lambda E_r, A_{r+1}, \ldots, A_n] + \cdots \\
& + \det [A_1, A_2, \ldots, A_n].
\end{aligned}$$

The expansion of each of these determinants is a power of $-\lambda$, from the diagonal entries, times a principal minor of A. (To see this more easily, write out the formula in full for $n = 3$.) We have therefore

Theorem 8.4.1: *The coefficient of λ^r $(r \leqslant n)$ in $\varphi(\lambda)$ is $(-1)^r$ times the sum of the principal minors of order $n - r$ of A. In particular, the coefficient of λ^n is $(-1)^n$; the constant term is $\det A$.*

In $\varphi(\lambda)$, the coefficient of λ^{n-1}, namely $(-1)^{n-1}(a_{11} + a_{22} + \cdots + a_{nn})$, is of special interest. We have called the expression in parentheses, namely $\sum a_{ii}$, the **trace** of A (Exercise 23, Section 1.9). Some writers call it the **spur** of A. (*Spur* is a German word, one English translation of which is **trace**.) Next to det A, the trace is perhaps the most important coefficient of $\varphi(\lambda)$.

We may use the preceding theorem to expand $\varphi(\lambda)$ if we wish. For example,

$$
\begin{vmatrix} 1 - \lambda & -1 & 1 \\ 0 & 1 - \lambda & 0 \\ 1 & -1 & 1 - \lambda \end{vmatrix} = \begin{vmatrix} 1 & -1 & 1 \\ 0 & 1 & 0 \\ 1 & -1 & 1 \end{vmatrix}
$$

$$
- \left(\begin{vmatrix} 1 & -1 \\ 0 & 1 \end{vmatrix} + \begin{vmatrix} 1 & 0 \\ -1 & 1 \end{vmatrix} + \begin{vmatrix} 1 & 1 \\ 1 & 1 \end{vmatrix} \right) \lambda
$$

$$
+ (1 + 1 + 1)\lambda^2 - \lambda^3 = -2\lambda + 3\lambda^2 - \lambda^3.
$$

For the proof of Theorem 8.4.3, we need

Lemma 8.4.2: *If $\lambda = \lambda_1$ is an r_1-fold characteristic root of A, then $\lambda = 0$ is an r_1-fold characteristic root of $A - \lambda_1 I_1$.*

By hypothesis, if $\varphi(\lambda)$ is the characteristic polynomial of A, we have

$$
\varphi(\lambda) \equiv (\lambda - \lambda_1)^{r_1} \psi(\lambda),
$$

where $\psi(\lambda_1) \neq 0$. Hence

$$
\begin{aligned}
\det[(A - \lambda_1 I) - \lambda I] &\equiv \det[A - (\lambda + \lambda_1)I] \\
&\equiv \varphi(\lambda + \lambda_1) \\
&\equiv [(\lambda + \lambda_1) - \lambda_1]^{r_1} \psi(\lambda + \lambda_1) \\
&\equiv \lambda^{r_1} \psi(\lambda + \lambda_1).
\end{aligned}
$$

Here $\psi(\lambda + \lambda_1) \neq 0$ when $\lambda = 0$, because $\psi(\lambda_1) \neq 0$. Therefore $\lambda = 0$ is an r_1-fold characteristic root of $A - \lambda_1 I$ and the lemma is proved.

Now in the expansion of $\det[(A - \lambda_1 I) - \lambda I]$, the coefficient of λ^{r_1} is $(-1)^{r_1} \sum$ (principal minors of order $n - r_1$ of $A - \lambda_1 I$). If λ_1 is an r_1-fold characteristic root of A, by Lemma 8.4.2, $\lambda = 0$ is an r_1-fold characteristic root of $A - \lambda_1 I$, and, hence, the coefficients of $\lambda^0, \lambda^1, \ldots, \lambda^{r-1}$ in this expansion are all zero, but the coefficient of λ^{r_1} is *not zero*. Therefore at least one principal minor of order $n - r_1$ of $A - \lambda_1 I$ is not zero, so that the rank of $A - \lambda_1 I$ is at least $n - r_1$.

It may well be that minors of $A - \lambda_1 I$ of order higher than $n - r_1$ are also unequal to zero. The last example of Section 8.2 illustrates this case. In summary, we have

Theorem 8.4.3: *If λ_1 is an r_1-fold characteristic root of a matrix A, then the rank of $A - \lambda_1 I$ is not less than $n - r_1$, and the dimension of the associated space of characteristic vectors is not greater than r_1.*

Now let the distinct characteristic roots of A be $\lambda_1, \lambda_2, \ldots, \lambda_p$, with multiplicities $r_1, r_2, \ldots, r_p$. Let $\rho_1, \rho_2, \ldots, \rho_p$ be the dimensions of the associated spaces of characteristic vectors respectively. Then we have

$$\sum_1^p r_j = n \quad \text{and} \quad 1 \leqslant \rho_j \leqslant r_j, \quad j = 1, 2, \ldots, p.$$

Hence, adding these inequalities, we have

(8.4.2) $$p \leqslant \sum_1^p \rho_j \leqslant n.$$

We shall see later that, in the case of a Hermitian or real symmetric matrix, $\rho_j = r_j$ in every case, so that then

$$\sum_1^p r_j = \sum_1^p \rho_j = n.$$

This is the most important case as far as applications are concerned.

We have, of course, for any matrix A, one case in which the result can be stated exactly:

Theorem 8.4.4: *If λ_1 is a simple root of $\varphi(\lambda) = 0$, the rank of $A - \lambda_1 I$ is $n - 1$, and the dimension of the associated space of characteristic vectors is 1.*

8.5 Exercises

*1. Show that A and $B^{-1}AB$ have the same determinant and the same trace. (See Exercise 23, Section 1.9.) (This means that a linear operator on a $\mathscr{V}_n^\circ{}^n$ has the same characteristic polynomial in every reference system.)

2. Use Theorem 8.4.1 to expand

$$\det \begin{bmatrix} 1 - \lambda & 1 & 0 & 0 \\ 1 & 2 - \lambda & 0 & 2 \\ 0 & 0 & 3 - \lambda & 3 \\ 0 & 2 & 3 & 4 - \lambda \end{bmatrix}.$$

3. Show that A and A^T have the same characteristic roots.

4. Show that, for each r, the sums of the corresponding principal minors of order r of AB and BA are equal, where A and B are of order n, so that AB and BA have exactly the same characteristic roots, but not necessarily the same characteristic vectors.

5. By differentiating $\det(A - \lambda I)$ repeatedly, prove that the rth derivative of $\varphi(\lambda)$ is given by $(-1)^r r!$ times the sum of the principal minors of order $n - r$ of the characteristic matrix if $r \leqslant n$ and by 0 if $r \geqslant n$. (The principal minor of order 0 is by definition 1.) Then use this result and Taylor's theorem to prove Theorem 8.4.1.

6. Show that $\det (A - I) = \sum (\pm$ principal minors of all orders of A). This includes the principal minor of order 0, which is by definition 1.

7. Show that, if $a_{ij} \geqslant 0$ for all i and j and $\sum_{i=1}^{n} a_{ij} \leqslant 1$ for each j, then

$$\det (A - I) \geqslant 0, \qquad \text{if } n \text{ is even,}$$

$$\leqslant 0, \qquad \text{if } n \text{ is odd.}$$

8. A linear transformation $Y = AX$ takes the vector $\{1, 2, 1\}$ into the vector $\{1, 2, 1\}$, $\{2, 1, 0\}$ into $\{-4, -2, 0\}$, and $\{1, 1, 1\}$ into $\{0, 0, 0\}$. Without finding A itself, write the characteristic equation of A and find the trace and the determinant of A.

*9. Show that if the rank of A is r, then at least $n - r$ characteristic roots of A are zero. Given an example to show that the "at least" here is justified.

*10. By expanding $\varphi(\lambda) \equiv (-1)^n \prod_{j=1}^{n} (\lambda - \lambda_j)$, where $\lambda_1, \lambda_2, \ldots, \lambda_n$ are the roots of the characteristic equation $\varphi(\lambda) = 0$ of a matrix A, show with the aid of Theorem 8.4.1 that

$$\operatorname{tr} A = \sum_{i=1}^{n} a_{ii} = \sum_{i=1}^{n} \lambda_i,$$

and that

$$\det A = \prod_{j=1}^{n} \lambda_j.$$

11. How is the characteristic polynomial of A^* related to the characteristic polynomial $\varphi(\lambda)$ of A? What is the nature of the coefficients of $\varphi(\lambda)$ in the event that A is Hermitian? Skew-Hermitian?

12. Given that A is $m \times n$, show that $A^{\mathsf{T}}A$ and AA^{T} have the same characteristic roots, except possibly for zero roots.

13. Prove that, if X is any nonzero-vector of $\mathscr{U}_n$, the nonzero characteristic root of XX^* is $X^*X = \sum |x_i|^2$.

POLYNOMIAL FUNCTIONS OF A MATRIX

8.6 The Cayley-Hamilton Theorem

In the manner of Section 1.17, we now associate with the characteristic polynomial $\varphi(\lambda)$ of a matrix A the polynomial in A,

$$(8.6.1) \qquad \varphi(A) = a_0 I_n + a_1 A + a_2 A^2 + \cdots + a_n A^n, \, a_n = (-1)^n,$$

which is called the **characteristic function** of A. Concerning this function, we have the famous **Cayley-Hamilton theorem**:

Theorem 8.6.1: $\varphi(A) = 0$, *that is, a matrix satisfies its own characteristic equation.*

The characteristic matrix of A is $A - \lambda I_n$. Let us use C to denote the adjoint matrix of $A - \lambda I_n$. [See Section 3.1.] The cofactors of $A - \lambda I_n$ are of degree at most $n - 1$ in λ, so that the same is true of the elements of C. Hence we may represent C as a matrix polynomial

$$(8.6.2) \qquad C = C_0 + C_1\lambda + C_2\lambda^2 + \cdots + C_{n-1}\lambda^{n-1},$$

where C_k is the matrix whose elements are the coefficients of λ^k in the corresponding elements of C. The following example illustrates the idea. Let

$$A = \begin{bmatrix} 1 & 2 & 0 \\ 2 & -1 & 0 \\ 0 & 0 & 1 \end{bmatrix}, \quad \text{so} \quad A - \lambda I_n = \begin{bmatrix} (1-\lambda) & 2 & 0 \\ 2 & (-1-\lambda) & 0 \\ 0 & 0 & (1-\lambda) \end{bmatrix},$$

and hence

$$C = \begin{bmatrix} \lambda^2 - 1 & 2\lambda - 2 & 0 \\ 2\lambda - 2 & \lambda^2 - 2\lambda + 1 & 0 \\ 0 & 0 & \lambda^2 - 5 \end{bmatrix}$$

$$= \begin{bmatrix} -1 & -2 & 0 \\ -2 & 1 & 0 \\ 0 & 0 & -5 \end{bmatrix} + \begin{bmatrix} 0 & 2 & 0 \\ 2 & -2 & 0 \\ 0 & 0 & 0 \end{bmatrix}\lambda + \begin{bmatrix} 1 & 0 & 0 \\ 0 & 1 & 0 \\ 0 & 0 & 1 \end{bmatrix}\lambda^2.$$

From (3.1.1), we have the relation

$$(A - \lambda I_n)C = (\det (A - \lambda I_n))I_n,$$

that is,

$$AC - \lambda C = \varphi(\lambda)I_n.$$

Substituting the expansion of C given in (8.6.2) and also putting

$$\varphi(\lambda) = \sum_{k=0}^{n} a_k \lambda^k,$$

we have

$$\sum_{k=0}^{n-1} AC_k \lambda^k - \sum_{k=0}^{n-1} C_k \lambda^{k+1} = \sum_{k=0}^{n} (a_k I_n)\lambda^k.$$

In this identity in λ, we may equate corresponding coefficients and obtain the following set of equations:

$$AC_0 \qquad\qquad = a_0 I_n,$$
$$AC_1 \quad - C_0 \quad = a_1 I_n,$$
$$AC_2 \quad - C_1 \quad = a_2 I_n,$$
$$\vdots$$
$$AC_{n-1} - C_{n-2} = a_{n-1} I_n,$$
$$\qquad - C_{n-1} = a_n I_n.$$

In order now to eliminate the matrices C_k from these equations, we need only to multiply them on the left by

$$I_n, A, A^2, \ldots, A^{n-1}, A^n$$

respectively and add the results, thus obtaining

(8.6.3) $$0 = a_0 I + a_1 A + a_2 A^2 + \cdots + a_{n-1} A^{n-1} + a_n A^n,$$

or $\varphi(A) = 0$, so that the theorem is proved.

In the case of the above example, we have

$$\varphi(\lambda) = \begin{vmatrix} 1-\lambda & 2 & 0 \\ 2 & -1-\lambda & 0 \\ 0 & 0 & 1-\lambda \end{vmatrix} = -5 + 5\lambda + \lambda^2 - \lambda^3.$$

Hence

$$\varphi(A) = -5 \begin{bmatrix} 1 & 0 & 0 \\ 0 & 1 & 0 \\ 0 & 0 & 1 \end{bmatrix} + 5 \begin{bmatrix} 1 & 2 & 0 \\ 2 & -1 & 0 \\ 0 & 0 & 1 \end{bmatrix}$$

$$+ \begin{bmatrix} 1 & 2 & 0 \\ 2 & -1 & 0 \\ 0 & 0 & 1 \end{bmatrix}^2 - \begin{bmatrix} 1 & 2 & 0 \\ 2 & -1 & 0 \\ 0 & 0 & 1 \end{bmatrix}^3$$

$$= \begin{bmatrix} -5 & 0 & 0 \\ 0 & -5 & 0 \\ 0 & 0 & -5 \end{bmatrix} + \begin{bmatrix} 5 & 10 & 0 \\ 10 & -5 & 0 \\ 0 & 0 & 5 \end{bmatrix}$$

$$+ \begin{bmatrix} 5 & 0 & 0 \\ 0 & 5 & 0 \\ 0 & 0 & 1 \end{bmatrix} + \begin{bmatrix} -5 & -10 & 0 \\ -10 & 5 & 0 \\ 0 & 0 & -1 \end{bmatrix} = 0.$$

An important application of the Cayley-Hamilton theorem is in the representation of high powers of a matrix. Suppose that in fact we have computed A^2, $A^3, \ldots, A^{n-1}$. Then from the equation $\varphi(A) = 0$, we obtain

(8.6.4) $$A^n = -\frac{a_0}{a_n} I - \frac{a_1}{a_n} A - \cdots - \frac{a_{n-1}}{a_n} A^{n-1}.$$

Multiplying through by A, and then substituting from (8.6.4) for A^n on the right, we obtain

$$(8.6.5) \quad A^{n+1} = \frac{a_{n-1}a_0}{a_n^2} I_n + \left(\frac{a_{n-1}a_1}{a_n^2} - \frac{a_0}{a_n}\right) A + \cdots$$

$$+ \left(\frac{a_{n-1}^2}{a_n^2} - \frac{a_{n-2}}{a_n}\right) A^{n-1}.$$

By continuing this process, we can express any positive integral power of A as a linear combination of $I, A, \ldots, A^{n-1}$.

If A^{-1} exists, by multiplying (8.6.3) by A^{-1} and then solving for A^{-1}, we obtain

$$(8.6.6) \qquad A^{-1} = -\frac{a_1}{a_0} I - \frac{a_2}{a_0} A - \cdots - \frac{a_n}{a_0} A^{n-1}.$$

Multiplying again by A^{-1} and then substituting for A^{-1} on the right from (8.6.6), we obtain

$$(8.6.7) \qquad A^{-2} = \left(\frac{a_1^2}{a_0^2} - \frac{a_2}{a_0}\right) I_n + \left(\frac{a_1 a_2}{a_0^2} - \frac{a_3}{a_0}\right) A + \cdots$$

$$+ \left(\frac{a_1 a_{n-1}}{a_0^2} - \frac{a_n}{a_0}\right) A^{n-2} + \left(\frac{a_1 a_n}{a_0^2}\right) A^{n-1}.$$

Thus all negative integral powers of A may also be expressed as linear combinations of $I_n, A, \ldots, A^{n-1}$ when A^{-1} exists.

These procedures are used in deriving formulas for automatic computation.

Another possible application of the Cayley-Hamilton theorem is to the evaluation of $\varphi(\lambda)$ itself. In fact, dividing $\varphi(A)$ by $a_n = (-1)^n$, we obtain an equation

$$A^n + \alpha_1 A^{n-1} + \cdots + \alpha_{n-1}A + \alpha_n I_n = 0,$$

from which

$$(8.6.8) \qquad (A^n X) + \alpha_1(A^{n-1}X) + \cdots + \alpha_{n-1}(AX) + \alpha_n X = 0,$$

where X is an arbitrarily chosen fixed vector. This matrix equation is equivalent to n scalar equations in the n unknowns $\alpha_1, \alpha_2, \ldots, \alpha_n$, which may be solved by any appropriate procedure provided the coefficient matrix is nonsingular. *This method of determining $\varphi(\lambda)$ often involves very tedious computations.*

8.7 The Minimum Polynomial of a Matrix

There are, of course, polynomial functions of a square matrix A, other than its characteristic function $\varphi(A)$, which reduce to zero. In fact, if $f(\lambda) = \varphi(\lambda)g(\lambda)$ where $g(\lambda)$ is any polynomial in λ, then $f(A) = 0$ also.

Among all not identically zero polynomials $p(\lambda)$ such that $p(A) = 0$, there must exist some of lowest degree. If this degree is μ, then $0 < \mu \leqslant n$.

Let each such polynomial of degree μ be divided by the coefficient of λ^μ. Then the result must be the same in every case, for if different polynomials were obtained, the difference of two of these, say $p_1(\lambda)$ and $p_2(\lambda)$, would be free of λ^μ,

$$p_1(\lambda) - p_2(\lambda) = \alpha_{\mu-1}\lambda^{\mu-1} + \alpha_{\mu-2}\lambda^{\mu-2} + \cdots + \alpha_1\lambda + \alpha_0.$$

Substitution of A would now yield

$$p_1(A) - p_2(A) \equiv \alpha_{\mu-1}A^{\mu-1} + \alpha_{\mu-2}A^{\mu-2} + \cdots + \alpha_1 A + \alpha_0 I_n = 0,$$

so that we would have an equation of degree less than μ satisfied by A. The contradiction proves our claim. This unique polynomial of lowest degree μ which vanishes at A is called the **minimum polynomial** of A and is denoted by $m(\lambda)$. We summarize in

Theorem 8.7.1:   *For a given square matrix A, there exists a unique polynomial $m(\lambda)$ of lowest degree μ, in which the coefficient of λ^μ is equal to unity, such that $m(A) = 0$.*

To illustrate, consider the scalar matrix

$$A = \begin{bmatrix} \alpha & 0 \\ 0 & \alpha \end{bmatrix}.$$

Here $\varphi(\lambda) = (\alpha - \lambda)^2$, but the minimum polynomial is just $\lambda - \alpha$ since $A - \alpha I = 0$ here.

We prove now

Theorem 8.7.2:   *Every polynomial $p(\lambda)$ such that $p(A) = 0$ is exactly divisible by $m(\lambda)$.*

To prove this, let the quotient when $p(\lambda)$ is divided by $m(\lambda)$ be $q(\lambda)$ and let the remainder, which is of degree less than μ, be $r(\lambda)$. Then we have

$$p(\lambda) \equiv m(\lambda)\, q(\lambda) + r(\lambda).$$

Substitution of A now yields

$$r(A) = 0.$$

Since $r(\lambda)$ is of degree less than μ, this implies $m(\lambda)$ is not a minimum polynomial unless $r(\lambda) \equiv 0$. Thus

$$p(\lambda) \equiv m(\lambda)\, q(\lambda),$$

and the theorem is proved.

A particular case of this result is that the minimum polynomial is a divisor of the characteristic polynomial $\varphi(\lambda)$. The relation between $\varphi(\lambda)$ and $m(\lambda)$ is more closely defined in the next two theorems.

Theorem 8.7.3:   *Every linear factor $\lambda - \lambda_1$ of $\varphi(\lambda)$ is also a factor of $m(\lambda)$.*

We know in fact that dividing $m(\lambda)$ by $\lambda - \lambda_1$ yields an identity

$$m(\lambda) \equiv (\lambda - \lambda_1) \, s(\lambda) + r,$$

where r is a constant. Substituting A for λ, we have

$$m(A) = (A - \lambda_1 I_n) \, s(A) + rI_n = 0,$$

so that, if $r \neq 0$, we have

$$(A - \lambda_1 I_n) \left(\frac{-s(A)}{r} \right) = I_n.$$

This means $A - \lambda_1 I_n$ has an inverse whereas, since λ_1 is a characteristic root, it is singular. The contradiction shows that r must be zero, so that

$$m(\lambda) \equiv (\lambda - \lambda_1) \, s(\lambda),$$

as was to be proved.

An immediate consequence is

Theorem 8.7.4:   *If the characteristic roots of A are distinct,*

$$\varphi(\lambda) = (-1)^n \, m(\lambda).$$

Indeed, in this case $\varphi(\lambda) = (-1)^n \prod_{j=1}^{n} (\lambda - \lambda_j)$ and $m(\lambda) = \prod_{j=1}^{n} (\lambda - \lambda_j)$, by the preceding theorem.

One might be tempted to conclude at this point that the minimum polynomial is simply the product of the distinct factors of $\varphi(\lambda)$. That this is not the case may be shown by an example. Let

$$A = \begin{bmatrix} 1 & 1 & 1 & \cdots & 1 \\ 0 & 1 & 1 & \cdots & 1 \\ 0 & 0 & 1 & \cdots & 1 \\ \vdots & & & & \\ 0 & 0 & 0 & \cdots & 1 \end{bmatrix}_n$$

so that $\varphi(\lambda) \equiv (-1)^n (\lambda - 1)^n$.

Then $A - I \neq 0$ so that $\lambda - 1$ is not the minimum polynomial. However, it is easily verified that $(A - I)^n = 0$ while no lesser power of $A - I$ is zero. Thus the minimum polynomial is $(\lambda - 1)^n$ in this case.

An equation $A^p + \alpha_{p-1} A^{p-1} + \cdots + \alpha_1 A + \alpha_0 I = 0$, which is satisfied by a fixed matrix A, says that the matrices $I, A, A^2, \ldots, A^p$ are linearly dependent. Hence the minimum polynomial of A may be found by determining the smallest positive integer p for which such a dependence exists. Since $\varphi(A) = 0$, we have $p \leqslant n$. For small values of n, in the case of matrices with integer entries, the computation is sometimes practicable by the following scheme.

We begin by computing $A^2, A^3, \ldots, A^n$. We then form a row matrix B_i for each A^i (B_0 for I) such that

$$B_i = [A_1{}^i, A_2{}^i, \ldots, A_n{}^i],$$

where $A_j{}^i$ is the jth row of A^i. Thus each row B_i has n^2 elements. Now we form an $(n + 1) \times n^2$ matrix

$$B = \begin{bmatrix} B_0 \\ B_1 \\ \vdots \\ B_n \end{bmatrix}.$$

The problem is to find the smallest integer p such that the first p rows of B are dependent. To record conveniently the row operations required to determine this, we append an identity matrix of order $n + 1$ to B, thus obtaining an $(n + 1) \times (n^2 + n + 1)$ array $[B, I_{n+1}]$. We perform on the identity matrix I_{n+1} the same row operations as on B. However, the dependence of the rows of B is all that is at issue. For example, if

$$A = \begin{bmatrix} -1 & 3 & 0 & 3 \\ -1 & 3 & 1 & 3 \\ 1 & -1 & -2 & 0 \\ 1 & -1 & -1 & -1 \end{bmatrix},$$

we obtain this 5×21 matrix:

I:	1	0	0	0	0	1	0	0	0	0	1	0	0	0	0	1	1	0	0	0	0
A:	-1	3	0	3	-1	3	1	3	1	-1	-2	0	1	-1	-1	-1	0	1	0	0	0
A^2:	1	3	0	3	2	2	-2	3	-2	2	3	0	-2	2	2	1	0	0	1	0	0
A^3:	-1	9	0	9	-3	11	3	9	3	-3	-4	0	3	-3	-3	-1	0	0	0	1	0
A^4:	1	15	0	15	4	12	-4	15	-4	4	5	0	-4	4	4	1	0	0	0	0	1

Now any column among the first n^2, which is linearly dependent on preceding columns, may be deleted without altering the dependence of the rows in any way. This permits the successive deletion of columns 3, 4, 7, 8, 9, 10, 12, 13, 14, 15, 16 in this example, so that only this matrix needs to be considered:

$$\left[\begin{array}{ccccc:ccccc}
1 & 0 & 0 & 1 & 1 & 1 & 0 & 0 & 0 & 0 \\
-1 & 3 & -1 & 3 & -2 & 0 & 1 & 0 & 0 & 0 \\
1 & 3 & 2 & 2 & 3 & 0 & 0 & 1 & 0 & 0 \\
-1 & 9 & -3 & 11 & -4 & 0 & 0 & 0 & 1 & 0 \\
1 & 15 & 4 & 12 & 5 & 0 & 0 & 0 & 0 & 1
\end{array}\right].$$

By sweep-out, *using row operations only*, we now obtain:

$$\left[\begin{array}{ccccc:ccccc}
1 & 0 & 0 & 1 & 1 & 1 & 0 & 0 & 0 & 0 \\
0 & 3 & -1 & 4 & -1 & 1 & 1 & 0 & 0 & 0 \\
0 & 0 & 3 & -3 & 3 & -2 & -1 & 1 & 0 & 0 \\
0 & 0 & 0 & 0 & 0 & -2 & -3 & 0 & 1 & 0 \\
0 & 0 & 0 & 0 & 0 & 0 & -2 & -3 & 0 & 1
\end{array}\right].$$

The 5×5 matrix on the right, being in fact a product of matrices of elementary transformations, records what has been done to the abbreviated rows representing I, A, A^2, A^3, A^4 respectively. Indeed, if we interpret I, A, A^2, A^3, A^4 to mean *rows*, the product

$$\left[\begin{array}{ccccc}
1 & 0 & 0 & 0 & 0 \\
1 & 1 & 0 & 0 & 0 \\
-2 & -1 & 1 & 0 & 0 \\
-2 & -3 & 0 & 1 & 0 \\
0 & -2 & -3 & 0 & 1
\end{array}\right] \cdot \left[\begin{array}{c}
I \\
A \\
A^2 \\
A^3 \\
A^4
\end{array}\right]$$

represents exactly what we must do to the original array in order to reduce rows four and five to rows of zeros. From the fourth row, we have, then,

$$-2I - 3A + 0 \cdot A^2 + A^3 + 0 \cdot A^4 = 0,$$

that is,

(8.7.1) $$A^3 - 3A - 2I = 0,$$

so that the minimal equation is

$$\lambda^3 - 3\lambda - 2 = 0,$$

with roots -1, -1, 2.

Notice that the fifth row yields

$$A^4 - 3A^2 - 2A = 0,$$

which is an immediate consequence of the equation (8.7.1) yielded by row four.

Although this method of finding the minimum polynomial is perfectly general, the computational difficulties increase rapidly with n, as is the case with most matrix calculations. This explains why effective procedures for use with digital computers are so essential.

8.8 Characteristic Roots of a Polynomial Function of a Matrix A

The following theorem, for which Exercises 9 and 15, Section 8.3 have been preparation, is also useful in applications:

Theorem 8.8.1: *If $\lambda_1, \lambda_2, \ldots, \lambda_n$ are the characteristic roots, distinct or not, of a matrix A of order n, and if $g(A)$ is any polynomial function of A, then the characteristic roots of $g(A)$ are $g(\lambda_1), g(\lambda_2), \ldots, g(\lambda_n)$.*

We know that

$$\det (A - \lambda I_n) \equiv (-1)^n(\lambda - \lambda_1)(\lambda - \lambda_2) \cdots (\lambda - \lambda_n),$$

and we wish to prove that, for any polynomial function $g(A)$,

$$\det (g(A) - \lambda I_n) \equiv (-1)^n(\lambda - g(\lambda_1))(\lambda - g(\lambda_2)) \cdots (\lambda - g(\lambda_n)).$$

Now suppose that $g(x)$ is of degree r in x and that, for a fixed value of λ, the roots of $g(x) - \lambda = 0$ are $x_1, x_2, \ldots, x_r$. Then we have

$$g(x) - \lambda \equiv \alpha(x - x_1)(x - x_2) \cdots (x - x_r),$$

where α is the coefficient of x^r in $g(x)$. Hence

$$g(A) - \lambda I_n \equiv \alpha(A - x_1 I_n)(A - x_2 I_n) \cdots (A - x_r I_n),$$

so that, if $\varphi(\lambda)$ is the characteristic polynomial of A,

$$\det (g(A) - \lambda I_n) = \alpha^n \det (A - x_1 I_n) \det (A - x_2 I_n) \cdots \det (A - x_r I_n)$$

$$= \alpha^n \varphi(x_1)\, \varphi(x_2) \cdots \varphi(x_r)$$

$$= \alpha^n(-1)^n(x_1 - \lambda_1)(x_1 - \lambda_2) \cdots (x_1 - \lambda_n)$$

$$\times (-1)^n(x_2 - \lambda_1)(x_2 - \lambda_2) \cdots (x_2 - \lambda_n)$$

$$\vdots$$

$$\times (-1)^n(x_r - \lambda_1)(x_r - \lambda_2) \cdots (x_r - \lambda_n).$$

By rearranging the orders and the signs of the factors, we now obtain

$$\det (g(A) - \lambda I_n) = \alpha(\lambda_1 - x_1)(\lambda_1 - x_2) \cdots (\lambda_1 - x_r)$$
$$\times \alpha(\lambda_2 - x_1)(\lambda_2 - x_2) \cdots (\lambda_2 - x_r)$$
$$\vdots$$
$$\times \alpha(\lambda_n - x_1)(\lambda_n - x_2) \cdots (\lambda_n - x_r)$$
$$= (g(\lambda_1) - \lambda)(g(\lambda_2) - \lambda) \cdots (g(\lambda_n) - \lambda),$$

and this relation holds true for each value of λ. Thus

$$\det (g(A) - \lambda I_n) \equiv (-1)^n(\lambda - g(\lambda_1))(\lambda - g(\lambda_2)) \cdots (\lambda - g(\lambda_n)),$$

as was to be proved.

8.9 Exercises

1. Given that

$$A = \begin{bmatrix} 1 & \sqrt{3} & 0 \\ \sqrt{3} & -1 & 0 \\ 0 & 0 & 1 \end{bmatrix}, \qquad g(A) = A^2 + A + I,$$

find the characteristic roots of A and of $g(A)$.

*2. Why may Theorem 8.8.1 *not* be used to prove that the characteristic roots of A^{-1}, when A is nonsingular, are the reciprocals of those of A? (See Exercise 14, Section 8.3.)

*3. Prove that the characteristic roots of A^p are $\lambda_1{}^p, \lambda_2{}^p, \ldots, \lambda_n{}^p$ where $\lambda_1, \lambda_2, \ldots, \lambda_n$ are those of A and p is any positive integer, whether or not the λ's are distinct. Using Exercise 14, Section 8.3, show that the result also holds true for p zero or a negative integer if A is nonsingular. (See also Exercise 9, Section 8.3.)

*4. Prove that if $AX = \lambda X$, then $A^2X = \lambda^2 X$ and, in fact, $A^pX = \lambda^p X$ for every positive integer p. Hence show that, if $AX = \lambda X$ and if $f(A)$ is any polynomial function of A, then $f(A)X = f(\lambda)X$. What is the geometrical interpretation of this?

5. Find A^3 and A^4, where A is the matrix given in Exercise 1, by the method of Section 8.6.

6. In proving the Cayley-Hamilton theorem, we in effect assumed that, if $F_0, F_1, \ldots, F_p$ and $G_0, G_1, \ldots, G_p$ are fixed matrices of order n, and if

$$F_0 + F_1\lambda + \cdots + F_p\lambda^p \equiv G_0 + G_1\lambda + \cdots + G_p\lambda^p,$$

that is, if these two polynomials yield the same matrix for all values of the scalar λ, then we must have $F_0 = G_0, F_1 = G_1, \ldots, F_p = G_p$. This is equivalent to the fact that, if $H_0, H_1, \ldots, H_p$ are matrices of order n, then $H_0 + H_1\lambda + \cdots + H_p\lambda^p \equiv 0$ if and only if $H_0 = H_1 = \cdots = H_p = 0$. Show that this last result follows from the corresponding fact for ordinary polynomials.

*7. The determination of the values of λ and the associated vectors X which satisfy the equation

$$AX = \lambda BX$$

is the **generalized characteristic value problem**. In the most important applications, B is nonsingular. Show that, if also $AB = BA$ and A and B have distinct characteristic roots, the "characteristic roots" are given by $\lambda_j = \mu_j/\nu_{k_j}$, where the μ_j's are the characteristic roots of A and the ν_{k_j}'s are those of B, in a suitable order.

8. Show that the characteristic vectors of A are all characteristic vectors of $g(A)$, where $g(A)$ is any polynomial function of A. Show by an example (for example, a matrix A such that $A^2 = 0$) that the converse is not true for all A and $g(A)$. One can also choose g so that $g(\lambda_1) = g(\lambda_2)$, with $\lambda_1 \neq \lambda_2$.

9. Compute $\varphi(\lambda)$ with the aid of (8.6.8) if

$$
A = \begin{bmatrix} 1 & 0 & 1 \\ -1 & -1 & 0 \\ 0 & 1 & 1 \end{bmatrix}.
$$

10. With the aid of Exercise 10, Section 8.3, show that every polynomial equation of degree n in an unknown matrix A of order n has at least one solution.

11. Compute the minimum polynomial of the matrix

$$
\begin{bmatrix} 0 & 1 & 0 & 0 & 0 \\ 0 & 0 & 1 & 0 & 0 \\ 1 & 0 & 0 & 0 & 0 \\ 0 & 0 & 0 & 0 & 1 \\ 0 & 0 & 0 & 1 & 0 \end{bmatrix}
$$

by the method given in Section 8.7.

12. Prove that $\operatorname{tr}(A^p) = \sum \lambda_j^p$, where the λ_j's are the characteristic roots of A. Then prove $\sum \lambda_j^2 = (\sum \lambda_j)^2 - 2 \sum_{i<j} \lambda_i \lambda_j$, so that

$$
\sum_{i<j} \lambda_i \lambda_j = \tfrac{1}{2}((\operatorname{tr} A)^2 - \operatorname{tr}(A^2)).
$$

(By Newton's formulas expressing arbitrary symmetric functions of the roots in terms of sums of powers, all symmetric functions, and hence the coefficients of the characteristic polynomial itself, can be expressed in terms of the traces of the powers of A.)

13. Find the powers and the characteristic roots of the powers of the cyclic permutation matrix

$$
\begin{bmatrix} 0 & 1 & 0 & 0 & 0 \\ 0 & 0 & 1 & 0 & 0 \\ 0 & 0 & 0 & 1 & 0 \\ 0 & 0 & 0 & 0 & 1 \\ 1 & 0 & 0 & 0 & 0 \end{bmatrix}.
$$

14. A matrix A is said to be **diagonalizable** if there exists a matrix B such that $B^{-1}AB = D[d_1, d_2, \ldots, d_n]$. Let A be diagonalizable and let $\varphi(\lambda) = 0$ be the characteristic equation of A. Show that $\varphi(D) = 0$ and hence that $\varphi(BDB^{-1}) = 0$, that is, $\varphi(A) = 0$. This proves the Cayley-Hamilton theorem for a diagonalizable matrix.

HERMITIAN AND REAL SYMMETRIC MATRICES

8.10 The Characteristic Roots of a Hermitian Matrix

A Hermitian matrix has been defined as one which is equal to its tranjugate: $A = A^*$. Concerning such matrices, which include real symmetric matrices as a special case, we prove first

Theorem 8.10.1:   *The characteristic roots of a Hermitian matrix are all real.*

Let A be Hermitian, let λ be any root of the characteristic equation of A and let Y be an associated *unit* characteristic vector. Then from the equation

$$(8.10.1) \qquad\qquad AY = \lambda Y,$$

we deduce

$$(8.10.2) \qquad\qquad Y^*AY = \lambda Y^*Y = \lambda.$$

But we also have, since $A = A^*$ and Y^*AY is a scalar,

$$Y^*AY = Y^*A^*Y = (Y^*AY)^* = \overline{Y^*AY}.$$

Thus, the scalar Y^*AY is equal to its own conjugate and hence is real. That is, by (8.10.2), λ is real.

As a special case, we have

Theorem 8.10.2:   *The characteristic roots of a real symmetric matrix are all real.*

Because in this case all the coefficients in the system of equations $AX = \lambda X$ are real, we have also

Theorem 8.10.3:   *The linear spaces of characteristic vectors of a real symmetric matrix may all be spanned by real vectors.*

We prove next

Theorem 8.10.4:   *If X and Y are characteristic vectors associated with distinct characteristic roots λ and μ of a Hermitian matrix A, then X and Y are orthogonal.*

Suppose in fact that

$$AX = \lambda X \qquad \text{and} \qquad AY = \mu Y, \qquad \lambda \neq \mu.$$

Then from these equations, we have,

$$Y^*AX = \lambda Y^*X \quad \text{and} \quad X^*A Y = \mu X^*Y.$$

Forming the transposed conjugate of the first of these equations, we have

$$X^*A Y = \lambda X^*Y,$$

since $A = A^*$ and λ is real. It then follows that

$$\mu X^*Y = \lambda X^*Y,$$

so that, since $\lambda \neq \mu$, we must have

$$X^*Y = 0,$$

that is, X and Y are orthogonal.

Again, an important special case is:

Theorem 8.10.5: *Characteristic vectors associated with distinct characteristic roots of a real symmetric matrix are orthogonal.*

8.11 Exercises

1. Prove that, if $A^* = -A$, the nonzero characteristic roots of A are pure imaginaries which occur in conjugate pairs if A is real.

2. Prove that, if $X_1 + iX_2$, where X_1 and X_2 are real, is a complex characteristic vector associated with a complex characteristic root $\lambda_1 + i\lambda_2$ of a *real* matrix A, then AX_1 and AX_2 are both linear combinations of X_1 and X_2.

3. Determine the characteristic roots and vectors of the Hermitian matrix

$$\begin{bmatrix} 1 & 0 & 0 \\ 0 & 0 & \omega^2 \\ 0 & \omega & 0 \end{bmatrix},$$

where ω is a complex cube root of unity: $\omega = e^{2\pi i/3}$.

*4. By Descartes' rule of signs, show that a Hermitian or real symmetric matrix has all positive characteristic roots if and only if the coefficients of $\varphi(\lambda)$ alternate in sign. Show also that Descartes' rule gives the exact numbers of positive and negative roots.

5. Prove that the characteristic roots of A^*A are all nonnegative.

6. Show that a real, skew-symmetric matrix has an even or odd number of zero characteristic roots according as its order is even or odd and, hence, that its rank is even. (Use Exercise 1.)

7. Prove that the characteristic roots of a real symmetric matrix A are all equal if and only if A is scalar.

8. Prove that a real symmetric matrix is the matrix of a projection if and only if each characteristic root of A is 0 or 1.

9. Given that A is a real orthogonal matrix and that $X + iY$ is a characteristic vector associated with the root $\alpha + i\beta$, $\beta \neq 0$, prove that $X^{\mathsf{T}}Y = 0$ and that $X^{\mathsf{T}}X = Y^{\mathsf{T}}Y$.

8.12 The Diagonal Form of a Hermitian Matrix

In the following, the notation $D[\lambda_1, \lambda_2, \ldots, \lambda_n]$ for a diagonal matrix with diagonal elements $\lambda_1, \lambda_2, \ldots, \lambda_n$ will be useful.

We prove first an existence theorem:

Theorem 8.12.1: *If A is Hermitian, there exists a unitary matrix U such that $U*AU$ is a diagonal matrix whose diagonal elements are the characteristic roots of A: $U*AU = D[\lambda_1, \lambda_2, \ldots, \lambda_n]$.*

We shall prove the theorem by induction on the order of A, and then later show how the matrix U may be computed.

First we observe that, if A is Hermitian, and if V is any matrix of order n, then $V*AV$ is also Hermitian since $(V*AV)* = V*A*(V*)* = V*AV$ because $A* = A$. From this we have the result that if $V*AV = B$ and $b_{21} = b_{31} = \cdots = b_{n1} = 0$, then, if A is Hermitian, $b_{12} = b_{13} = \cdots = b_{1n} = 0$ also.

A second observation useful in our proof is that, if V is unitary and if $V*AV = B$, where B is diagonal, then the diagonal elements of B are necessarily the characteristic roots of A (Exercise 17, Section 8.3).

In case A is of order 2, we must show there exists a unitary matrix U of order 2 such that

$$U*AU = D[\lambda_1, \lambda_2],$$

where λ_1 and λ_2 are the characteristic roots of A. That is, since $U* = U^{-1}$, we must show there exists a unitary matrix U such that

$$\begin{bmatrix} a_{11} & a_{12} \\ a_{21} & a_{22} \end{bmatrix} \cdot \begin{bmatrix} u_{11} & u_{12} \\ u_{21} & u_{22} \end{bmatrix} = \begin{bmatrix} u_{11} & u_{12} \\ u_{21} & u_{22} \end{bmatrix} \cdot \begin{bmatrix} \lambda_1 & 0 \\ 0 & \lambda_2 \end{bmatrix}.$$

Forming both products and equating their first columns, we obtain the equations

$$(a_{11} - \lambda_1)u_{11} + a_{12}u_{21} = 0,$$

$$a_{21}u_{11} + (a_{22} - \lambda_1)u_{21} = 0,$$

which have nontrivial solutions for u_{11}, u_{21} since λ_1 is a characteristic root of A. We select one of these solutions for the first column of U. Since the equations are homogeneous, this solution may be assumed normalized, that is, we may assume $\{u_{11}, u_{21}\}$ is a unit 2-vector, so that

$$\bar{u}_{11}u_{11} + \bar{u}_{21}u_{21} = 1.$$

Now we use for the second column of U any unit vector orthogonal to the first, so that

$$\bar{u}_{12}u_{12} + \bar{u}_{22}u_{22} = 1, \qquad \bar{u}_{11}u_{12} + \bar{u}_{21}u_{22} = 0.$$

Because it then has mutually orthogonal unit vectors as columns, U is a unitary matrix. Also, the product U^*AU has as its first column the vector $\{\lambda_1, 0\}$. By the first observation above, it then follows that the 1, 2-entry of this product is also zero, and, therefore, from the second observation we conclude that the lower right element is necessarily λ_2. This proves the theorem for $n = 2$.

Now let $n - 1$ be any integer $\geqslant 2$ such that the theorem holds true for all Hermitian matrices of order $n - 1$, and let A be any Hermitian matrix of order n. We shall determine first a unitary matrix V such that

$$V^*AV = \begin{bmatrix} \lambda_1 & \vdots & 0 \\ \cdots & \vdots & \cdots \\ 0 & \vdots & B \end{bmatrix},$$

that is, such that

$$AV = V \begin{bmatrix} \lambda_1 & \vdots & 0 \\ \cdots & \vdots & \cdots \\ 0 & \vdots & B \end{bmatrix},$$

where λ_1 is any characteristic root of A and B is a matrix of order $n - 1$.

Once again, we equate the elements of the first columns of the left and right members of this last equation and obtain the equations

$$(a_{11} - \lambda_1)v_{11} + a_{12}v_{21} + \cdots + a_{1n}v_{n1} = 0,$$

$$a_{21}v_{11} + (a_{22} - \lambda_1)v_{21} + \cdots + a_{2n}v_{n1} = 0,$$

$$\vdots$$

$$a_{n1}v_{11} + a_{n2}v_{21} + \cdots + (a_{nn} - \lambda_1)v_{n1} = 0,$$

for the determination of the first column $V_1 = \{v_{11}, v_{21}, \ldots, v_{n1}\}$ of V. Since λ_1 is a characteristic root of A, this homogeneous system has nontrivial solutions, one of which we normalize and use for V_1.

The remaining columns of V we simply choose in such a way that $V_1, V_2, \ldots, V_n$ form a set of mutually orthogonal unit vectors so that V is indeed unitary (Theorem 7.16.1).

It now follows from the first observation at the beginning of this proof that V^*AV actually has the required form

$$\begin{bmatrix} \lambda_1 & \vdots & 0 \\ \cdots & \vdots & \cdots \\ 0 & \vdots & B \end{bmatrix}.$$

Since V^*AV is Hermitian, B must be Hermitian also. Furthermore, by an argument like that used in the second observation above, it follows that the characteristic roots of B are just the remaining characteristic roots

$\lambda_2, \lambda_3, \ldots, \lambda_n$ of A. Hence, by the induction hypothesis, there exists a unitary matrix W of order $n - 1$ such that

$$W*BW = D[\lambda_2, \lambda_3, \ldots, \lambda_n].$$

It then follows that

$$\begin{bmatrix} 1 & 0 \\ \hline 0 & W* \end{bmatrix} V*AV \begin{bmatrix} 1 & 0 \\ \hline 0 & W \end{bmatrix} = \begin{bmatrix} 1 & 0 \\ \hline 0 & W* \end{bmatrix} \cdot \begin{bmatrix} \lambda_1 & 0 \\ \hline 0 & B \end{bmatrix} \cdot \begin{bmatrix} 1 & 0 \\ \hline 0 & W \end{bmatrix}$$

$$= \begin{bmatrix} \lambda_1 & 0 \\ \hline 0 & W*BW \end{bmatrix} = D[\lambda_1, \lambda_2, \ldots, \lambda_n].$$

Thus the unitary matrix

$$U = V \begin{bmatrix} 1 & 0 \\ \hline 0 & W \end{bmatrix}$$

has the property stated in the theorem, which is therefore true for all positive integers $n \geqslant 2$.

Specializing once again to the real case, we have

Theorem 8.12.2: *If A is a real symmetric matrix, there exists an orthogonal matrix U such that $U^{\mathsf{T}}AU$ is a diagonal matrix whose diagonal elements are the characteristic roots of A.*

The geometric interpretation of this result is simple. Let A be the matrix of a real symmetric linear operator in the natural reference system. If U is the matrix of an orthogonal transformation of coordinates, then the matrix representing the operator in the new coordinate system is $U^{\mathsf{T}}AU$, since $U^{-1} = U^{\mathsf{T}}$ here. Because all characteristic roots of a real symmetric matrix are real, the theorem says that, given a symmetric linear operator over the real field, we can always find a reference system in $\mathscr{E}_n$ in which the matrix of that operator is diagonal. In this reference system, the effect of the operator is simply to multiply each component of a vector by a factor which is one of the characteristic roots of the operator.

Theorem 8.12.3: *The unitary matrix U of Theorem 8.12.1 may be chosen so that the characteristic roots $\lambda_1, \lambda_2, \ldots, \lambda_n$ appear in any desired order in the diagonal matrix $U*AU$.*

This follows from the mode of proof of Theorem 8.12.1, and it also follows readily from the fact that a permutation matrix, which one may use to permute the rows or columns of a given matrix, is unitary. The reader may supply the details.

8.13 The Diagonalization of a Hermitian Matrix

Theorem 8.12.1 permits us now to deduce a chain of theorems which show how the matrix U of that theorem may be computed. First we prove

Theorem 8.13.1: *If λ_1 is a k_1-fold characteristic root of a Hermitian matrix A, then the rank of $A - \lambda_1 I_n$ is $n - k_1$.*

By Theorems 8.12.1 and 8.12.3, there exists a unitary matrix U such that

$$U^*AU = D[\lambda_1, \lambda_1, \ldots, \lambda_1; \lambda_{k_1+1}, \ldots, \lambda_n],$$

the λ_1 occurring k_1 times and $\lambda_{k_1+1}, \ldots, \lambda_n$ all being distinct from λ_1. Since U is unitary, subtracting $\lambda_1 I_n$ from both sides of this equation gives

$$U^*(A - \lambda_1 I_n)U = D[0, 0, \ldots, 0; (\lambda_{k_1+1} - \lambda_1), \ldots, (\lambda_n - \lambda_1)].$$

From this, since U is nonsingular, it follows that the rank of $A - \lambda_1 I_n$ is the same as that of the matrix on the right, which is precisely $n - k_1$ since $(\lambda_{k_1+1} - \lambda_1), \ldots, (\lambda_n - \lambda_1)$ are all unequal to zero.

An immediate consequence is

Theorem 8.13.2: *If λ_1 is a k_1-fold characteristic root of a Hermitian matrix A, there exist k_1 linearly independent characteristic vectors of A associated with λ_1, that is, with λ_1 there is associated a k_1 dimensional space of characteristic vectors.*

We have next

Theorem 8.13.3: *With every Hermitian matrix A we can associate an orthonormal set of n characteristic vectors.*

The characteristic vectors associated with a given characteristic root of A form a vector space for which we can construct an orthonormal basis, by the Gram-Schmidt process if necessary. For each A, there are altogether n vectors in the bases so constructed, by the preceding theorem. Since characteristic vectors associated with distinct characteristic roots of a Hermitian matrix are orthogonal, it follows then that these n basis vectors will serve as the orthonormal set mentioned in the theorem.

This result indicates how the diagonalization process may be effected. For let the n vectors of such an orthonormal system be $U_1, U_2, \ldots, U_n$. Then

(8.13.1) $$AU_j = \lambda_j U_j, \qquad j = 1, 2, \ldots, n,$$

where, in each case, λ_j is the characteristic root associated with U_j. Hence, if

$$U = [U_1, U_2, \ldots, U_n],$$

equations (8.13.1) may be combined in the single equation

$$[AU_1, AU_2, \ldots, AU_n] = [\lambda_1 U_1, \lambda_2 U_2, \ldots, \lambda_n U_n],$$

or

$$AU = UD[\lambda_1, \lambda_2, \ldots, \lambda_n],$$

or, since U is unitary by construction,

$$U^*AU = D[\lambda_1, \lambda_2, \ldots, \lambda_n].$$

We summarize in

Theorem 8.13.4: *If $U_1, U_2, \ldots, U_n$ is an orthonormal system of characteristic vectors associated respectively with the characteristic roots $\lambda_1, \lambda_2, \ldots, \lambda_n$ of a Hermitian matrix A, and if U is the unitary matrix $[U_1, U_2, \ldots, U_n]$, then*

$$U^*AU = D[\lambda_1, \lambda_2, \ldots, \lambda_n].$$

The vectors $U_1, U_2, \ldots, U_n$ are often called a set of **principal axes** of A and the transformation with matrix U used to diagonalize A is called a **principal axis transformation**.

8.14 Examples

We illustrate the preceding theorem with some examples of the real symmetric case.

(a) Let

$$A = \begin{bmatrix} 1 & 2 \\ 2 & 1 \end{bmatrix},$$

so that $\varphi(\lambda) = (\lambda - 3)(\lambda + 1)$. Then normalized characteristic vectors associated with the characteristic roots 3 and -1 are respectively,

$$\begin{bmatrix} \dfrac{1}{\sqrt{2}} \\[2mm] \dfrac{1}{\sqrt{2}} \end{bmatrix} \quad \text{and} \quad \begin{bmatrix} \dfrac{-1}{\sqrt{2}} \\[2mm] \dfrac{1}{\sqrt{2}} \end{bmatrix},$$

so that we may put

$$U = \begin{bmatrix} \dfrac{1}{\sqrt{2}} & \dfrac{-1}{\sqrt{2}} \\[2mm] \dfrac{1}{\sqrt{2}} & \dfrac{1}{\sqrt{2}} \end{bmatrix}.$$

It is then easy to verify that $U^*AU = D[3, -1]$ by computing the product.

(b) Let

$$A = \begin{bmatrix} 5 & 2 & 0 & 0 \\ 2 & 2 & 0 & 0 \\ 0 & 0 & 5 & -2 \\ 0 & 0 & -2 & 2 \end{bmatrix}.$$

Then the characteristic roots are 1, 1, 6, 6. Putting $\lambda = 1$ in $AX = \lambda X$, we obtain the system of equations

$$
\begin{aligned}
4x_1 + 2x_2 \quad\quad\quad\quad &= 0, \\
2x_1 + x_2 \quad\quad\quad\quad &= 0, \\
4x_3 - 2x_4 &= 0, \\
-2x_3 + x_4 &= 0,
\end{aligned}
$$

with the complete solution

$$X = k_1 \begin{bmatrix} 1 \\ -2 \\ 0 \\ 0 \end{bmatrix} + k_2 \begin{bmatrix} 0 \\ 0 \\ 1 \\ 2 \end{bmatrix}.$$

The basis vectors here are already orthogonal so that we need only normalize them to obtain two columns of U

$$U_1 = \left\{ \frac{1}{\sqrt{5}}, \frac{-2}{\sqrt{5}}, 0, 0 \right\}, \quad U_2 = \left\{ 0, 0, \frac{1}{\sqrt{5}}, \frac{2}{\sqrt{5}} \right\}.$$

Proceeding in the same fashion with the root $\lambda = 6$, we obtain for the other two columns of U

$$U_3 = \left\{ \frac{2}{\sqrt{5}}, \frac{1}{\sqrt{5}}, 0, 0 \right\}, \quad U_4 = \left\{ 0, 0, \frac{-2}{\sqrt{5}}, \frac{1}{\sqrt{5}} \right\}.$$

Then if $U = [U_1, U_2, U_3, U_4]$, it is easy to check that

$$U^*AU = D[1, 1, 6, 6].$$

NORMAL MATRICES

8.15 Triangularization of an Arbitrary Matrix

Not every matrix can be reduced to diagonal form by a unitary transformation. On the other hand, it is always possible to attain a triangular form:

Theorem 8.15.1: *Every square matrix A over the complex field can be reduced by a unitary transformation to upper triangular form with the characteristic roots on the diagonal.*

The theorem is proved by induction. We begin with the case $n = 2$. Let A have characteristic roots λ_1, λ_2. With λ_1 we can associate a unit characteristic vector U_1. (It may be that A has only one independent characteristic vector, but it has at least one.) Let U_2 be any unit vector orthogonal to U_1. Then $U = [U_1, U_2]$ is unitary. Moreover

$$U*AU = \begin{bmatrix} U_1{}^* \\ U_2{}^* \end{bmatrix} \cdot [AU_1, AU_2] = \begin{bmatrix} U_1{}^*AU_1 & U_1{}^*AU_2 \\ U_2{}^*AU_1 & U_2{}^*AU_2 \end{bmatrix}.$$

Since $AU_1 = \lambda_1 U_1$, $U_1{}^*U_1 = 1$, and $U_2{}^*U_1 = 0$, this reduces to

$$U*AU = \begin{bmatrix} \lambda_1 & U_1{}^*AU_2 \\ 0 & U_2{}^*AU_2 \end{bmatrix}.$$

Since A and $U*AU$ have the same characteristic roots, it now follows that $U_2{}^*AU_2 = \lambda_2$, and the theorem is proved for $n = 2$.

Now suppose the result holds for all matrices of order $n - 1$, and let A be of order n. Let λ_1 be any characteristic root of A, and let U_1 denote a corresponding unit characteristic vector. Let $U_2, \ldots, U_n$ be so chosen that $U_1, U_2, \ldots, U_n$ is an orthonormal set, that is, so that $U = [U_1, U_2, \ldots, U_n]$ is unitary. Then, just as in the case where $n = 2$, we obtain

$$U*AU = \begin{bmatrix} \lambda_1 & U_1{}^*AU_2 & \cdots & U_1{}^*AU_n \\ 0 & U_2{}^*AU_2 & \cdots & U_2{}^*AU_n \\ \vdots & & & \\ 0 & U_n{}^*AU_2 & \cdots & U_n{}^*AU_n \end{bmatrix} = \begin{bmatrix} \lambda_1 & B \\ \hline 0 & C \end{bmatrix}.$$

By the induction hypothesis, there exists a unitary matrix W of order $n - 1$ which will triangularize the lower right submatrix of order $n - 1$. Let

$$V = \begin{bmatrix} 1 & 0 \\ \hline 0 & W \end{bmatrix}.$$

Then V is unitary and

$$V*(U*AU)V = \begin{bmatrix} 1 & 0 \\ \hline 0 & W^* \end{bmatrix} \cdot \begin{bmatrix} \lambda_1 & B \\ \hline 0 & C \end{bmatrix} \cdot \begin{bmatrix} 1 & 0 \\ \hline 0 & W \end{bmatrix} = \begin{bmatrix} \lambda_1 & B \\ \hline 0 & W^*CW \end{bmatrix},$$

where W^*CW is upper triangular. Introducing symbols b_{ij} to simplify the notation, we can rewrite this in the form

(8.15.1)
$$(UV)^*A(UV) = \begin{bmatrix} \lambda_1 & b_{12} & b_{13} & \cdots & b_{1n} \\ 0 & \lambda_2 & b_{23} & \cdots & b_{2n} \\ \vdots & & & & \\ 0 & 0 & 0 & \cdots & \lambda_n \end{bmatrix}.$$

Since UV is unitary, the characteristic roots of the triangular matrix are the same as those of A, that is, the diagonal elements are indeed the λ's, and the theorem is proved.

This theorem is often used in deriving other important results, as is illustrated in the next section.

8.16 Normal Matrices

A matrix A is said to be **normal** if and only if

$$A^*A = AA^*.$$

Simple examples are unitary, Hermitian, and skew-Hermitian matrices. So are diagonal matrices with arbitrary diagonal elements, which are not necessarily unitary, Hermitian or skew-Hermitian. We prove first

Theorem 8.16.1:   *If U is unitary, then A is normal if and only if U^*AU is normal.*

We have

$$(U^*AU)^*(U^*AU) = U^*A^*AU,$$

and

$$(U^*AU)(U^*AU)^* = U^*AA^*U.$$

Now $A^*A = AA^*$ if and only if $U^*A^*AU = U^*AA^*U$, which proves the theorem.

The importance of the concept of normality is indicated by

Theorem 8.16.2:   *A matrix A over the complex field can be diagonalized by a unitary transformation if and only if A is normal.*

First, suppose U is unitary and $U^*AU = D[\lambda_1, \lambda_2, \ldots, \lambda_n]$. Then $A = UDU^*$ and $A^*A = UD^*DU$, while $AA^* = UDD^*U$. But D and D^*, being diagonal, commute. Hence $A^*A = AA^*$ and A is normal.

Conversely, suppose A is normal. Then, by Theorem 8.15.1 there exists a unitary matrix U such that $U^*AU = B$, where B is upper triangular and, by Theorem 8.16.1, B is also normal. Let

$$
B = \begin{bmatrix}
\lambda_1 & b_{12} & b_{13} & \cdots & b_{1n} \\
0 & \lambda_2 & b_{23} & \cdots & b_{2n} \\
\vdots & & & & \\
0 & 0 & 0 & \cdots & \lambda_n
\end{bmatrix}.
$$

Since $B^*B = BB^*$, we have from the 1, 1-entries that

$$
\bar{\lambda}_1 \lambda_1 = \lambda_1 \bar{\lambda}_1 + b_{12}\bar{b}_{12} + \cdots + b_{1n}\bar{b}_{1n},
$$

or

$$
0 = |b_{12}|^2 + |b_{13}|^2 + \cdots + |b_{1n}|^2,
$$

which implies that $b_{12} = b_{13} = \cdots = b_{1n} = 0$. In the same way, comparison of the 2, 2-entries now implies that $b_{23} = b_{24} = \cdots = b_{2n} = 0$, and so on, for all entries above the diagonal. That is, the assumption that A is normal implies that B is diagonal and the theorem is proved.

We have thus characterized fully the class of matrices which can be diagonalized by unitary transformations.

8.17 Exercises

*1. Show that the determinant, the trace, and the characteristic polynomial of a linear operator are invariant under any nonsingular transformation of coordinates.

2. Show that, if $U_1{}^*A_1U_1 = D[\lambda_1, \ldots, \lambda_k]$ and $U_2{}^*A_2U_2 = D[\lambda_{k+1}, \ldots, \lambda_n]$, then

$$
\begin{bmatrix} U_1 & 0 \\ 0 & U_2 \end{bmatrix}^* \cdot \begin{bmatrix} A_1 & 0 \\ 0 & A_2 \end{bmatrix} \cdot \begin{bmatrix} U_1 & 0 \\ 0 & U_2 \end{bmatrix} = D[\lambda_1, \ldots, \lambda_k, \lambda_{k+1}, \ldots, \lambda_n].
$$

3. Show that, if there exists a nonsingular matrix C such that

$$
C^{-1}AC = D[\lambda_1, \ldots, \lambda_n] \quad \text{and} \quad C^{-1}BC = D[\mu_1, \ldots, \mu_n],
$$

then $AB = BA$ and the characteristic roots of AB are $\lambda_1\mu_1, \lambda_2\mu_2, \ldots, \lambda_n\mu_n$.

4. Show that, if U is a unitary matrix such that $U^*AU = D[\lambda_1, \lambda_2, \ldots, \lambda_n]$, then $U^*A^*U = D[\bar{\lambda}_1, \bar{\lambda}_2, \ldots, \bar{\lambda}_n]$, and if A is nonsingular, $U^*A^{-1}U = D[\lambda_1{}^{-1}, \lambda_2{}^{-1}, \ldots, \lambda_n{}^{-1}]$.

5. Show that, if λ is a characteristic root of a unitary matrix, then $|\lambda| = 1$ so that if λ is real, λ must be 1 or -1.

6. Show that, if A is a real, orthogonal matrix of odd order, then A has 1 or -1 as a characteristic root depending on whether det A is 1 or -1.

7. Find unitary matrices which diagonalize the matrices

(a) $\begin{bmatrix} 1 & -1 & 0 \\ -1 & 1 & 0 \\ 0 & 0 & 1 \end{bmatrix}$,   (b) $\begin{bmatrix} 4 & 1 & 0 \\ 1 & 4 & 0 \\ 0 & 0 & 4 \end{bmatrix}$,   (c) $\begin{bmatrix} 4 & 1 & 0 & 0 \\ 1 & 2 & 0 & 0 \\ 0 & 0 & 3 & -1 \\ 0 & 0 & -1 & 3 \end{bmatrix}$.

8. Diagonalize this matrix, the characteristic roots of which are irrational:

$$\begin{bmatrix} 0 & 2 & 4 \\ 2 & 0 & 8 \\ 4 & 8 & 0 \end{bmatrix}.$$

*9. Show that, if

$$A = \begin{bmatrix} 1 & 1 \\ 0 & 1 \end{bmatrix},$$

there exists no nonsingular matrix B of order 2 such that $B^{-1}AB = D[d_1, d_2]$. This example shows that *not every square matrix can be diagonalized by a non-singular transformation of coordinates.*

10. Use Theorem 8.15.1 to construct an example of the triangularization of a 3×3 non-Hermitian matrix. (That is, start with the triangular form, pick an arbitrary unitary matrix, etc.)

11. Show that, if a Hermitian matrix H has characteristic roots $\lambda_1, \lambda_2, \ldots, \lambda_n$ such that $|\lambda_j| < 1$ for all j, then as $p \to \infty$, each element of H^p approaches zero.

12. If U^*AU is diagonal, where U is unitary, and if

$$B = \begin{bmatrix} A & 0 \\ 0 & D[\alpha_1, \alpha_2, \ldots, \alpha_n] \end{bmatrix},$$

what transformation will diagonalize B?

13. Let A be a symmetric matrix and let $U_1, U_2, \ldots, U_n$ be an orthonormal set of characteristic vectors corresponding to the characteristic roots $\lambda_1, \lambda_2, \ldots, \lambda_n$ respectively. Show that the solution of

$$(A - \lambda I)X = B, \qquad \lambda \neq \lambda_j, \qquad j = 1, 2, \ldots, n,$$

is given by

$$X = \sum_{j=1}^{n} \frac{U_j^{\mathsf{T}}B}{\lambda_j - \lambda} U_j.$$

14. Find a unitary transformation U such that

$$U^* \begin{bmatrix} a & -b \\ b & a \end{bmatrix} U = \begin{bmatrix} \lambda_1 & 0 \\ 0 & \lambda_2 \end{bmatrix},$$

where a and b are real numbers.

15. Show that, if A has distinct characteristic roots, then there exists a *unique* unitary matrix U such that

$$U^*AU = D[\lambda_1, \lambda_2, \ldots, \lambda_n],$$

where the λ's appear *in a specified order* on the right.

16. Prove that, if B is nonsingular and commutes with A, and if U diagonalizes A, then BU also diagonalizes A.

17. Prove that a real symmetric matrix is also orthogonal if and only if its characteristic roots are all ± 1. Use the argument of the proof to help you construct an example of a real, symmetric, orthogonal matrix of order 3.

*18. Given that U^*AU is diagonal, where U is unitary, obtain a simple formula for A^p, where p is any positive integer.

19. Let A be a Hermitian matrix with characteristic roots $\lambda_1, \lambda_2, \ldots, \lambda_r, 0, 0, \ldots, 0$, where no λ_j is 0. Prove that A has rank r.

20. Prove that, if A and B are Hermitian matrices with the same characteristic roots $\lambda_1, \lambda_2, \ldots, \lambda_n$, then there exists a unitary matrix U such that $U^*AU = B$, and conversely.

21. Given the real nonzero vector B, show that the system

$$BB^\mathsf{T}X = B$$

is consistent. What is its rank? Show that the complete solution of the system is

$$X = \sum_{i=1}^{n-1} \alpha_i P_i + \frac{1}{B^\mathsf{T}B} B,$$

where $P_1, P_2, \ldots, P_{n-1}$ are independent characteristic vectors of BB^T associated with the zero characteristic roots, and the α_i are parameters.

22. Construct an example of a normal matrix which is not unitary, Hermitian, skew-Hermitian, or diagonal.

*23. Show that every proper orthogonal matrix A in $\mathscr{E}_3$ represents a rotation about the characteristic vector corresponding to the root $\lambda = 1$, the angle of rotation being defined by

$$\cos \theta = \frac{(\operatorname{tr} A) - 1}{2}.$$

(*Hint:* Introduce the characteristic vector in question as a coordinate axis.)

CHAPTER NINE

Bilinear, Quadratic, and Hermitian Forms

EQUIVALENCE OF BILINEAR FORMS

9.1 Bilinear Forms

In this chapter we consider three types of scalar functions of vector variables which are used widely both in pure mathematics and in applications. We consider first the bilinear form.

The concept of a bilinear form was introduced informally in Section 5.13. We now define it in terms of its essential properties. Consider two vector spaces $\mathscr{V}_m^{\,m}$ and $\mathscr{V}_n^{\,n}$ over the same field $\mathscr{F}$. Let X represent an arbitrary vector of $\mathscr{V}_m^{\,m}$ and Y represent an arbitrary vector of $\mathscr{V}_n^{\,n}$, each with respect to the natural reference system in its space. Then a **bilinear form** over $\mathscr{F}$ is a function b of the two vector variables X and Y with the following properties:

(a) To each pair of vectors X and Y it relates a unique scalar $b(X, Y)$ of $\mathscr{F}$.

(b) For each scalar α of $\mathscr{F}$, $b(\alpha X, Y) = b(X, \alpha Y) = \alpha\, b(X, Y)$.

(c) For all vectors X, X_1, X_2 of the $\mathscr{V}_m^{\,m}$ and Y, Y_1, Y_2 of the $\mathscr{V}_n^{\,n}$,

$$b(X_1 + X_2, Y) = b(X_1, Y) + b(X_2, Y),$$

and

$$b(X, Y_1 + Y_2) = b(X, Y_1) + b(X, Y_2).$$

That is, b possesses the characteristic properties of linearity with respect to both of the variables X and Y.

Let $E_1, E_2, \ldots, E_m$ denote the elementary vectors of the $\mathscr{V}_m^{\,m}$ and $E_1', E_2', \ldots, E_n'$ denote those of the $\mathscr{V}_n^{\,n}$. Then, by (a), there exist unique scalars a_{ij} such that $b(E_i, E_j') = a_{ij}$, $i = 1, 2, \ldots, m; j = 1, 2, \ldots, n$. Then, since $X = \sum_{i=1}^{m} x_i E_i$ and $Y = \sum_{j=1}^{n} y_j E_j'$, repeated application of (b) and (c) yields

(9.1.1) $$b(X, Y) = \sum_{i=1}^{m} \sum_{j=1}^{n} x_i y_j a_{ij} = X^{\mathsf{T}} A Y,$$

where $A = [a_{ij}]_{m \times n}$. For example,

$$[x_1, x_2, x_3] \cdot \begin{bmatrix} 1 & 0 \\ 0 & 2 \\ -1 & -2 \end{bmatrix} \cdot \begin{bmatrix} y_1 \\ y_2 \end{bmatrix} = x_1 y_1 + 2x_2 y_2 - x_3 y_1 - 2x_3 y_2$$

is a bilinear form over the real field, or simply a **real bilinear form**.

The $m \times n$ matrix A which contains all the coefficients of a bilinear form is called the **matrix of the form** and if the x's and y's are independent variables, the rank of A is called the **rank of the form**. In the example just given, the rank of the form is 2. When the matrix of the form is symmetric, the form itself is called a **symmetric bilinear form**. The most important example of a symmetric bilinear form is the inner product $X^{\mathsf{T}} Y = X^{\mathsf{T}} I Y$, where $\mathscr{F}$ is the field of real numbers or a subfield thereof.

Since every $m \times n$ matrix may be used as the matrix of a bilinear form in $m + n$ variables, many definitions and theorems about matrices have simple counterparts in the theory of bilinear forms, as will appear in following paragraphs.

It is important to note that in (9.1.1) a_{ij} is the coefficient of the product $x_i y_j$, for by this observation we are enabled to go from the form to its matrix representation and vice versa *by inspection*. A useful example is provided by a form much used in statistics, namely the **covariance** of X and Y,

(9.1.2) $$\operatorname{cov}(X, Y) = \frac{1}{n-1} \sum_{j=1}^{n} (x_j - m_x)(y_j - m_y),$$

where

$$m_x = \frac{1}{n} \sum_{j=1}^{n} x_j \quad \text{and} \quad m_y = \frac{1}{n} \sum_{j=1}^{n} y_j$$

are the means of the x's and the y's respectively. This form may be regarded most simply as a bilinear form in the $2n$ "deviations" $x_j - m_x$ and $y_j - m_y$, its matrix being the identity matrix divided by $n - 1$. However, since $\sum (x_j - m_x) = 0$ and $\sum (y_j - m_y) = 0$, the deviations are not independent variables. To determine the rank of the form, we therefore expand the product in (9.1.2), sum the individual terms, and substitute for m_x and m_y, thus obtaining the expansion

(9.1.3) $\operatorname{cov}(X, Y) = \dfrac{1}{n-1}\left(\dfrac{n-1}{n}\sum\limits_{j=1}^{n} x_j y_j - \dfrac{1}{n}\sum\limits_{j \neq k} x_j y_k\right).$

Hence the matrix of the covariance is

(9.1.4) $\dfrac{1}{n(n-1)}\begin{bmatrix} (n-1) & -1 & \cdots & -1 \\ -1 & (n-1) & \cdots & -1 \\ \vdots & & & \\ -1 & -1 & \cdots & (n-1) \end{bmatrix}_n,$

which may be shown to have rank $n - 1$. Assuming the x's and y's to be independent, $n - 1$ is then the rank of the form.

9.2 The Equivalence of Bilinear Forms

Frequently it is necessary or desirable to introduce new variables into a bilinear form in place of X and Y, that is, to effect linear transformations of coordinates in the spaces $\mathscr{V}_m{}^m$ and $\mathscr{V}_n{}^n$.

We next investigate the effect of this operation and some of the results which can be accomplished thereby.

Let $X^{\mathsf{T}}A\,Y$ be a bilinear form over a field $\mathscr{F}$. Let $X = B\tilde{X}$ and $Y = C\tilde{Y}$ be nonsingular linear transformations relating X and Y to new variables $\tilde{X}$ and $\tilde{Y}$, the matrices B and C also being over $\mathscr{F}$. Then we have

$$X^{\mathsf{T}}A\,Y = (B\tilde{X})^{\mathsf{T}} A(C\tilde{Y}) = \tilde{X}^{\mathsf{T}}(B^{\mathsf{T}}AC)\tilde{Y},$$

which gives the representation of the form in the new reference systems. The matrix $B^{\mathsf{T}}AC$ has the same rank as A since B^{T} and C are nonsingular.

Alternatively, we can regard the transformations $X = B\tilde{X}$, $Y = C\tilde{Y}$ as nonsingular operators in their vector spaces, the effect of which is to take the bilinear form $X^{\mathsf{T}}A\,Y$ into the new form $\tilde{X}^{\mathsf{T}}(B^{\mathsf{T}}AC)\tilde{Y}$, which always has the same value as the given one at the corresponding pair of vectors.

We have then, in summary,

Theorem 9.2.1:   *The rank of a bilinear form is the same in all reference systems. Nonsingular linear operators on $\mathscr{V}_m{}^m$ and $\mathscr{V}_n{}^n$ take a bilinear form over $\mathscr{F}$ into a bilinear form of the same rank and also over $\mathscr{F}$. The values of the two forms are always the same at corresponding pairs of vectors (X, Y) and $(\tilde{X}, \tilde{Y})$.*

For example, let us apply the real transformations of coordinates

$$X = \begin{bmatrix} 1 & 1 & 0 \\ 0 & 1 & 0 \\ 0 & 0 & -1 \end{bmatrix}\tilde{X} \quad \text{and} \quad Y = \begin{bmatrix} 1 & 1 & 0 \\ 0 & 1 & 0 \\ 0 & 0 & -1 \end{bmatrix}\tilde{Y}$$

to the symmetric bilinear form

$$X^\mathsf{T} A Y = X^\mathsf{T} \begin{bmatrix} 1 & -1 & 0 \\ -1 & 2 & 0 \\ 0 & 0 & 1 \end{bmatrix} Y = x_1 y_1 - x_1 y_2 - x_2 y_1 + 2 x_2 y_2 + x_3 y_3.$$

We obtain

$$X^\mathsf{T} A Y = \tilde{X}^\mathsf{T} \begin{bmatrix} 1 & 0 & 0 \\ 1 & 1 & 0 \\ 0 & 0 & -1 \end{bmatrix} \cdot \begin{bmatrix} 1 & -1 & 0 \\ -1 & 2 & 0 \\ 0 & 0 & 1 \end{bmatrix} \cdot \begin{bmatrix} 1 & 1 & 0 \\ 0 & 1 & 0 \\ 0 & 0 & -1 \end{bmatrix} \tilde{Y}$$

$$= \tilde{X}^\mathsf{T} \begin{bmatrix} 1 & 0 & 0 \\ 0 & 1 & 0 \\ 0 & 0 & 1 \end{bmatrix} \tilde{Y} = \tilde{x}_1 \tilde{y}_1 + \tilde{x}_2 \tilde{y}_2 + \tilde{x}_3 \tilde{y}_3,$$

so that, in the new reference systems, the bilinear form is diagonal, that is, it has a diagonal matrix.

This example also illustrates the concept of equivalent bilinear forms. We shall say that two bilinear forms in $m + n$ variables, whose matrices A_1 and A_2 have elements in a field $\mathscr{F}$, are **equivalent** over $\mathscr{F}$ if and only if there exist nonsingular matrices B and C over $\mathscr{F}$, of orders m and n respectively, such that $B^\mathsf{T} A_1 C = A_2$, that is, if and only if the matrices of the two forms are equivalent. If we write the forms as $X^\mathsf{T} A_1 Y$ and $\tilde{X}^\mathsf{T} A_2 \tilde{Y}$, the definition amounts to saying that the two forms are equivalent over $\mathscr{F}$ if and only if there exist nonsingular transformations $X = B\tilde{X}$ and $Y = C\tilde{Y}$ over $\mathscr{F}$ which transform the first form into the second. The reader should show that the inverse transformations will then carry the second form into the first, so that equivalence is actually symmetric in character, even though it is not symmetrically defined. Because the equivalence of forms as thus defined is identical to the equivalence of the corresponding matrices, it is in fact an equivalence relation as defined in Chapter One.

If we choose to regard the equivalent forms as being related by linear transformations of coordinates, it follows that, in this case, *distinct but equivalent forms are representations of the same bilinear function but in different reference systems.*

In the event that the transformations are regarded as operators, two forms are equivalent if and only if there exist nonsingular operators on $\mathscr{V}_m^\circ{}^m$ and $\mathscr{V}_n^\circ{}^n$ such that the forms always have equal values at corresponding pairs of vectors. Since two matrices over a field $\mathscr{F}$ are equivalent if and only if they have the same order and the same rank, we may conclude

Theorem 9.2.2: *Two bilinear forms over a field $\mathscr{F}$, each with an $m \times n$ matrix, are equivalent over $\mathscr{F}$ if and only if they have the same rank.*

In particular, every bilinear form $X^\mathsf{T} A Y$ in $m + n$ variables and of rank r is equivalent to the **canonical form**

$$(9.2.1) \qquad \tilde{X}^\mathsf{T} \begin{bmatrix} I_r & \vdots & 0 \\ \cdots & \vdots & \cdots \\ 0 & \vdots & 0 \end{bmatrix} \tilde{Y} = \tilde{x}_1 \tilde{y}_1 + \tilde{x}_2 \tilde{y}_2 + \cdots + \tilde{x}_r \tilde{y}_r.$$

In fact, if B^T and C are matrices such that $B^\mathsf{T} A C$ is the normal form of A, then the transformations $X = B\tilde{X}$ and $Y = C\tilde{Y}$ effect the reduction of $X^\mathsf{T} A Y$ to the canonical form.

By determining first what transformations reduce each of two equivalent bilinear forms to the canonical form, we can determine by what transformations either may be transformed into the other.

9.3 Cogredient and Contragredient Transformations

Suppose that a bilinear form has a matrix A of order n and that X and Y are both n-vectors belonging to the same $\mathscr{V}_n{}^n$, the problem now being to determine the effect of a linear transformation of coordinates in $\mathscr{V}_n{}^n$ or of an operator on $\mathscr{V}_n{}^n$. That is, we now wish to subject both X and Y to the *same* transformation: $X = B\tilde{X}$ and $Y = B\tilde{Y}$. In this case, we say that X and Y are **transformed cogrediently**. The effect of a cogredient transformation of X and Y is to take the form $X^\mathsf{T} A Y$ into the form $\tilde{X}^\mathsf{T} (B^\mathsf{T} A B) \tilde{Y}$. If A and B are over $\mathscr{F}$ and B in addition is nonsingular, the matrices A and $B^\mathsf{T} A B$ are equivalent over $\mathscr{F}$, but in a special way. We recognize this by introducing a special term. In general, if A_1, A_2 of order n are over $\mathscr{F}$ and if there exists an $n \times n$ nonsingular matrix B over $\mathscr{F}$ such that $B^\mathsf{T} A_1 B = A_2$, then we call A_1 and A_2 **congruent** over $\mathscr{F}$. The reader may verify that congruence is a true equivalence relation. Using this terminology, we summarize in

Theorem 9.3.1: *Two bilinear forms over a field $\mathscr{F}$ are equivalent under cogredient transformation of the variables if and only if their matrices are congruent over $\mathscr{F}$.*

When A is square and X and Y both belong to the $\mathscr{V}_n{}^n$ over $\mathscr{F}$, then $X^\mathsf{T} A Y$ is often called a **bilinear form on the $\mathscr{V}_n{}^n$ over $\mathscr{F}$**. In this case, X and Y are, of course, transformed cogrediently.

However, when A is square it is not *necessary*, nor is it always useful, to require that the vectors X and Y of a bilinear form be transformed cogrediently. Indeed, at times they must be regarded as belonging to geometrically distinct $\mathscr{V}_n{}^n$'s over $\mathscr{F}$, and in such a case they may be subjected to distinct linear transformations.

An instance of this which is of special importance is the following. We assume that X and Y need *not* be transformed cogrediently. Under this condition, we wish to know what transformations leave identically invariant the matrix of the canonical bilinear form

$$X^\mathsf{T} I_n Y = x_1 y_1 + x_2 y_2 + \cdots + x_n y_n.$$

If we put $X = B\tilde{X}$ and $Y = C\tilde{Y}$, we have

$$X^\mathsf{T} I_n Y = \tilde{X}^\mathsf{T} B^\mathsf{T} C \tilde{Y},$$

in which we require that $B^\mathsf{T} C = I_n$. From this it follows that B and C must be nonsingular and that $C = (B^\mathsf{T})^{-1}$. The transformations $X = B\tilde{X}$ and $Y = (B^\mathsf{T})^{-1} \tilde{Y}$ are called **contragredient transformations**.

In particular, if B is a real orthogonal matrix, we have $B^\mathsf{T} B = I_n$, or $B = (B^\mathsf{T})^{-1}$. Hence an orthogonal transformation is contragredient to itself. Consequently, when one subjects the $\mathscr{V}^\circ{}_n{}^n$ over the real field to an orthogonal transformation of coordinates or to an orthogonal operator, the variables X and Y of a bilinear form $X^\mathsf{T} A Y$ are transformed both cogrediently and contragrediently, a fact which is of particular importance in the geometry of $\mathscr{E}_n$.

9.4 Exercises

*1. Given that the products $B_1 A_1 C_1$ and $B_2 A_2 C_2$ are in the same normal form and that the B's and the C's are nonsingular, write the transformations that will take the bilinear form $X^\mathsf{T} A_1 Y$ into the bilinear form $\tilde{X}^\mathsf{T} A_2 \tilde{Y}$.

2. Use the methods and theorems developed in Chapter Four to reduce the bilinear form

$$X^\mathsf{T} \begin{bmatrix} 1 & 1 & 0 & 3 \\ 2 & 0 & 2 & 2 \\ 3 & -2 & 5 & -1 \end{bmatrix} Y$$

to the canonical form defined in Section 9.2.

3. Supply the details of the reduction of (9.1.2) to (9.1.3).

4. Under what conditions are the real transformations $X = B\tilde{X}$ and $Y = C\tilde{Y}$ simultaneously cogredient and contragredient?

5. Show that the matrix (9.1.4) has rank $n - 1$.

6. Show that, if A is symmetric, then $X^\mathsf{T} A Y = Y^\mathsf{T} A X$.

7. Show that, if $X^\mathsf{T} A Y$ is symmetric, and if X and Y are transformed cogrediently, then the new form is also symmetric.

8. Determine the transformation contragredient to

$$X = \begin{bmatrix} 1 & 0 & 1 \\ 0 & 1 & 1 \\ 1 & 1 & 1 \end{bmatrix} \tilde{X}.$$

9. Let $X^\mathsf{T} A Y$ be a *real* bilinear form with A of order n and nonsingular. Then $X^\mathsf{T} A^{-1} Y$ is called the **reciprocal bilinear form** of the given one. Show that

$$X^\mathsf{T} A^{-1} Y = -\det \begin{bmatrix} 0 & \vdots & X^\mathsf{T} \\ \cdots & \vdots & \cdots \\ Y & \vdots & A \end{bmatrix} \det A^{-1}.$$

Show also that if reciprocal bilinear forms are transformed cogrediently by the same orthogonal transformation, reciprocal bilinear forms result.

10. Show that an identity in the y's, $Y^\mathsf{T} A X \equiv Y^\mathsf{T} B$, where X, Y, and B are vectors, can hold if and only if X is a solution of the system of equations $A X = B$.

11. Prove that, if A is real and symmetric and if $A X = \lambda X$, $A Y = \mu Y$, where $\lambda \neq \mu$, then $X^\mathsf{T} A Y = 0$.

12. Consider the set of bilinear forms over the real field. Show that the values of each such form for n-vectors X and Y may be regarded as the inner product of two vectors.

13. Prove that the matrix A of a bilinear form on the $\mathscr{V}_n{}^n$ over a field $\mathscr{F}$ is symmetric if and only if $X^\mathsf{T} A Y = Y^\mathsf{T} A X$ for all X and Y of the $\mathscr{V}_n{}^n$.

14. If B is a square matrix over $\mathscr{F}$ such that $B^\mathsf{T} A B = A$, then the operator with matrix B is said to **preserve** the bilinear form $X^\mathsf{T} A Y$. Show that the set of all nonsingular operators over $\mathscr{F}$ which preserve a fixed bilinear form constitutes a group. What group is it when $A = I$?

15. Let A, B be $m \times n$ matrices over a field $\mathscr{F}$. Show that tr $(A^\mathsf{T} B)$ is a symmetric bilinear form in the elements of A and B.

16. Prove that the set of all bilinear forms over a field $\mathscr{F}$, which have $m \times n$ matrices, constitutes a vector space. What is its dimension? What set of bilinear forms constitutes a particularly simple basis for this space?

17. Let $L_1(X)$ and $L_2(Y)$ denote linear forms on a $\mathscr{V}_n{}^n$ over $\mathscr{F}$. Show that $L_1(X) L_2(Y)$ is a bilinear form on the $\mathscr{V}_n{}^n$, and that every bilinear form on the $\mathscr{V}_n{}^n$ is representable as a sum of at most n such products. What is the significance of the *least* number required for such a representation?

18. Given the bilinear form $b = X^\mathsf{T} A Y$, in which A is square and X and Y belong to the same $\mathscr{V}_n{}^n$, we say that b is **nonsingular** if and only if A is nonsingular. Prove that b is nonsingular, if and only if for each $X \neq 0$ there exists a Y such that $X^\mathsf{T} A Y \neq 0$, and for each $Y \neq 0$ there exists an X such that $X^\mathsf{T} A Y \neq 0$.

*19. Let f be a function of n vector variables whose common domain is the $\mathscr{V}_n{}^n$ over a field $\mathscr{F}$. Assume f has these properties for all X's of the $\mathscr{V}_n{}^n$:

(a) $f(X_1, X_2, \ldots, X_n)$ is a scalar in $\mathscr{F}$.

(b) $f(X_1, \ldots, X_{j-1}, \alpha X_j, X_{j+1}, \ldots, X_n) = \alpha f(X_1, \ldots, X_j, \ldots, X_n)$ for $j = 1, 2, \ldots, n$ and α any scalar in $\mathscr{F}$.

(c) $f(X_1, \ldots, X_{j-1}, X_j + X_j', X_{j+1}, \ldots, X_n) = f(X_1, \ldots, X_{j-1}, X_j, X_{j+1}, \ldots, X_n) + f(X_1, \ldots, X_{j-1}, X_j', X_{j+1}, \ldots, X_n)$, $j = 1, 2, \ldots, n$.

(d) $f(E_1, E_2, \ldots, E_n) = 1$.

(e) If $X_1, X_2, \ldots, X_n$ are linearly dependent, $f(X_1, X_2, \ldots, X_n) = 0$.

Prove that:

(α) $f(E_1, \ldots, E_{j-1}, X, E_{j+1}, \ldots, E_n) = x_j$.

(β) $f(E_{j_1}, E_{j_2}, \ldots, E_{j_n}) = \epsilon_{j_1 j_2 \cdots j_n}$.

(γ) $f(X_1, X_2, \ldots, X_n) = \det [X_1, X_2, \ldots, X_n]$.

Properties (a), (b), (c) say that f is a **multi-linear form** on the given $\mathscr{V}_n{}^n$. Properties (d), (e) restrict the form enough to make it, in fact, the determinant. Prove that (e) can be replaced by (e'): If any two of $X_1, X_2, \ldots, X_n$ are the same, $f(X_1, X_2, \ldots, X_n) = 0$.

QUADRATIC FORMS

9.5 Quadratic Forms

A homogeneous polynomial q of the type

$$(9.5.1) \qquad q = X^\mathsf{T} AX = \sum_{i,j=1}^{n} a_{ij} x_i x_j,$$

the coefficients of which are in a field $\mathscr{F}$, is called a **quadratic form over $\mathscr{F}$** or a **quadratic form on the $\mathscr{V}_n{}^n$ over $\mathscr{F}$**. Such forms have many applications, for example, in the physical sciences and engineering, in the mathematics of computation, in statistics, in geometry, etc. In most applications, the field $\mathscr{F}$ is the field of real numbers or the field of rational numbers.

As in the case of bilinear forms, the expansion of the quadratic form $X^\mathsf{T}AX$ may be written by inspection when needed. In this expansion the similar terms $a_{ij}x_ix_j$ and $a_{ji}x_jx_i$ would naturally be combined into a single term. It is clear then that distinct products $X^\mathsf{T}A_1X$ and $X^\mathsf{T}A_2X$ lead to the same expansion provided only that all corresponding sums of the type $a_{ij} + a_{ji}$ are the same for both matrices. Conversely, a quadratic form q can be rewritten in infinitely many ways as a matrix product $X^\mathsf{T}AX$. We agree, however, to eliminate the ambiguity once and for all in the following way. We replace each member of every pair of coefficients a_{ij} and a_{ji} of a given form q by their mean, $(a_{ij} + a_{ji})/2$. Thus we obtain an equal quadratic form whose coefficients define a symmetric matrix $(A + A^\mathsf{T})/2$. For example, we would consider

$$q = x_1{}^2 - 3x_1x_2 + x_2{}^2 + x_1x_3$$

to be a convenient abbreviation for

$$q = x_1{}^2 - \tfrac{3}{2}x_1x_2 - \tfrac{3}{2}x_2x_1 + x_2{}^2 + \tfrac{1}{2}x_1x_3 + \tfrac{1}{2}x_3x_1.$$

In matrix notation, this last form becomes

$$X^\mathsf{T} \begin{bmatrix} 1 & -\tfrac{3}{2} & \tfrac{1}{2} \\ -\tfrac{3}{2} & 1 & 0 \\ \tfrac{1}{2} & 0 & 0 \end{bmatrix} X,$$

since the coefficient of x_ix_j becomes the element a_{ij} of the matrix.

The result of our agreement is then that, unless otherwise stated, *every quadratic form $X^\mathsf{T}AX$ with which we work will have a symmetric matrix A.* This restriction to the symmetric case has many advantages in addition to elimination of ambiguity. If the x's are independent variables, the rank of A is called the **rank of the form** and det A is called the **discriminant of the form.**

9.6 Equivalence of Quadratic Forms

The nonsingular transformation $X = B\tilde{X}$ with coefficients in a field $\mathscr{F}$ takes a quadratic form $X^\mathsf{T}AX$, where A is over $\mathscr{F}$, into the form $\tilde{X}^\mathsf{T}(B^\mathsf{T}AB)\tilde{X}$ where $B^\mathsf{T}AB$ is also over $\mathscr{F}$ and has the same rank as A. Note that $B^\mathsf{T}AB$ is symmetric because A is. We say that two quadratic forms $X^\mathsf{T}A_1X$ and $\tilde{X}^\mathsf{T}A_2\tilde{X}$ over $\mathscr{F}$ are **equivalent** over $\mathscr{F}$ if and only if there is a nonsingular transformation $X = B\tilde{X}$ over $\mathscr{F}$ such that

$$X^\mathsf{T}A_1X = \tilde{X}^\mathsf{T}(B^\mathsf{T}A_1B)\tilde{X} = \tilde{X}^\mathsf{T}A_2\tilde{X},$$

that is, if and only if, for a suitable nonsingular matrix B over $\mathscr{F}$,

$$A_2 = B^\mathsf{T}A_1B.$$

From this follows at once

Theorem 9.6.1: *Two quadratic forms over a field $\mathscr{F}$ are equivalent over $\mathscr{F}$ if and only if their matrices are congruent over $\mathscr{F}$.*

This is analogous to Theorem 9.3.1 for bilinear forms. Geometrically, the theorem says that, if $X = B\tilde{X}$ represents a linear transformation of co-ordinates in the $\mathscr{V}_n{}^n$ over $\mathscr{F}$, then two distinct quadratic forms are equivalent if and only if they are, in fact, representations of the same function in different reference systems. Alternatively, if $X = B\tilde{X}$ represents an operator on the $\mathscr{V}_n{}^n$ over $\mathscr{F}$, then two quadratic forms are equivalent over $\mathscr{F}$ if and only if there exists a nonsingular linear operator which transforms one into the other, that is, such that the two forms always have equal values at corresponding vectors X and $\tilde{X}$.

As an example, consider the form

$$29x_1{}^2 + 24x_1x_2 + 5x_2{}^2 = X^\mathsf{T}\begin{bmatrix} 29 & 12 \\ 12 & 5 \end{bmatrix}X.$$

Let us put

$$X = \begin{bmatrix} 1 & -2 \\ -2 & 5 \end{bmatrix}\tilde{X}.$$

Then

$$X^\mathsf{T}\begin{bmatrix} 29 & 12 \\ 12 & 5 \end{bmatrix}X = \tilde{X}^\mathsf{T}\begin{bmatrix} 1 & -2 \\ -2 & 5 \end{bmatrix} \cdot \begin{bmatrix} 29 & 12 \\ 12 & 5 \end{bmatrix} \cdot \begin{bmatrix} 1 & -2 \\ -2 & 5 \end{bmatrix}\tilde{X}$$

$$= \tilde{X}^\mathsf{T}\begin{bmatrix} 1 & 0 \\ 0 & 1 \end{bmatrix}\tilde{X} = \tilde{x}_1{}^2 + \tilde{x}_2{}^2.$$

Thus the real quadratic forms $29x_1{}^2 + 24x_1x_2 + 5x_2{}^2$ and $\tilde{x}_1{}^2 + \tilde{x}_2{}^2$ are equivalent over the real field.

9.7 Exercises

*1. Show that, if A_1 and A_2 are symmetric, $X^{\mathsf{T}}A_1X$ is identical to $X^{\mathsf{T}}A_2X$ in the x's if and only if $A_1 = A_2$. (This proves that the symmetric matrix of a quadratic form is unique.)

2. Show that $X^{\mathsf{T}}AX \equiv X^{\mathsf{T}}A^{\mathsf{T}}X$, whether or not A is symmetric, and that $X^{\mathsf{T}}BX \equiv 0$ if B is skew-symmetric.

3. Show by means of an example that, if A_1 and A_2 are *not* both symmetric, we can have $X^{\mathsf{T}}A_1X \equiv X^{\mathsf{T}}A_2X$ even though A_1 and A_2 have different ranks. (This is another reason for agreeing to use only symmetric matrices in quadratic forms.)

4. Rewrite $(a_1x_1 + a_2x_2 + \cdots + a_nx_n)^2$ in the form $X^{\mathsf{T}}AX$, where A is a symmetric matrix. What is the rank of A?

5. If $m_x = \dfrac{1}{n}\sum_1^n x_j$, rewrite the quadratic form

$$s_x{}^2 = \frac{1}{n-1}\sum_{j=1}^n (x_j - m_x)^2$$

in the form $X^{\mathsf{T}}AX$, where A is symmetric. What is the rank of A? For what sets of values of the x's will this form have the value zero? (This form is the **variance**, much used in statistics.)

6. Show that equivalence of quadratic forms, as above defined, is a true equivalence relation.

7. Show that the matrix of a sum of quadratic forms is the sum of their matrices, and that the rank of their sum is equal to or less than the sum of their ranks.

8. Show that a quadratic form $X^{\mathsf{T}}AX$ over a field $\mathscr{F}$ may be factored into a product $(X^{\mathsf{T}}V_1)(X^{\mathsf{T}}V_2)$, where V_1 and V_2 are n-vectors over $\mathscr{F}$ if and only if its rank is 1 or 0.

9. Find the matrix and the rank of the quadratic form

$$(A_1{}^{\mathsf{T}}X)^2 + (A_2{}^{\mathsf{T}}X)^2 + \cdots + (A_k{}^{\mathsf{T}}X)^2,$$

where $A_1, A_2, \ldots, A_k$ are linearly independent n-vectors.

10. Apply the transformation

$$X = \begin{bmatrix} 2 & -1 & -2 & 1 \\ 2 & 1 & 0 & 0 \\ 0 & 0 & 2 & -1 \\ 0 & 0 & 2 & 1 \end{bmatrix} Y$$

to the form

$$X^{\mathsf{T}} \begin{bmatrix} 0 & 1 & 0 & 0 \\ 1 & 0 & 1 & 0 \\ 0 & 1 & 0 & 1 \\ 0 & 0 & 1 & 0 \end{bmatrix} X.$$

11. Write the quadratic form

$$\det \begin{bmatrix} 0 & | & X^T \\ \hline X & | & A \end{bmatrix},$$

where A is $n \times n$ and X is $n \times 1$, in the form $X^T BX$. Then do the same for

$$\det \begin{bmatrix} 0 & | & X^T \\ \hline X & | & B \end{bmatrix}.$$

(This operation is important in geometry.)

12. The potential energy of a certain mechanical system is given by

$$V = \tfrac{1}{2}(k_1 x_1{}^2 + k_2 x_2{}^2 + k_3 x_3{}^2 + l_1(x_1 - x_2)^2 + l_2(x_1 - x_3)^2$$
$$+ l_3(x_2 - x_3)^2 + m(x_1 + x_2 + x_3)^2).$$

Write this quadratic form in matrix form. Given that k_1, k_2, k_3, l_1, l_2, l_3, m are all positive, prove that $V(X) > 0$ unless $X = 0$.

THE DIAGONALIZATION OF QUADRATIC FORMS

9.8 Diagonalization by Orthogonal Transformation

A given quadratic form can be reduced in various ways to equivalent forms which emphasize certain of its basic properties. The most important of these reductions is probably diagonalization by means of an orthogonal transformation.

We have already seen in Chapter Eight that, for every real symmetric matrix A, there exists an orthogonal matrix U such that

$$U^T A U = D[\lambda_1, \lambda_2, \ldots, \lambda_n],$$

where $\lambda_1, \lambda_2, \ldots, \lambda_n$ are characteristic roots of A. As a consequence, the transformation

$$X = UY$$

applied to the quadratic form $X^T A X$ gives

(9.8.1) $$X^T A X = \lambda_1 y_1{}^2 + \lambda_2 y_2{}^2 + \cdots + \lambda_n y_n{}^2.$$

If the rank of A is r, then $n - r$ characteristic roots are zero so that (9.8.1) becomes

(9.8.2) $$X^T A X = \lambda_1 y_1{}^2 + \lambda_2 y_2{}^2 + \cdots + \lambda_r y_r{}^2$$

where $\lambda_1, \lambda_2, \ldots, \lambda_r$ are the non-zero characteristic roots.

The computational aspects of this method of reduction are, of course, the same as those discussed in Chapter Eight in connection with the determination of the matrix U.

The orthogonal transformations of quadratic forms in $\mathscr{E}_2$ and $\mathscr{E}_3$ have a ready geometrical interpretation.

In $\mathscr{E}_2$, the quadratic equation

$$a_{11}x_1{}^2 + 2a_{12}x_1x_2 + a_{22}x_2{}^2 = b,$$

where b is a constant, or

$$X^\mathsf{T} \begin{bmatrix} a_{11} & a_{12} \\ a_{12} & a_{22} \end{bmatrix} X = b,$$

represents a conic section of some kind. Let U be the orthogonal matrix which diagonalizes the matrix

$$A = \begin{bmatrix} a_{11} & a_{12} \\ a_{12} & a_{22} \end{bmatrix}$$

of the quadratic form. Then, making the nonsingular transformation $X = UY$, we obtain the equation

$$Y^\mathsf{T} \begin{bmatrix} \lambda_1 & 0 \\ 0 & \lambda_2 \end{bmatrix} Y = b,$$

or

$$\lambda_1 y_1{}^2 + \lambda_2 y_2{}^2 = b,$$

where λ_1 and λ_2 are the characteristic roots of A.

If we interpret the transformation $X = UY$ as a transformation of coordinates, the new conic is identical with the original one—only the reference system has been altered. The alteration is such that the equation of the conic is particularly simple in the new reference system. In this case, the columns of U define respectively the unit vectors along the positive y_1 and y_2 axes, with respect to the x-coordinate system. The y axes are called the **principal axes** of the conic and the transformation is called a **principal axis transformation**.

If we interpret $X = UY$ as an operator, the reference system is unaltered. The transformation yields a new conic congruent to the original one, and also located so that its equation has a particularly simple form. In either case, if λ_1, λ_2, and b are all different from zero, we may write the new equation in the form

$$\frac{y_1{}^2}{\left(\dfrac{b}{\lambda_1}\right)} + \frac{y_2{}^2}{\left(\dfrac{b}{\lambda_2}\right)} = 1.$$

If both denominators here are positive, the equation represents an ellipse; if they are opposite in sign, it represents a hyperbola; if they are both negative, the equation has no real locus. If one or more of λ_1, λ_2, b is zero, the equation represents two lines, a point, or again no real locus. (The reader may discuss these cases in detail.)

In $\mathscr{E}_3$, the equation

$$X^\mathsf{T} A X = X^\mathsf{T} \begin{bmatrix} a_{11} & a_{12} & a_{13} \\ a_{12} & a_{22} & a_{23} \\ a_{13} & a_{23} & a_{33} \end{bmatrix} X = b$$

represents a quadratic surface of some kind. Again, let U be the orthogonal matrix which diagonalizes the symmetric matrix A. Then a nonsingular transformation $X = UY$ yields the equation

$$\lambda_1 y_1{}^2 + \lambda_2 y_2{}^2 + \lambda_3 y_3{}^2 = b,$$

where λ_1, λ_2, λ_3 are the characteristic roots of A.

If λ_1, λ_2, λ_3, and b are all different from zero, we may write this in the form

$$\frac{y_1{}^2}{\left(\dfrac{b}{\lambda_1}\right)} + \frac{y_2{}^2}{\left(\dfrac{b}{\lambda_2}\right)} + \frac{y_3{}^2}{\left(\dfrac{b}{\lambda_3}\right)} = 1.$$

If all three denominators here are positive, the equation represents an ellipsoid; if one is negative, it represents a hyperboloid of one sheet; if two are negative, it represents a hyperboloid of two sheets; if all three are negative, the equation has no real locus. (For details of the analytic geometry, see C. E. Love and E. O. Rainville: *Analytic Geometry*, New York, Macmillan, 1955.) If one or more of λ_1, λ_2, λ_3, b is zero, the equation may represent a conical surface, a cylindrical surface, two planes, a point, or no real locus. (Here, too, we leave it to the reader to discuss these cases in detail.)

Again, if $X = UY$ is a transformation of coordinates, the columns of U define respectively the unit vectors along the positive y_1, y_2, and y_3 axes with respect to the x-coordinate system. The y axes are called the **principal axes** of the quadric.

In $\mathscr{E}_n$, the equation

$$X^\mathsf{T} A X = b$$

represents what is called a **hyperquadric**, an **n-quadric**, or simply a **quadric** in $\mathscr{E}_n$. As in $\mathscr{E}_2$ and $\mathscr{E}_3$, we can use an appropriate orthogonal transformation of coordinates $X = UY$ to reduce the equation to the form

$$\sum_{j=1}^{n} \lambda_j y_j^2 = b.$$

The most important special case here is that in which all the λ's are positive. In this event, the locus of the equation is commonly called an **ellipsoid**. As in $\mathscr{E}_2$ and $\mathscr{E}_3$, the columns of U define the **principal axes** of the quadric in $\mathscr{E}_n$.

9.9 Lagrange's Reduction

A second manner of reducing a quadratic form to a particularly simple form which sets its rank in evidence is known as **Lagrange's reduction**. The process involves basically just a repeated completing of the square. Before stating the general theorem, we illustrate the process with two examples.

Consider first the quadratic form of rank 3,

$$q = 2x_1^2 + x_1 x_2 - 3x_1 x_3 + 2x_2 x_3 - x_3^2.$$

We first group all the terms containing x_1 and factor out the coefficient of x_1^2:

$$q = 2(x_1^2 + (\tfrac{1}{2}x_2 - \tfrac{3}{2}x_3)x_1) + 2x_2 x_3 - x_3^2.$$

Now we complete the square on x_1 and pay for the inserted terms:

$$q = 2\big(x_1^2 + (\tfrac{1}{2}x_2 - \tfrac{3}{2}x_3)x_1 + (\tfrac{1}{4}x_2 - \tfrac{3}{4}x_3)^2\big) - 2(\tfrac{1}{4}x_2 - \tfrac{3}{4}x_3)^2 + 2x_2 x_3 - x_3^2,$$

so that

$$q = 2(x_1 + \tfrac{1}{4}x_2 - \tfrac{3}{4}x_3)^2 - \tfrac{1}{8}(x_2^2 - 22x_2 x_3) - \tfrac{17}{8}x_3^2.$$

Now we complete the square on x_2, thus obtaining

$$q = 2(x_1 + \tfrac{1}{4}x_2 - \tfrac{3}{4}x_3)^2 - \tfrac{1}{8}(x_2 - 11x_3)^2 + 13x_3^2.$$

The substitution

$$y_1 = x_1 + \tfrac{1}{4}x_2 - \tfrac{3}{4}x_3,$$
$$y_2 = \phantom{x_1 + \tfrac{1}{4}x_2} x_2 - 11x_3,$$
$$y_3 = \phantom{x_1 + \tfrac{1}{4}x_2 - 11} x_3,$$

has determinant 1 and is, therefore, nonsingular. It gives

$$q = 2y_1^2 - \tfrac{1}{8}y_2^2 + 13y_3^2,$$

which also has rank 3.

In matrix form, we have

$$Y = \begin{bmatrix} 1 & \frac{1}{4} & -\frac{3}{4} \\ 0 & 1 & -11 \\ 0 & 0 & 1 \end{bmatrix} X \quad \text{or} \quad X = \begin{bmatrix} 1 & -\frac{1}{4} & -2 \\ 0 & 1 & 11 \\ 0 & 0 & 1 \end{bmatrix} Y,$$

so that

$$X^{\mathsf{T}} \begin{bmatrix} 2 & \frac{1}{2} & -\frac{3}{2} \\ \frac{1}{2} & 0 & 1 \\ -\frac{3}{2} & 1 & -1 \end{bmatrix} X = Y^{\mathsf{T}} \begin{bmatrix} 1 & 0 & 0 \\ -\frac{1}{4} & 1 & 0 \\ -2 & 11 & 1 \end{bmatrix}$$

$$\times \begin{bmatrix} 2 & \frac{1}{2} & -\frac{3}{2} \\ \frac{1}{2} & 0 & 1 \\ -\frac{3}{2} & 1 & -1 \end{bmatrix} \begin{bmatrix} 1 & -\frac{1}{4} & -2 \\ 0 & 1 & 11 \\ 0 & 0 & 1 \end{bmatrix} Y$$

$$= Y^{\mathsf{T}} \begin{bmatrix} 2 & 0 & 0 \\ 0 & -\frac{1}{8} & 0 \\ 0 & 0 & 13 \end{bmatrix} Y.$$

If there had been no x_1^2 term in q, our completing the square on x_1 would have been impossible. Similarly, after this was done, if no x_2^2 term had appeared, we could not have completed the square on x_2. The same difficulty may, of course, arise at any stage. To show how to deal with this situation, we consider the form in three variables,

$$q = 2x_1x_2 + 2x_2x_3 + x_3^2.$$

Let us first put

$$x_1 = \tilde{x}_1,$$

(9.9.1) $$x_2 = \tilde{x}_1 + \tilde{x}_2,$$

$$x_3 = \tilde{x}_3.$$

This transformation has determinant 1 and is therefore nonsingular. It gives

$$q = 2\tilde{x}_1^2 + 2\tilde{x}_1\tilde{x}_2 + 2\tilde{x}_1\tilde{x}_3 + 2\tilde{x}_2\tilde{x}_3 + \tilde{x}_3^2,$$

from which, proceeding as before, we obtain

$$q = 2(\tilde{x}_1 + \tfrac{1}{2}\tilde{x}_2 + \tfrac{1}{2}\tilde{x}_3)^2 - \tfrac{1}{2}(\tilde{x}_2 - \tilde{x}_3)^2 + \tilde{x}_3^2.$$

The transformation with determinant 1 defined by

$$y_1 = \tilde{x}_1 + \tfrac{1}{2}\tilde{x}_2 + \tfrac{1}{2}\tilde{x}_3,$$

(9.9.2)
$$y_2 = \qquad\quad \tilde{x}_2 - \tilde{x}_3,$$

$$y_3 = \qquad\qquad\qquad \tilde{x}_3,$$

then gives

$$q = 2y_1{}^2 - \tfrac{1}{2}y_2{}^2 + y_3{}^2,$$

so that the reduction is now complete. (We could, of course, have begun by completing the square on x_3 in order to avoid using a transformation of type (9.9.1).)

Combining (9.9.1) and (9.9.2), we obtain the transformation of determinant unity

$$y_1 = \tfrac{1}{2}x_1 + \tfrac{1}{2}x_2 + \tfrac{1}{2}x_3, \qquad\qquad x_1 = y_1 - \tfrac{1}{2}y_2 - y_3,$$

$$y_2 = -x_1 + x_2 - x_3, \qquad \text{or} \qquad x_2 = y_1 + \tfrac{1}{2}y_2,$$

$$y_3 = \qquad\qquad x_3, \qquad\qquad\quad x_3 = \qquad\qquad y_3,$$

which effects the reduction in one step. The reader should check this assertion by the matrix method used in the previous example.

The device used in this problem may be introduced at any stage of the reduction process. A systematic scheme permitting this is contained in the proof of

Theorem 9.9.1: *Every not identically zero quadratic form over a number field $\mathscr{F}$ can be reduced by a nonsingular transformation with coefficients in $\mathscr{F}$ to the form*

$$c_1 y_1{}^2 + c_2 y_2{}^2 + \cdots + c_r y_r{}^2,$$

where the c's are not zero but are in $\mathscr{F}$ and where r is necessarily the rank of the given quadratic form.

We prove the theorem by induction.

When $n = 1$, $r = 1$ also. The quadratic form is simply

$$a_{11} x_1{}^2, \qquad a_{11} \neq 0,$$

and the identity transformation

$$y_1 = x_1$$

is the transformation mentioned in the theorem.

Suppose now that the theorem is true for quadratic forms in $n - 1$ or fewer variables and consider a quadratic form

$$q = \sum_{i,j=1}^{n} a_{ij} x_i x_j$$

of rank r in n variables. In the argument to follow it is necessary to have an x_1^2 term present. If $a_{11} \neq 0$, that is good enough. If, however, $a_{11} = 0$, but $a_{kk} \neq 0$ for some $k > 1$, then we may put

(9.9.3)
$$x_1 = \tilde{x}_k,$$
$$x_k = \tilde{x}_1,$$
$$x_j = \tilde{x}_j, \qquad j \neq 1, k.$$

This is a transformation with determinant -1 which takes the term $a_{kk}x_k^2$ into the term $a_{kk}\tilde{x}_1^2$. Since no other $\tilde{x}_1^2$ can appear, $\tilde{x}_1^2$ has a nonzero coefficient in the new form. The new form has the same rank as the old, and its coefficients are also in the same field.

If every coefficient a_{kk} is zero, then some coefficient a_{ij}, $i < j$, is not zero, and we put

(9.9.4)
$$x_j = \tilde{x}_i + \tilde{x}_j,$$
$$x_k = \tilde{x}_k, \qquad k \neq j.$$

As a result of this nonsingular transformation (determinant 1) the term $a_{ij}x_ix_j$ is replaced by the terms $a_{ij}\tilde{x}_i^2 + a_{ij}\tilde{x}_i\tilde{x}_j$, and similarly for the symmetric term $a_{ji}\tilde{x}_j\tilde{x}_i$. Hence, since $a_{ii} = a_{jj} = 0$ by hypothesis, the total coefficient of $\tilde{x}_i^2$ in the new form will be $2a_{ij}$, which is not zero. Then an application of the first transformation discussed will give us a quadratic form with an $\tilde{x}_1^2$-type term actually present. Again, the new form will have the same rank as the original form, and its coefficients will be in the same field.

We may thus assume that we are in fact dealing with a quadratic form q_1 equivalent to q in which $a_{11} \neq 0$. Using the fact that $a_{ij} = a_{ji}$, we rearrange q_1 and complete the square on x_1 as follows:

$$q_1 = \sum_{i,j=1}^{n} a_{ij}x_ix_j = a_{11}x_1^2 + 2 \sum_{j=2}^{n} a_{1j}x_1x_j + \sum_{i,j=2}^{n} a_{ij}x_ix_j$$

$$= a_{11}\left[x_1^2 + 2\left\{ \sum_{j=2}^{n} \frac{a_{1j}}{a_{11}}x_j \right\}x_1 \right] + \sum_{i,j=2}^{n} a_{ij}x_ix_j$$

$$= a_{11}\left[x_1^2 + 2\left\{ \sum_{j=2}^{n} \frac{a_{1j}}{a_{11}}x_j \right\} x_1 + \left\{ \sum_{j=2}^{n} \frac{a_{1j}}{a_{11}}x_j \right\}^2 \right]$$

$$+ \left[\sum_{i,j=2}^{n} a_{ij}x_ix_j - a_{11}\left\{ \sum_{j=2}^{n} \frac{a_{1j}}{a_{11}}x_j \right\}^2 \right]$$

$$= a_{11}\left(x_1 + \frac{a_{12}}{a_{11}}x_2 + \cdots + \frac{a_{1n}}{a_{11}}x_n \right)^2 + q_2.$$

Here q_2 is a quadratic form in $x_2, \ldots, x_n$ only, with coefficients in $\mathscr{F}$. We now make the transformation

(9.9.5)
$$\tilde{x}_1 = x_1 + \frac{a_{12}}{a_{11}} x_2 + \cdots + \frac{a_{1n}}{a_{11}} x_n,$$

$$\tilde{x}_i = x_i, \qquad i = 2, 3, \ldots, n,$$

which is over $\mathscr{F}$ and also has determinant 1, thus obtaining

(9.9.6)
$$q_1 = a_{11}\tilde{x}_1^{\,2} + q_2(\tilde{x}_2, \ldots, \tilde{x}_n).$$

Now by the induction hypothesis, there exists over $\mathscr{F}$ a nonsingular transformation taking $\tilde{x}_2, \tilde{x}_3, \ldots, \tilde{x}_n$ into $y_2, y_3, \ldots, y_n$ and such that

$$q_2 = c_2 y_2^{\,2} + c_3 y_3^{\,2} + \cdots + c_k y_k^{\,2},$$

where $k - 1$ is the rank of q_2. Let the matrix of order $n - 1$ of this transformation be B. Then the transformation

(9.9.7)
$$Y = \begin{bmatrix} 1 & 0 \\ \hline 0 & B \end{bmatrix} \tilde{X}$$

is also nonsingular and over $\mathscr{F}$. Applying this to (9.9.6) and putting $a_{11} = c_1$ for the sake of uniformity, we obtain

(9.9.8)
$$q_1 = c_1 y_1^{\,2} + c_2 y_2^{\,2} + \cdots + c_k y_k^{\,2}.$$

Similarly, starting with an arbitrary quadratic form q, we may combine any transformations of the types (9.9.3), (9.9.4), (9.9.5), and (9.9.7) we may have used and thus obtain a single transformation $X = MY$ which reduces q at once to a form of the type (9.9.8). Furthermore, M is nonsingular and has elements in $\mathscr{F}$.

Hence

(9.9.9)
$$q = X^{\mathsf{T}}AX = Y^{\mathsf{T}}(M^{\mathsf{T}}AM)Y = \sum_{j=1}^{k} c_j y_j^{\,2},$$

where

$$M^{\mathsf{T}}AM = D[c_1, c_2, \ldots, c_k, 0, 0, \ldots, 0].$$

But since M is nonsingular, the diagonal matrix on the right must have the same rank as A. Hence $k = r$ and the theorem is proved.

9.10 Kronecker's Reduction

By each of the two preceding methods of reduction, a quadratic form of rank $r < n$ is reduced to a form in which only r variables appear. Another way of accomplishing this is by means of **Kronecker's reduction**.

Theorem 9.10.1: *Let the quadratic form* $q = \sum\limits_{i,j=1}^{n} a_{ij}x_ix_j$ *over a number field $\mathscr{F}$ have rank $r < n$. Then if the leading principal minor of order r is not zero, there exists a nonsingular linear transformation over $\mathscr{F}$ with determinant equal to 1 which reduces q to the form* $q = \sum\limits_{i,j=1}^{r} a_{ij}y_iy_j$.

We write the matrix of the given form partitioned into columns thus: $A = [A_1, A_2, \ldots, A_n]$. By hypothesis, A has rank r with $A_1, A_2, \ldots, A_r$ linearly independent. Hence there exist relations

(9.10.1) $$A_k = \sum_{j=1}^{r} c_{kj}A_j, \qquad k = r+1, \ldots, n,$$

expressing the dependence of all later columns on the first r independent ones. Then, if we postmultiply A by the matrix

$$
C = \left[
\begin{array}{cccc:cccc}
1 & 0 & \cdots & 0 & -c_{r+1,1} & -c_{r+2,1} & \cdots & -c_{n1} \\
0 & 1 & \cdots & 0 & -c_{r+1,2} & -c_{r+2,2} & \cdots & -c_{n2} \\
 & \vdots & & & \vdots & & & \\
0 & 0 & \cdots & 1 & -c_{r+1,r} & -c_{r+2,r} & \cdots & -c_{nr} \\
\hdashline
 & & & & 1 & 0 & \cdots & 0 \\
 & & \mathbf{0} & & 0 & 1 & \cdots & 0 \\
 & & & & \vdots & & & \\
 & & & & 0 & 0 & \cdots & 1
\end{array}
\right]_n,
$$

we will obtain as the product the matrix $[A_1, \ldots, A_r, 0, \ldots, 0]$. Next, because of the symmetry of A, if we premultiply this product by C^{T}, the corresponding result will be effected with respect to the rows. We therefore have

$$
C^{\mathsf{T}}AC = \left[
\begin{array}{ccc:c}
a_{11} & \cdots & a_{1r} & \\
\vdots & & & 0 \\
a_{r1} & \cdots & a_{rr} & \\
\hdashline
 & 0 & & 0
\end{array}
\right].
$$

From this it follows that the transformation

$$X = CY$$

effects the desired reduction of the given quadratic form. Moreover, $\det C = 1$. Also, since finding the coefficients c_{kj} in (9.10.1) involves solving linear equations with coefficients in $\mathscr{F}$, it follows that the c_{kj}'s may be chosen in $\mathscr{F}$, so that C is over $\mathscr{F}$.

If now $X^{\mathsf{T}}AX$ is any quadratic form of rank r, with $r < n$, we know by Theorem 5.22.6 that the symmetric matrix A has at least one nonvanishing principal minor of order r. Then a suitable symmetric rearrangement of the rows and columns of A, which amounts to renaming the variables of the quadratic form, may be used to bring the rows and columns of this minor into the leading position. A little thought will reveal that a suitable renaming of the variables can always be effected with the aid of a permutation matrix—in fact, a matrix with determinant $+1$ if desired. Hence any quadratic form of rank r may be reduced in the manner of the theorem to a form of rank r in r variables only. Moreover, the net transformation that does the job may be chosen so as to have determinant $+1$ if desired.

We illustrate by reducing the form of rank 2,

$$X^{\mathsf{T}}AX = X^{\mathsf{T}} \begin{bmatrix} 1 & -1 & 0 \\ -1 & 1 & 0 \\ 0 & 0 & 2 \end{bmatrix} X.$$

Since the leading principal minor of order 2 is zero, but the lower right one is not, we rename the variables thus:

$$\begin{cases} x_1 = z_2 \\ x_2 = z_3 \\ x_3 = z_1 \end{cases} \quad \text{or} \quad X = \begin{bmatrix} 0 & 1 & 0 \\ 0 & 0 & 1 \\ 1 & 0 & 0 \end{bmatrix} Z.$$

This gives

$$X^{\mathsf{T}}AX = Z^{\mathsf{T}} \begin{bmatrix} 2 & 0 & 0 \\ 0 & 1 & -1 \\ 0 & -1 & 1 \end{bmatrix} Z,$$

which meets the conditions of the theorem. Using the notation of the proof,

$$A_3 = 0 \cdot A_1 + (-1)A_2.$$

Hence

$$C = \begin{bmatrix} 1 & 0 & 0 \\ 0 & 1 & 1 \\ 0 & 0 & 1 \end{bmatrix}.$$

Putting $Z = CY$, we obtain the form

$$Y^{\mathsf{T}} \begin{bmatrix} 1 & 0 & 0 \\ 0 & 1 & 0 \\ 0 & 1 & 1 \end{bmatrix} \cdot \begin{bmatrix} 2 & 0 & 0 \\ 0 & 1 & -1 \\ 0 & -1 & 1 \end{bmatrix} \cdot \begin{bmatrix} 1 & 0 & 0 \\ 0 & 1 & 1 \\ 0 & 0 & 1 \end{bmatrix} Y$$

$$= Y^{\mathsf{T}} \begin{bmatrix} 2 & 0 & 0 \\ 0 & 1 & 0 \\ 0 & 0 & 0 \end{bmatrix} Y = 2y_1{}^2 + y_2{}^2.$$

Combining the two transformations, we have the single transformation

$$X = \begin{bmatrix} 0 & 1 & 1 \\ 0 & 0 & 1 \\ 1 & 0 & 0 \end{bmatrix} Y,$$

whose determinant is $+1$ and which effects the reduction in one step.

9.11 Exercises

*1. Prove that, over the field of complex numbers, every quadratic form of rank r may be reduced to the form

$$z_1{}^2 + z_2{}^2 + \cdots + z_r{}^2$$

by a nonsingular transformation. (Begin by assuming the result of Theorem 9.9.1.)

*2. Prove that, over the complex field, two quadratic forms in n variables are equivalent if and only if they have the same rank.

3. Reduce by Kronecker's method:

(a) $\quad X^\mathsf{T} \begin{bmatrix} 1 & 2 & 4 \\ 2 & 4 & 8 \\ 4 & 8 & 16 \end{bmatrix} X,$ (b) $\quad X^\mathsf{T} \begin{bmatrix} 1 & -1 & 0 & 2 \\ -1 & 2 & 1 & -3 \\ 0 & 1 & 1 & -1 \\ 2 & -3 & -1 & 5 \end{bmatrix} X.$

4. Reduce by Lagrange's method:

(a) $\quad X^\mathsf{T} \begin{bmatrix} 4 & 2 & 1 \\ 2 & 4 & 2 \\ 1 & 2 & 4 \end{bmatrix} X,$ (b) $\quad X^\mathsf{T} \begin{bmatrix} 0 & 1 & 0 & 0 \\ 1 & 0 & 2 & 0 \\ 0 & 2 & 0 & 3 \\ 0 & 0 & 3 & 0 \end{bmatrix} X.$

*5. Show that Lagrange's reduction can always be effected by a single transformation whose determinant is 1. [*Hint:* Use an extra interchange of two variables and (or) a change of sign of one variable, if necessary.]

6. Show how the result of Exercise 5 is useful in the evaluation over a region R in $\mathscr{E}_n$ of the multiple integral

$$\int\int \cdots \int_R \left(\sum_{i,j} a_{ij} x_i x_j \right) dx_1 dx_2 \cdots dx_n.$$

7. Using Exercise 5, show how Lagrange's method of reduction may be used to evaluate the determinant of a symmetric matrix.

8. Diagonalize the forms

$$q_1(X) = 2x_1 x_2 + 2x_2 x_3,$$
$$q_2(X) = 2x_1 x_2 + 2x_2 x_3 + 2x_3 x_1,$$

means of orthogonal transformations ($n = 3$).

9. Diagonalize the forms

$$q_1(X) = 2(x_1x_2 + x_2x_3 + \cdots + x_{n-1}x_n),$$
$$q_2(X) = 2(x_1x_2 + x_2x_3 + \cdots + x_{n-1}x_n + x_nx_1).$$

SYLVESTER'S LAW OF INERTIA

9.12 Sylvester's Law of Inertia for Real Quadratic Forms

Suppose now that a quadratic form q of rank r is over the real field, so that, in the equivalent form

$$q = c_1y_1{}^2 + c_2y_2{}^2 + \cdots + c_ry_r{}^2$$

of Theorem 9.9.1, or of (9.8.2), in which case the c's are the λ's, each coefficient c_i is also real. It is not hard to see that, in effecting the reduction of q to this form, we can assign the names of the variables in such a way that all the positive terms appear first, followed by all the negative terms. We may therefore assume that q is given by

(9.12.1) $\qquad q = h_1y_1{}^2 + \cdots + h_py_p{}^2 - h_{p+1}y_{p+1}^2 - \cdots - h_ry_r{}^2,$

where $h_i > 0$ in every case. Then p is called the **index** of the form and the difference between the numbers of positive and negative terms, $p - (r - p)$, is called the **signature** of the form. These definitions are given significance by

Theorem 9.12.1: *Every quadratic form q over the field of real numbers may be reduced by a real nonsingular transformation to the form*

(9.12.2) $\qquad z_1{}^2 + \cdots + z_p{}^2 - z_{p+1}^2 - \cdots - z_r{}^2,$

where p is the index of the form and r is its rank, p and r being uniquely determined integers for a given form q.

The reduction of (9.12.1) to (9.12.2) is effected by the real, nonsingular transformation

(9.12.3)
$$z_i = h_i{}^{1/2}y_i, \qquad i = 1, 2, \ldots, r,$$
$$z_i = y_i, \qquad i = r + 1, \ldots, n.$$

Since r is unique by Theorem 9.9.1, it remains only to establish the uniqueness of p. Suppose that a different chain of real transformations had reduced the form q to the form

(9.12.4) $\qquad w_1{}^2 + \cdots + w_k{}^2 - w_{k+1}^2 - \cdots - w_r{}^2.$

We examine first the possibility that $p > k$. From preceding results we know there exist nonsingular transformations

$$Z = CX \qquad \text{and} \qquad W = DX$$

which reduce q to (9.12.2) and (9.12.4) respectively. These transformations express each z and each w as a linear function of the x's, so that, when the z's and w's are replaced by their expressions in terms of the x's, we have the *identities* in $x_1, x_2, \ldots, x_n$,

$$z_1{}^2 + \cdots + z_p{}^2 - z_{p+1}^2 - \cdots - z_r{}^2 \equiv q$$

$$\equiv w_1{}^2 + \cdots + w_k{}^2 - w_{k+1}^2 - \cdots - w_r{}^2.$$

That is, the values taken on by these three quadratic forms will be equal for each given set of values of $x_1, x_2, \ldots, x_n$.

Now consider the possibility of picking a set of values of $x_1, x_2, \ldots, x_n$ to satisfy the set of $k + (n - p)$ simultaneous equations,

$$w_1 = 0 \qquad z_{p+1} = 0$$

$$w_2 = 0 \qquad z_{p+2} = 0$$

$$\vdots \qquad\qquad \vdots$$

$$w_k = 0, \qquad z_n = 0.$$

Suppose first $p > k$. Then we have here $k + (n - p) = n - (p - k) < n$ equations, which necessarily have real, nontrivial, simultaneous solutions. For each such solution we have

$$z_1{}^2 + \cdots + z_p{}^2 = -w_{k+1}^2 - \cdots - w_r{}^2.$$

Since we are dealing with *squares* of real numbers, this equation then implies the vanishing of each term on both left and right, so that we have also

$$z_1 = 0 \qquad\qquad w_{k+1} = 0$$

$$z_2 = 0 \qquad \text{and} \qquad w_{k+2} = 0$$

$$\vdots \qquad\qquad\qquad \vdots$$

$$z_p = 0, \qquad\qquad w_r = 0.$$

Thus the n equations in the x's

$$z_1 = z_2 = \cdots = z_n = 0,$$

or, more briefly, since $Z = CX$,

$$CX = 0,$$

have a nontrivial solution. This, in turn, implies $\det C = 0$, which is not true since the transformation $Z = CX$ is nonsingular. Hence, $p \not> k$. Similarly, $k \not> p$ so that $p = k$. Thus p is a uniquely defined integer, and the proof of the theorem is complete.

Putting the conclusion another way, since every real reduction of q to the form (9.12.2) must lead to the same p and the same r, *the rank and the index are invariants of the real quadratic form q with respect to real, nonsingular transformations*. This fact is known as **Sylvester's law of inertia**.

It is now simple to prove

Theorem 9.12.2:   *Two real quadratic forms are equivalent under nonsingular real transformations if and only if they have the same rank r and the same index p.*

Suppose first that $X^\mathsf{T} A_1 X$ and $\tilde{X}^\mathsf{T} A_2 \tilde{X}$ have the same rank r and the same index p. Then there exist, by Theorem 9.12.1, real, nonsingular transformations

$$X = B_1 Y \qquad \text{and} \qquad \tilde{X} = B_2 Y$$

such that

$$Y^\mathsf{T}(B_1{}^\mathsf{T} A_1 B_1) Y \qquad \text{and} \qquad Y^\mathsf{T}(B_2{}^\mathsf{T} A_2 B_2) Y$$

are the same form

$$y_1{}^2 + y_2{}^2 + \cdots + y_p{}^2 - y_{p+1}^2 - \cdots - y_r{}^2.$$

Hence we must have

$$B_1{}^\mathsf{T} A_1 B_1 = B_2{}^\mathsf{T} A_2 B_2,$$

so that

$$A_1 = (B_2 B_1{}^{-1})^\mathsf{T} A_2 (B_2 B_1{}^{-1}),$$

and the forms are equivalent.

On the other hand, if $X^\mathsf{T} A_1 X$ and $\tilde{X}^\mathsf{T} A_2 \tilde{X}$ are equivalent under a real, nonsingular linear transformation $X = B\tilde{X}$, we will have

(9.12.5) $A_2 = B^\mathsf{T} A_1 B.$

Suppose now that $\tilde{X} = CY$ reduces $\tilde{X}^\mathsf{T} A_2 \tilde{X}$ to a form

$$y_1{}^2 + y_2{}^2 + \cdots + y_p{}^2 - y_{p+1}^2 - \cdots - y_r{}^2.$$

Then, from (9.12.5),

$$\tilde{X}^\mathsf{T} A_2 \tilde{X} = Y^\mathsf{T}(C^\mathsf{T} A_2 C) Y = Y^\mathsf{T}(BC)^\mathsf{T} A_1 (BC) Y.$$

We conclude that the transformation

$$X = (BC) Y$$

will reduce $X^\mathsf{T} A_1 X$ to the same result. Thus p and r are the same for the two forms and the theorem is proved.

An analogous result proved in the same manner as the one just established is given by

Theorem 9.12.3: *Two real bilinear forms with symmetric matrices of the same order are equivalent under real, nonsingular, cogredient transformations if and only if they may both be reduced to the same form*

$$x_1 y_1 + x_2 y_2 + \cdots + x_p y_p - x_{p+1} y_{p+1} - \cdots - x_r y_r.$$

Thus the equivalence over the real field of the two bilinear forms also rests on the equality of the two numbers r (the rank) and p (the index) which are uniquely defined for each form.

The forms

$$y_1{}^2 + y_2{}^2 + \cdots + y_p{}^2 - y_{p+1}^2 - \cdots - y_r{}^2$$

and

$$x_1 y_1 + x_2 y_2 + \cdots + x_p y_p - x_{p+1} y_{p+1} - \cdots - x_r y_r$$

are called canonical forms for real quadratic and bilinear forms with symmetric matrices. Correspondingly,

$$\begin{bmatrix} I_p & 0 & 0 \\ 0 & -I_{r-p} & 0 \\ 0 & 0 & 0 \end{bmatrix}$$

is a canonical form for a real, symmetric matrix A. That is, given A, there always exists a real, nonsingular matrix B such that $B^{\mathsf T} A B$ is in the stated normal form.

The normal form,

$$\begin{bmatrix} I_r & 0 \\ 0 & 0 \end{bmatrix},$$

developed in Chapter Four for an arbitrary constant matrix of rank r over a number field $\mathscr{F}$ is another canonical form. There are other canonical forms for matrices and for quadratic and bilinear forms, each designed to exhibit certain important properties thereof.

VALUES OF REAL QUADRATIC FORMS

9.13 Values of a Quadratic Form

Consider an arbitrary real quadratic form $q(X) = X^{\mathsf T} A X$. It is often important to know certain properties of the set of values of q when X is a unit vector. To study this problem, we need to know a little more of the geometry of $\mathscr{E}_n$.

The angle between two nonzero-vectors X and Y of $\mathscr{E}_n$ is defined, as in $\mathscr{E}_2$ and $\mathscr{E}_3$, by the formula

(9.13.1) $$\cos \theta = \frac{X^{\mathsf T} Y}{|X| \cdot |Y|}, \qquad 0 \leqslant \theta \leqslant \pi.$$

This is acceptable since, by the Cauchy-Schwarz inequality,

$$|X^\mathsf{T} Y| \leqslant |X| \cdot |Y|,$$

so that we have $-1 \leqslant \cos \theta \leqslant 1$. If X and Y are unit vectors, we have simply

$$\cos \theta = X^\mathsf{T} Y = Y^\mathsf{T} X, \qquad |X| = |Y| = 1.$$

The vectors X and Y are orthogonal if and only if $\theta = \pi/2$, that is, $X^\mathsf{T} Y = 0$.

Now let $B_1, B_2, \ldots, B_n$ represent an arbitrary orthonormal reference system in $\mathscr{E}_n$, and let θ_i denote the angle between an arbitrary nonzero-vector X and B_i. There exist unique scalars α_j not all zero such that $X = \sum\limits_{j=1}^{n} \alpha_j B_j$. Hence, since $B_i^\mathsf{T} B_j = \delta_{ij}$,

$$\cos \theta_i = \frac{B_i^\mathsf{T} X}{|X|} = \frac{1}{|X|} \sum_{j=1}^{n} \alpha_j B_i^\mathsf{T} B_j = \frac{\alpha_i}{|X|},$$

That is,

(9.13.2)
$$X = |X| \cdot \sum_{j=1}^{n} (\cos \theta_j) B_j.$$

Now,

$$X^\mathsf{T} X = |X| \sum_{j=1}^{n} (\cos \theta_j) X^\mathsf{T} B_j$$

$$= |X|^2 \sum_{j=1}^{n} (\cos \theta_j)^2 = X^\mathsf{T} X \sum_{j=1}^{n} (\cos \theta_j)^2.$$

Since $X^\mathsf{T} X \neq 0$, we have

(9.13.3)
$$\sum_{j=1}^{n} (\cos \theta_j)^2 = 1.$$

We return again to the quadratic form $q(X) = X^\mathsf{T} A X$. Let $U_1, U_2, \ldots, U_n$ be an orthonormal set of characteristic vectors of A, and let X be an arbitrary unit vector. Let θ_j denote the angle between X and U_j, so that

$$\cos \theta_j = U_j^\mathsf{T} X.$$

Also, let $U = [U_1, U_2, \ldots, U_n]$, and define Y by the equation $X = UY$ or $Y = U^\mathsf{T} X$. Then,

$$Y = \begin{bmatrix} U_1^\mathsf{T} \\ U_2^\mathsf{T} \\ \vdots \\ U_n^\mathsf{T} \end{bmatrix} X = \begin{bmatrix} \cos \theta_1 \\ \cos \theta_2 \\ \vdots \\ \cos \theta_n \end{bmatrix}.$$

Hence,

$$q(X) = X^\mathsf{T} A X = Y^\mathsf{T} U^\mathsf{T} A U Y = Y^\mathsf{T} D[\lambda_1, \lambda_2, \ldots, \lambda_n] Y$$

$$= \sum_{j=1}^{n} \lambda_j \cos^2 \theta_j.$$

We have, therefore, what is known as **Euler's theorem**:

Theorem 9.13.1: *The value of a quadratic form $q(X) = X^\mathsf{T}AX$ at a unit vector X is $\sum \lambda_j \cos^2 \theta_j$, where the λ's are the characteristic roots of A, and the angles θ_j are the angles between X and the vectors U_j of an orthonormal set of characteristic vectors of A corresponding to the λ_j's respectively.*

Again, let $B_1, B_2, \ldots, B_n$ denote an arbitrary orthonormal reference system in $\mathscr{E}_n$, and let θ_{ij} denote the angle between B_i and U_j, where U_j is as defined above. Then, by the preceding theorem, $q(B_i) = \sum\limits_{j=1}^{n} \lambda_j \cos^2 \theta_{ij}$. Also, since the B's are an orthonormal reference system, $\sum\limits_{i=1}^{n} \cos^2 \theta_{ij} = 1$, by (9.13.3) above. Hence,

$$\sum_{i=1}^{n} q(B_i) = \sum_{i=1}^{n} \left(\sum_{j=1}^{n} \lambda_j \cos^2 \theta_{ij} \right)$$
$$= \sum_{j=1}^{n} \lambda_j \left(\sum_{i=1}^{n} \cos^2 \theta_{ij} \right) = \sum_{j=1}^{n} \lambda_j.$$

We thus have

Theorem 9.13.2: *The sum of the values of a real quadratic form at the n vectors of an arbitrary orthonormal reference system is equal to the sum of the characteristic roots of A, that is, it is equal to the trace of A.*

Now let the characteristic roots of A be indexed in descending order:

$$\lambda_1 \geqslant \lambda_2 \geqslant \cdots \geqslant \lambda_n,$$

and let a corresponding set of orthonormal characteristic vectors be $U_1, U_2, \ldots, U_n$. Let X be an arbitrary unit vector making the angle θ_i with U_i, so that

$$X^\mathsf{T}U_i = \cos \theta_i,$$

and, by Euler's theorem,

$$q(X) = \sum_{i=1}^{n} \lambda_i \cos^2 \theta_i.$$

Suppose we choose X so that $X^\mathsf{T}U_i = 0$, $i = 1, 2, \ldots, m - 1$. Then $\cos \theta_i = 0$, $i = 1, 2, \ldots, m - 1$, and hence, for each such X,

$$q(X) = \lambda_m \cos^2 \theta_m + \cdots + \lambda_n \cos^2 \theta_n.$$

Because of the ordering of the λ's and (9.13.3), we now have

$$q(X) \leqslant \lambda_m(\cos^2 \theta_m + \cdots + \cos^2 \theta_n) = \lambda_m.$$

On the other hand, if we choose $X = U_m$, we have $\cos \theta_m = 1$, $\cos \theta_i = 0$, $i \neq m$. Hence, $q(U_m) = \lambda_m$. (See also Exercise 13, Section 8.3.) Thus the value λ_m is actually attainable. In summary, we have

Theorem 9.13.3: *Given the real quadratic form $q(X) = X^\mathsf{T}AX$. Let the characteristic roots of A be $\lambda_1 \geqslant \lambda_2 \geqslant \cdots \geqslant \lambda_n$, and let an associated set of orthonormal characteristic vectors be $U_1, U_2, \ldots, U_n$. Then λ_m is the maximum value of q over the set of unit vectors which are orthogonal to $U_1, U_2, \ldots, U_{m-1}$. In particular, λ_1 is the maximum value of q over the set of all unit vectors.*

Thus appropriate knowledge of the values of a quadratic form gives us important knowledge about the characteristic roots of the corresponding symmetric matrix.

Another important aspect of the values of a quadratic function is simply the sign of $q(X)$. Let $q(X) = X^{\mathsf{T}}AX$ be a real quadratic form in n variables. Let the rank be r and the index be p. Let U be an orthogonal matrix such that

$$U^{\mathsf{T}}AU = D[\alpha_1, \alpha_2, \ldots, \alpha_p, \beta_1, \beta_2, \ldots, \beta_{r-p}, 0, 0, \ldots, 0],$$

where each α_i is positive and each β_j is negative. Now let

(9.13.4)
$$X = U\tilde{X}, \qquad \tilde{X} = \sum_{i=1}^{p} b_i E_i.$$

If not all the b's are 0, that is, if $X \neq 0$, we have

$$X^{\mathsf{T}}AX = \tilde{X}^{\mathsf{T}}U^{\mathsf{T}}AU\tilde{X} = \left(\sum_{i=1}^{p} b_i E_i^{\mathsf{T}}\right) D \left(\sum_{i=1}^{p} b_i E_i\right)$$

$$= \sum_{i=1}^{p} \alpha_i b_i^2 > 0.$$

Thus the given quadratic form is positive for every nonzero-vector X of the $\mathscr{V}_n^p$ defined by (9.13.4).

Similarly, if we let

(9.13.5)
$$Y = U\tilde{Y}, \qquad \text{where} \qquad \tilde{Y} = \sum_{j=1}^{r-p} c_j E_{j+p},$$

we obtain for any $Y \neq 0$,

$$Y^{\mathsf{T}}AX = \tilde{Y}^{\mathsf{T}}U^{\mathsf{T}}AU\tilde{Y} = \left(\sum_{j=1}^{r-p} c_j E^{\mathsf{T}}_{j+p}\right) D \left(\sum_{j=1}^{r-p} c_j E_{j+p}\right)$$

$$= \sum_{j=1}^{r-p} \beta_j c_j^2 < 0.$$

The given quadratic form is therefore negative for every nonzero-vector Y of the $\mathscr{V}_n^{r-p}$ defined by (9.13.5).

Note next that, for arbitrary vectors X and Y of the two spaces just defined,

$$X^{\mathsf{T}}Y = \tilde{X}^{\mathsf{T}}U^{\mathsf{T}}U\tilde{Y} = \tilde{X}^{\mathsf{T}}\tilde{Y} = \left(\sum_{i=1}^{p} b_i E_i^{\mathsf{T}}\right)\left(\sum_{j=1}^{r-p} c_j E_{j+p}\right) = 0,$$

that is, the $\mathscr{V}_n^p$ and the $\mathscr{V}_n^{r-p}$ are orthogonal. Hence, in the case when $r = n$, we have two orthogonal spaces whose dimensions total n so that $\mathscr{V}_n^n$ is the sum of these spaces. (It should not be overlooked that these spaces vary with the orthogonal transformation U.) In summary, we have

Theorem 9.13.4: *Given a real quadratic form q of rank r and index p, there exist real spaces of dimension p on which q is positive if $p > 0$, and real spaces of dimension $r - p$ on which q is negative if $r - p > 0$. One can choose (but not uniquely) pairs of spaces, one of each kind, which are orthogonal. Any two such orthogonal spaces span the $\mathscr{V}_n^n$ over the real field in the case when $r = n$.*

As a simple example in $\mathscr{E}_2$, consider the form $q = x_1^2 - x_2^2$ for which $p = 1$ and $r = n = 2$. This form is positive on the $\mathscr{V}_2^1$ with basis E_1, and negative on the $\mathscr{V}_2{}^1$ with basis E_2. E_1 is orthogonal to E_2 and, together, E_1 and E_2 span $\mathscr{V}_2{}^2$. The form is also positive on any $\mathscr{V}_2{}^1$ with basis $\{a, b\}$, where $|a| > |b|$, and negative on any $\mathscr{V}_2{}^1$ with basis $\{a, b\}$, where $|a| < |b|$. Suppose $|a| > |b|$. Then $\{a, b\}$ and $\{-b, a\}$ span orthogonal spaces on which q is positive and negative respectively.

A simple and important application of values of quadratic forms occurs in the theory of maxima and minima of differentiable functions. Let $f(x_1, x_2, \ldots, x_n)$ $\equiv f(X)$ be differentiable with continuous third partial derivatives. Then the point X_0 (endpoint of the vector X_0) is called a **critical point** of f if

$$\frac{\partial f}{\partial x_i}(X_0) = 0, \qquad i = 1, 2, \ldots, n.$$

The symmetric matrix,

$$H(X_0) = \left[\frac{\partial^2 f}{\partial x_i \, \partial x_j}(X_0)\right],$$

is called the **Hessian matrix of f at X_0**.

The point X_0 is called a **nondegenerate critical point of index** $n - p$ if the quadratic form $Y^{\mathsf{T}}H(X_0)Y$ has rank n and index p.

At any point X_0, the finite Taylor expansion up to the second order can be written in the form

$$f(X) = f(X_0) + \left[\frac{\partial f}{\partial x_1}, \frac{\partial f}{\partial x_2}, \cdots, \frac{\partial f}{\partial x_n}\right]_{X_0} \Delta X + \frac{1}{2}(\Delta X)^{\mathsf{T}}H(X_0)\,\Delta X + \sigma(|\Delta X|^3),$$

where $\Delta X = X - X_0$ and $\sigma(|\Delta X|^3)$ is a quantity which approaches 0 at least as fast as $|\Delta X|^3$. It follows that the approximate behavior of $f(X) - f(X_0)$ in a neighborhood of a nondegenerate critical point X_0 is the same as the behavior of $Y^{\mathsf{T}}H(X_0)Y$ in a neighborhood of $Y = 0$, for here

$$f(X) - f(X_0) = \tfrac{1}{2}\Delta X^{\mathsf{T}}\,H(X_0)\,\Delta X.$$

In particular:

(1) If $p = 0$, X_0 is a relative maximum point;

(2) if $p = n$, X_0 is a relative minimum point;

(3) if $0 < p < n$, then X_0 is neither a maximum point nor a relative minimum point, for every neighborhood of X_0 contains points X, X' for which $f(X) > f(X_0)$ and $f(X') < f(X_0)$, as follows from Theorem 9.13.4.

9.14 Exercises

1. Show that the range of values of a real quadratic form over the set of all unit vectors remains the same in all orthonormal reference systems.

2. Show that in the notation of Theorem 9.13.3, λ_m is the *minimum* value assumed by q over the set of all unit vectors X such that

$$X^{\mathsf{T}}U_{m+1} = 0, \, X^{\mathsf{T}}U_{m+2} = 0, \ldots, X^{\mathsf{T}}U_n = 0.$$

In particular, λ_n is the minimum value of q over the set of all unit vectors.

***3.** Prove that the number of positive characteristic roots of a real symmetric matrix A of rank r is equal to the index p of A, and that the number of negative characteristic roots is equal to the difference $r - p$.

4. Given the quadratic form in $\mathscr{E}_2$, $x_1{}^2 + 2x_1x_2$, find a $\mathscr{V}_2{}^p$ over which the form is positive, and an orthogonal $\mathscr{V}_2{}^{r-p}$ over which the form is negative. Show that together these spaces span $\mathscr{V}_2{}^2$.

5. Proceed as in Exercise 4 for the quadratic form in $\mathscr{E}_3$, $x_1{}^2 + x_2{}^2 - 2x_2x_3$.

6. Determine the nature of the critical points of the functions:

(a) $4x_1x_2 - x_1{}^2 - x_2{}^2 + 12x_1$.

(b) $x_1{}^2 + x_2{}^2 + x_3{}^2 + x_1x_2 + x_2x_3 + 4x_1 - 8x_3$.

DEFINITE QUADRATIC FORMS AND DEFINITE MATRICES

9.15 Definite Forms

A real, quadratic form $q \equiv X^\mathsf{T}AX$ with a *nonsingular* symmetric matrix of order n is called **positive** or **positive definite** if its rank and its index are equal. This means that $n = r = p$ so that there are no negative or zero terms in its canonical form. Hence, under a suitable nonsingular transformation $X = BY$, we have

$$(9.15.1) \qquad q \equiv X^\mathsf{T}AX \equiv y_1{}^2 + y_2{}^2 + \cdots + y_n{}^2 = Y^\mathsf{T}Y,$$

so that every positive definite quadratic form is equivalent to the unit quadratic form $Y^\mathsf{T}Y$, which is the simplest positive definite form. The fact that $Y^\mathsf{T}Y$ is positive definite is what guarantees that the length $\sqrt{Y^\mathsf{T}Y}$ of Y will always be real and will always be different from 0 when $Y \neq 0$. For every nontrivial set of real y's, the left member will be greater than zero and hence, because of the identity (9.15.1), q must be greater than zero for every nontrivial set of real x's, which explains the name. The converse is also true: If q is greater than zero for every nontrivial set of real x's, then $p = r = n$, so that the form is positive definite. The reader should prove this in detail.

A real, *singular* quadratic form $q \equiv X^\mathsf{T}AX$ with a symmetric matrix of order n is called **positive semidefinite** if its rank and its index are equal. This means that there are no negative terms in its canonical form, which therefore reads

$$(9.15.2) \qquad q \equiv X^\mathsf{T}AX \equiv y_1{}^2 + y_2{}^2 + \cdots + y_r{}^2, \qquad r < n,$$

where r is the rank of the form. For any set of values of the y's, the right member here is positive or zero, and hence, because of the identity, q must be positive or zero for all sets of values of the x's. Again, if q is positive or zero for all sets of x's, then $p = r$, so that q is at least positive semidefinite. The forms on the right in (9.15.1) and (9.15.2) are the simplest definite and semidefinite forms respectively.

A form that may be either positive semidefinite or positive definite is called **nonnegative definite**.

A form is **negative definite** ($r = n$) or **negative semidefinite** ($r < n$) if its index is zero. Its canonical form is then

$$q = -y_1{}^2 - y_2{}^2 - \cdots - y_r{}^2,$$

where r is the rank of the form.

Since the negative forms are simply the negatives of positive forms, it is not necessary to develop a separate theory for them. They are, however, useful in certain applications. The positive definite and semidefinite forms on the other hand, are more widely used. To illustrate, the *variance* of X

$$s_X{}^2 = \frac{1}{n-1} \sum_{j=1}^{n} (x_j - m_x)^2$$

is a particularly useful positive semidefinite form of rank $n - 1$. (See Exercise 5, Section 9.7.) On the other hand, the quadratic forms representing potential and kinetic energy in theoretical mechanics are positive definite.

The basic theorem on definite forms is

Theorem 9.15.1: *If $X^{\mathsf{T}}AX$ is positive definite, then $\det A > 0$.*

For there exists a nonsingular transformation $X = BY$ such that

$$X^{\mathsf{T}}AX = Y^{\mathsf{T}}(B^{\mathsf{T}}AB)Y = Y^{\mathsf{T}}I_n Y.$$

Hence

$$B^{\mathsf{T}}AB = I_n,$$

so that

$$\det B^{\mathsf{T}} \det A \det B = 1,$$

or

$$\det A = (\det B)^{-2} > 0.$$

Theorem 9.15.2: *If $X^{\mathsf{T}}AX$ is positive definite, then every principal minor determinant of A is positive.*

Such a minor is the determinant of the matrix of a quadratic form obtained by putting one or more of the variables $x_1, x_2, \ldots, x_n$ equal to zero, and the resulting quadratic form is positive definite in the remaining variables. Theorem 9.15.1 now applies.

Theorem 9.15.3: *If $X^{\mathsf{T}}AX$ is positive definite, then $a_{ii} > 0$ for $i = 1, 2, \ldots, n$.*

This is just a special case of the preceding result.

Theorem 9.15.4: *If $X^\mathsf{T}AX$ is positive semidefinite, every principal minor determinant of A is $\geqslant 0$.*

For again, any such minor is the determinant of the matrix of a quadratic form obtained by putting one or more of the variables $x_1, x_2, \ldots, x_n$ equal to zero. Such a quadratic form is either positive semidefinite or positive definite in the remaining variables. Hence the principal minor must either be zero or be positive by Theorem 9.15.1.

Theorem 9.15.5: *If $X^\mathsf{T}AX$ is positive semidefinite and x_i actually appears in $X^\mathsf{T}AX$, then $a_{ii} > 0$.*

From the previous theorem, we have that $a_{ii} \geqslant 0$ in any case, since a_{ii} is a principal minor of A. Since x_i actually appears in $X^\mathsf{T}AX$, $a_{ik} \neq 0$ for some k. If $k = i$, then $a_{ii} > 0$ by Theorem 9.15.4. If $k \neq i$, then by the preceding theorem we have

$$\det \begin{bmatrix} a_{ii} & a_{ik} \\ a_{ki} & a_{kk} \end{bmatrix} \geqslant 0,$$

or

$$a_{ii}a_{kk} - (a_{ik})^2 \geqslant 0,$$

which would be impossible were $a_{ii} = 0$. Hence $a_{ii} > 0$.

9.16 Definite Matrices

A real symmetric matrix A is called a **positive definite matrix** (or a **positive semidefinite matrix**) if and only if the corresponding quadratic form $X^\mathsf{T}AX$ is positive definite (or positive semidefinite). In some cases (for example in the preceding sequence of theorems) one usually employs forms in discussing definiteness. In others, as will be illustrated in some of the theorems to follow, it may be convenient to deal with the matrices directly.

Theorem 9.16.1: *The diagonal matrix $D[\lambda_1, \lambda_2, \ldots, \lambda_n]$ is positive definite if and only if all the λ's are positive.*

For the rank and the index of the form

$$X^\mathsf{T}DX = \lambda_1 x_1{}^2 + \lambda_2 x_2{}^2 + \cdots + \lambda_n x_n{}^2,$$

both equal n if and only if all the λ's are > 0.

Theorem 9.16.2: *A real matrix A is symmetric and positive definite if and only if for every real nonsingular matrix B of the same order, $B^\mathsf{T}AB$ is symmetric and positive definite.*

When A is symmetric and positive definite, the form $X^\mathsf{T}AX$ is positive for *all* real, nonzero-vectors X. Since B is nonsingular, when $Y \neq 0$, the vector $X = BY$ is also different from zero. Hence, for all $Y \neq 0$,

$$Y^\mathsf{T}(B^\mathsf{T}AB)Y = (BY)^\mathsf{T}A(BY) = X^\mathsf{T}AX > 0,$$

that is, $B^\mathsf{T}AB$ is positive definite. It is easily checked that $B^\mathsf{T}AB$ is symmetric.

The converse is proved by observing that $I^\mathsf{T}AI = A$ is a positive definite symmetric matrix by hypothesis.

Theorem 9.16.3: *A real, symmetric matrix A is positive definite if and only if all its characteristic roots are positive.*

First there exists a nonsingular, orthogonal matrix U such that $U^\mathsf{T}AU = D[\lambda_1, \lambda_2, \ldots, \lambda_n]$, where $\lambda_1, \lambda_2, \ldots, \lambda_n$ are the characteristic roots of A. By the preceding theorem, if A is positive definite, $D[\lambda_1, \lambda_2, \ldots, \lambda_n]$ must also be positive definite, so that by Theorem 9.16.1, $\lambda_i > 0$, $i = 1, 2, \ldots, n$. Conversely, if each $\lambda_i > 0$, again by Theorem 9.16.1, $D[\lambda_1, \lambda_2, \ldots, \lambda_n]$ is positive definite so that, now by the preceding theorem, $A = UD[\lambda_1, \lambda_2, \ldots, \lambda_n]U^\mathsf{T}$ is also positive definite.

Theorem 9.16.4: *The real matrix A is symmetric and positive definite if and only if A^{-1} exists and is symmetric and positive definite.*

If A is symmetric, so is A^{-1} (Exercise 10, Section 3.2), and conversely. If A is positive definite, all its characteristic roots are positive by the preceding theorem. The roots of A^{-1} are $\lambda_1^{-1}, \lambda_2^{-1}, \ldots, \lambda_n^{-1}$ (Exercise 14, Section 8.3). Hence they are also all positive, so that A^{-1} is positive definite, also by the preceding theorem. Applying the same argument to A^{-1} instead of A will now prove the remainder of the theorem.

Theorem 9.16.5: *If a real symmetric matrix A is positive definite, then so is A^p where p is any integer.*

This follows from the fact that the characteristic roots of A^p are λ_1^p, $\lambda_2^p, \ldots, \lambda_n^p$ (Exercise 3, Section 8.9) and from Theorem 9.16.3.

Theorem 9.16.6: *A real matrix A is symmetric and positive definite if and only if there exists a real nonsingular matrix B such that $A = B^\mathsf{T}B$.*

If A is symmetric and positive definite, there exists a nonsingular real matrix B^{-1} such that $(B^{-1})^\mathsf{T}A(B^{-1}) = I_n$. Then $A = B^\mathsf{T}B$.

Conversely, suppose $A = B^\mathsf{T}B$ with B real and nonsingular. Then $A^\mathsf{T} = B^\mathsf{T}B$ also, so that A is symmetric and is real because B is. Since B is nonsingular, we have $(B^{-1})^\mathsf{T}AB^{-1} = I_n$. Then A is positive definite since I_n is.

The theorems of this section are important in a variety of applications.

9.17 A Necessary and Sufficient Condition for Positive Definiteness

In a matrix A of order n, the **leading principal minor determinants** are defined thus:

$$p_0 = 1, \qquad p_1 = a_{11},$$

$$p_2 = \begin{vmatrix} a_{11} & a_{12} \\ a_{21} & a_{22} \end{vmatrix}, \qquad p_3 = \begin{vmatrix} a_{11} & a_{12} & a_{13} \\ a_{21} & a_{22} & a_{23} \\ a_{31} & a_{32} & a_{33} \end{vmatrix}, \ldots, p_n = \det A.$$

These minors play an important role in Lagrange's method of reduction, as we shall now show.

Let us suppose that at each stage of the process the necessary square term is present, so that we can first complete the square on x_1, then on x_2, and so on until the task is complete. Then we can write q as a linear combination of squares of linear forms

$$(9.17.1) \quad q = c_1(x_1 + \alpha_{12}x_2 + \cdots + \alpha_{1n}x_n)^2 + c_2(x_2 + \alpha_{23}x_3 + \cdots$$
$$+ \alpha_{2n}x_n)^2 + \cdots + c_r(x_r + \alpha_{r,r+1}x_{r+1} + \cdots + \alpha_{r,n}x_n)^2,$$

where $r \leqslant n$ and where the coefficient of x_j in the jth linear form is 1. The nonsingular transformation

$$(9.17.2) \quad \begin{aligned} y_1 &= x_1 + \alpha_{12}x_2 + \quad \cdots + \alpha_{1n}x_n \\ y_2 &= \qquad x_2 + \quad \cdots + \alpha_{2n}x_n \\ &\;\vdots \\ y_r &= \qquad\qquad x_r + \cdots + \alpha_{rn}x_n \\ y_{r+1} &= \qquad\qquad x_{r+1} \\ &\;\vdots \\ y_n &= \qquad\qquad\qquad x_n \end{aligned}$$

then gives

$$q = c_1 y_1^2 + c_2 y_2^2 + \cdots + c_r y_r^2.$$

We have, of course,

$$c_1 = a_{11} = \frac{p_1}{p_0} \neq 0.$$

The coefficient of x_2^2 in q is a_{22}, but from (9.17.1) it is also $c_1\alpha_{12}^2 + c_2$. Now from Section 9.9,

$$\alpha_{12} = \frac{a_{12}}{a_{11}},$$

so that after a little manipulation we have

$$c_2 = a_{22} - c_1\alpha_{12}{}^2 = \frac{a_{11}a_{22} - a_{12}{}^2}{a_{11}} = \frac{p_2}{p_1}.$$

The pattern suggested here is perfectly general:

Theorem 9.17.1:   *Let A be symmetric and of rank r. Then there exists an identity*

(9.17.3) $$X^{\mathsf{T}}AX \equiv \frac{p_1}{p_0} y_1{}^2 + \frac{p_2}{p_1} y_2{}^2 + \cdots + \frac{p_r}{p_{r-1}} y_r{}^2,$$

where $p_0 = 1$ and where y_j has the form $y_j = x_j + \alpha_{j,j+1}x_{j+1} + \cdots + \alpha_{jn}x_n$, if and only if $p_j \neq 0, j = 1, 2, \ldots, r$.

By inspection of (9.17.3), we see that it is necessary that $p_1, p_2, \ldots, p_{r-1}$ be different from zero in order for an identity of the form (9.17.3) to exist, and that p_r be different from zero for the form on the right to have the rank r.

The sufficiency of the condition is proved by induction. Suppose that $p_1, p_2, \ldots, p_{r-1}$ are all different from zero. Then $a_{11} \neq 0$, and we can write

$$q = X^{\mathsf{T}}AX = a_{11}\left(x_1 + \frac{a_{12}}{a_{11}} x_2 + \cdots + \frac{a_{1n}}{a_{11}} x_n\right)^2 + q_2(x_2, \ldots, x_n),$$

as in Section 9.9, or

$$q = \frac{p_1}{p_0} y_1{}^2 + q_2(x_2, \ldots, x_n),$$

where

$$y_1 = x_1 + \frac{a_{12}}{a_{11}} x_2 + \cdots + \frac{a_{1n}}{a_{11}} x_n.$$

That is, since $p_1 \neq 0$, the first step of the reduction can be carried out. Let us suppose then that we have been able to write

$$q = \frac{p_1}{p_0} y_1{}^2 + \frac{p_2}{p_1} y_2{}^2 + \cdots + \frac{p_{k-1}}{p_{k-2}} y_{k-1}^2 + q_k(x_k, \ldots, x_n),$$

where

(9.17.4) $$y_j = x_j + \alpha_{j,j+1}x_{j+1} + \cdots + \alpha_{jn}x_n, \qquad j = 1, 2, \ldots, k-1.$$

Let us put

$$q_k = \sum_{i,j=k}^{n} c_{ij}x_i x_j, \qquad c_{ij} = c_{ji}.$$

Then we have $k-1$ equations of the form

(9.17.5a) $$\frac{1}{2}\frac{\partial q}{\partial x_s} \equiv \sum_{j=1}^{n} a_{sj}x_j \equiv \sum_{j=1}^{s} \frac{p_j}{p_{j-1}} y_j \frac{\partial y_j}{\partial x_s}, \qquad s = 1, 2, \ldots, k-1,$$

and one equation of the form

(9.17.5b) $$\frac{1}{2}\frac{\partial q}{\partial x_k} \equiv \sum_{j=1}^{n} a_{kj}x_j \equiv \sum_{j=1}^{k-1} \frac{p_j}{p_{j-1}}\, y_j\, \frac{\partial y_j}{\partial x_k} + \sum_{j=k}^{n} c_{kj}x_j.$$

In these identities and in (9.17.4) let us put $x_{k+1} = \cdots = x_n = 0$, and then let us choose $x_1, x_2, \ldots, x_k$ so that, in (9.17.4),

$$y_1 = y_2 = \cdots = y_{k-1} = 0.$$

We have here $k-1$ equations in the k remaining unknowns, $x_1, x_2, \ldots, x_k$, so that a nontrivial solution certainly exists. For such a solution, together with $x_{k+1} = \cdots = x_n = 0$, we deduce from (9.17.5a, b) that

$$\sum_{j=1}^{k} a_{sj}x_j = 0, \qquad s = 1, 2, \ldots, k-1,$$

$$\sum_{j=1}^{k} a_{kj}x_j = c_{kk}x_k.$$

Here we have k homogeneous equations in k unknowns which have by hypothesis a nontrivial solution. Hence the determinant of the system must vanish:

$$\begin{vmatrix} a_{11} & a_{12} & \cdots & a_{1k} \\ a_{21} & a_{22} & \cdots & a_{2k} \\ \vdots & & & \\ a_{k1} & a_{k2} & \cdots & (a_{kk} - c_{kk}) \end{vmatrix} = 0.$$

Expanding, we have

$$p_k - c_{kk}p_{k-1} = 0,$$

or, since $p_{k-1} \neq 0$, $p_k \neq 0$,

$$c_{kk} = \frac{p_k}{p_{k-1}} \neq 0.$$

We can therefore proceed with the next step of the reduction, obtaining $(p_k/p_{k-1})y_k^2$ as the next term. Finally, since A has rank r, the process must stop with the term in y_r^2, so that the proof of the theorem is complete.

We are now able to prove the following result:

Theorem 9.17.2:   *A real quadratic form q of rank r is positive semidefinite, or definite if $r = n$, and actually contains the variables $x_1, x_2, \ldots, x_r$ if $p_1, p_2, \ldots, p_r$ are all positive.*

Since $p_1, p_2, \ldots, p_r$ are all $\neq 0$ and q has rank r, we have, by the preceding theorem,

$$q \equiv \frac{p_1}{p_0} y_1{}^2 + \frac{p_2}{p_1} y_2{}^2 + \cdots + \frac{p_r}{p_{r-1}} y_r{}^2.$$

Hence, all the p's being positive, q is positive semidefinite if $r < n$ and positive definite if $r = n$. Furthermore, q must contain $x_1, x_2, \ldots, x_r$, for the absence of x_j, say, with $j \leqslant r$, would imply the vanishing of the jth row and the jth column in the matrix of q so that $p_j, p_{j+1}, \ldots, p_r$ would all vanish, contrary to hypothesis.

Combining results from Theorems 9.15.2 and 9.17.2, we have

Theorem 9.17.3:   *A real quadratic form is positive definite if and only if* $p_1 > 0, p_2 > 0, \ldots, p_n > 0$, *that is, if and only if the leading principal minors of the matrix of the form are all positive.*

9.18 Examples

(1) Under what circumstances will a real matrix of the type

$$A = \begin{bmatrix} x & a & a & \cdots & a \\ a & x & a & \cdots & a \\ \vdots & & & & \\ a & a & a & \cdots & x \end{bmatrix}_n$$

be positive definite? Positive semidefinite?

We have, after a little manipulation,

$$\det A = (x - a)^{n-1}(x + (n-1)a).$$

The leading principal minor determinants are

$$p_k = (x - a)^{k-1}(x + (k-1)a), \qquad k = 1, 2, \ldots, n.$$

We will have A positive definite if and only if each $p_k > 0$. This will certainly be the case, regardless of the sign of a, if the inequalities

$$x > 0, \qquad x > a, \qquad x > -(n-1)a,$$

are all satisfied. That is, these are *sufficient* conditions for the positive definiteness of A. Suppose now that A is positive definite. Then $p_1 \equiv x > 0$ and therefore, since $p_2 \equiv (x - a)(x + a) > 0$, it follows that $x > a$ (and $x > -a$). Finally, from the hypothesis that $\det A > 0$ it follows also that $x > -(n-1)a$. Thus the conditions are also *necessary*.

If A is to be semidefinite, we must have $\det A = 0$ so that either $x = a$ or $x = -(n-1)a$. If $x = a$,

$$A = a \begin{bmatrix} 1 & 1 & \cdots & 1 \\ 1 & 1 & \cdots & 1 \\ \vdots & & & \\ 1 & 1 & \cdots & 1 \end{bmatrix}_n.$$

Hence $X^{\mathsf{T}}AX = a(x_1 + x_2 + \cdots + x_n)^2$, which is positive semidefinite of rank 1 if $a > 0$. If $x = -(n - 1)a$, we have

$$A = (-a) \begin{bmatrix} n-1 & -1 & \cdots & -1 \\ -1 & n-1 & \cdots & -1 \\ \vdots & & & \\ -1 & -1 & \cdots & n-1 \end{bmatrix}_n,$$

which may be shown to have rank $n - 1$. Since we have, in this case,

$$p_k = (n - k)n^{k-1}(-a)^k,$$

we will have $p_1 > 0, \ldots, p_{n-1} > 0$ and, hence, A positive semidefinite if and only if $a < 0$.

Various special cases of the preceding example and of the next are useful in statistics.

(2) Show that, for any real matrix A, the form $X^{\mathsf{T}}(A^{\mathsf{T}}A)X$ is positive definite or semidefinite.

This is because $X^{\mathsf{T}}(A^{\mathsf{T}}A)X = (AX)^{\mathsf{T}}(AX)$ which is a nonnegative scalar since AX is a real vector.

If A has order (m, n), then $A^{\mathsf{T}}A$ is of order n. Also the rank of $A^{\mathsf{T}}A$ is not greater than either m or n. Hence, if $n > m$, $A^{\mathsf{T}}A$ is certainly singular and therefore positive semidefinite. If $n \leqslant m$, $A^{\mathsf{T}}A$ is positive semidefinite or definite, depending on whether the rank of A is or is not less than n. This follows from the fact that $\det A^{\mathsf{T}}A$ is a sum of squares of major determinants of A, these majors having order n.

When A is of order n and nonsingular, the nonsingular transformation $Y = AX$ gives $X^{\mathsf{T}}A^{\mathsf{T}}AX = Y^{\mathsf{T}}Y = \sum_{i=1}^{n} y_i^2$, which again shows that the form is positive definite. This same reduction to a sum of n squares works even if A is singular, but in this case $A^{\mathsf{T}}A$ is only semidefinite. This illustrates the fact that a form of rank r may be written as a sum of more than r squares of linear forms. When this is done, however, the linear forms—the y's in this example—are *not linearly independent*.

Let $X = [x_{ij}]_{(n,p)}$ be a matrix of p sets of n numerical observations each, each column of X comprising a set of observations. Let $Y = [(x_{ij} - m_j)]_{(n,p)}$, where m_j is the mean of the observations in the jth column. Then

$$\frac{1}{n-1} Y^{\mathsf{T}}Y = \left[\frac{1}{n-1} \sum_{k=1}^{n} (x_{ki} - m_i)(x_{kj} - m_j) \right]_p$$

is known as the **covariance matrix** of the given observations. From the previous example, we see that this matrix is positive definite if the rank of Y is p, but that otherwise it is positive semidefinite.

For further examples of the use of positive definite matrices in statistics, the reader is referred to C. R. Rao: *Advanced Statistical Methods in Biometric Research*, New York, John Wiley, 1952, and other references cited in the bibliography.

9.19 Cochran's Theorem

In previous sections we have often been concerned with reducing a positive definite quadratic form to a sum of squares. In this section, we examine such sums of squares further and develop two theorems which are of considerable importance in statistics. We begin with an example to illustrate the issues involved.

A familiar identity in statistics is the following:

$$\sum_{i=1}^{n} x_i^2 = nm_x^2 + \sum_{i=1}^{n} (x_i - m_x)^2,$$

where

$$m_x = \frac{1}{n} \sum_{i=1}^{n} x_i.$$

(The reader not familiar with this identity may establish it by expanding $\sum_{i=1}^{n} (x_i - m_x)^2$. It is also instructive to verify that when $n = 2$, the identity reduces to $x_1^2 + x_2^2 = (x_1 + x_2)^2/2 + (x_1 - x_2)^2/2$.)

We have here an example of a decomposition of $\sum_{i=1}^{n} x_i^2$ into a sum of two quadratic forms, neither of which is simply a sum of squares of the x's. We note that

$$nm_x^2 = \left(\frac{x_1}{\sqrt{n}} + \frac{x_2}{\sqrt{n}} + \cdots + \frac{x_n}{\sqrt{n}} \right)^2,$$

so that, if we put $Y = BX$, this being any orthogonal transformation such that

$$y_1 = \frac{x_1}{\sqrt{n}} + \frac{x_2}{\sqrt{n}} + \cdots + \frac{x_n}{\sqrt{n}},$$

we will thereby reduce nm_x^2 to y_1^2. (Since $[1/\sqrt{n}, 1/\sqrt{n}, \ldots, 1/\sqrt{n}]$ is a *unit* row n-vector, it follows from Theorems 6.7.3 and 7.16.1 that such orthogonal transformations actually exist.) Then, applying this transformation to the initial identity, we obtain, because B is orthogonal,

$$\sum_{i=1}^{n} x_i^2 = \sum_{i=1}^{n} y_i^2 = y_1^2 + \left(\text{transform of } \sum_{i=1}^{n} (x_i - m_x)^2 \right).$$

Hence, under such a transformation, we must have

$$\sum_{i=1}^{n} (x_i - m_x)^2 = \sum_{i=2}^{n} y_i^2.$$

It now follows that the rank of nm_x^2 is 1 and that of $\sum_{i=1}^{n} (x_i - m_x)^2$ is $n - 1$, since rank is not altered by a nonsingular transformation. Note also that the sum of these two ranks is n.

The general situation of which the above is an illustration is given in **Cochran's theorem:**

Theorem 9.19.1: *If* $\sum_{i=1}^{n} x_i^2 \equiv q_1 + q_2 + \cdots + q_k$ *where each* q_i *is a positive semidefinite or definite form in* $x_1, x_2, \ldots, x_n$ *and is of rank* r_i, *then there exists an orthogonal transformation* $Y = BX$ *such that*

$$q_1 = y_1^2 + y_2^2 + \cdots + y_{r_1}^2$$

$$q_2 = y_{r_1+1}^2 + \cdots + y_{r_1+r_2}^2$$

$$\vdots$$

$$q_k = y_{r_1+\cdots+r_{k-1}+1}^2 + \cdots + y_{r_1+r_2+\cdots+r_k}^2,$$

if and only if $r_1 + r_2 + \cdots + r_k = n$.

In the first place, suppose such a transformation exists. Then, being orthogonal, it preserves the length of a vector and the rank of a quadratic form. Applying it, we have therefore

$$\sum_{i=1}^{n} x_i^2 = \sum_{i=1}^{n} y_i^2 = (y_1^2 + \cdots + y_{r_1}^2) + \cdots$$

$$+ (y_{r_1+\cdots+r_{k-1}+1}^2 + \cdots + y_{r_1+\cdots+r_k}^2),$$

so that $n = r_1 + r_2 + \cdots + r_k$ since the rank must be the same on both sides.

Secondly, let us suppose that $\sum_{i=1}^{k} r_i = n$. Now q_1 is positive semidefinite or definite by hypothesis. Hence, as we have seen earlier, (9.15.2), there exists an identity

$$q_1 = y_1^2 + y_2^2 + \cdots + y_{r_1}^2,$$

where

(9.19.1)
$$
\begin{aligned}
y_1 &= b_{11}x_1 + b_{12}x_2 + \cdots + b_{1n}x_n \\
y_2 &= b_{21}x_1 + b_{22}x_2 + \cdots + b_{2n}x_n \\
&\ \vdots \\
y_{r_1} &= b_{r_1 1}x_1 + b_{r_1 2}x_2 + \cdots + b_{r_1 n}x_n.
\end{aligned}
$$

and where, as far as the reduction of q_1 is concerned, it does not matter what linear forms we write for the remaining y's so long as the net transformation is nonsingular. In the same way, we can write

$$q_2 = y_{r_1+1}^2 + \cdots + y_{r_1+r_2}^2,$$

where

(9.19.2)
$$
\begin{aligned}
y_{r_1+1} &= b_{r_1+1,1}x_1 + \cdots + b_{r_1+1,n}x_n \\
&\ \vdots \\
y_{r_1+r_2} &= b_{r_1+r_2,1}x_1 + \cdots + b_{r_1+r_2,n}x_n.
\end{aligned}
$$

We continue thus for each of the q_i's. Since $\sum_{i=1}^{k} r_i = n$, the equations (9.19.1),

(9.19.2), . . ., all taken together, define a transformation $Y = BX$ such that under it we have

$$\sum_{i=1}^{n} x_i{}^2 = \sum_{i=1}^{k} q_i = \sum_{i=1}^{n} y_i{}^2.$$

Since $Y = BX$ thus leaves the sum $\sum x_i{}^2$ invariant, it is orthogonal (Theorem 7.10.1), and the theorem is proved.

Theorem 9.19.2: *The characteristic roots of the matrix of each q_i, where the q_i's are as in Theorem 9.19.1, are all either 1 or 0: r_i of them are 1 and $n - r_i$, of them are 0.*

Let A_i be the symmetric matrix of the form q_i so that $q_i = X^{\mathsf{T}}A_iX$. Now putting $Y = BX$, where B is formed as in the proof above, we have, by the preceding theorem,

$$X^{\mathsf{T}}A_iX = Y^{\mathsf{T}}(BA_iB^{\mathsf{T}})Y = y^2_{r_1 + r_2 + \cdots + r_{i-1} + 1} + \cdots + y^2_{r_1 + r_2 + \cdots + r_i}.$$

The matrix of the form on the right has r_i characteristic roots equal to 1, the other $n - r_i$ being 0. Since B is orthogonal, $B^{\mathsf{T}} = B^{-1}$, and hence A_i and BA_iB^{T} have the same characteristic roots (Exercise 4, Section 8.3) which proves the theorem.

9.20 Pairs of Quadratic Forms

In certain applications it is necessary to effect the simultaneous reduction of two real symmetric matrices or two real quadratic forms, at least one of which is, ordinarily, positive definite. We begin with the problem of finding the scalars λ and the vectors X which satisfy the equation

$$(9.20.1) \qquad\qquad AX = \lambda BX.$$

This is a generalization of the characteristic value problem of Chapter Eight, to which this reduces if $B = I$. The solutions λ and X of this problem are respectively called the **characteristic roots** and the **characteristic vectors** of the pair of matrices A and B *in that order*.

As before, there will exist vectors X satisfying this equation if and only if λ is a root of the **characteristic equation**

$$(9.20.2) \qquad\qquad \det [A - \lambda B] = 0.$$

For our present purposes, we *assume that A is symmetric and that B is positive definite and symmetric*. Then there exists an orthogonal matrix U such that

$$U^{\mathsf{T}}BU = D[\mu_1, \mu_2, \ldots, \mu_n],$$

where $\mu_1, \mu_2, \ldots, \mu_n$ are the characteristic roots of B and are all positive, since B is positive definite. If we now put

$$R = D[\mu_1{}^{-1/2}, \mu_2{}^{-1/2}, \ldots, \mu_n{}^{-1/2}],$$

we have

$$R^\mathsf{T}(U^\mathsf{T}BU)R = R^\mathsf{T}D[\mu_1, \mu_2, \ldots, \mu_n]R = I,$$

which, by putting $S = UR$, we may write as

$$S^\mathsf{T}BS = I.$$

Now S is nonsingular and therefore we may replace (9.20.2) by the equivalent equation

$$\det S^\mathsf{T}[A - \lambda B]S = 0,$$

that is, by

(9.20.3) $\det [S^\mathsf{T}AS - \lambda I] = 0.$

Thus we have reduced our characteristic value problem to one of the bâsic type treated in Chapter Eight.

In (9.20.3), $S^\mathsf{T}AS$ is a real symmetric matrix. Hence all its characteristic roots are real. We have, therefore,

Theorem 9.20.1:   *The roots $\lambda_1, \lambda_2, \ldots, \lambda_n$ of the equation $\det [A - \lambda B]$ $= 0$, where A and B are symmetric and B is positive definite, are all real.*

Next, since $S^\mathsf{T}AS$ is symmetric, there exists an orthogonal matrix Q which will diagonalize it:

$$Q^\mathsf{T}(S^\mathsf{T}AS)Q = D[\lambda_1, \lambda_2, \ldots, \lambda_n],$$

that is,

$$(SQ)^\mathsf{T}A(SQ) = D[\lambda_1, \lambda_2, \ldots, \lambda_n].$$

if we now transform B by the matrix SQ, we obtain

$$(SQ)^\mathsf{T}B(SQ) = Q^\mathsf{T}(S^\mathsf{T}BS)Q = Q^\mathsf{T}IQ = I,$$

since Q is orthogonal. If we write $V = SQ$, we may summarize thus:

Theorem 9.20.2:   *If A and B are real matrices of order n and if A is symmetric and B is positive definite and symmetric, then there exists a real nonsingular matrix V such that $V^\mathsf{T}AV$ is diagonal and $V^\mathsf{T}BV$ is the identity matrix.*

Now consider the pair of quadratic forms $X^\mathsf{T}AX$ and $X^\mathsf{T}BX$ associated with the real symmetric matrices A and B. If we put $X = VY$, we have

$$X^\mathsf{T}AX = Y^\mathsf{T}(V^\mathsf{T}AV)Y = \sum_{i=1}^{n} \lambda_i y_i^2,$$

and

$$X^\mathsf{T}BX = Y^\mathsf{T}(V^\mathsf{T}BV)Y = \sum_{i=1}^{n} y_i^2.$$

Thus a restatement of the preceding theorem is

Theorem 9.20.3:   *If $X^{\mathsf{T}}AX$ is an arbitrary quadratic form and if $X^{\mathsf{T}}BX$ is any positive definite quadratic form in the same number of variables, then there exists a nonsingular transformation $X = VY$ which reduces $X^{\mathsf{T}}AX$ to the form $\sum \lambda_i y_i^2$, where the λ's are the roots of the equation $\det [A - \lambda B] = 0$, and which reduces $X^{\mathsf{T}}BX$ to the unit form $\sum y_i^2$.*

In the theory of small vibrations, the quadratic form $X^{\mathsf{T}}AX$ is a positive definite form representing the potential energy, $X^{\mathsf{T}}BX$ is a positive definite form representing the kinetic energy, and the λ's are used to compute the "normal modes of vibration."

9.21 Exercises

1. Examine for definiteness

$$
\text{(a)} \quad
\begin{bmatrix}
1 & -1 & -1 \\
-1 & 2 & 4 \\
-1 & 4 & 6
\end{bmatrix},
\qquad
\text{(b)} \quad
\begin{bmatrix}
4 & 2 & -2 \\
2 & 4 & 2 \\
-2 & 2 & 4
\end{bmatrix}.
$$

2. What is the condition that the quadratic form $Ax^2 + Bxy + Cy^2$ be positive definite? Test $x^2 + xy + y^2$, $x^2 + 2xy + y^2$, $x^2 + 4xy + y^2$, and $x^2 + 2kxy + my^2$ for definiteness.

3. Show that a matrix A is positive definite and symmetric if and only if $B^{\mathsf{T}}AB$ is positive definite and symmetric for each nonsingular B of the same order.

4. Show that a necessary and sufficient condition that a real symmetric matrix A be negative definite is that $p_1 < 0, p_2 > 0, p_3 < 0, \ldots$.

5. Show that, if $\alpha > 1$, the matrix A of order n for which $a_{i,i \pm k} = \alpha^{(n-1)-k}$ is positive definite.

6. If

$$
X^{\mathsf{T}}AX = \left(\sum_{j=2}^{n^2+n+1} x_j \right)^2 + n \sum_{j=2}^{n^2+n+1} \left(\frac{x_1}{n} + x_j \right)^2, \qquad n \geqslant 2,
$$

determine the symmetric matrix A and show it is positive definite.

7. Show that the problem of reducing the quadratic form $X^{\mathsf{T}}AX$ to the form $\tilde{X}^{\mathsf{T}}D[\lambda_1, \lambda_2, \ldots, \lambda_n]\tilde{X}$ by an orthogonal transformation is equivalent to the problem of reducing a linear vector function $Y = AX$ to the form $\tilde{Y} = D[\lambda_1, \lambda_2, \ldots, \lambda_n]\tilde{X}$ by an orthogonal transformation of coordinates.

8. Show that Cochran's theorem still holds true if we replace $\sum_{i=1}^{n} x_i^2$ by any positive definite quadratic form in $x_1, x_2, \ldots, x_n$.

*9. Show that every real positive definite or semidefinite symmetric matrix A has for each positive integer p a real symmetric pth root given by

$$
UD\left[\lambda_1^{\frac{1}{p}}, \lambda_2^{\frac{1}{p}}, \ldots, \lambda_n^{\frac{1}{p}} \right]U^{\mathsf{T}},
$$

where U is an orthogonal matrix depending only on A.

10. Show that, if X_1 and X_2 are characteristic vectors associated with distinct characteristic roots λ_1 and λ_2 of the pair of real symmetric matrices A and B, then $X_1^{\mathsf{T}} B X_2 = 0$. To what result does this reduce when $B = I$?

11. Prove that, if A is real, positive definite, and symmetric, and if C has rank r, then $C^{\mathsf{T}} A C$ has rank r also.

12. Find a linear transformation that will simultaneously diagonalize the quadratic forms

$$X^{\mathsf{T}} \begin{bmatrix} 1 & 2 \\ 2 & 1 \end{bmatrix} X \quad \text{and} \quad X^{\mathsf{T}} \begin{bmatrix} 2 & 1 \\ 1 & 2 \end{bmatrix} X.$$

13. Show that there is no linear transformation which will simultaneously diagonalize the quadratic forms

$$X^{\mathsf{T}} \begin{bmatrix} 1 & 0 \\ 0 & -1 \end{bmatrix} X \quad \text{and} \quad X^{\mathsf{T}} \begin{bmatrix} 0 & 1 \\ 1 & 0 \end{bmatrix} X.$$

*14. Let $q(X)$ denote a non-negative definite quadratic form $X^{\mathsf{T}} A X$, and let $b(X, Y)$ denote the associated bilinear form $X^{\mathsf{T}} A Y$. Prove that, for all real t, X, and Y,

$$q(X + tY) = t^2 q(Y) + 2t\, b(X, Y) + q(X) \geqslant 0,$$

and, hence, that the **Cauchy-Schwarz inequality**

$$b(X, Y)^2 \leqslant q(X)\, q(Y)$$

holds. To what does this reduce when $A = I$?

15. Prove that, if

$$\begin{bmatrix} P & Q \\ Q^{\mathsf{T}} & S \end{bmatrix},$$

where S is nonsingular, is a real, positive semidefinite matrix, then $P - QS^{-1}Q^{\mathsf{T}}$ is also positive semidefinite.

16. Let A, B be of order n and symmetric, B positive definite, $A - B$ positive definite or semidefinite. Prove that $\det A \geqslant \det B$ and that A is positive definite.

17. A student asserted that, if $R = [r_{ij}]_{n \times n}$ is symmetric and real with

$$r_{ii} > 0,$$

$$r_{ii} > \sum_{j \neq i} |r_{ij}|, \quad i = 1, 2, \ldots, n,$$

then R is positive definite. Prove or disprove his assertion.

HERMITIAN FORMS

9.22 Hermitian Forms

Another type of form, useful in applications in the complex number field, is the **Hermitian** form. Such a form h is defined by

$$(9.22.1) \qquad h = X^{*} H X = \sum_{i,j=1}^{n} h_{ij} \bar{x}_i x_j,$$

where H is a Hermitian matrix and the components of X are in the complex field. If X and H are real, the Hermitian form (9.22.1) reduces to a real quadratic form as a special case. This explains why many results here parallel those of earlier sections. The rank of H is called the **rank of the form**.

Since h is a scalar, we have $\bar{h} = h^*$. Hence, since H is Hermitian

$$\bar{h} = h^* = (X^*HX)^* = X^*HX = h.$$

Thus h, being equal to its own conjugate, is real for every choice of X.

Conversely, suppose h is real for every choice of X. Then $h = \bar{h} = h^*$, so that we have the identity

$$X^*HX \equiv (X^*HX)^* \equiv X^*H^*X.$$

Hence $H^* = H$ and H is Hermitian (see Exercise 6, Section 9.24, below). Summing up, we have

Theorem 9.22.1: *A matrix H is Hermitian if and only if the form X^*HX is real for every choice of the vector X.*

In Chapter Eight we saw that for every Hermitian matrix H, there exists a unitary matrix U such that

$$U^*HU = D[\lambda_1, \lambda_2, \ldots, \lambda_n],$$

where the λ's are the characteristic roots of H and are all real. For a Hermitian form (9.22.1) this implies

Theorem 9.22.2: *By a suitable unitary transformation $X = UY$, X^*HX can be reduced to the form*

$$Y^*D[\lambda_1, \lambda_2, \ldots, \lambda_n]Y = \sum_{j=1}^{n} \lambda_j \bar{y}_j y_j,$$

where the λ's are the characteristic roots of the Hermitian matrix H.

It is possible to use other nonsingular transformations to reduce a given Hermitian form to the diagonal form

$$Y^*D[g_1, g_2, \ldots, g_n]Y = \sum_{j=1}^{n} g_j \bar{y}_j y_j,$$

where the g's are not necessarily the characteristic roots of H. Thus, for example, the nonunitary transformation

$$X = \begin{bmatrix} 1 & -i \\ 0 & 1 \end{bmatrix} Y$$

applied to the Hermitian form

$$X^* \begin{bmatrix} 1 & i \\ -i & 0 \end{bmatrix} X$$

with characteristic roots $(1 \pm \sqrt{5})/2$ yields the Hermitian form

$$Y^* \begin{bmatrix} 1 & 0 \\ 0 & -1 \end{bmatrix} Y = \bar{y}_1 y_1 - \bar{y}_2 y_2,$$

as the reader may verify.

Concerning such transformations, we have

Theorem 9.22.3:   *If X^*HX is Hermitian and if the substitution $X = AY$ yields $X^*HX = Y^*(A^*HA)Y = \sum\limits_{j=1}^{n} g_j \bar{y}_j y_j$, then the g's are all real.*

Indeed, $Y^*(A^*HA)Y$ is also Hermitian and is, therefore, real for all Y. If $y_j = 1$ and all other y's $= 0$, then $Y^*(A^*HA)Y = g_j$. Thus all of the g_j's must be real.

If A in the preceding theorem is *nonsingular*, we define the number p of positive terms in $\sum g_j \bar{y}_j y_j$ to be the **index** of the form. The number of nonzero g's is evidently the rank r of the form. The **signature** is then defined to be $2p - r$. As in the case of quadratic forms, **Sylvester's law of inertia** applies:

Theorem 9.22.4:   *No matter by what nonsingular transformation a given Hermitian form is reduced to a form*

$$g_1 \bar{z}_1 z_1 + \cdots + g_p \bar{z}_p z_p - g_{p+1} \bar{z}_{p+1} z_{p+1} - \cdots - g_r \bar{z}_r z_r,$$

where the g's are all positive, the integers p and r will be the same.

The proof of this theorem is like that of Theorem 9.12.1 and is left to the reader to supply in detail.

We define two Hermitian forms X^*H_1X and Y^*H_2Y to be **equivalent** if and only if there exists a nonsingular transformation $X = AY$ such that $X^*H_1X \equiv Y^*(A^*H_1A)Y \equiv Y^*H_2Y$, that is, if and only if for some nonsingular A, $H_2 = A^*H_1A$ (see Exercise 6, Section 9.24, below). Then, analogously to Theorem 9.12.2, we have

Theorem 9.22.5:   *Two Hermitian forms are equivalent if and only if they have the same rank and the same index.*

9.23 Definite Hermitian Forms

A *nonsingular* Hermitian form is called **positive definite** if and only if its rank and its index are equal, that is, $p = r = n$. A *singular* Hermitian form is called **positive semidefinite** if and only if its rank and its index are equal, that is, $p = r < n$.

Concerning definite Hermitian forms, we have the following theorems, all proved in much the same way as the corresponding theorems for quadratic forms:

Theorem 9.23.1:   *If X^*HX is positive definite (semidefinite), then its value is > 0 ($\geqslant 0$) for all nonzero-vectors X.*

Theorem 9.23.2:   *If $X*HX$ is positive definite, then* det H, *and every principal minor determinant of H, is positive.*

Theorem 9.23.3:   *If $X*HX$ is positive semidefinite, every principal minor determinant of H is $\geqslant 0$.*

Theorem 9.23.4:   *If $X*HX$ is positive semidefinite and x_i actually appears in $X*HX$, then $h_{ii} > 0$.*

Theorem 9.23.5:   *A Hermitian matrix H is positive definite if and only if any one of the following conditions is satisfied:*

(a) *$A*HA$ is positive definite for arbitrary, nonsingular A.*
(b) *H^p is positive definite for every integer p.*
(c) *There exists a nonsingular matrix A such that $H = A*A$.*

9.24 Exercises

1. Prove Theorems 9.22.4 and 9.22.5 in detail.

2. Write proofs for Theorems 9.23.1 through 9.23.5.

3. Show that every positive definite Hermitian form may be reduced to the form $\sum_{j=1}^{n} |z_j|^2$ by a nonsingular transformation.

4. Determine the unitary transformation which will diagonalize the Hermitian form

$$X* \begin{bmatrix} 1 & \sqrt{42}i \\ -\sqrt{42}i & 2 \end{bmatrix} X.$$

5. Determine whether or not the matrix

$$\begin{bmatrix} 4 & i & 0 \\ -i & 8 & -i \\ 0 & i & 4 \end{bmatrix}$$

is positive definite.

6. Prove in detail that $X*H_1X = X*H_2X$ for all vectors X if and only if $H_1 = H_2$.

7. Prove that if H is positive definite and Hermitian, then $H^{\frac{1}{p}}$ is defined for each positive integer p. (See Exercise 9, Section 9.21.)

8. Prove that for arbitrary A, the matrix $A*A$ has a Hermitian square root.

*9. Let H be a nonnegative definite Hermitian matrix such that

$$H^2 = D[\lambda_1, \lambda_2, \ldots, \lambda_n].$$

Prove that each λ_j is $\geqslant 0$ and that

$$H = D[\lambda_1^{\frac{1}{2}}, \lambda_2^{\frac{1}{2}}, \ldots, \lambda_n^{\frac{1}{2}}].$$

Thus a nonnegative definite diagonal matrix has a unique nonnegative definite square root and this root is also diagonal.

10. Prove that a matrix H of order n is a positive definite Hermitian matrix if and only if C^*HC is a positive definite Hermitian matrix for every nonsingular matrix C of order n.

11. Restate the theorems of Section 9.20 for Hermitian matrices and prove the results.

*12. Show that, if $A = B^2 = C^2$, where B and C are nonnegative definite and Hermitian, then $B = C$, that is, if a nonnegative definite Hermitian square root exists, it is unique. Exercise 9 will help.

13. Investigate for definiteness where $\omega^3 = 1$ but $\omega \neq 1$:

$$\begin{bmatrix} 1 & \omega & \omega^2 \\ \omega^2 & 1 & \omega \\ \omega & \omega^2 & 1 \end{bmatrix}.$$

*14. Represent the Hermitian form X^*A^*AX as a sum of squares of absolute values of linear forms in the x's. Here A is an arbitrary $m \times n$ matrix. (*Hint:* Let $Y = AX$, etc.)

15. Let X and Y be vectors of the $\mathscr{V}_n{}^n$ over the complex number field. Let the complex matrix H be Hermitian. Define X and Y to be **conjugate** with respect to H if and only if $X^*HY = 0$. Prove that a fixed Y is conjugate to *all* X if and only if $HY = 0$. To what does conjugacy reduce if $H = I$?

*16. Given that A is nonsingular, prove that there exist unique positive definite Hermitian matrices R and S and a unique unitary matrix U such that $A = RU = US$. This is called the **polar representation** of A. (First prove that if $A = RU = US$ with R, S, U, as described, then $AA^* = R^2$ and $A^*A = S^2$ so that R and S, and hence U, are unique (Exercise 12). To prove the converse, define R by $A^*A = R^2$ (Exercise 8), U by $A = RU$. Show U is unitary and then define $S = U^*RU$. Show S is positive definite and Hermitian and that $A = US$.)

The Notations Σ and $\prod$

Through his previous work in mathematics, the reader may already have become somewhat familiar with the notations Σ and $\prod$ for sums and products respectively, but there are operations with these symbols which we use rather frequently in this book and which may well be new to him. For his convenience, we therefore provide a discussion of these symbols.

THE Σ NOTATION

I.1 Definitions

The Σ notation is simply a shorthand method for designating sums. Thus, for example, we write

$$x_1 + x_2 + x_3 + x_4 + x_5 = \sum_{j=1}^{5} x_j.$$

Here j is a variable ranging over the integers 1, 2, 3, 4, 5. The symbols $j = 1$ below the Σ sign indicate that 1 is the initial value taken on by j, and the 5 written above the Σ sign indicates that 5 is the terminal value of j. We call j the **index of summation**. The **summand**, x_j, is a function of j which takes on the values x_1, x_2, x_3, x_4, x_5 respectively as j takes on successively the values 1, 2, 3, 4, 5. Finally, the Σ sign denotes the fact that the values x_1, x_2, x_3, x_4, x_5 taken on by x_j are to be *added*. The entire symbol $\sum_{j=1}^{5} x_j$ is read, "the summation of x_j as j ranges from 1 to 5."

In the same way, we have

$$x_6 + x_7 + x_8 = \sum_{j=6}^{8} x_j,$$

where now the initial value of j is 6, and the terminal value is 8. Combining these two examples we have

$$x_1 + x_2 + x_3 + x_4 + x_5 + x_6 + x_7 + x_8 = \sum_{j=1}^{5} x_j + \sum_{j=6}^{8} x_j,$$

so that

$$\sum_{j=1}^{8} x_j = \sum_{j=1}^{5} x_j + \sum_{j=6}^{8} x_j.$$

Our first example above is an illustration of the basic definition:

(I.1.1) $$\sum_{j=1}^{n} x_j = x_1 + x_2 + \cdots + x_n.$$

Our third example above is an illustration of the theorem:

(I.1.2) $$(x_1 + x_2 + \cdots + x_p) + (x_{p+1} + \cdots + x_n) = \sum_{j=1}^{n} x_j = \sum_{j=1}^{p} x_j + \sum_{j=p+1}^{n} x_j.$$

A familiar function of n quantities $x_1, x_2, \ldots, x_n$ is their "average" or arithmetic mean m_x, namely, their sum divided by n. Using the above notation, we can write

$$m_x = \frac{x_1 + x_2 + \cdots + x_n}{n} = \frac{1}{n} \sum_{j=1}^{n} x_j.$$

The compactness of the Σ notation, as here demonstrated, is one indication of its value.

In the above examples, the values actually represented by $x_1, x_2, \ldots, x_n$, of course, have to be given before the sums can be evaluated. Sometimes, however, the notation is such as to designate the values of the various terms. An example of such a sum is

$$1^2 + 2^2 + 3^2 + 4^2 + 5^2 = \sum_{k=1}^{5} k^2,$$

or, more generally,

$$1^2 + 2^2 + \cdots + n^2 = \sum_{k=1}^{n} k^2.$$

Here the index of summation k ranges over the values 1, 2, 3, 4, 5 in the first case, while the summand k^2 ranges over the values 1^2, 2^2, 3^2, 4^2, 5^2. In the second case the range of the index k is from 1 to n while that of the summand k^2 is from 1^2 to n^2, inclusive, of course.

It should also be pointed out that sometimes the initial value of the summation index is zero or a negative integer. For example,

$$\sum_{j=0}^{k} \frac{1}{2^j} = \frac{1}{2^0} + \frac{1}{2^1} + \cdots + \frac{1}{2^k},$$

and

$$\sum_{j=-n}^{n} a_j x^j = a_{-n} x^{-n} + a_{-n+1} x^{-n+1} + \cdots$$

$$+ a_{-1} x^{-1} + a_0 x^0 + a_1 x^1 + a_2 x^2 + \cdots + a_n x^n \qquad (x \neq 0).$$

As a final illustration, we recall that infinite series are also commonly written with a Σ sign. Thus, for example, we might have

$$\frac{1}{1^p} + \frac{1}{2^p} + \frac{1}{3^p} + \cdots + \frac{1}{n^p} + \cdots = \sum_{n=1}^{\infty} \frac{1}{n^p},$$

or

$$\frac{x}{1+2} + \frac{2x^2}{1+2^2} + \frac{3x^3}{1+2^3} + \cdots + \frac{nx^n}{1+2^n} + \cdots = \sum_{n=1}^{\infty} \frac{nx^n}{1+2^n}.$$

In each case we can obtain the first three terms on the left by substituting $n = 1, 2, 3$ respectively into the **general term** of the series, namely the term containing the index n which appears on both the left and the right in the appropriate equation. As many more terms as may be desired may, of course, be found in the same way. Here the $\sum$ sign denotes a *purely formal sum* which may or may not represent a number depending on whether the series does or does not converge.

I.2 Exercises

1. Given that $x_1 = -2$, $x_2 = 1$, $x_3 = -1$, $x_4 = 3$, $x_5 = 7$, $x_6 = -8$, find

$$\sum_{j=1}^{6} x_j, \qquad \sum_{j=1}^{6} x_j^2, \qquad \sum_{j=1}^{6} (2x_j + 3) \qquad \text{and} \qquad \sum_{j=1}^{6} (x_j + 2)(x_j - 2).$$

2. Rewrite in the $\sum$ notation:

(a) $2t + 4t^2 + 8t^3 + 16t^4 + 32t^5 + 64t^6$.

(b) $1 + 3 + 5 + \cdots + (2n - 1)$.

(c) $1 \cdot 2 + 2 \cdot 3 + \cdots + n(n + 1)$.

(d) $(x_1 - m_x)(y_1 - m_y) + (x_2 - m_x)(y_2 - m_y) + \cdots + (x_n - m_x)(y_n - m_y)$.

3. Rewrite in the ordinary notation:

(a) $\displaystyle\sum_{k=0}^{5} k(k-1)$; $\qquad \displaystyle\sum_{k=2}^{5} k(k-1)$; $\qquad \displaystyle\sum_{k=-5}^{5} k(k-1)$.

(b) $\displaystyle\sum_{j=1}^{n} a_j x_j$; $\qquad \displaystyle\sum_{j=1}^{n} a_j x^j$.

(c) $\displaystyle\sum_{n=0}^{\infty} \frac{x^n}{n!}$ (0! is defined to be 1, in case you have forgotten, and $x^0 = 1$ here).

(d) $\displaystyle\sum_{n=0}^{\infty} \left(\frac{x^n}{n!} + n(n-1)(n-2) \right).$ (Compare with (c).)

(e) $\displaystyle\sum_{n=0}^{\infty} \left(\frac{x^n}{n!} \right) (1 + \sin n(n-1)(n-2)x).$ (Compare with (d), (c).)

4. Show that:

(a) $\displaystyle\left(\sum_{j=1}^{n} x_j \right) + x_{n+1} = \sum_{j=1}^{n+1} x_j.$

(b) $\displaystyle\sum_{j=p+1}^{n} x_j = \sum_{j=1}^{n} x_j - \sum_{j=1}^{p} x_j, \ (n \geq p + 1).$

(c) $\displaystyle\sum_{j=1}^{k} x_j + \sum_{j=1}^{n-k} x_{k+j} = \sum_{j=1}^{n} x_j.$

I.3 Basic Rules of Operation

In each of the examples given in I.1, the symbol used for the index of summation is entirely arbitrary, so that it is called a **dummy index**. Thus we have, for example,

$$x_1 + x_2 + \cdots + x_n = \sum_{i=1}^{n} x_i = \sum_{j=1}^{n} x_j = \sum_{p=1}^{n} x_p = \cdots,$$

$$1^2 + 2^2 + \cdots + n^2 = \sum_{j=1}^{n} j^2 = \sum_{k=1}^{n} k^2 = \sum_{v=1}^{n} v^2 = \cdots.$$

There is another kind of arbitrariness in the summation index which is indicated by the following examples which the student should examine carefully.

$$\sum_{j=1}^{n} x_j = \sum_{j=0}^{n-1} x_{j+1} = \sum_{j=2}^{n+1} x_{j-1} = \cdots,$$

and

$$\sum_{n=0}^{\infty} \frac{x^n}{n!} = \sum_{n=1}^{\infty} \frac{x^{n-1}}{(n-1)!} = \sum_{n=-1}^{\infty} \frac{x^{n+1}}{(n+1)!} = \cdots.$$

Here we have altered the initial value of the index of summation, but we have altered the function being summed in a compensating way, so that the net sum remains unaltered. Can you write in words a rule for how this is to be done? This sort of shift in the range of summation is often useful.

Let us consider again the sum

(I.3.1) $$\sum_{j=1}^{n} x_j = x_1 + x_2 + \cdots + x_n.$$

If each of the x's here is equal to the same fixed quantity c, we have

$$\sum_{j=1}^{n} x_n = c + c + \cdots + c = nc,$$

or, as we write it in this case,

(I.3.2) $$\sum_{j=1}^{n} c = nc.$$

For example,

$$\sum_{j=1}^{5} 10 = 50.$$

Equation (I.3.2) is, in fact, a *definition* of the symbol $\sum_{j=1}^{n} c$, which is *a priori* meaningless since the constant c does not depend on the index of summation j.

Next let us suppose that in (I.3.1) we have $x_j = ky_j$, where k is a constant. Then,

$$\sum_{j=1}^{n} x_j = \sum_{j=1}^{n} (ky_j) = ky_1 + ky_2 + \cdots + ky_n = k(y_1 + y_2 + \cdots + y_n)$$

$$= k \sum_{j=1}^{n} y_j.$$

Thus we have our second basic rule,

(I.3.3)
$$\sum_{j=1}^{n} (ky_j) = k \sum_{j=1}^{n} y_j.$$

Finally, let us suppose that $x_j = y_j + z_j$ in (I.3.1). Then we have

$$\sum_{j=1}^{n} x_j = \sum_{j=1}^{n} (y_j + z_j) = (y_1 + z_1) + (y_2 + z_2) + \cdots + (y_n + z_n)$$

$$= (y_1 + y_2 + \cdots + y_n) + (z_1 + z_2 + \cdots + z_n) = \sum_{j=1}^{n} y_j + \sum_{j=1}^{n} z_j,$$

which gives our third basic rule,

(I.3.4)
$$\sum_{j=1}^{n} (y_j + z_j) = \sum_{j=1}^{n} y_j + \sum_{j=1}^{n} z_j.$$

We make one more observation in this section. When there is no possible misinterpretation, the index of summation is often omitted. Thus we write simply $\sum x$ in place of $\sum_{j=1}^{n} x_j$ if the range of summation is clearly indicated by the context. Similarly, we could write $\sum x^2 - (\sum x)^2$ in place of $\sum_{j=1}^{n} x_j^2 - (\sum_{j=1}^{n} x_j)^2$, and so on.

I.4 Exercises

1. Use (I.3.3) and (I.3.4) above to show that

$$\sum_{j=1}^{n} (ax_j + by_j) = a \sum_{j=1}^{n} x_j + b \sum_{j=1}^{n} y_j.$$

2. Show that

$$\sum_{j=1}^{n} x_j(x_j - 1) = \sum_{j=1}^{n} x_j^2 - \sum_{j=1}^{n} x_j,$$

and that

$$\sum_{j=1}^{n} (x_j - 1)(x_j + 1) = \left(\sum_{j=1}^{n} x_j^2 \right) - n.$$

3. Using the fact that $m_x = (\sum x)/n$, (I.3.2), and Exercise 1 above, show that $\sum (x_j - m_x) = 0$. (Fill in the missing indices of summation first of all. The differences $x_j - m_x$ are called *the deviations of the x's from their mean*. You are thus to prove that the sum of the deviations of a set of quantities from their mean is zero.)

4. Show that

(a) $\displaystyle\sum_{j=1}^{k} (x_j + 1)^2 f_j = \sum_{j=1}^{k} x_j^2 f_j + 2 \sum_{j=1}^{k} x_j f_j + \sum_{j=1}^{k} f_j,$

(b) $\displaystyle\sum_{j=1}^{n} (x_j - m_x)^2 = \left(\sum_{j=1}^{n} x_j^2 \right) - n m_x^2.$

These two results are used in deriving various formulas in statistics.

I.5 Finite Double Sums

We shall now consider the matter of **double sums**. Let us suppose that we have a set of nm quantities U_{ij}, where $i = 1, 2, \ldots, n$ and $j = 1, 2, \ldots, m$. We arrange these in a rectangular pattern, thus:

$$
\begin{array}{cccc}
U_{11} & U_{12} & \cdots & U_{1m} \\
U_{21} & U_{22} & \cdots & U_{2m} \\
\vdots & & & \\
U_{n1} & U_{n2} & \cdots & U_{nm}.
\end{array}
$$

If we wish to add all the U's, we may add first the various rows and then add the row totals to get the desired result,

$$
\sum_{j=1}^{m} U_{1j} + \sum_{j=1}^{m} U_{2j} + \cdots + \sum_{j=1}^{m} U_{nj},
$$

which may be written more compactly by using a second summation sign thus:

$$
\sum_{i=1}^{n} \left(\sum_{j=1}^{m} U_{ij} \right).
$$

If we had found the column totals first instead of the row totals, we would have obtained in the same way the result

$$
\sum_{j=1}^{m} \left(\sum_{i=1}^{n} U_{ij} \right).
$$

Since the sum will be the same in either case, we have

(I.5.1)
$$
\sum_{i=1}^{n} \left(\sum_{j=1}^{m} U_{ij} \right) = \sum_{j=1}^{m} \left(\sum_{i=1}^{n} U_{ij} \right),
$$

which says that *in a finite double sum, the order of summation is immaterial*. This result does not necessarily hold for sums of infinitely many terms.

Such double sums are usually written without parentheses:

$$
\sum_{i=1}^{n} \sum_{j=1}^{m} U_{ij} = \sum_{j=1}^{m} \sum_{i=1}^{n} U_{ij}.
$$

The indices of summation here are, of course, dummy indices, just as in the case of simple sums.

An important kind of double sum is obtained when we put

$$
U_{ij} = a_{ij} x_i y_j \begin{cases} i = 1, 2, \ldots, n, \\ j = 1, 2, \ldots, m, \end{cases}
$$

and obtain

$$
\sum_{i=1}^{n} \sum_{j=1}^{m} a_{ij} x_i y_j.
$$

The expanded form of this sum is a polynomial in the $m + n$ variables $x_1, x_2, \ldots,$ $x_n, y_1, y_2, \ldots, y_m$. Since each term of this polynomial is of the first degree in the x variables as well as in the y variables, we call it a *bilinear form* in these variables.

If we had, for example, $n = 2$, $m = 3$ and $a_{11} = a_{12} = a_{13} = 1$, $a_{21} = a_{22} = a_{23} = -1$, the bilinear form would be

$$\sum_{i=1}^{2} \sum_{j=1}^{3} a_{ij}x_iy_j = a_{11}x_1y_1 + a_{12}x_1y_2 + a_{13}x_1y_3 + a_{21}x_2y_1 + a_{22}x_2y_2 + a_{23}x_2y_3$$

$$= x_1y_1 + x_1y_2 + x_1y_3 - x_2y_1 - x_2y_2 - x_2y_3.$$

Another special situation of prime importance is obtained when $m = n$ and $U_{ij} = a_{ij}x_ix_j$, $i, j = 1, 2, \ldots, n$. We have then

$$\sum_{i=1}^{n} \sum_{j=1}^{n} a_{ij}x_ix_j,$$

or, as it is more commonly written,

$$\sum_{i,j=1}^{n} a_{ij}x_ix_j.$$

(When several indices of summation have the same range, as here, it is convenient to write them on one summation sign. This is permissible because the order of summation is irrelevant in a finite sum.) If, for example, $n = 2$, the expanded form of the sum is

$$a_{11}x_1x_1 + a_{12}x_1x_2 + a_{21}x_2x_1 + a_{22}x_2x_2 = a_{11}x_1^2 + (a_{12} + a_{21})x_1x_2 + a_{22}x_2^2.$$

A polynomial of this kind is called a *quadratic form* in $x_1, x_2, \ldots, x_n$, since every term in it is of the second degree in those variables. In most applications, the requirement $a_{ij} = a_{ji}$, $i, j = 1, 2, \ldots, n$, is useful. In this case we call the quadratic form *symmetric*. More details are given in Chapter Nine.

I.6 Exercises

1. Write out in full the *trilinear* form

$$\sum_{i=1}^{2} \sum_{j=1}^{2} \sum_{k=1}^{3} a_{ijk}x_iy_jz_k.$$

2. Show in Exercise 1 that the same result is obtained independently of the order in which the various summations are carried out.

3. Write out the quadratic form for which $a_{ij} = 0$, $i \neq j$, and $a_{ii} = 1$, $i, j = 1, 2, \ldots, n$.

4. In how many different orders may the summation in

$$\sum_{i_1=1}^{n_1} \sum_{i_2=1}^{n_2} \cdots \sum_{i_k=1}^{n_k} U_{i_1 i_2 \cdots i_k}$$

be carried out? Are the results all equal? By what method of proof would you establish your answer to this last question?

5. Show that

$$\left(\sum_{j=1}^{n} x_j \right)^2 - \sum_{j=1}^{n} x_j^2 = \sum_{\substack{i,j=1 \\ i \neq j}}^{n} x_ix_j = 2 \sum_{\substack{i,j=1 \\ i < j}}^{n} x_ix_j.$$

(When, as here, a restriction is imposed on a summation process, the intention is that the summation should proceed as usual except that only those terms satisfying the restriction are to be written.)

6. Show that, if $\sum\limits_{j=1}^{n} x_j = 0$, then

$$\sum_{j=1}^{n} x_j^2 = -\sum_{\substack{i,j=1 \\ i \neq j}}^{n} x_i x_j.$$

7. Given that $n_i m_{x_i} = \sum\limits_{j=1}^{n_i} x_{ij}$, $i = 1, 2, \ldots, k$ and that

$$\left(\sum_{i=1}^{k} n_i\right) m_x = \sum_{i=1}^{k} \sum_{j=1}^{n_i} x_{ij},$$

show that

$$\sum_{i=1}^{k} n_i(m_{x_i} - m_x) = 0$$

and

$$\sum_{i=1}^{k} \sum_{j=1}^{n_i} (x_{ij} - m_x)^2 = \sum_{i=1}^{k} \sum_{j=1}^{n_i} (x_{ij} - m_{x_i})^2 + \sum_{i=1}^{k} n_i(m_{x_i} - m_x)^2.$$

These are more formulas useful in statistics.

8. Write out in full the "triangular" sums

(a) $\sum\limits_{\substack{i,j=1 \\ i<j}}^{6} U_{ij}$ or $\sum\limits_{1 \leqslant i < j \leqslant 6} U_{ij}$,

and

(b) $\sum\limits_{\substack{i,j=1 \\ i \leqslant j}}^{6} U_{ij}$.

9. Show that the sum of the elements in the triangular array

$$a_{11}$$
$$a_{12} \quad a_{22}$$
$$a_{13} \quad a_{23} \quad a_{33}$$
$$\vdots$$
$$a_{1n} \quad a_{2n} \quad a_{3n} \quad \cdots \quad a_{nn}$$

may be represented as either

$$\sum_{i=1}^{n} \left(\sum_{j=i}^{n} a_{ij}\right) \quad \text{or} \quad \sum_{j=1}^{n} \left(\sum_{i=1}^{j} a_{ij}\right).$$

It is instructive to compare this with the change of order in a double integration (Figure I.6.1):

$$\int_0^a \int_x^a f(x, y) \, dy \, dx = \int_0^a \int_0^y f(x, y) \, dx \, dy.$$

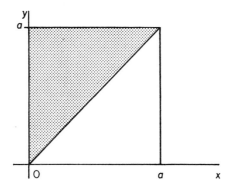

Figure I.6.1

10. Show that, if

$$\frac{1}{N}\left(\sum_{i=1}^{N}\alpha_{ik}\right) = \mu, \qquad k = 1, 2, \ldots, M,$$

and

$$\frac{1}{M}\left(\sum_{k=1}^{M}\beta_{kj}\right) = \nu, \qquad j = 1, 2, \ldots, R,$$

then

$$\frac{1}{NRM}\sum_{i=1}^{N}\sum_{j=1}^{R}\sum_{k=1}^{M}\alpha_{ik}\beta_{kj} = \mu\nu.$$

THE Π NOTATION

I.7 Definitions and Basic Properties

We have for **products** a notation, analogous to the $\sum$ notation for sums, the definition of which is contained in the equation

(I.7.1)
$$\prod_{j=1}^{n} x_j = x_1 x_2 \cdots x_n.$$

Here again, j is an index whose range is indicated by the notations on the Π symbol, and x_j is a function of j, just as before. The values taken on by x_j are, however, multiplied in this case, as the symbol Π (for "product") is intended to imply.

We have the further definition

(I.7.2)
$$\prod_{j=1}^{n} c = c^n,$$

and the properties

(I.7.3)
$$\prod_{j=1}^{n} (kx_j) = k^n \left(\prod_{j=1}^{n} x_j\right),$$

(I.7.4) $$\prod_{j=1}^{n} x_j y_j = \left(\prod_{j=1}^{n} x_j\right)\left(\prod_{j=1}^{n} y_j\right),$$

(I.7.5) $$\prod_{i=1}^{n} \left(\prod_{j=1}^{m} U_{ij}\right) = \prod_{j=1}^{m} \left(\prod_{i=1}^{n} U_{ij}\right).$$

We also have **triangular products**, just as we have triangular sums. (See Exercises 8 and 9, Section I.6.) An important example of this type of product is

$$\prod_{1 \leqslant i < j \leqslant n} (x_i - x_j),$$

or, as it is also written,

$$\prod_{\substack{i=1,2\cdots,n-1 \\ j=i+1,\cdots,n}} (x_i - x_j).$$

The notations under the Π's here mean that we are to use all factors of the form $(x_i - x_j)$ as i and j range over the values $1, 2, \ldots, n$, subject to the restriction that i be always less than j. We have, therefore,

$$\prod_{1 \leqslant i < j \leqslant n} (x_i - x_j) = (x_1 - x_2)(x_1 - x_3) \cdots (x_1 - x_n)$$
$$(x_2 - x_3) \cdots (x_2 - x_n)$$
$$\vdots$$
$$(x_{n-1} - x_n).$$

How many factors are there in this product?

This function of $x_1, x_2, \ldots, x_n$ is known as the **alternating function**. It is zero unless the x's are all distinct, and when it is not zero, it changes its sign if any two x's are interchanged. (Verify this last statement for x_1 and x_2.)

For further ways of writing triangular products, see Exercise 5 below.

I.8 Exercises

1. Prove rules (I.7.3), (I.7.4), (I.7.5).

2. Show that

(a) $$\left(\prod_{j=1}^{n} x_j\right) x_{n+1} = \prod_{j=1}^{n+1} x_j.$$

(b) $$\prod_{j=1}^{k} x_j \cdot \prod_{j=k+1}^{n} x_j = \prod_{j=1}^{n} x_j, \qquad (n > k).$$

(c) $$\prod_{i=1}^{k} x_i \cdot \prod_{j=1}^{n-k} x_{k+j} = \prod_{p=1}^{n} x_p, \qquad (n > k).$$

3. Show by examples that the index in the Π notation is a dummy index and that the range of the index may be shifted if desired.

4. Simplify

$$\left(\prod_{k=1}^{n} (a^{1/2^k} + b^{1/2^k})\right)(a^{1/2^n} - b^{1/2^n}), \qquad a, b > 0.$$

5. Show that

$$\prod_{j=1}^{n} \left(\prod_{i=1}^{j} a_{ij}\right) = \prod_{i=1}^{n} \left(\prod_{j=i}^{n} a_{ij}\right).$$

6. Write in expanded notation:

(a) $\displaystyle\sum_{i=1}^{n} \left(\prod_{j=1}^{n} x_{ij} \right).$

(b) $\displaystyle\prod_{j=1}^{n} \left(\sum_{i=1}^{n} x_{ij} \right).$

(c) $\displaystyle\sum_{i=1}^{n} \left\{ \frac{y_i}{x_0 - x_i} \prod_{\substack{1 \leqslant j \leqslant n \\ j \neq i}} \left(\frac{x - x_j}{x_0 - x_j} \right) \right\}.$

7. Show that

$$\prod_{\substack{i,j=1,2,\cdots n \\ i \neq j}} (x_i - x_j) = (-1)^{n(n-1)/2} \left[\prod_{\substack{i,j=1,2,\cdots n \\ i < j}} (x_i - x_j) \right]^2.$$

8. Show that

$$\prod_{i=1}^{n} \left(\sum_{j=1}^{m} x_{ij} \right) = \sum_{j_1,\cdots,j_n = 1}^{m} \left(\prod_{i=1}^{n} x_{ij_i} \right).$$

The Algebra of Complex Numbers

Since complex numbers are used rather extensively in this book, and since some readers may have only a passing acquaintance with them, we give in this appendix a brief review of their more important algebraic properties.

II.1 Definitions and Fundamental Operations

If a and b are real numbers, symbols of the form $a + bi$ (subject to the rules of operation listed below) are called **complex numbers**. The real number a is called the **real part** of $a + bi$, and the real number b is called its **imaginary part**. It is often convenient to denote complex numbers by single letters from the end of the alphabet: $a + bi = z$, etc.

Two complex numbers $a + bi$ and $c + di$ are defined to be equal if and only if the real and imaginary parts of one are respectively equal to the real and imaginary parts of the other, that is, if and only if $a = c$ and $b = d$.

The complex numbers which are the **sum** and the **product** of two complex numbers are defined as follows:

$$(\text{II.1.1}) \qquad (a + bi) + (c + di) = (a + c) + (b + d)i,$$

$$(\text{II.1.2}) \qquad (a + bi)(c + di) = (ac - bd) + (ad + bc)i.$$

From the preceding equations, we note that

$$(a + 0i) + (c + 0i) = (a + c) + 0i,$$

$$(a + 0i)(c + 0i) = (ac) + 0i.$$

Thus, complex numbers of the form $a + 0i$ behave just like the corresponding real numbers a with respect to addition and multiplication. This fact leads us to redefine the symbol $a + 0i$ as the real number a:

$$(\text{II.1.3}) \qquad a + 0i = a$$

for every real number a. In particular, we have

$$0 + 0i = 0 \qquad \text{and} \qquad 1 + 0i = 1.$$

The first of these special cases leads to:

Theorem II.1.1: *A complex number is zero if and only if its real and imaginary parts are both zero.*

The preceding definitions have the consequence that the set of real numbers is contained in the set of complex numbers: Every real number a is a complex number of the special form $a + 0i$. Every statement true for complex numbers in general is thus true in particular for real numbers, but not conversely, of course.

Since

$$(a + bi) + 0 = (a + bi) + (0 + 0i) = (a + 0) + (b + 0)i = a + bi,$$

we see that 0 is an **identity element for addition**.

We define the **negative** of $a + bi$ to be the complex number

$$-(a + bi) = (-a) + (-b)i,$$

so that

$$(a + bi) + (- (a + bi)) = (a + bi) + ((-a) + (-b)i) = 0.$$

Subtraction is next defined thus:

$$(a + bi) - (c + di) = (a + bi) + (-(c + di)),$$

so that

(II.1.4) $$\qquad (a + bi) - (c + di) = (a - c) + (b - d)i.$$

This makes subtraction the operation inverse to addition, that is, we will have $(z + w) - w = z$ for all complex numbers z and w.

It is consistent with these definitions of addition and subtraction to define also

(II.1.5) $$\qquad a + (-b)i = a - bi.$$

We could establish easily, but not in little space, that the associative, commutative, and distributive laws, the laws of signs and parentheses, and the laws of positive integral exponents apply in the above operations with complex numbers just as in the case of real numbers. We shall simply assume these results and proceed.

The equation

$$(a + bi)1 = (a + bi)(1 + 0i) = a + bi,$$

which follows from (II.1.2), shows that 1 is an **identity element for multiplication**.

For economy of representation, we define

(II.1.6) $$\qquad 0 + bi = bi.$$

A complex number of this form is called a **pure imaginary number**. The pure imaginary number $1i = i$ is called the **imaginary unit**. From (II.1.2), by putting $a = c = 0$, $b = d = 1$, we obtain the equation

$$i^2 = -1.$$

Thus, when multiplying complex numbers, we proceed as though we were multiplying polynomials of the form $a + bx$, except that now we replace i^2 by

-1 whenever it appears. It is helpful in this connection to observe that $i^3 = -i$, $i^4 = 1$, etc. For some purposes it is helpful to rewrite the relation $i^2 = -1$ in the form $i = \sqrt{-1}$, in which case $-\sqrt{-1} = -i$.

Using (II.1.2), we may now verify that

$$(c + di) \left(\left(\frac{c}{c^2 + d^2} \right) + \left(\frac{-d}{c^2 + d^2} \right) i \right) = 1,$$

provided that $c^2 + d^2 \neq 0$. Hence we define the **inverse** or **reciprocal** of $c + di$ as follows:

(II.1.7) $\qquad (c + di)^{-1} = \left(\frac{c}{c^2 + d^2} \right) + \left(\frac{-d}{c^2 + d^2} \right) i = \frac{c - di}{c^2 + d^2}.$

Since c^2 and d^2 are both nonnegative, $c^2 + d^2 = 0$ if and only if $c = d = 0$. Thus *the only complex number $c + di$ which has no reciprocal is zero.*

This definition of the reciprocal leads us to define **division** of complex numbers thus:

(II.1.8) $\qquad \dfrac{a + bi}{c + di} = (a + bi)(c + di)^{-1}, \qquad c^2 + d^2 \neq 0.$

Substituting and expanding, we obtain

$$\frac{a + bi}{c + di} = \frac{(a + bi)(c - di)}{c^2 + d^2} = \left(\frac{ac + bd}{c^2 + d^2} \right) + \left(\frac{bc - ad}{c^2 + d^2} \right) i,$$

which is again a complex number. With this definition, we have $(zw) \div w = z$ for all z and w except $w = 0$, so that division as defined here is indeed the inverse of multiplication.

Any collection $\mathscr{F}$ of complex numbers which has the property that the sum, difference, product, and quotient (division by zero excepted) of any two numbers of $\mathscr{F}$ also belong to $\mathscr{F}$ is called a **number field**. In particular, the set of all complex numbers is a field since, as has been shown above, the four operations applied to any two complex numbers each yield a complex number. The set of all complex numbers of the form $a + 0i$, namely the set of all real numbers, is likewise a number field since

$$(a + 0i) \pm (b + 0i) = (a \pm b) + 0i,$$

$$(a + 0i)(b + 0i) = (ab) + 0i,$$

$$(a + 0i) \div (b + 0i) = \frac{a}{b} + 0i, \qquad b \neq 0.$$

that is, the four operations applied to two real numbers again result in real numbers. The real field is a **subfield** of the complex number field. A third example of a number field is the set of all rational real numbers, that is, the set of all real numbers of the form a/b where a and b are integers ($b \neq 0$). There are many other examples of number fields. See Chapter Four for a more extended discussion.

II.2 Exercises

1. Simplify $(1 - i)^3 - (1 + i)^3$.

2. If x and y are real, what can we conclude about them from the equation

$$(x - y + 2) + (2x + y)i = 3 + 5i?$$

3. Let n be any integer, so that $n = 4q + r$ where q is an integer and $r = 0, 1,$ 2, or 3. Give a rule for evaluating i^n.

4. Show that the complex numbers $1, -1, i, -i$ form a group with respect to the operation of multiplication. (See Chapter Seven for the definition of a group.)

5. Use (II.1.1) and (II.1.2) to show that, for arbitrary complex numbers $z_j = x_j + iy_j, j = 1, 2, 3$, the commutative law

$$z_1 z_2 = z_2 z_1$$

and the distributive law

$$z_1(z_2 + z_3) = z_1 z_2 + z_1 z_3$$

hold.

6. Show that, for all complex numbers z, $z \cdot 0 = 0$. [Use (II.1.2) and the fact that $0 = 0 + 0i$.]

7. Prove that, if $z_1 + w = z_2 + w$, then $z_1 = z_2$, and that, if $z_1 w = z_2 w$ and $w \neq 0$, then $z_1 = z_2$. (**Cancellation laws** for addition and multiplication.)

8. Given that

$$\omega = \frac{-1 + \sqrt{3}i}{2},$$

show that

$$\omega^2 = \frac{-1 - \sqrt{3}i}{2},$$

and that

$$\omega^3 = 1.$$

Show also that

$$\omega^2 + \omega + 1 = 0.$$

9. Show that, for every complex number $x_1 + x_2 i$, there exist unique real numbers y_1, y_2 such that

$$x_1 + x_2 i = y_1 \frac{1 + i}{\sqrt{2}} + y_2 \frac{1 - i}{\sqrt{2}}.$$

II.3 Conjugate Complex Numbers

The complex numbers $a + bi$ and $a - bi$ are called **conjugate complex numbers,** each being the conjugate of the other. A real number is its own conjugate. The conjugate of a complex number z is denoted by $\bar{z}$.

If $z = a + bi$, then $\bar{z} = a - bi$, and

$$z + \bar{z} = 2a, \qquad z - \bar{z} = 2bi, \qquad z\bar{z} = a^2 + b^2.$$

We have therefore:

Theorem II.3.1: *The sum, difference, and product of conjugate complex numbers are respectively a real number, a pure imaginary number, and a nonnegative real number.*

Again, by the definition of equality, if $z = \bar{z}$, we have $b = -b$ so that $b = 0$ and $z = a$. If $z = -\bar{z}$, then $a = -a$ so that $a = 0$ and $z = bi$. This yields

Theorem II.3.2: *If a complex number equals its conjugate it is a real number, but if it equals the negative of its conjugate it is a pure imaginary number.*

An important use of the conjugate of a complex number is in the evaluation of a quotient according to the process

$$\frac{a + bi}{c + di} = \frac{(a + bi)(c - di)}{(c + di)(c - di)} = \frac{(ac + bd) + (bc - ad)i}{c^2 + d^2}.$$

The rule "multiply numerator and denominator by the conjugate of the denominator" is easier to use and remember than is the formula for the quotient.

By direct computation, we can show readily that for any two complex numbers w and z, we have

$$\overline{(\bar{z})} = z,$$

$$\overline{w + z} = \bar{w} + \bar{z},$$

(II.3.1) $$\overline{wz} = \bar{w}\,\bar{z},$$

$$\overline{\left(\frac{w}{z}\right)} = \frac{\bar{w}}{\bar{z}}, \qquad z \neq 0.$$

For example, if

$$w = a + bi, \qquad z = c + di,$$

then

$$\overline{wz} = \overline{(ac - bd) + (ad + bc)i} = (ac - bd) - (ad + bc)i,$$

and

$$\bar{w}\bar{z} = (a - bi)(c - di) = (ac - bd) + (-ad - bc)i,$$

so that

$$\overline{wz} = \bar{w}\bar{z}.$$

Similar procedures apply in the other cases.

The **absolute value** of the complex number $z = a + bi$, denoted by $|z|$, is by definition the nonnegative real number $\sqrt{z\bar{z}} = \sqrt{a^2 + b^2}$. The square of the absolute value, namely $z\bar{z}$ or $a^2 + b^2$, appears in the process of division:

$$z^{-1} = \frac{1}{z} = \frac{\bar{z}}{z\bar{z}},$$

and similarly

$$\frac{w}{z} = \frac{w\bar{z}}{z\bar{z}}, \qquad z \neq 0.$$

In particular, the reciprocal of a complex number is its conjugate divided by the square of its absolute value.

Concerning the absolute value, we may show, again by direct computation, that

$$|\bar{z}| = |z|,$$

$$|wz| = |w| \cdot |z|,$$

(II.3.2)

$$\left|\frac{w}{z}\right| = \frac{|w|}{|z|}.$$

For example, if $w = a + bi$, $z = c + di$, we have

$$|wz| = |(ac - bd) + (ad + bc)i|$$
$$= \sqrt{(ac - bd)^2 + (ad + bc)^2} = \sqrt{(a^2 + b^2)(c^2 + d^2)}$$
$$= |w| \cdot |z|.$$

Alternatively,

$$(wz) \cdot (\overline{wz}) = wz\bar{w}\bar{z} = (w\bar{w})(z\bar{z}).$$

Hence, taking positive square roots on both sides,

$$\sqrt{(wz)(\overline{wz})} = \sqrt{w\bar{w}} \cdot \sqrt{z\bar{z}},$$

or

$$|wz| = |w| \cdot |z|.$$

Similar proofs may be developed for the other rules.

The absolute value of a complex number also appears in some important inequalities:

(II.3.3)
$$\text{If } z = a + bi, \text{ then } |a| \leqslant |z| \text{ and } |b| \leqslant |z|.$$
$$|w + z| \leqslant |w| + |z|.$$

The first two of these are left to the reader to prove. To prove the last one, we note that

$$(w + z)\overline{(w + z)} = (w + z)(\bar{w} + \bar{z}) = w\bar{w} + z\bar{z} + \bar{w}z + w\bar{z},$$

or

$$|w + z|^2 = |w|^2 + |z|^2 + (\bar{w}z + \overline{\bar{w}z}).$$

The quantity in parentheses is twice the real part of $\bar{w}z$ and hence, by the first of (II.3.3), we have

$$\bar{w}z + \overline{\bar{w}z} \leqslant 2|\bar{w}z| = 2|w|\,|z|.$$

Therefore,

$$|w + z|^2 \leqslant |w|^2 + 2|w|\,|z| + |z|^2 = (|w| + |z|)^2.$$

Taking the positive square root on both sides, we then have the desired result:

$$|w + z| \leqslant |w| + |z|.$$

II.4 Exercises

1. Complete the proof of (II.3.1) and (II.3.2).

*2. Prove that, if f is a polynomial with *real coefficients*, $f(\bar{z}) = \overline{f(z)}$.

3. Given an example of a function g such that $g(\bar{z}) \neq \overline{g(z)}$.

*4. Prove that, if f is a polynomial with real coefficients and if $f(z) = 0$, then $f(\bar{z}) = 0$ also. In words, this says that in the case of polynomial equations with real coefficients, complex roots occur in conjugate pairs.

5. Prove that $|w + z| \geqslant |\,|w| - |z|\,|$.

6. For what complex numbers do we have $|z| = z$? $|z| = -z$?

7. Simplify $(1 + i)^3/(1 - i)^3$.

*8. Show that $\sum\limits_{j=1}^{n} |w_j|^2 \geqslant 0$ for arbitrary complex numbers w_j, and that, if

$$\sum_{j=1}^{n} |w_j|^2 = 0,$$

then

$$w_j = 0, \qquad j = 1, 2, \ldots, n.$$

9. Show that, if $wz = 1$ and $|w| = 1$, where w and z are complex numbers, then $|z| = 1$ and $w^{-1} = \bar{w}$.

The General Concept
of Isomorphism

III.1 Sets and Correspondences

In mathematics there is occasion to consider a wide variety of **sets** of objects: sets of numbers, sets of rotations of axes, sets of matrices, sets of lines, etc. Such a set is said to be **defined** when all of its **members**, also called **elements**, are listed or named, or when enough properties which its members are required to possess are given so that we can decide whether or not any given object belongs to the set. For example, "the set consisting of the integers 0 and 1" is defined by naming its members. On the other hand, "the set of real solutions of the matrix equation $A^2 - 2A + 5I_2 = 0$" is defined by a property by which we can decide whether or not any given object belongs to the set.

Frequently it is useful or necessary to associate with each member of one set $\mathscr{S}$ a corresponding member of a set $\mathscr{T}$. Such a correspondence is called a **mapping** of $\mathscr{S}$ into $\mathscr{T}$, and the member t of $\mathscr{T}$ which corresponds to an element s of $\mathscr{S}$ is called the **image** of s under the mapping. For example, if $\mathscr{S}$ denotes the set of all integers and $\mathscr{T}$ denotes the set consisting of the integers 0 and 1, one might choose to assign to every even integer of $\mathscr{S}$ the integer 0 of $\mathscr{T}$ as an image and to every odd integer of $\mathscr{S}$ the integer 1 of $\mathscr{T}$ as an image. (This particular mapping is often useful.)

If each member of $\mathscr{S}$ has exactly one image in $\mathscr{T}$ and if each member of $\mathscr{T}$ is the image of exactly one member of $\mathscr{S}$, we say $\mathscr{S}$ and $\mathscr{T}$ are in **one-to-one correspondence**. If the particular elements s of $\mathscr{S}$ and t of $\mathscr{T}$ are related to each other in this way, we write "$s \leftrightarrow t$." For example, let $\mathscr{S}$ denote the set of all complex numbers $a + bi$ and let $\mathscr{T}$ denote the set of all 2×2 matrices of the form $\begin{bmatrix} a & -b \\ b & a \end{bmatrix}$, with a and b real numbers. If now we require that to each complex number $a + bi$ there correspond the matrix $\begin{bmatrix} a & -b \\ b & a \end{bmatrix}$ *and vice versa,* we have a

one-to-one correspondence between $\mathscr{S}$ and $\mathscr{T}$ which is conveniently symbolized thus:

$$a + bi \leftrightarrow \begin{bmatrix} a & -b \\ b & a \end{bmatrix}.$$

III.2 Operations

Ordinarily we are interested in the properties of certain appropriate operations to be performed on members of the sets under investigation. For example, it is useful to add and to multiply matrices, but one must also know whether or not these operations are commutative, associative, distributive, etc., in order to be able to compute correctly and efficiently.

Not infrequently the elements of two sets are subjected to analogous operations which possess the same basic properties. Consider, for example, a set $\mathscr{R}$ consisting of four symbols r^0, r^1, r^2, r^3, subject to an operation of multiplication for which the ordinary laws of exponents hold but also for which, for nonnegative integers n, $r^{n+4} = r^n$. Let us denote this operation of "multiplication" by the symbol $\circ$. Then $r^2 \circ r^1 = r^3$, $r^2 \circ r^2 = r^0$, $r^2 \circ r^3 = r^1$, etc. The complete multiplication table is as follows:

$\circ$	r^0	r^1	r^2	r^3
r^0	r^0	r^1	r^2	r^3
r^1	r^1	r^2	r^3	r^0
r^2	r^2	r^3	r^0	r^1
r^3	r^3	r^0	r^1	r^2.

(Here the left factor appears at the left, the right factor at the top.)

From the table we can conclude $r^i \circ r^j = r^j \circ r^i$ in all cases and also that $(r^i \circ r^j) \circ r^k = r^i \circ (r^j \circ r^k)$ in all cases. That is, the operation $\circ$ is both commutative and associative as applied to this set of four elements. (There exist many useful interpretations of these r's and of the operation $\circ$.)

As a similar example, consider a set $\mathscr{I}$ consisting of the four complex numbers 1, i, -1, $-i$, subject to the ordinary operation of multiplication, which is also associative and commutative. The multiplication table is:

$\times$	1	i	-1	$-i$
1	1	i	-1	$-i$
i	i	-1	$-i$	1
-1	-1	$-i$	1	i
$-i$	$-i$	1	i	-1.

III.3 The Concept of Isomorphism

Now the sets $\mathscr{R}$ and $\mathscr{I}$ listed above each contain four objects, so that we may establish a one-to-one correspondence between the two. This may be done in various ways, but one that is useful at this point is symbolized by:

$$r^0 \leftrightarrow 1,$$
$$r^1 \leftrightarrow i,$$
$$r^2 \leftrightarrow -1,$$
$$r^3 \leftrightarrow -i.$$

The above shows, for example, that the image of r^1 is i, and that the image of r^2 is -1. We observe next that $r^1 \circ r^2 = r^3$ and $i \times (-1) = -i$ and then that $-i$ *is the image of* r^3. That is, in this instance, *the product of the images of two members of* $\mathscr{R}$ *is the image of their product.* Moreover, comparison of the two multiplication tables shows at once that this property holds *without exception.* This fact is expressed by saying that the two sets are *isomorphic with respect to the corresponding operations* $\circ$ *and* $\times$.

The preceding example, like that of Section 1.13, illustrates a general concept of isomorphism which we now define. Let $\mathscr{C}$ and Γ denote two sets of elements subject to certain operations of interest, the operations $\circ_1, \circ_2, \ldots, \circ_k$ applying to elements of $\mathscr{C}$, and the respectively corresponding operations $\omega_1, \omega_2, \ldots, \omega_k$ applying to elements of Γ. Let operations $\circ$ yield only elements of $\mathscr{C}$, operations ω only elements of Γ. Assume there exists a one-to-one correspondence between the elements of $\mathscr{C}$ and the elements of Γ such that the *image* of the result of performing an operation $\circ$ on elements c of $\mathscr{C}$ is always equal to the result of performing the corresponding operation ω on the respective image elements γ of Γ. Then we say that $\mathscr{C}$ and Γ are **isomorphic** with respect to the operations $\circ_1, \circ_2, \ldots, \circ_k$ and $\omega_1, \omega_2, \ldots, \omega_k$, and that the mapping is an **isomorphism**.

There are several specialized illustrations of this general concept of isomorphism in the various chapters of this book. In every case, the isomorphism is established by demonstrating that "the product of the images is the image of the product" for each of the operations involved, the word "product" being suitably interpreted in each case.

III.4 Exercise

1. Show that if $\mathscr{C}$ and Γ are isomorphic as defined above, and if $a \circ_j b = b \circ_j a$ holds for all a and b of $\mathscr{C}$, then $\alpha \omega_j \beta = \beta \omega_j \alpha$ for all α, β of Γ. Show also that, if $a \circ_i (b \circ_j c) = (a \circ_i b) \circ_j (a \circ_i c)$ for all a, b, c of $\mathscr{C}$, then $\alpha \omega_i (\beta \omega_j \gamma) = (\alpha \omega_i \beta) \omega_j (\alpha \omega_i \gamma)$ for all α, β, γ of Γ. Finally, show that the image of an identity element with respect to an operation $\circ_j$ is an identity element with respect to the corresponding operation ω_j.

A Bibliography of Vector Spaces, Matrices, Determinants, and Their Applications

This list of books is intended to be selective rather than exhaustive. It provides references to major areas of application as well as to more mature, more extensive, classical, or different treatments of these subjects.

The relevant papers are too many in number to be listed here. However, specialized bibliographies of the applications can readily be made by consulting the technical journals in the field of the reader's interest and by examining bibliographies in the books listed herein.

GENERAL REFERENCES TO ABSTRACT ALGEBRA

A. A. Albert. *Modern Higher Algebra*. Chicago: U. of Chicago Press, 1937.

_____. *Introduction to Algebraic Theories*. Chicago: U. of Chicago Press, 1941.

_____. *Fundamental Concepts of Higher Algebra*. Chicago: U. of Chicago Press, 1956.

G. Birkhoff and S. Mac Lane. *A Survey of Modern Algebra*, rev. ed. New York: Macmillan, 1953.

M. Bôcher. *Introduction to Higher Algebra*. New York: Macmillan, 1907.

L. E. Dickson. *Modern Algebraic Theories*. Chicago: Sanborn, 1926; New York: Dover, 1959.

H. Hasse. *Higher Algebra* and *Exercises to Higher Algebra*. New York: Ungar, 1954.

N. Jacobson. *Lectures in Abstract Algebra*. New York: Van Nostrand, Vol. I, *Basic Concepts*, 1951; Vol. II, *Linear Algebra*, 1953.

C. C. MacDuffee. *An Introduction to Abstract Algebra*. New York: Wiley, 1940.

N. H. McCoy. *Introduction to Modern Algebra*. Boston: Allyn and Bacon, 1960.

O. Schreier and E. Sperner. *An Introduction to Modern Algebra and Matrix Theory*. New York: Chelsea, 1952.

B. L. van der Waerden. *Modern Algebra* (English). New York: Ungar, Vol. I, 1949; Vol. II, 1950.

_____. *Algebra* (German). Berlin: Springer, Vol. I, 5th Ed., 1960; Vol. II, 4th Ed., 1959.

M. J. Weiss and R. Dubisch. *Higher Algebra for the Undergraduate*. 2nd Ed. New York: Wiley, 1962.

LINEAR ALGEBRA, MATRICES, AND DETERMINANTS

A. C. Aitken. *Determinants and Matrices.* 8th Ed. New York: Interscience, 1954.

R. Bellman. *Introduction to Matrix Analysis.* New York: McGraw-Hill, 1960.

S. K. Berberian. *Introduction to Hilbert Space.* New York: Oxford U. Press, 1961.

W. L. Ferrar. *Algebra, A Text-Book of Determinants, Matrices, and Algebraic Forms.* Oxford: Clarendon Press, 1941.

————. *Finite Matrices.* Oxford: Clarendon Press, 1951.

D. T. Finkbeiner, II. *Matrices and Linear Transformations.* San Francisco: Freeman, 1960.

R. A. Frazer, W. J. Duncan, and A. R. Collar. *Elementary Matrices and Some Applications to Dynamics and Differential Equations.* Cambridge: Cambridge U. Press, 1950.

F. R. Gantmacher. *The Theory of Matrices,* Vols. I, II. New York: Chelsea, 1959.

P. R. Halmos. *Finite-Dimensional Vector Spaces.* 2nd Ed. Princeton: Van Nostrand, 1958.

————. *Introduction to Hilbert Space.* New York: Chelsea, 1951.

H. L. Hamburger and M. E. Grimshaw. *Linear Transformations in n-Dimensional Vector Space, an Introduction to the Theory of Hilbert Spaces.* Cambridge: Cambridge U. Press, 1951.

B. Higman. *Applied Group-Theoretic and Matrix Methods.* Oxford: Clarendon Press, 1955.

K. Hoffman and R. Kunze. *Linear Algebra.* Englewood Cliffs, N.J.: Prentice-Hall, 1961.

A. Lichnerowicz. *Lineare Algebra und lineare Analysis.* Berlin: VEB. Deutscher Verlag der Wissenschaften, 1956; *Algèbre et analyse linéaires.* Paris: Masson, 1947.

C. C. MacDuffee. *The Theory of Matrices.* 2nd Ed. New York: Chelsea, 1946.

————. *Vectors and Matrices.* Carus Mathematical Monograph No. 7. Ithaca, New York: Mathematical Association of America, 1943.

L. Mirsky. *An Introduction to Linear Algebra.* Oxford U. Press, 1955.

T. Muir and W. H. Metzler. *A Treatise on the Theory of Determinants.* New York: Longmans, 1933.

D. C. Murdoch. *Linear Algebra for Undergraduates.* New York: Wiley, 1957.

L. Pipes. *Matrix Methods for Engineering.* Englewood Cliffs, N.J.: Prentice-Hall, 1962.

W. Schmeidler. *Vorträge über Determinanten und Matrizen mit Anwendungen in Physik und Technik.* Berlin: Akademie-Verlag GmbH., 1949.

R. F. Scott and G. B. Mathews. *The Theory of Determinants and Their Applications.* Cambridge: Cambridge U. Press, 1904.

G. E. Shilov. *An Introduction to the Theory of Linear Spaces.* Englewood Cliffs, N.J.: Prentice-Hall, 1961.

H. W. Turnbull. *Theory of Determinants, Matrices, and Invariants.* London: Blackie, 1928; New York: Dover, 1960.

————. and A. C. Aitken. *An Introduction to the Theory of Canonical Matrices.* London: Blackie, 1932; New York: Dover, 1961.

B. L. van der Waerden. *Gruppen von linearen Transformationen.* Berlin: Springer, 1935; New York: Chelsea, 1948.

J. H. M. Wedderburn. *Lectures on Matrices.* Providence, R.I.: American Mathematical Society, 1934.

P. Zurmühl. *Matrizen, eine Darstellung für Ingenieure.* 3rd Ed. Berlin: Springer, 1961.

GROUP THEORY

H. Boerner. *Darstellungen von Gruppen.* Berlin: Springer, 1955.

C. W. Curtis and I. Reiner. *Representation Theory of Finite Groups.* New York: Interscience, 1963.

M. Hall. *The Theory of Groups.* New York: Macmillan, 1959.

M. Hamermesh. *Group Theory and its Applications to Physical Problems.* Reading, Mass.: Addison-Wesley, 1962.

D. E. Littlewood. *The Theory of Group Characters and Matrix Representations of Groups.* Oxford: Clarendon Press, 1950.

L. Mariot. *Group Theory and Solid State Physics.* Englewood Cliffs, N.J.: Prentice-Hall, 1962.

F. D. Murnaghan. *The Theory of Group Representations.* Baltimore: Johns Hopkins U. Press, 1938.

A. Speiser. *Die Theorie der Gruppen von endlicher Ordnung.* 4th Ed. Basel: Birkhäuser Verlag, 1956.

GEOMETRY AND TOPOLOGY

A. A. Albert. *Solid Analytic Geometry.* New York: McGraw-Hill, 1949.

J. A. Barrau. *Analytische Meetkunde.* 2nd Ed. Groningen, Netherlands: Noordhoff, 1933.

C. Berge. *The Theory of Graphs and its Applications.* New York: Wiley, 1962.

E. Bertini. *Einführung in die projective Geometrie mehrdimensionaler Räume.* Vienna: Seidel, 1924.

J. H. C. Gerretson. *Lectures on Tensor Calculus and Differential Geometry.* Groningen, Netherlands: Noordhoff, 1962.

W. C. Graustein. *Introduction to Higher Geometry.* New York: Macmillan, 1935.

W. V. D. Hodge and D. Pedoe. *Methods of Algebraic Geometry.* Cambridge: Cambridge U. Press, Vol. I, 1947; Vol. II, 1952; Vol. III, 1954.

D. Koenig. *Theorie der endlichen und unendlichen Graphen.* New York: Chelsea, 1950.

G. Köthe. *Topologische lineare Räume.* Berlin: Springer, 1960.

H. Levy. *Projective and Related Geometries.* New York: Macmillan, 1964.

O. Ore. *Theory of Graphs.* Providence: American Mathematical Society, 1962.

T. G. Room. *The Geometry of Determinantal Loci.* Cambridge: Cambridge U. Press, 1938.

S. Seshu and M. B. Reed. *Linear Graphs and Electrical Networks.* Reading, Mass.: Addison-Wesley, 1961.

D. M. Y. Sommerville. *Analytic Geometry of Three Dimensions.* Cambridge: Cambridge U. Press, 1934.

E. Sperner. *Einführung in die analytische Geometrie und Algebra.* Göttingen: Vandenhoeck und Ruprecht, Vol. I, 1941; Vol. II, 1951.

O. Veblen. *Analysis Situs.* New York: American Mathematical Society, 1931.

FUNCTIONS OF SEVERAL VARIABLES

R. Crowell and R. Williamson. *Calculus of Vector Functions*. Englewood Cliffs, N.J.: Prentice-Hall, 1962.

M. E. Munroe. *Modern Multidimensional Calculus*. Reading, Mass.: Addison-Wesley, 1963.

DIFFERENTIAL, DIFFERENCE, AND INTEGRAL EQUATIONS

R. Bellman. *Stability Theory of Differential Equations*. New York: McGraw-Hill, 1953.

E. A. Coddington and N. Levinson. *Theory of Ordinary Differential Equations*. New York: McGraw-Hill, 1955.

L. Collatz. *Eigenwertaufgaben mit technischen Anwendungen*. Leipzig: Akademische Verlagsgesellschaft, 1949.

S. Goldberg. *Introduction to Difference Equations*. New York: Wiley, 1958.

W. Hurewicz. *Ordinary Differential Equations in the Real Domain with Emphasis on Geometric Methods*. New York: Wiley, 1958.

W. Kaplan. *Operational Methods for Linear Systems*. Reading, Mass.: Addison-Wesley, 1962.

C. Lanczos. *Linear Differential Operators*. Princeton: Van Nostrand, 1961.

S. Lefschetz. *Differential Equations, Geometric Theory*. 2nd Ed. New York: Interscience, 1963.

W. V. Lovitt. *Linear Integral Equations*. New York: Dover, 1950.

I. G. Petrovskii. *Lectures on the Theory of Integral Equations*. Rochester: Graylock Press, 1957.

L. S. Pontryagin. *Ordinary Differential Equations*. Reading, Mass.: Addison-Wesley, 1962.

G. Sansone. *Equazioni differenziali nello campo reali*. Bologna: Zanichelli, 1948.

W. Schmeidler. *Integralgleichungen mit Anwendungen in Physik und Technik*. Leipzig: Akademische Verlagsgesellschaft, 1950.

APPLIED MATHEMATICS TEXTS

R. Courant and D. Hilbert. *Methods of Mathematical Physics*. New York: Interscience, Vol. 1, 1953; Vol. 2, 1962.

J. W. Dettman. *Mathematical Methods in Physics and Engineering*. New York: McGraw-Hill, 1962.

B. Friedman. *Principles and Techniques of Applied Mathematics*. New York: Wiley, 1956.

T. von Kármán and M. A. Biot. *Mathematical Methods in Engineering*. New York: McGraw-Hill, 1940.

J. G. Kemeny, H. Mirkil, J. L. Snell, and G. L. Thompson. *Finite Mathematical Structures*. Englewood Cliffs, N.J.: Prentice-Hall, 1959.

J. G. Kemeny, J. L. Snell, and G. L. Thompson. *Introduction to Finite Mathematics*. Englewood Cliffs, N.J.: Prentice-Hall, 1957.

F. D. Murnaghan. *Introduction to Applied Mathematics*. New York: McGraw-Hill, 1957.

H. S. Wilf. *Mathematics for the Physical Sciences*. New York: Wiley, 1962.

NUMERICAL ANALYSIS AND COMPUTATION

E. Bodewig. *Matrix Calculus*, 2nd Ed. New York: Interscience, 1959.

S. H. Crandall. *Engineering Analysis, A Survey of Numerical Procedures*. New York: McGraw-Hill, 1956.

P. S. Dwyer. *Linear Computations*. New York: Wiley, 1951.

V. N. Faddeeva. *Computational Methods of Linear Algebra*. New York: Dover, 1959.

D. K. Faddeev and V. N. Faddeeva. *Numerical Methods in Linear Algebra*. San Francisco: Freeman, 1963.

L. Fox. *The Numerical Solution of Two-Point Boundary Problems in Ordinary Differential Equations*. Oxford: Clarendon Press, 1957.

L. Fox, *et al. Modern Computing Methods*. London: Her Majesty's Stationery Office, 1961.

D. R. Hartree. *Numerical Analysis*. Oxford: Clarendon Press, 1952.

A. S. Householder. *Theory of Matrices in Numerical Analysis*. Boston: Ginn, 1964.

K. S. Kunz. *Numerical Analysis*. New York: McGraw-Hill, 1957.

C. Lanczos. *Applied Analysis*. Englewood Cliffs, N.J.: Prentice-Hall, 1956.

A. S. Levens. *Nomography*. 2nd Ed. New York: Wiley, 1959.

W. E. Milne. *Numerical Solution of Differential Equations*. New York: Wiley, 1953.

R. Varga. *Matrix Iterative Analysis*. Englewood Cliffs, N.J.: Prentice-Hall, 1962.

PROBABILITY AND STATISTICS

T. W. Anderson. *Introduction to Multivariate Statistical Analysis*. New York: Wiley, 1958.

W. Feller. *Probability Theory and its Applications*. 2nd Ed. New York: Wiley, 1957.

F. A. Graybill. *An Introduction to Linear Statistical Models*. New York: McGraw-Hill, 1961.

J. G. Kemeny and J. L. Snell. *Finite Markov Chains*. Princeton: Van Nostrand, 1959.

O. Kempthorne. *The Design and Analysis of Experiments*. New York: Wiley, 1952.

B. W. Lindgren. *Statistical Theory*. New York: Macmillan, 1962.

C. R. Rao. *Advanced Statistical Methods in Biometric Research*. New York: Wiley, 1952.

S. N. Roy. *Some Aspects of Multivariate Analysis*. New York: Wiley, 1958.

H. Scheffé. *The Analysis of Variance*. New York: Wiley, 1959.

S. S. Wilks. *Mathematical Statistics*. New York: Wiley, 1962.

ECONOMICS, GAME THEORY, AND LINEAR PROGRAMMING

R. G. D. Allen. *Mathematical Economics*. New York: St. Martin's Press, 1957.

G. Avondo-Bodino. *Economic Applications of the Theory of Graphs*. New York: Gordon and Breach, 1962.

A. Charnes and W. Cooper. *Management Models and Industrial Applications of Linear Programming*. Vols. I, II. New York: Wiley, 1961.

R. Dorfman, P. A. Samuelson, and R. M. Solow. *Linear Programming and Economic Analysis.* New York: McGraw-Hill, 1958.

D. Gale. *The Theory of Linear Economic Models.* New York: McGraw-Hill, 1960.

G. Hadley. *Linear Algebra.* Reading, Mass.: Addison-Wesley, 1961.

S. Karlin. *Mathematical Methods and Theory in Games, Programming, and Economics.* Vols. I, II. Reading, Mass.: Addison-Wesley, 1959.

L. R. Klein. *Econometrics.* Evanston, Ill.: Row Peterson, 1953.

R. D. Luce and H. Raiffa. *Games and Decisions.* New York: Wiley, 1957.

J. C. C. McKinsey. *Introduction to the Theory of Games.* New York: McGraw-Hill, 1952.

O. Morgenstern. *Economic Activity Analysis.* New York: Wiley, 1954.

J. J. Schwartz. *Lectures on the Mathematical Method in Analytical Economics.* New York: Gordon and Breach, 1962.

J. von Neumann and O. Morgenstern. *Theory of Games and Economic Behavior.* Princeton: Princeton U., 1944.

PSYCHOLOGY AND SOCIOLOGY

R. R. Bush and F. Mosteller. *Stochastic Models for Learning.* New York: Wiley, 1955.

H. H. Harman. *Modern Factor Analysis.* Chicago: U. of Chicago Press, 1960.

P. Horst. *Matrix Algebra for Social Scientists.* New York: Holt, Rinehart and Winston, 1963.

R. D. Luce (Ed.). *Developments in Mathematical Psychology.* Glencoe, Ill.: Free Press, 1960.

H. Solomon (Ed.). *Mathematical Thinking in the Measurement of Behavior.* Glencoe, Ill.: Free Press, 1960.

L. L. Thurstone. *Multiple Factor Analysis.* Chicago: U. of Chicago Press, 1947.

LOGICAL DESIGN AND AUTOMATA

S. H. Caldwell. *Switching Circuits and Logical Design.* New York: Wiley, 1958.

A. Gill. *Introduction to the Theory of Finite State Machines.* New York: McGraw-Hill, 1962.

W. W. Peterson. *Error Correcting Codes.* New York: Wiley, 1961.

ELECTRICAL ENGINEERING

V. Belevich. *Théorie des circuits de télécommunication.* Paris: Gauthier-Villars, 1959.

W. Cauer. *Synthesis of Linear Communication Networks.* New York: McGraw-Hill, 1958.

E. A. Guillemin. *The Mathematics of Circuit Analysis.* New York: Wiley, 1949.

L. P. Huelsman. *Circuits, Matrices, and Linear Vector Spaces.* New York: McGraw-Hill, 1963.

W. H. Kim and R. T. Chien. *Topological Analysis and Synthesis of Communication Networks.* New York: Columbia U. Press, 1962.

M. B. Reed. *Alternating Current Circuit Theory.* New York: Harper, 1956.

L. Weinberg. *Network Analysis and Synthesis.* New York: McGraw-Hill, 1962.

AERONAUTICAL ENGINEERING

R. L. Bisplinghoff and H. Ashley. *Principles of Aeroelasticity*. New York: Wiley, 1962.

Y. C. Fung. *An Introduction to the Theory of Aeroelasticity*. New York: Wiley, 1955.

R. H. Scanlan and R. Rosenbaum. *Aircraft Vibration and Flutter*. New York: Macmillan, 1951.

MECHANICS

J. H. Argyris and S. Kelsey. *Energy Theorems in Structure Analysis*. London: Butterworth, 1960.

H. Baldauf. *Hochgradig statisch unbestimmte Tragwerke*. Leipzig: Hirzel, 1956.

P. G. Bergman. *Introduction to the Theory of Relativity*. Englewood Cliffs, N.J.: Prentice-Hall, 1942.

S. F. Borg. *Matrix-Tensor Methods in Continuum Mechanics*. Princeton: Van Nostrand, 1962.

H. C. Corben and P. Stehle. *Classical Mechanics*. New York: Wiley, 1950.

H. Goldstein. *Classical Mechanics*. Reading, Mass.: Addison-Wesley, 1950.

H. L. Langhaar. *Dimensional Analysis and Theory of Models*. New York: Wiley, 1951.

S. J. McMinn. *Matrices for Structural Analysis*. New York: Wiley, 1962.

F. D. Murnaghan. *Finite Deformation of an Elastic Solid*. New York: Wiley, 1951.

H. F. P. Purday. *Linear Equations in Applied Mechanics*. New York: Interscience, 1954.

I. S. Sokolnikoff. *Mathematical Theory of Elasticity*. 2nd Ed. New York: McGraw-Hill, 1956.

A. Wintner. *The Analytical Foundations of Celestial Mechanics*. Princeton: Princeton U. Press, 1947.

CHEMISTRY AND CRYSTALLOGRAPHY

H. Eyring, J. Walter, and G. E. Kimball. *Quantum Chemistry*. New York: Wiley, 1944.

H. Hartmann. *Theorie der chemischen Bindung*. Berlin: Springer, 1954.

J. F. Nye. *Physical Properties of Crystals: Their Representation by Tensors and Matrices*. Oxford: Clarendon Press, 1957.

J. C. Slater. *Quantum Theory of Atomic Structure*. Vols. I, II. New York: McGraw-Hill, 1960.

E. B. Wilson, J. C. Decius, and P. Cross. *Molecular Vibrations*. New York: McGraw-Hill, 1955.

QUANTUM MECHANICS

J. D. Jackson. *Mathematics for Quantum Mechanics*. New York: W. A. Benjamin, 1962.

E. Merzbacher. *Quantum Mechanics*. New York: Wiley, 1962.

A. Messiah. *Quantum Mechanics*. Vol. I. New York: Interscience, 1961.

J. I. Powell and B. Crasemann. *Quantum Mechanics*. Reading, Mass.: Addison-Wesley, 1961.

COLOR AND COLOR PHOTOGRAPHY

P. J. Bouma. *Physical Aspects of Color*. Eindhoven, Netherlands: N. V. Philips, 1957.

R. M. Evans, W. T. Hanson, Jr., and W. L. Brewer. *Principles of Color Photography*. New York: Wiley, 1953.

C. W. Miller. *Principles of Photographic Reproduction*. New York: Macmillan, 1942.

Index

A

C